TABLE OF CONTENTS

Case Study 1 .... *7*

Heave damage caused by root barrier - Extensive persistent deficit from poplars - Incorrect diagnosis of subsidence based on timing of damage and erroneous visual observations - Value of level distortion survey - Significance of dead roots - Heave damage can develop in summer.

Case Study 2 .... *19*

Oak causing damage to semi-detached house - Engineer's concern of heave - No evidence of persistent desiccation - Tree felled - Level monitoring shows 80% recovery in first winter - No subsequent damage.

Case Study 3 .... *33*

Mature oak tree 1.5m from building on London clay - No external damage and no movement - Water requirements of tree provided from within bands of sand - Settlement of floor slab unrelated to tree.

Case Study 4 .... *61*

Bungalow underpinned after subsidence in 1976 - Cypress trees felled - Subsequent damage diagnosed as settlement of underpinning caused by softening of soil - Such explanation inconsistent with damage - Monitoring demonstrates heave - Engineers negligent and liable - Heave continuing and bungalow demolished.

Case Study 5 .... *79*

Single storey school building on Boulder Clay - Damage caused by various adjacent poplars - Initial tree felling stabilised parts of building - Additional felling and eventually hedge removal required for complete stability - Level monitoring essential to demonstrate effects of tree removal.

TREE ROOT DAMAGE TO BUILDINGS

Ca ... EDY

Cover design. Oak tree on London Clay,
1.5m from an extension, but causing no damage.
See Case Study 3, page 33.

First published 1998

by

Willowmead Publishing Ltd.
Ickleton Road, Wantage, OX12 9JA

© P.G.Biddle 1998

ISBN for complete set of 2 volumes: 0 9533086 0 X

ISBN Volume 1: 0 9533086 1 8

This publication contains Crown copyright material from research projects
which were undertaken for the Department of the Environment, Transport and the Regions
and is reproduced with the permission of the Controller of Her Majesty's Stationery Office.

Meteorological data are published under licence from The Meteorological Office;
graphs of meteorological data in Chapter 8 are Crown copyright.

Printed by Acorn Press Swindon Ltd.
Westmead Drive, Westmead Industrial Estate, Swindon, SN5 7UU

Seasonal movements of reinforced raft on piles - Defective piles - Estimate of major heave potential - No allowance for heave in foundation design - Engineer liable for defective design - No options for tree management.

Block of flats with independent deep foundations for flank wall - Severe subsidence from closely adjacent tree- Polythene around foundations preventing seasonal recovery - Trees felled and recovery accelerated by watering-in, providing rapid and effective remedy.

Bungalow on sloping site with extensive fill, suffered extensive damage in 1980 - Insufficient funds for full remedial scheme - Partial underpinning - Further damage - Level monitoring confirms continued movements including underpinned areas - Lack of datum prevents distinction between heave or slope instability.

Victorian property on steeply sloping London Clay site - Trees closely adjacent down-slope - Long history of damage - Crack monitoring demonstrates seasonal and progressive movements - Removal of trees produces no benefit - Seasonal movements apparently caused by natural drainage.

Semi-detached house with reinforced raft foundations on Kimmeridge Clay - Comparison of level distortion surveys indicates about 30mm seasonal movement - Root barrier inappropriate - Trees felled - Level monitoring showed slight continuing recovery.

PREFACE

Introduction

Tree Root Damage to Buildings provides a comprehensive analysis of how the interaction of trees, soils and water can cause foundation movement and damage to buildings.

No other publication provides similar comprehensive cover of this subject. Thus, "Tree Roots and Buildings" by Cutler and Richardson (1989) provides details about the spread of tree roots and the proximity of trees to buildings where damage has occurred, but gives only a very brief overview of other topics. Various Digests by the Building Research Establishment cover specific topics, but provide no overall analysis. The report by the Institution of Structural Engineers (1994) on "Subsidence of low rise buildings" covers the various causes of subsidence, but was written by engineers and has negligible input about trees.

Trees are undoubtedly the biggest cause of subsidence, and a proper understanding of them is essential. My background in writing this book is as a research forester and arboriculturist, which provides me with knowledge of how trees are involved. More importantly, the research which is described in Volume 2 provides a unique insight into the interaction of trees and clay soils. This, and my practical experience of this topic built up during the investigation of more than 2000 cases over the past 23 years, enables me to approach the subject from a slightly different standpoint. In my opinion this points to the need for a radical re-appraisal of our methods of investigating and remedying damage, as well as many other aspects of this subject.

Although my background is in arboriculture, I have studied and sought to understand the input of other professions. As my university courses included some aspects of engineering, surveying and soil science, as well as forestry and geology, I suspect it may be easier for me to understand those parts of these disciplines which impinge on this subject, than it is for other professions to understand the behaviour of trees. I appreciate that, by writing about these other topics and covering such a wide spectrum of ideas, I may be accused of straying outside my own specialism. However, separate Chapters must either be written by different specialists, which can lead to an ill-coordinated presentation, or one must accept the inadequacies which may occur if a single author strays too far from their own expertise. I would like to believe that, during the past 23 years of study and practical involvement in this subject, I have acquired sufficient understanding of the other disciplines to allow me to present a coherent, and technically correct, overview.

I hope it also allows me to challenge some of the existing dogma, but I would always be interested to hear from anyone wishing to correct technical inaccuracies.

The problems are multi-disciplinary, involving structural engineers, surveyors, arboriculturists, soil scientists, insurers and their loss adjusters, architects, builders and planners, as well as giving work to solicitors and barristers. This book addresses all aspects of the problem, and so should be of value to all these professions.

Layout of book

This book is produced in two volumes:

i) Volume 1 which describes:

- The interaction of trees, soils, water and buildings (Chapters 1 - 10).
- The investigation of damage (Chapters 11-16).
- Remedy and prevention (Chapters 17-20).

ii) Volume 2, which presents the results of investigations into the patterns of soil drying in proximity to trees on clay soils.

At the end of each of the 20 Chapters there is a brief summary. Even if the complete text is not read, the reader is urged to study these summaries. If they suggest a different viewpoint, a more careful study of the whole Chapter should be warranted. In addition, as an aid to rapid reading, essential points have been highlighted like this with a green background. I hope this does not discourage reading the rest.

Colour coding of tables and graphs

Most of the diagrams are shown against a coloured background, the colour indicating the source of the information on which it is based. These colours are:

   i)   derived from research in Volume 2;

   ii)   derived from my own investigations;

   iii) derived from other sources.

Tables and graphs without colour are derived from non-specific sources.

Case Studies

At the end of each Chapter in Volume 1 there is a Case Study, selected from my consultancy work. These endeavour to show that problems of tree damage can be investigated by simple techniques, and simple remedial action can be used to rectify the problems. Where they relate to a particular topic, they have been placed at the end of the most appropriate Chapter; however most have no such direct link.

The Case Studies have been selected from my files over the past 20 years and therefore reflect my evolving approach to investigation. For instance, in the early cases I was undertaking level distortion surveys but no level monitoring, and sometimes placed greater emphasis on soil investigation than I now believe to be warranted. Some of the cases are taken to a full conclusion; in others my instructions were either limited or curtailed for various reasons. The cases thus reflect a typical spectrum of work. My reports on cases are usually more detailed and lengthy; for the Case Studies these have been précised, whilst retaining the important information. At the end of each Case Study is a section on "Lessons to be learnt", which identifies the good and bad points which emerge.

References in the text to the figures in the Case Studies are given as CS Figure ..., to distinguish them from the similar numbering used on the figures in the chapters.

The Case Studies presented in Volume 1 try to preserve the anonymity of the client and the site. The location is therefore only described in general terms, and features which identify the site are omitted. In some cases the plans and photographs are show as mirror images.

Acknowledgements

The research projects which are described in Volume 2 were only possible thanks to the generous funding by Milton Keynes Development Corporation, the National House-Building Council and the Department of Environment, to whom I express my special thanks.

These projects also relied on the co-operation of all those who provided suitable sites; Bedford Borough Council (trees 30, 31); Corpus Christi College, Cambridge (trees 45, 46); Emmanuel College, Cambridge (tree 37); London Borough of Brent (trees 1, 2, 3, 25, 26, 35, 36, 39, 43, 44); London Borough of Haringey (trees 4, 12, 27); London Borough of Harrow (trees 17, 18, 21, 22, 40); London Borough of Richmond upon Thames (tree 34); Milton Keynes Borough Council (trees 8, 10, 11, 15, 16, 32, 33, 38, 47, 48); Pembroke College, Cambridge (trees 28, 29); St. John's College, Cambridge (trees 5, 6); The National Trust (tree 7); Welwyn and Hatfield Borough Council (trees 19, 20, 23, 24, 41, 42); Willen Priory, Milton Keynes (tree 9, 13, 14). Particular thanks are due to the London Borough of Merton who provided the site with the 12 plane trees (trees 49 -60), and also allowed the variable pruning regime on these trees.

Much of the early field work on the research projects was undertaken by my assistant at that time, Mark Lazzeri. Members of my family have also kindly assisted in the neutron probe readings.

I am very grateful to those who provided photographs; these are acknowledged beneath the photograph.

Much of the typing and the entry of the research data has been undertaken by my secretary, Helen Walters, to whom I am most grateful.

I am also very grateful to my daughter-in-law, Dr Astrid Biddle who helped with the proof reading, and also to Caroline Davis, previously of the Department of Environment, who has commented on the technical content. However, I take full responsibility for all inaccuracies.

Finally, but most importantly, my special thanks to my wife, Hilary, who has supported me throughout this project. Not only has she tolerated my absence from other domestic chores, but has also done much of the data entry and preparation of the diagrams for Volume 2, undertaken much of the laboratory work and soil analyses, checked and commented on the drafts of both volumes, and provided the essential encouragement to finish the task.

The case for trees

Trees provide benefit by their beauty and visual amenity in softening and naturalising the hard landscape of the urban environment, by improving the microclimate of wind and temperature extremes, by reducing particulate and gaseous pollution, by enhancing social and property values and as a habitat for birds. More generally, they provide a carbon sink, with benefits for reducing global warming and climate change. For these and other reasons, the vast majority of people value the presence of trees and want them in proximity to buildings (Figure 1.1).

The case against trees

Trees can also cause problems. They obstruct light, and the fall of leaves, twigs and honeydew (from aphids) can be a source of inconvenience. More importantly, they can cause damage to buildings, very occasionally if the tree or branches fall but more commonly by the effects of their roots in causing subsidence or direct damage. During the past 25 years subsidence has become a major problem. The cost of repairs is a major drain on insurance reserves, and is also an expense for homeowners, either directly for repairs or indirectly in increased insurance premiums. Concern about the risk of subsidence gives rise to anxiety about trees close to buildings, which in turn is leading to felling or pruning of many trees.

Trees and buildings can co-exist with minimum conflict, provided there is proper understanding about the mechanism of tree root damage and how it can be prevented, or remedied if the need arises. It should be the duty of those responsible for trees and buildings (that is arboriculturists, architects, builders, building control officers, insurers, loss adjusters, planners, soil scientists, structural engineers, surveyors and valuers) to work with each other and the homeowner to try to ensure a harmonious relationship.

Figure 1.1

This mature oak provides a focal point and has been carefully retained within this new development. In some circumstances it could cause damage to adjacent buildings. Retention of trees of this sort, and of all trees in proximity to buildings, requires a thorough understanding of how they can cause damage, of the ways of preventing such damage, and of appropriate remedies in the event of damage occurring.

The nature of the problem

The allegation frequently made against trees growing near buildings is that "their roots have taken water from a clay soil causing it to shrink and the foundations to subside, resulting in structural damage to the building".

At first sight this allegation appears simple enough, but in reality it is a crude over-simplification which obscures the real picture and gives rise to misunderstandings about the mechanism of damage. In particular, foundations do not simply "subside". Where tree roots are the cause of damage, the foundations are invariably in a highly dynamic state, moving up or down, and sometimes laterally, depending on the circumstances. It is these movements, caused by the interaction of the tree with the soil, which are liable to produce structural damage.

In order to have a proper understanding of the mechanism of tree root damage to buildings, it is essential to understand the pattern of these movements, both in space and time. Once these concepts are grasped, the inadequacy of the commonly used existing methods for investigating cases of damage are apparent, and alternative simple diagnostic techniques become self-evident. More importantly, it is only when the mechanism of damage is properly understood and investigated that the most appropriate remedial measures can be identified and implemented. Improved knowledge can also show how to prevent damage from occurring in the first place.

The interaction of the tree and the soil involves water, and it is the constant movement of water within the system which produces the dynamic condition. These movements of water, and their interaction with the soil and the tree, are illustrated diagrammatically in Figure 1.2, where the thickness of the arrow is indicative of the volume of water movement.

In a bare field devoid of all buildings, trees, or other vegetation, there will be a simple balance, with water entering the system as rainfall and being lost as evaporation from the soil surface. Excess water will be lost from the system by vertical drainage or lateral run-off. If a building is introduced into this system, it will interfere with the balance by excluding rainfall from beneath the building and by preventing evaporation from the area it occupies. In Britain this has little effect and a balance is easily re-established. By contrast, in countries with a more arid climate where soils are normally desiccated, buildings allow the soil beneath them to retain moisture, resulting in expansion of the soil if it contains clay. In these countries, problems with expansive soils can be of far greater concern than problems of tree root damage in Britain.

If a tree is introduced into the system, it can have a major influence on the water balance. During the summer while the tree is in leaf it will loose large quantities of water through the leaves in the form of transpiration (Chapter 2). This water is obtained from the soil by the roots (Chapter 3). The amount of water which is absorbed by the roots is usually greater than that supplied by rainfall, so that the soil dries out progressively during the summer. In the winter the tree loses its leaves and transpiration stops. Water is no longer required and so water uptake by the roots also ceases. This allows the soil to recover the water deficit. In most situations the soil recovers fully each winter, so that the influence of the tree is entirely seasonal (Chapter 5). However, in some situations full recovery cannot occur during the winter, leaving the soil in a persistently desiccated state (Chapter 6).

The amount of water which is taken up by the roots depends on a number of factors, all of which can be very variable:

- the availability of water in the soil (Chapter 4);

- the species, size and vigour of the tree (Chapter 9);

- the rate of evaporation during the summer (Chapter 8).

In addition, the input of water as rainfall can be very variable, with serious deficiencies in years of drought. Overall this variation in both the uptake and input of water results in a very unstable water balance in the soil.

If the soil is sand or gravel, it will be stable to the changes in moisture content, and no foundation movement will occur. However, a clay soil which is subject to changes in moisture content will shrink when it is dried, and expand when it rehydrates. The amount of movement depends on the extent of change in moisture content and on the properties of the clay. Clay soils can behave very differently, depending on the origin of the clay particles and on their proportion in the soil (Chapter 4). The permeability of the clay is also important in determining the ability of the water to penetrate into the desiccated ground. As a result, the interaction between the tree and a clay soil can produce widely differing effects, which are generally very difficult to predict. At one extreme, there may be little change in moisture content and a soil of low

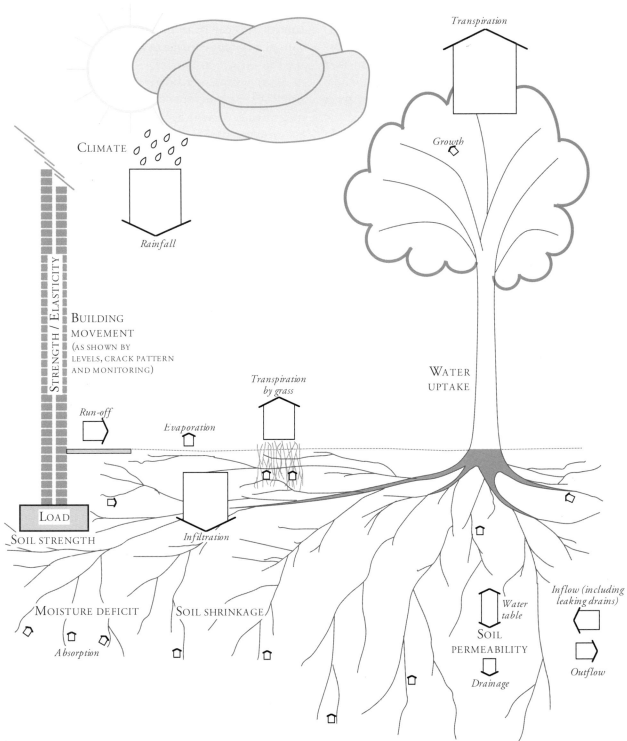

CLIMATE

Rainfall

Transpiration

Growth

STRENGTH / ELASTICITY

BUILDING
MOVEMENT
(AS SHOWN BY
LEVELS, CRACK PATTERN
AND MONITORING)

Run-off

Evaporation

Transpiration
by grass

WATER
UPTAKE

LOAD

SOIL STRENGTH

Infiltration

MOISTURE DEFICIT

SOIL SHRINKAGE

Absorption

Water
table

SOIL
PERMEABILITY

Inflow (including
leaking drains)

Outflow

Drainage

Figure 1.2

Diagram showing the role of water in the interaction between trees and buildings, and the factors which need to be considered when investigating cases of tree root damage to buildings.   The size of the blue arrows is indicative of typical water movements.

shrinkability, producing a comparatively stable system with little movement of the clay and a minimal risk to buildings. At the other extreme, with a soil of high shrinkability and a tree causing major changes in moisture content, the whole system can become highly dynamic, producing massive soil and foundation movement, with an associated high risk of damage.

Buildings are able to tolerate some foundation movement, but when differential movements become excessive, cracking occurs. Tree root activity is a common cause of damage, but there are many other possible causes. When damage does occur there is a tendency to assume that an adjacent tree is the cause, but such assumptions frequently lead to faulty diagnosis and to the wrong remedial works. Chapter 11 considers the merits of the various investigative techniques which I find to be most appropriate. These include investigation of the building, the soil and the tree (Chapters 12, 13, and 14) to provide an initial assessment of the possible involvement of a tree. Monitoring of levels is particularly valuable, and should be an essential part of most investigations (Chapter 15). Heave of the foundations, caused by rehydration of a persistent moisture deficit, introduces special problems and additional diagnostic techniques (Chapter 16). With a proper understanding and appropriate investigation, a variety of remedial options become apparent (Chapter 17).

The implications of tree root damage are widespread. Since the problem was first recognised, there have been a variety of guidelines and Codes of Practice which have shown an evolving change in attitudes to the prevention of damage. The most recent of these guidelines is the 1991 revision of National House-Building Council Standards, Chapter 4.2 (formerly NHBC Practice Note 3). The implications of this and other methods of preventing damage are considered in Chapter 18. This Chapter also considers whether predictions should be made about the risk of damage occurring and how this could be done.

The legal framework of statute and common law impinges on all aspects of investigation and responsibility (Chapter 19). In addition, the role of insurers, both for the cover provided against damage to buildings and for the professional liability of all those involved in this work, can have important ramifications.

The problems of tree root damage to buildings impinge on many professionals; architects, builders, building control officers, planners, surveyors, structural engineers, loss adjusters and insurers, as well as arboriculturists, are all concerned about particular facets of the problem. The implications of my conclusions for these professions are considered in Chapter 20.

A multi-disciplinary approach

Traditionally all problems of subsidence damage to buildings have been considered to fall within the professional domain of the *structural engineer*. This is certainly appropriate for other causes of subsidence damage (e.g. landslip or mining subsidence) or settlement (e.g. from compaction of fill or compression of peat) where the remedy will normally involve structural reinforcement of the foundations (i.e. underpinning). However, it is increasingly appreciated that damage caused by tree root activity does not necessarily require

expensive remedies such as underpinning. Alternative approaches, particularly those involving vegetation control, should often be preferred. This indicates a need to involve *arboriculturists* to advise on and undertake appropriate work to trees and shrubs.

Any such preventative or remedial work by arboriculturists cannot be undertaken in isolation. They will need to know the extent of the problem, and whether any applied remedy has been effective. This book places great emphasis on the importance of monitoring in this process. Work of this nature would normally fall outside the remit of the arboriculturist, but could involve either a *building surveyor*, or an *engineer*.

In many situations a *surveyor and arboriculturist*, or *engineer and arboriculturist*, working in tandem should be able to identify the cause of a problem and the most appropriate remedy, often without the need for any subsoil investigation. Where soil investigations are deemed necessary, their interpretation has usually been by structural engineers. However, I would suggest that much of the training of engineers, and the basic concepts under which they work, are based on assumptions of a saturated soil, but in practice these conditions are rarely applicable where tree root activity is involved. Most roots must have oxygen for growth; the necessary rates of diffusion of oxygen can only be achieved in air, i.e. in a non-saturated soil. In the absence of relevant methods, engineers seek to apply the concepts for saturated soils to these conditions, but in many situations, closer involvement of a *soil scientist* could be highly beneficial. Regrettably this profession is very rarely involved, although they could make a substantial contribution to a better understanding of soil behaviour and soil shrinkage, particularly in the zone of root activity near the soil surface (Chapter 4).

In many situations where damage has occurred *insurers* are likely to be involved. *Loss adjusters* acting on their behalf are ideally placed for ensuring that the owner of the damaged property gets relevant advice from the appropriate professionals. However, this will only be achieved if the loss adjuster has an understanding of the whole process and the available options.

Likewise, all of the professionals who give advice must have an adequate understanding of the whole process and their role within it; advice on one's own expertise cannot be given in isolation. Hopefully this book will help in achieving this goal. Any advice must take account of all evidence and be compatible with the input of others. If a number of professionals from different disciplines are involved, co-ordination in a team effort is required. The team leader must ensure that everyone is kept fully informed of all of the evidence as it becomes available. Like the loss adjuster, the team leader must have an adequate understanding of the whole process and the remedial options.

Other professions will have their role in the prevention of damage. Virtually all damage could be prevented by ensuring that the foundations are adequate. This will involve the *architect* and / or *builder;* where particular problems are identified, the engineer will be required for purpose-designed foundations. A supervisory role for all such work rests with *building control.* In addition, *planners* will have a role to play in ensuring that new housing incorporates foundations which are appropriate for future needs.

The extent of the problem

The extent of the problem has increased sharply during the past 25 years. Figure 1.3 shows the number and cost of insurance claims for subsidence each year during this period. Not all these cases are caused by trees, but it has been suggested that over 80% of subsidence claims on shrinkable clay soils can be attributed to trees and shrubs close to the property (Institution of Structural Engineers, 1994). If anything, this may be an underestimate.

This increase in claims is undoubtedly linked to the introduction of insurance cover for subsidence in 1971. If damage occurred prior to that date, it was down to the house owner to finance any repair, and they usually preferred to undertake minimal work. It was only if a third party tree owner was involved that other funds might become available, but even claims of this sort were comparatively rare. There was a general acceptance that buildings were liable to move seasonally and some damage was likely to occur in dry spells; the nec-

essary repairs were part of normal house maintenance and only if damage became severe was it deemed necessary to take more specific remedial action.

Insurance cover was introduced in 1971 at the request of the building societies who were concerned at the possibility of loss of equity in the event of severe damage. As there were so few cases of severe damage, insurers considered the risk to be minimal and provided cover for block policies taken out through the building societies without additional premium. Initially the public was unaware of the existence of this cover and so there were few claims, the numbers approximately doubling each year during the first 4 years. In 1975 the rate of increase was slightly greater, but this exploded to 21,400 claims in 1976, associated with the exceptional drought conditions of that year. Not surprisingly in 1977 there were still many claims, undoubtedly the residual effect of 1976, but by 1978 and 1979 it was hoped that the number of claims had reached a steady plateau at about 8,000 per annum. This hope was not realised. During the early 1980s the number of claims rose by about 25% each year, reaching a peak of 24,000 claims in 1984, thus exceeding the claims record of 1976. This number dropped back slightly in subsequent years, but again escalated greatly during the drought period of 1989/90/91 to 60,000 in 1991, with a further peak of 47,700 in 1995. The cost, in terms of insurance claims, was £540 million in 1991 and £333 million in 1996, but this does not recognise the full extent of the problem. There are also the uninsured losses, and the many cases where the cost of repairing minor damage is less than the policy excess.

The risk of damage, as indicated by the number of claims, is clearly related to the weather conditions; the succession of droughts in recent years has greatly increased the extent of the problem. Comparison of

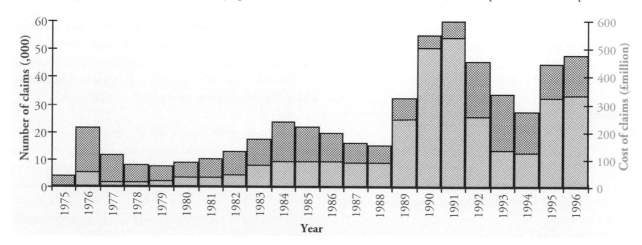

Figure 1.3
The number and cost of insurance claims since 1971.

(Data provided by Association of British Insurers.)

5

weather in different years will depend on the parameters which are used (Chapter 8), but the drought of 1975/76 was as bad, or worse, than any of the subsequent dry periods. Despite this, recent years, even of average or wet weather, have generated far more claims than arose in 1975/76. This dramatic rise is only partially caused by an increase in the amount of damage, but rather by a change in public awareness and public attitude. This has been fostered by the press; any brief period of drought will produce a spate of alarmist newspaper articles highlighting the problem, suggesting that the public should search for cracks, that such cracks are due to subsidence and that the house owner should claim on their insurance. The attitude of the public is now fundamentally different to that of 25 years ago. Movement and damage which was tolerated in the past now gives rise to claims.

In recent years there has also been an increase in the duty of care required of professionals when giving advice on this or any subject. Inadequate or wrong advice gives rise to claims for professional negligence. The simple way for professionals to protect themselves against such claims is to make sure that any potential risk is identified, however remote, and pre-emptive action taken. This approach would be reasonable if the risks could be properly identified, but accurate prediction is not possible (Chapter 18). If the risk cannot be identified, an alternative way of avoiding any possible claim is to adopt an ultra-cautious approach ensuring a massive safety factor. This may ensure that no damage ever occurs, but at a potential cost either in terms of additional precautions in house design and construction, or, more probably, in terms of damage or destruction of the treescape and the benefits which it provides. If this is to be avoided, it behoves all of us to ensure that we have a proper understanding of the cause, diagnosis, and remedy for cases of structural damage by trees. With proper understanding of the risks and the nature of the problem, it should be possible to restore public confidence and ensure a more enlightened attitude so that trees and buildings can co-exist in reasonable proximity.

Summary

1.   Trees have an essential role in the environment.

2.   Where there are shrinkable clay soils, trees are involved in at least 80% of cases of subsidence claims.

3.   Trees and buildings can co-exist harmoniously, provided there is a proper understanding of the mechanism of damage, how to prevent such damage from occurring, and of the appropriate remedies if damage does occur.

4.   Fundamental to this understanding is the role of water. The transpiration of water from the leaves during the summer is in excess of input from rainfall and other sources, leading to a moisture deficit in the summer. In almost all situations this deficit is corrected during the subsequent winter.

5.   On clay soils these changes in moisture content cause dimensional changes in the soil. If such movements occur below foundation level, they can cause damage to buildings.

6.   The extent of these movements is related to the soil properties. Soil permeability is crucial to the development and recovery of moisture deficits.

7.   In most situations moisture deficits and associated soil movements are seasonal, with full recovery during each winter. Only in exceptional circumstances does a persistent deficit develop.

8.   Level monitoring is the most effective method for investigating these movements and damage.

9.   Wherever movements are seasonal, they can be stabilized rapidly and effectively by curtailing the influence of the tree. Provided the movements are stopped in this way, the extent and cost of remedial works are minimal. In most situations this should be the preferred remedy where damage has occurred.

10.   Where trees are the cause, underpinning is only justified if there is a persistent moisture deficit and risk of unacceptable and long-term recovery or heave, or if the tree is of exceptional value. Such situations are rare.

11.   The whole interacting system of trees, soils and buildings, and the movements of water, is very variable and unpredictable. Guidelines which aim to prevent all damage will therefore inevitably need to be ultra cautious and impose unreasonable requirements.

12.   Instead of adopting a cautious approach, it should be accepted that minor damage will sometimes occur. This should be remedied by a rapid response to deal with the offending tree and to repair the damage.

13.   This approach will only be effective if there is a proper understanding of the mechanism of damage and a reappraisal of the methods of investigating and remedying this damage.

Heave damage caused by root barrier – Extensive persistent deficit from poplars – Incorrect diagnosis of subsidence based on timing of damage and erroneous visual observations – Value of level distortion survey – Significance of dead roots – Heave damage can develop in summer.

Background

The site is in south Essex, on London Clay. I was instructed in early 1978 by the solicitors acting for the owners of the trees who were defendants in an action which had been brought for the costs of remedial underpinning to an adjacent building.

The trees

The relevant trees were three poplars, located at the positions shown on the site plan in CS Figure 1.1. These trees had been felled and all evidence removed prior to my involvement; the location and dimensions are therefore based on other reports. From the description, and development of suckers, at least one was white poplar (*Populus alba*); the others were probably hybrid black poplars (*P.* x *euramericana*). There was no information on previous management of the trees.

History of building

The property, a chalet bungalow, had been built in 1973/74 by a relative of the plaintiff, working to standard plans. These plans had specified that the foundations should suit local requirements, and the plaintiff was advised by local authority building control to construct foundations using concrete to a depth of 0.9m.

While digging the trenches, tree roots were encountered up to 50mm in diameter, and on seeing these roots, whose origin was obviously the poplars on the adjoining property, the building inspector instructed that a tree root barrier be constructed. It was specified that the underground parts of this barrier should be concrete, taken to a depth of 2m. It was located 1m from the flank wall of the garage (extending further to the front than shown in the site plan).

Construction was completed in November 1974, and during that winter minor cracking was noted.

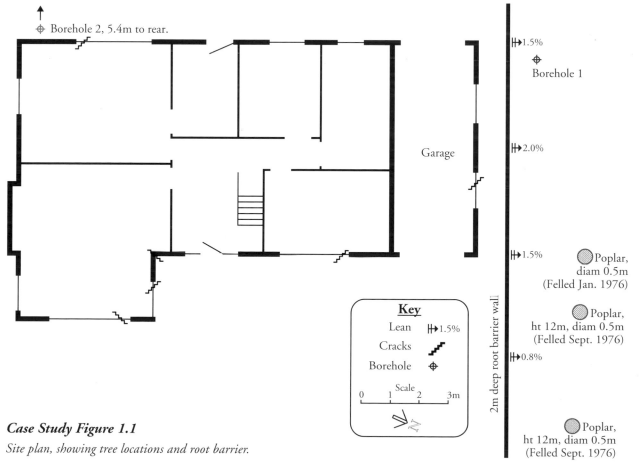

Case Study Figure 1.1

Site plan, showing tree locations and root barrier.

By September 1975 extensive damage was present throughout the building. It was agreed to remove the nearest of the poplar trees, and to reduce another by 50%. This work was undertaken in January 1976.

At the same time an underpinning contractor excavated a trial hole adjacent to the projecting front section of the building. This confirmed the 900mm deep foundations. This hole was extended by auger to 3.25m, with roots up to 4mm diameter observed to a depth of 2.25m. These roots were thought to be dead, and this was subsequently confirmed from samples submitted to the Royal Botanic Gardens at Kew. The contractor concluded:-

> "There is little doubt that the right hand section of the property and part of the front have suffered due to the cumulative effect of the dry summers of recent years culminating in the very dry one we experienced last year [1975], together with the dehydrating influence of the poplar tree roots. The resultant severe shrinkage of the supporting clay strata must have consequently caused differential settlement of the foundation itself."

The location and direction of the main cracks in the building are shown on the plan in CS Figure 1.1.

A structural engineer inspected and reported in May 1976. The following extracts are taken from his report:-

> "During my survey on viewing the whole property at front and rear elevations there were noticeable signs of a structure having tilted downwards at the garage end. The external brickwork cracks were all wider at the top than at the bottom."

> "It is plain to me from all the evidence available including the pattern of damage to the external walls that differential settlement within the property's foundations has occurred and that this settlement is on account of shrinkage to the clay substrata supporting the foundations. It is clear that the roots from the poplar trees on the adjoining land ... ... have encroached, the root barrier being too shallow. It cannot be impossible that the root barrier may have cut off all the original roots growing from the poplars because they are basically shallow-rooting trees. This of itself however does not mean that the roots cannot have found their way both beneath and round the barrier and then come back to their normal shallow rooting so as to cause the clear subsidence which I found. Had the root barrier been taken to a depth of 3.5m and been made sufficiently long then it may have well served to prevent the roots from encroaching at all but there is no doubt in my mind that 2m was a totally inadequate depth."

He concluded his report with:

> "The pattern of damage to the external walls are text book examples of differential settlement"

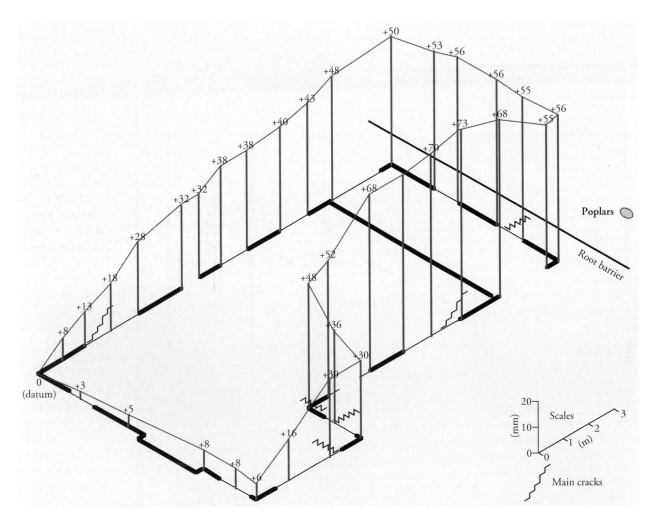

Case Study Figure 1.2

Level distortion survey (February 1978). Note high part of building closest to trees.

8

The engineer instructed that the remaining poplars should be felled, with this work undertaken in September 1976.

The whole property was underpinned, using a pier and beam system, in autumn 1976. The underpinning of the right hand flank wall of the garage was taken to 3.5m. During this work it was noted that the ground near the garage was very hard and dry; elsewhere desiccation was less noticeable.

I was instructed, on behalf of the owners of the poplars, 15 months after the underpinning was complete, and undertook my site investigations in February 1978.

Site investigations.

I used a water level for a level distortion survey; the results are shown in CS Figure 1.2. There was a zero closing error. The site plan (CS Figure 1.1) shows the lean which I recorded in the boundary wall, which was founded on the root barrier.

I drilled two boreholes at the locations shown on the site plan. Borehole 1 was to a depth of 5.0m and borehole 2 to 4.0m. Soil samples were taken at 0.25m intervals for determination of moisture content. Moisture content profiles are shown in CS Figure 1.3.

When drilling borehole 1 I recorded fine root activity to 2.0m and occasional fine roots to 2.75m. None of these roots were large enough for identification. No roots were found below 1m in borehole 2.

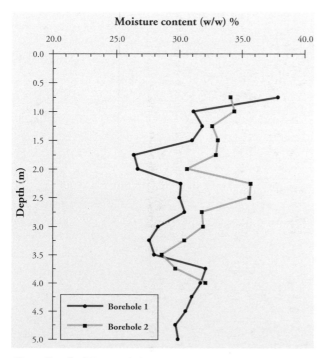

Case Study Figure 1.3
Moisture content profiles for boreholes drilled February 1978.

DISCUSSION

Cause of damage

The level distortion survey is entirely inconsistent with the allegation of damage caused by subsidence. The lowest part of the building was the point furthest from the trees where there should be least root activity, whereas the highest point was on the frontage close to the trees.

The logical explanation is that the damage was caused by rehydration and swelling of the clay, producing heave of the foundations. The property was built on clay which was already severely desiccated. At the same time, the root barrier, although only 2m deep, severed virtually all of the roots which extended beneath the house. These roots ceased water uptake so that the process of rehydration and swelling of the clay could start. Within 12 months it was beginning to cause damage, with this damage continuing to develop until the property was underpinned. This underpinning effectively locked the building into its distorted state.

It is notable that, on the basis of visual observation, the engineer acting for the house owner concluded that there was subsidence at the right hand end, particularly in the region of the garage. He later dismissed my level distortion survey as "building error" and maintained that the development of cracking in the autumn of 1975, with further worsening of the damage in the summer of 1976, indicated that heave could not be involved and that damage must have been caused by subsidence.

There is a simple explanation for his misinterpretation. The level distortion survey shows that the amount of heave is less in the front corner of the building closest to the trees. The angular distortion produced by this makes it appear that the garage is tilted down, but the distortion survey shows this is an optical illusion. The reduced heave in this area was probably caused by some continuing root activity extending beneath the barrier wall. In the summer this was sufficient to reduce, or perhaps even reverse, the rehydration and heave. This accentuated the angular distortion at that time of year so that the cracks became more obvious.

It was also claimed that heave could not be involved because of the absence of any evidence of lateral movement of the foundations. However, as these foundations were laid in the winter and were comparatively shallow, it is unlikely that they would have enclosed desiccated clay, and there was therefore no reason why they should have been vulnerable to such damage. It is notable that the deep foundations of the barrier wall had rotated.

The moisture content profiles indicate that the soil close to the trees was significantly drier than the control. However, as the last of the trees had been felled 18 months prior to the investigation, these soil investigations provide little information on the cause of the damage. It can be estimated that the soil moisture deficit below foundation level in borehole 1 was 128mm, indicating a potential for a further 32mm of heave, assuming WSF = 4.

9

It is more relevant to note that the roots observed in the engineer's trial hole and borehole adjacent to the property in February 1976 were dead, and so could not have been causing soil drying and subsidence.

The engineer's criticism that the 2m deep barrier was inadequate is meaningless. It was sufficient to sever and kill all, or at least the vast majority, of the roots extending right under the building. A deeper barrier might have prevented any localised drying under the front corner of the garage, but any action which severed the roots was sufficient to cause heave.

The most definitive way for proving that heave, rather than subsidence, was the cause would have been level monitoring. However, by the time of my involvement the building was already underpinned so that such exercise was no longer practical. If the house owner's engineer had investigated the matter more carefully and thus appreciated the pattern of distortion, he should at least have undertaken such work.

Lessons to be learnt

- It does not require trees to be removed for heave to occur. Any factor, such as the root barrier, which severs or damages the roots, can allow heave to develop.

- The eye is easily deceived. Do not rely on visual observation to determine the pattern of distortion; a level distortion survey is essential.

- Even where the movements are primarily caused by heave, there can be a localised reversal if there is any remaining vegetation. In this way, cracks may develop in late summer, even where heave is the primary cause of movement.

- To my disappointment, the defendant's insurance company were not prepared to back my opinion in court against that of the plaintiff's engineer. The case occurred early in my career, but I trust that these days the opinions of an arboriculturist would be endorsed more firmly.

The growth and function of all plants is essentially similar. They seek to expose a large surface area (i.e. the leaves) to the sun to absorb energy for growth, and they have a structure to conduct materials such as water, nutrients and sugars to and from these leaves. This structure is composed of individual cells which have specialised to fulfil these various functions. Trees are only different in that they have evolved a more complex woody structure to provide strength and support for the leaves which enables them to compete more effectively for the sunlight.

The tissues which conduct materials within the plant are the xylem, which takes water and nutrient from the roots up to the leaves, and the phloem which distributes sugars and other plant growth materials down from the leaves through the plant. In grass and herbaceous plants these two systems are bundled together, but the evolution of woody plants (trees and bushes) has created two distinct systems, both of which can undergo secondary thickening into specialised tissues and thereby continue to grow throughout their life. On woody plants in the summer it is easy to peel the bark off a twig or branch to leave the underlying smooth surface of the wood. This wood is the xylem, and the innermost part of the bark is the phloem. Technically the term "bark" should be restricted to the outermost corky layers which protect the surface of the trunk, branches and twigs. This distinction between xylem and phloem applies to all woody tissue (i.e. twigs, branches, trunk and roots), all of which have an essentially similar structure (Figure 2.1).

Xylem

The xylem has two main functions:

i)   to provide strength to support the plant;

ii) to conduct water from the roots to the leaves.

To perform these functions, the cells are differentiated into three main types: fibres, vessels and rays. The different proportion and distribution of these cell types within the wood produces the characteristic variation in the structure of timber and forms the basis for identifying wood or root samples.

Fibres are the most common cell, which make up the bulk of wood tissue. They are normally long, thin tapering cells, often several millimetres long, and aligned parallel with the trunk. It is this mass of fibres which provides the main strength in timber.

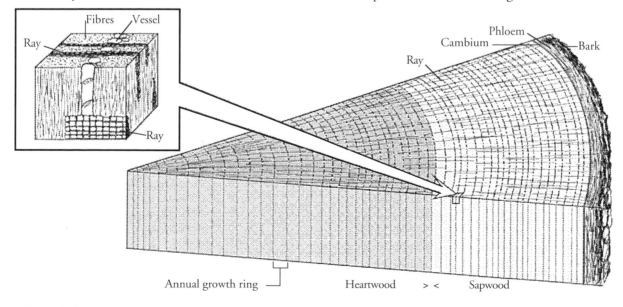

Figure 2.1
Diagram of main components of wood structure (of a ring porous hardwood)

Vessels consist of hollow cylinders made up of individual cells stacked on top of each other to form a continuous tube. The sole function of these vessels is to conduct water, and the mineral nutrients dissolved in the water, from the roots to the leaves. Theoretically a vessel can extend as a single tube from a root right through the trunk, branches and twigs to a leaf, but in practice there are some junctions and forks. The lumen (internal diameter) of the vessels is comparatively large for a cell (up to 0.3mm), and visible to the naked eye in many species of tree.

Conifers have not evolved this distinction between fibres and vessels, but instead have tracheids which fulfil the functions of both strength and water conduction.

Fibres and vessels are all dead tissues which have lost their cell contents. Although they are dead, it is necessary for the tree to be able to maintain control of them; this is achieved by the **ray cells**. These cells are aggregated together to form the medullary rays which radiate out from the centre of the tree, and are akin to vertical flanges. These rays maintain their cell contents and provide transport radially within the tree. They may be many cells wide and easily visible on a cross section of timber, or merely a single layer of cells. They may be only a few cells in height or extend for several millimetres. This variation, which is characteristic for different species, is an important aid for identifying wood or root samples.

Phloem

The main constituent of all cell walls is cellulose. This is a complex polysaccharide derived from simple sugar molecules. These sugars are produced in the leaves in the process of photosynthesis, but they must be transported from the leaf to wherever they are required for conversion to cellulose. This downward transport of sugars from the leaves to the roots occurs exclusively in the phloem. Unlike the vessels which lose their cell contents to form hollow tubes, the phloem remains a living tissue with living cells, connected by intercellular strands through which the sugars move.

The rays in the xylem extend into the phloem. By this means, there is continuity between living cells in the outermost phloem and the centre of the tree.

On the outside of the phloem is the inner bark and the corky outer bark. This is usually ridged and furrowed into the characteristic patterns which are seen on the trunk of any tree.

Cambium and growth

A tree increases in size by the carefully regulated production of fresh xylem and phloem. This takes place in a layer of cells between the phloem and the xylem known as the cambium. The cambial layer is a complete envelope between the xylem and the phloem. During growth the cells are constantly dividing longitudinally, the majority of these differentiating on the inside into fibres or vessels, but sometimes cells form on the outer side to produce phloem. It is because of the weakness induced by the layer of dividing cambial cells that the phloem can be easily peeled away from the xylem during the time when the cambium is active in the summer.

In temperate climates, such as Britain, growth of the aerial parts only occurs during the summer months when the tree is in leaf and photosynthesising to produce the sugar which is needed for this growth. Energy is needed for this process and the reduced temperature and light in winter are inadequate, so that deciduous species lose their leaves and the growth of evergreen species is inhibited. In the early summer, growth tends to be rapid and the fibres and vessels (or tracheids in conifers) produce large cells with thin walls. Towards the end of the summer the walls become thicker until growth finally stops. This seasonal variation in cell dimensions produces a discernible annual growth ring.

Not only the dimensions but also the distribution of vessels can vary. Some species of hardwood, e.g. oak and ash, form most of their vessels in the spring, and predominantly fibres for the rest of the season (these are known as ring-porous species). The large size of the vessels makes these annual rings very easy to distinguish. In other species (diffuse porous), the formation of vessels occurs throughout the season, and the only variation is in cell wall dimensions or the production of special cells at the end of the season.

These growth rings in the aerial parts are produced every year, so that counting their number at the base of the trunk will reveal the age of the tree (or in a branch, will reveal the age of the branch). This should be done with care, preferably by inspecting the rings under a low power microscope, as sudden fluctuations in growth rate can produce a mis-leading "false ring" (Chapter 14, page 228).

The factors which control the growth of the root system are different (see Chapter 3), and so roots do not produce regular annual growth rings.

Water transport in the xylem vessels of the trunk and branches only occurs in the outermost annual rings, mostly in the current season's ring. There is frequently a clear distinction between the central heartwood of the tree, and the outer sapwood, but not all of the sapwood is necessarily functional for water transport. The heartwood becomes totally non-functional; gums and other materials are deposited in the vessels by the rays. By contrast, the whole cross section of a root will normally remain functional and active for water transport.

In addition to the growth in diameter of the trunk, branches, shoots and roots (secondary growth), extension growth also occurs at the end of all shoots and roots (primary growth). At the ends of these there is a cap of dividing cells which rapidly differentiate into xylem and phloem. The cambium then forms between these elements and starts to divide, so as to increase the diameter of the young shoot or root.

In a shoot the tip overwinters in a terminal bud. In some species (e.g. beech) this bud contains the complete shoot and leaves in miniature, merely waiting for the cells to expand and the cell walls to harden. In other species (e.g. poplar) the shoot tip extends throughout the season, forming fresh leaves at intervals as it grows, finally pausing in the autumn to form another terminal resting bud. These terminal buds often leave a characteristic scar on the twig which can be identified for several years. These scars allow the annual extension growth of twigs to be measured, just as the annual growth rings can be counted in the stem.

The age of some species can also be determined by the branching pattern which is produced by the development of the lateral buds. These can produce a whorl of branches, with the number of these whorls indicating the age (Chapter 14, page 231).

The control of growth, and carbon economy

The growth of a tree, like all plants, is highly organized and ordered. They possess a very complex control mechanism, mediated through growth hormones which influence all parts of the growth and development of the tree.

The prime objective is to maximise the production and utilization of the energy reserves of the tree. This energy is in the form of carbon compounds, which are obtained from carbon dioxide in the atmosphere via the process of photosynthesis; this is described in further detail in the next section. The end product of photosynthesis is sugar ($C_6H_{12}O_6$). This sugar can then be converted to cellulose or lignin and laid down in the cell walls, or converted to starch as a food reserve. The processes of growth, form and function have evolved to optimise the use of carbon by the plant, and are best understood in terms of this carbon balance.

To maximise photosynthesis, the tree must project its leaves to the light in the most advantageous way. These leaves must be supported by a twig and branch structure which must be sufficiently robust to withstand gravity and exposure to extreme wind conditions, and this whole structure must be robustly anchored to the ground by the root system. All of these processes are influenced by the allocation and utilisation of carbon reserves.

Trees often compete with each other to obtain maximum light and so may have to adapt their shape by additional height growth if the light is from above, or by growing with a lean of the trunk or developing long lateral branches to obtain lateral light. Any additional growth of this sort utilizes additional energy. If there is this competition, it may be essential to use energy in this way, but for an isolated tree it is more efficient to develop a compact and rounded crown shape, as this minimises the amount of wood tissue (or energy) which is needed in the twig and branch structure. This also reduces the stresses from gravity and the exposure to wind. Thus the general shape of the tree must strike a balance between these conflicting requirements.

In engineering terms, the tree achieves this shape with incredible efficiency. It has been shown (Mattheck 1990) that growth of the load-carrying parts of the tree are determined by the law of uniform surface stress, so that the tree achieves a uniform mechanical stress along the whole length of a stem from the structural roots through the trunk to the top of the tree. If parts are subjected to higher stresses, they are supported by additional adaptive growth so as to reduce the stress peak. This ensures that the most efficient use is made of available carbon resources so as to optimise the mechanical strength of all parts. At the same time the tree is balancing this allocation of carbon resources between the need for mechanical support by the twigs, branches, trunk and structural roots, as well as the need to maximise the leaf area.

However, maximising light is only a part of the overall balance. Photosynthesis requires water (see next section) which must be obtained from the soil by the roots. Growth also needs essential nutrients such as nitrogen, phosphorus, potassium and many trace elements, which are also obtained from the soil. The roots must be capable of exploiting the soil to obtain the essential water and nutrients. This involves a balance between the carbon allocation for mechanical strength and the requirements for growth of both roots and leaves. Resources must also be allocated for reproduction (flowers and seeds), resisting attack by pests or diseases, wound repair after pruning or other injury, and to provide for the major variations in the growth rate which are imposed by the seasonal cycle of weather.

There are many different factors which influence growth, but the availability of water is one of the most important. If there is a shortage of water the growth rate will be reduced, and if the availability falls even lower it will stop all growth. For this reason, agricultural crops are often irrigated to maintain optimum growth. However, excess water can lead to waterlogging of the soil, which will prevent the roots from functioning or even kill them. There is therefore an optimum level of water for growth, with either a shortage or excess leading to reduced growth.

Other factors which can influence growth rate are light, temperature, exposure (including a whole range of climatic variables) and nutrient availability. There are optimum values for all these factors, with higher or lower levels reducing the growth rate until limiting values are reached where growth stops. Indeed, only under exceptional or artificially controlled circumstances are these factors maintained at their optimum. Growth will almost always be limited by one or more of these factors. Under different circumstances, it will be a different combination of factors which are critical to the growth rate.

Leaf function and transpiration

The main function of the leaf is to absorb the energy of sunlight and use this to produce the sugar which is the essential basis for all plant growth. This is the process known as photosynthesis. The energy of the sun is absorbed by the green chlorophyll pigment within the leaf, and this energy is used to convert carbon dioxide and water into sugar.

Carbon dioxide + water $\xrightarrow{\text{energy from sun}}$ sugar + oxygen

$$6CO_2 + 6H_2O = C_6H_{12}O_6 + 6O_2$$

Although this process uses water, less than 1% of the water required by a tree (or any plant) is incorporated into sugar or forms part of the cell contents. The

remaining more than 99% is lost in the form of transpiration from the leaves. It is therefore necessary to have an understanding of this transpirational loss.

Chlorophyll which absorbs the sunlight is contained within chloroplasts in the cells of the leaf. For photosynthesis to occur, it is necessary for carbon dioxide from the air to be absorbed into the cells containing these chloroplasts. This absorption is a two part process. The gaseous carbon dioxide is first dissolved in water on the outside of the individual cells, and this solution then passes through the cell wall to the chloroplasts. To enable rapid absorption of carbon dioxide the cells require a large surface area covered by a thin film of water. For this reason the centre of a leaf consists of vertically aligned palisade cells and loosely packed spongy, mesophyll cells, which expose an enormous surface area for gaseous diffusion (Figure 2.2). This is similar to the internal surface of our lungs which are adapted for dissolving oxygen.

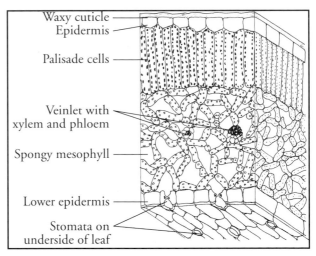

Figure 2.2
Diagrammatic cross section of typical leaf

At the same time as the carbon dioxide is being dissolved in the film of water, water is also evaporating and being lost from the surface of the cells. It is this loss of water which is known as "transpiration". Once again it is analogous to our lungs; as we breathe out, we also lose water.

Much of the structure of a leaf is adapted to control this transpirational loss of water. It is for this reason that the spongy mesophyll cells are in the centre of the leaf where they are protected by an outer layer of epidermal cells and by a thick waxy cuticle on both upper and lower surfaces of the leaf. However, they cannot be completely enclosed as it is also necessary for carbon dioxide to reach the mesophyll. The epidermis and cuticle are therefore punctured by minute pores known as stomata, which allow gas to diffuse into the centre of the leaf. At the same time as the carbon dioxide enters, water vapour diffuses out through the stomata and is lost.

Stomata occur in enormous numbers, mostly on the underside of the leaf. A single oak leaf can have in excess of a million stomata. Each consists of a pair of crescent-shaped guard cells. When these have adequate water they become swollen and turgid. The pressure caused by the swelling opens a pore between the guard cells and gaseous diffusion can occur. If the leaf loses excessive water, the first cells to lose their turgidity are the guard cells, which causes the pores to close. Once they have closed further gaseous diffusion and loss of water is restricted. Stomata only reopen when turgidity is restored by additional water reaching the leaf.

Stomatal control thereby provides a very efficient self-regulating means of controlling the transpirational water loss from the leaf. Whenever there is an adequate supply of water, the stomata are open and carbon dioxide can diffuse in while water vapour diffuses out, but if there is insufficient water the stomata close to prevent further water loss. Although closure of the stomata will stop water loss, it also stops carbon dioxide entering, and therefore stops the process of photosynthesis. For this reason, it is important that the stomata stay open as much as possible, but this can only be achieved if there is adequate water supply to maintain turgidity. Differences in stomatal number, size, location and overall control account for some of the differences between tree species.

Once the stomata have closed, very little further water loss occurs from the leaf. The waxy cuticle over the surface of the leaf is virtually impervious to water, and the leaf can therefore remain flaccid and inactive for long periods. Only in extreme drought does irreversible water loss occur, resulting in death of the leaf. There is very little water lost through the bark, twigs, branches or trunk of the tree.

Moisture deficits, suction and water potential

As water is lost from the leaf, it sets up a suction within the leaf. The leaf is at the extremity of a continuous system of vessel cells, which extend from the roots, through the trunk, branches and twigs to terminate in the fine veins of the leaf. The loss of water from the leaf sets up a gradient throughout this continuous system, so that water flows from the roots to the leaves.

These suctions are quantified in terms of water potential. As described in later chapters, the concept of water potential can be applied throughout the plant and soil, and provides a unifying and coherent approach to the study of water movement. Water potential (ψ) is defined as the difference between the chemical potential of water in the system and that of pure free water at the same temperature and atmospheric pressure. It quantifies the capacity of the water to do work in comparison to the work an equal mass of pure free water could do. Water will always move from a region of high potential to one of low potential. It is measured in energy per unit volume, which under the standardised system of SI measurement is the Pascal (Pa). As this is a very small unit it is more usual to refer to kilo pascals (kPa; where 1kPa = 1000Pa).

Unfortunately throughout the literature there is a wide variety of different methods used for expressing this same concept. Although it is preferable to use the term water potential, in plants and soils these values are usually negative. It is often easier to think of this negative water potential as a suction, with the suction expressed in the same units (kPa), but as a positive value. As measurement of soil suctions is now becoming a practical technique (see Chapter 13, page 206) with results usually presented as positive suction values, suction, rather than negative potential, has been used throughout this book. Although the kilopascal should be preferred, engineers tend to favour newtons/m² or kilonewtons/m², with 1kN/m² being the same as 1 kPa. Prior to implementation of the SI units, the favoured unit using the CGS system was the 'bar', 1 bar being equal to 100 kPa. As a further complication, as many correlations between soil properties produce a straight-line relationship if they are expressed on a logarithmic scale, suctions are often expressed on the pF scale, which is $\log_{10}$ of the equivalent height of water expressed in cm. These different units are compared in Figure 2.3.

Bar	kPa	kN/m²	cm water	pF
0.1	10	10	100	2
1	100	100	1000	3
1.5	150	150	1500	3.2
10	1000	1000	10000	4
15	1500	1500	15000	4.2
100	10000	10000	100000	5

Figure 2.3

Units for measurement of water suction in plants or soil.

15

Water potential in the plant has been extensively studied and quantified (see Kozlowski (1982) for a detailed review). The potential which develops in a leaf can vary widely, with some desert plants and also alpine plants being capable of developing very high suctions (6000 kPa or greater), but in temperate climates maximum suction in the leaf is typically between 1500 and 2000 kPa. Within the branches and main trunk of trees there is a decrease in the suction as a result of the resistance to water flow. This gradient between the leaf and root is about 200 to 500 kPa, so that the maximum suction exerted by the roots on the soil is typically about 1500 kPa. It is the development of this suction which causes water to move from the soil into the plant. 1500 kPa is commonly considered the maximum suction achieved by tree roots in temperate climates at their wilting point. Although there have been extensive investigations into the potentials developed by agricultural and forestry crops, there is little comparable information which is directly relevant to amenity trees. It is known that it varies greatly between species and cultivars, and will also be influenced both by the availability of moisture in the soil and by the evaporative conditions. For instance, open crowned trees or those in more exposed situations may have an increased rate of water loss.

Where water is freely available, maximum photosynthesis will occur and water flow and loss will be rapid. The rate of this will depend on the weather conditions and the daylength, but peak rates in June/July in southern England will be in excess of 5mm per day (Chapter 8, page 121). This equates to a loss of 50,000 litres per hectare. If there is a continuous forest canopy, it would be possible to convert this to the water use per individual trees (i.e. at 100 trees/hectare, each would be losing 500 litres/day). An isolated tree will potentially have a far higher use as it will have a far larger leaf area (extending down the side of the crown to ground level) and be exploiting soil from a surface area extending beyond the canopy spread.

In practice, even if water is freely available and conditions are conducive to high transpiration rates (i.e. high temperature, low vapour pressure and sufficient air movement), the absorption of water usually cannot keep pace with transpiration loss and a deficit develops within the plant which may be sufficient to lead to loss of turgidity and temporary closure of the stomata. As a result, there are marked diurnal variations in deficit, with the minimum at or near dawn and a maximum in late afternoon. For instance, the suction in leaves of sugar maple (*Acer saccharum*) and paper bark birch (*Betula papyrifera*) trees increased from about 300 kPa in the morning to as much as 2000 kPa for the maple and 1600 kPa for birch in the early afternoon (Periera and Kozlowski, 1978). This increase in the suction and build-up of a water deficit results in stomatal closure to reduce the amount of water loss. Under conditions of extreme drought, a tree can remain under permanent water stress with the stomata closed and negligible further water loss.

For these reasons, and because it is unusual for water to be freely available, the actual rates of transpiration are far lower than the theoretical maxima. In such circumstances it becomes a meaningless exercise to try to calculate the amounts of water which might be lost from a tree, or to use this as a basis for comparison. Water loss will always be heavily dependent on water availability.

Relationship between growth and transpiration rate

The sugar which is produced in the leaf during photosynthesis is the chemical building block for growth. This sugar is converted by a process of polymerisation into cellulose and more complex lignin. These materials form the cell walls and the solid "woody" part of the plant. Before sugar can be used in this way, it is moved in solution down the plant in the phloem to the location where it is required for growth. The sugar is then converted to cellulose and laid down in the walls of the cells as they divide and grow.

If a plant is to keep growing in this way it must maintain photosynthesis and the associated sugar and cellulose production. However, whenever the tree is photosynthesising, water is also being lost from the leaf as transpiration and so growth can only be sustained if there is adequate water available to make good this transpirational loss and to maintain turgidity of the leaf. This is one reason for the close correlation between availability of water and growth.

In practice the situation is far more complicated, with low water availability having an influence on many aspects of growth (Zahner, 1968). A biological model showing the inter-relationship of many of the factors which are affected by water availability and thereby influence growth has been proposed by Fritts (1966), and is reproduced in Figure 2.4. Even this model is over-simplified.

The overall effect of these inter-relationships can be demonstrated by comparing the width of the annual growth rings with the rainfall (Figure 2.5). In this example the situation is complicated by the fact

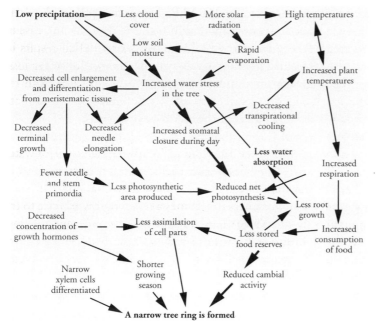

Figure 2.4

Proposed model for the effect of hot dry weather in the formation of a narrow growth ring. *(from Fritts, 1966).*

will be reflected in a drop in growth rate until new roots regenerate to restore uptake and growth. Alternatively, a tree which is pruned (or defoliated by insects) will have reduced leaf area and therefore reduced water loss, and will be unable to produce as much cellulose for growth. This will result in narrower growth rings. Initially the roots of a tree which has been pruned will be capable of providing the previous amounts of water so that water stress is less likely, but new root growth will be curtailed by the lack of photosynthates.

Inspection of the width of the annual growth rings can therefore provide an assessment of the amount of water used by the tree in any previous year or years. Details of the methods of assessing growth rate and interpreting the past patterns of growth are described in Chapter 14.

Although there is a relationship between growth rate and water use, direct comparison should only be made between individuals of the same species. Different species can have very different rates for producing photosynthates per unit of water lost as transpiration, and mechanisms which control the growth rate can be very different so that they respond in different ways to water stress. Chapter 9 considers the variation in the water requirements of different species.

Care should also be taken to avoid too literal an interpretation of the relationship between growth and water use, as other factors can confound it. In particular, a vigorous tree will generate surplus sugar during the summer and polymerise this to starch which is deposited as granules in the cell. All cells can be used for starch storage in this way, but roots are particularly important for this purpose. In times of stress, or at times when growth is particularly rapid so that demand for sugar for cell production outstrips supply, these starch reserves can be reconverted to sugar and utilised. The starch thus acts as a buffer, cushioning between the periods of excess production and demand. If a vigorous tree with abundant reserves is pruned or defoliated so as to reduce the rate of photosynthesis, it can use these starch reserves to maintain growth, thereby using far less water than might be expected from the growth.

that pine trees (as well as many other species) make much of their growth early in the season, whereas late season photosynthesis is allocated more to replenishment of energy reserves. For this reason the best correlation is achieved by comparing growth with rainfall in the current + previous season. With most species the effect on ring width is particularly apparent during extreme drought conditions such as in 1976 when growth of most trees was severely curtailed. This can usually be seen in a very narrow annual growth ring for that year.

In addition to the factors shown in Figure 2.4, many other factors can influence growth rate, but these usually also have a direct or indirect effect on the water use. For instance, a tree which suffers root damage will be unable to obtain water as easily as in previous years. This will cause water stress more rapidly, which

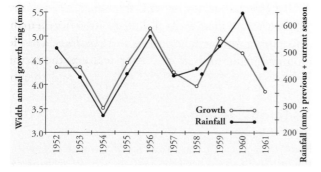

Figure 2.5

Relationship between ring width and rainfall for Pinus resinosa. *(derived from Zahner and Donnelly, 1967)*

Brief mention should also be made of the significance of respiration. All of the biochemical processes which are occurring in the cells, whether in cell division, production of cellulose or starch, for water and nutrient absorption or the myriad of other essential processes, all require energy. This energy is obtained in the same way as we obtain our energy; that is by the oxidation of sugar back to carbon dioxide and water. Just as we must have oxygen for this, so also must the plant.

Annual cycle of growth

There is a popular misconception that water uptake is synonymous with rising sap in the spring. Water pressure in the plant often increases in the spring as the roots become more active and mobilise the sugar reserves which have been stored as starch, but the extra quantity of water which can be absorbed within the plant is minimal. Significant water loss only starts to occur once the leaves have started to expand and photosynthesis and transpiration commences. Subject to water availability, transpiration will then continue throughout the summer.

As long as the plant is able to maintain turgidity in the leaves, the process of photosynthesis continues, but, as seen in the previous section, water availability is usually limiting to growth.

In the autumn, prior to leaf fall, the conducting vessels taking water to the leaf are blocked off and an abscission layer forms. The leaf also undergoes extensive changes as materials, particularly the green chlorophyll, are re-absorbed into the tree. This produces the autumn colours. As the abscission layer forms, further water loss ceases. Water loss during the winter is negligible.

The loss of water from the leaf is therefore highly seasonal, but occurs at a comparatively uniform rate through the summer, subject to day length, weather conditions and water availability. The influence which this has on the moisture in the soil is considered in Chapter 5.

Evergreen trees obviously retain their leaves throughout the winter and will continue to have some water loss during this period. However, the low temperatures greatly reduce growth rate and photosynthesis, and so the amount of water loss will be far less than during the summer months.

Summary

1.   The leaves are the site of photosynthesis which produces the raw materials for plant growth.

2.   For photosynthesis to occur, carbon dioxide must dissolve in a film of water within the leaf. This film of water is constantly evaporating, and being lost from the leaf as water vapour. This water loss is known as transpiration.

4.   The loss of water by transpiration and the entry of carbon dioxide into the leaf are controlled by minute pores, the stomata, on the undersurface of the leaf. They only open and allow photosynthesis and transpiration to occur when water is available.

5.   **More than 99% of water required by the plant is lost as transpiration.** Less than 1% goes into direct growth.

6.   The loss of water from the leaf sets up a negative potential (or suction gradient) through the tree, and water is drawn along this gradient from the roots to the leaves. The negative potential in the root draws the moisture from the soil. The loss of water from the leaves is therefore the driving force behind all of the water movements involved in soil drying.

7.   When water is available to the leaf, transpiration loss for a given species is approximately proportional to the leaf area, although other factors such as crown exposure also influence the rate of loss.

8.   If water is freely available, growth and transpiration are rapid, but availability of water is usually a limiting factor. Different species of tree differ in their efficiency in utilising water. This is not necessarily related to the growth rate of that species.

9.   Other factors, notably light, temperature, exposure and nutrient status also influence growth rate. All of these factors are only rarely at their optimum level, but are usually limiting growth rate. Under different circumstances, there will be different factors which limit growth.

10.   Trees, in common with all plants, have a complex control mechanism over their growth. This is mediated through growth hormones and ensures optimum production and utilisation of energy reserves.

Additional reading

Kozlowski, T.T. (1982). Water supply and tree growth. Review in Forestry Abstracts 43, 2, 57 - 95.

Zahner, R. (1968). Water deficits and growth of trees. Vol.2, Ch. 5 of Water deficits and plant growth. Ed. T.T. Kozlowski. Academic Press. 191-254

Oak causing damage to semi-detached house – Engineer's concern of heave – No evidence of persistent desiccation – Tree felled – Level monitoring shows 80% recovery in first winter – No subsequent damage.

Background

The site is in a village in Cambridgeshire.

The property is a semi-detached chalet bungalow which was built in 1968 (CS Figure 2.1, and site plan at CS Figure 2.2).

In 1983 the left semi-detached was sold, with a standard House Buyer's Report and Valuation undertaken by a chartered surveyor. This survey made no mention of any trees, and reported that the dwelling was free from major structural defects.

In 1985 the new owners were contacted by an engineer who was investigating damage to the right half. He drew attention to damage in the left half of which the owners were unaware. Once alerted to this damage they notified their insurers, who intimated a claim against the surveyor, alleging a negligent survey. At the same time, the engineer who was acting for the owners of the right half agreed to act for both owners.

My instructions came in February 1986 from the solicitors acting for the professional indemnity insurers of the surveyor.

The tree

The only tree of relevance was an oak (*Quercus robur*). This stood in the front garden of the left half, close to the common boundary and 8.9m from the front elevation. The tree was approximately 13m high, with a trunk diameter of 71cm. The crown structure showed that it had been heavily, but expertly, pruned, probably in 1968 at the time of construction of the building.

Engineer's initial investigations

The engineer described the worst damage around the front door and porch of the right half, where there was up to 10mm of outward displacement of the bricks below d.p.c.. This gradually diminished across the front elevation, being 2mm at the party wall and reducing to zero beneath the lounge window of the left half. Associated with the movement of the front wall, there was an 8mm wide crack in the floor of the porch. A 15mm diagonal fracture was recorded beneath the lounge window (although I could find no evidence for a crack of this size). He assessed the overall damage as BRE Category 3.

A trial pit beneath the lounge window of the right half recorded 260mm thick strip footings, founded 940mm below ground level. The hole was extended by soil auger, revealing a firm to stiff clay with chalk inclusions and small sand lenses. The soil was described as too dry for easy augering (in November 1985).

The engineer considered two options:-

i) Removal of tree. He dismissed this on the grounds that the tree was older than the building and that there was an unacceptable risk of heave.

ii) Underpinning. He recommended this to a depth of 3m as a continuous strip across the full width of the front elevation of both properties, and extending 4m along both ends, with additional precautions internally against the risk of heave.

Case Study Figure 2.1
Oak tree in front garden of chalet bungalow.

My investigations

My initial investigations were restricted to the left half. The results of the level distortion survey of this half are shown on CS Figure 2.2.

I drilled a borehole 1m in front of the party wall in March 1986. This revealed:-

0 - 0.25m   Gravelly topsoil/fill
0.25 - 0.6m   Yellow sandy clay with small flints and chalk
0.6 - 1.8m   Blue/grey sandy clay with small flints and chalk, and sandy lenses
1.8 - 3.2m   Uniform blue/grey clay with occasional small stones

The Geological survey map indicated that the site lay on Chalk Marl of the Lower Chalk, with the underlying Gault Clay outcropping about 75m away on a virtually level site. This borehole suggested that the surface of this Gault was at a depth of about 1.8m beneath the property.

When drilling this hole, water started to seep in at 1.8m making it impractical to take soil samples for moisture content determination. However, the condition and texture of the soil did not suggest any significant desiccation.

When drilling the borehole a 20mm diameter oak root was encountered at 0.25m. There were abundant fine roots to a depth of 1.6m and occasional fine roots down to 2.5m with very occasional roots to 2.9m. The majority of the fine roots below 2m appeared to be dead.

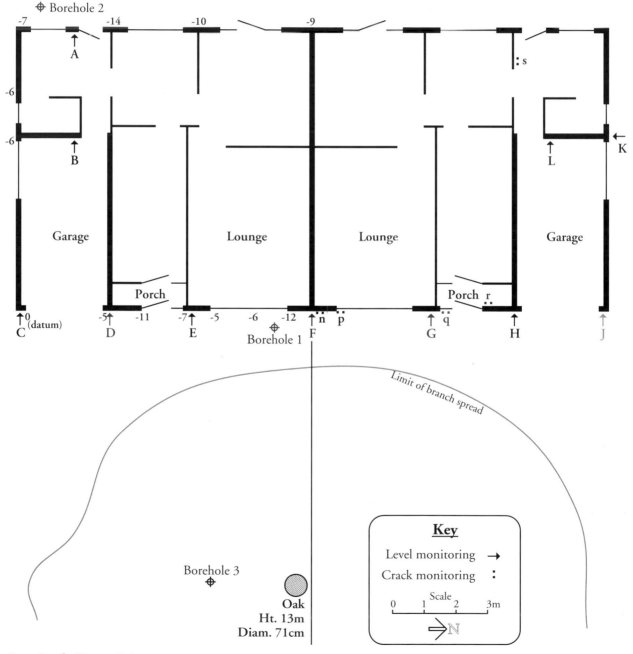

Case Study Figure 2.2

Site plan including location of level monitoring markers, and results of level distortion survey (mm) relative to datum at highest point on brickcourse.

Changes in level (mm) compared to 30/9/86:-						
Marker	11.3.86	30.9.86	8.1.87	7.5.87	22.9.87	29.3.87
A	Datum	Datum	Datum	Datum	Datum	Datum
B	+3.9	0	+3.1	+3.9	+4.2	+4.4
C	+2.0	0	+1.4	+1.7	+2.4	+2.9
D	+3.5	0	+2.6	+3.9	+4.6	+5.2
E	+4.0	0	+3.0	+5.0	+5.9	+6.9
F	+10.7	0	+8.6	+12.0	+13.2	+14.6
G	-	0	+13.9	+18.5	+19.5	+20.7
H	-	0	+8.7	+12.5	+13.2	+14.0
J	-	0	+4.1	+6.0	+6.2	+6.7
K	-	0	+0.6	+2.0	+1.6	-
L	-	0	+1.5	+2.4	-	+3.1
Crack monitoring (mm) compared to 30/9/86:-						
n	Front wall	0	-1.003	-1.089	-1.134	-1.162
p	Below window	0	-0.921	-1.162	-1.170	-1.142
q	D.P.C.	0	-8.26	-8.96	-9.14	-9.12
r	Porch floor	0	-7.06	-7.82	-7.94	-8.04
s	Over door	0	-0.238	-0.549	-0.577	-0.581

Case Study Figure 2.3

Results of level and crack monitoring.

In March 1986 I attached level monitoring markers in the left half at the locations shown in CS Figure 2.2. On 30th September this was extended to the right half. Changes in level have been calculated by reference to station A on the rear elevation as an assumed stable datum. To facilitate comparison of all of the measurements, they are compared with the readings taken on 30/9/86. The results are tabulated in CS Figure 2.3, and shown graphically for selected stations in CS Figure 2.4. Crack monitoring was also started on 30/9/86; the results are included in CS Figure 2.3 and shown graphically in CS Figure 2.5.

Further soils investigations

In June 1986 the engineer undertook further soils investigations, drilling three boreholes at the locations shown on CS Figure 2.2. Borehole 1 confirmed my observation of a silty clay with chalk, gravel and traces of sand to a depth of 1.9m, with a firm grey silty clay below this level. In the control borehole 2 to the rear, the interface with the Gault Clay was at only 0.9m, whereas at borehole 3 in the front garden, the mix of soils extended to 3.0m. Moisture content profiles (and also the values for plastic limit, and 0.4 x liquid limit) for boreholes 1 and 2 are shown in CS Figure 2.6 (the results for borehole 3 are not included as conditions were too variable).

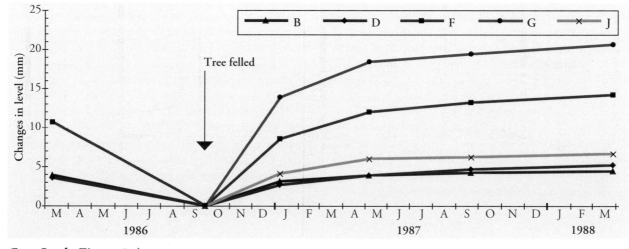

Case Study Figure 2.4

Diagram of level monitoring results.

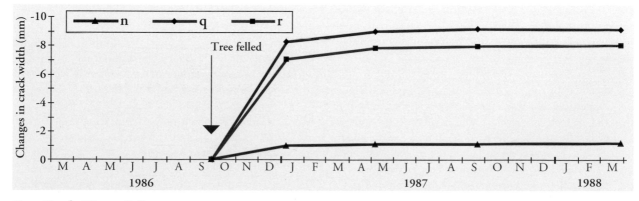

Case Study Figure 2.5

Diagram of crack monitoring results.

21

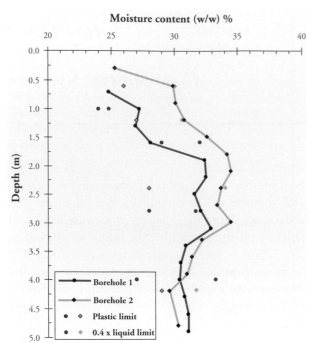

Moisture content (w/w) %

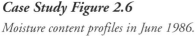

Case Study Figure 2.6

Moisture content profiles in June 1986.

DISCUSSION

From the outset there was agreement that the damage was being caused by soil movement associated with root activity of the oak tree. The worst of this damage was affecting the right half of the bungalow. Discussion centred on the appropriate remedial action, and in particular whether removal of the tree would cause an unacceptable extent and duration of heave movement.

On the basis of my initial investigations I had urged the immediate removal of the oak tree. This opinion was based on the conditions revealed in my borehole, in particular the presence of free water overlying the Gault and my assessment that the Gault was not significantly desiccated.

The previous history of the tree also suggested that significant heave could not occur. The tree had been heavily reduced at the time the bungalow was constructed. If the soil had been desiccated at that time, heave would have occurred as a result of that treatment; the lack of evidence of previous damage showed this had not occurred. A persistent moisture deficit could not have developed since the bungalow was built, as this would have shown up as distortion in the level survey.

At first sight the moisture content profiles (CS Figure 2.6) suggest that the soil at borehole 1 is significantly drier than the control. However, conditions in the two boreholes are not strictly comparable, with the interface of the underlying Gault 1m nearer the surface at the control. The engineer considered the soil at borehole 1 to be desiccated on the basis of the comparison with plastic limit and 0.4 x liquid limit; on this basis, it would only be the sample from 1.6m depth which is desiccated. It is perhaps more relevant to note that this alleged desiccation was in soil where there was free water at the time when I drilled my borehole in March.

In the light of the engineer's concern about the risk of heave, the tree was not felled prior to the summer, as a result of which my level monitoring recorded significant subsidence by September, particularly at the front of the party wall (station F, which subsided by 10.5mm).

The owner of the right half was anxious that the property should be underpinned, whereas the owner of the left half, where there was negligible damage, was anxious to avoid such work. It was eventually agreed that the tree would be felled, with this work undertaken in October 1986. This was a somewhat inappropriate time, as the seasonal movements during that summer were already over, whilst it did not allow opportunity to consider any implications from the rate of recovery in the subsequent winter.

Subsequent events confirmed that the correct decision had been taken. By 8th January 1987 station F at the front of the party wall had recovered by 8.6mm, compared with the 10.7mm of subsidence during the summer. If 80% of the seasonal movement could occur by early January, it indicated that the rate of recovery movement must already be diminishing. This was borne out by the subsequent readings. There was a further 3.4mm of recovery at station F by 7/5/87, with only another 2.6mm in the subsequent 10 months. The recovery around the front door of the right half (station G) is even more dramatic, with 18.5mm during the winter after the tree was felled, but only a further 2.2mm in the subsequent 10 months.

During the winter of 1987 the properties were re-decorated with appropriate re-stitching of the brickwork on the front elevation. Although the monitoring showed that very slight further recovery movements were still occurring, I understand there was no further damage.

Lessons to be learnt

- Consideration of the soil conditions, combined with the past history of the tree, indicated that heave was unlikely. This information is more relevant than rigid adherence to comparison of moisture content profiles, or the relative ages of the tree and building.

- Removal of the tree allowed the building to restabilise very rapidly, with about 80% of the total potential recovery occurring within the first winter. With this rate of recovery, underpinning was quite unnecessary.

- The failure to take prompt action in spring 1986 allowed another cycle of subsidence, and delayed the restabilisation by 12 months.

- Level monitoring was able to show that some slight recovery was still continuing, whereas crack monitoring indicated complete stability after the first winter.

Introduction

The root system has four main functions:

i) to support and anchor the tree in the soil;

ii) to absorb and conduct water;

iii) to absorb and conduct nutrients required for growth;

iv) to act as a storage organ for starch.

Roots are adapted to perform these functions. These functions are totally different from those of the aerial parts of the tree (the crown), which is adapted to absorb carbon dioxide from the air and to convert it to carbohydrate using the energy of sunlight. As the functions of the two systems are so different and as they develop in such different environments, it should not be surprising that their development, morphology and physiology should reflect these differences.

The aerial parts of all vegetation have evolved a structure designed to display the maximum leaf area to sunlight, and to compete for this sunlight with other vegetation. In trees this has led to the development of a tall rigid trunk and an extensive branch system with most of the leaf surface carried on the twigs towards the periphery of the crown. The size of this structure means that it has to withstand the effects of gravity and the buffeting of wind. It is all of these factors which influence the shape of the crown. The outcome is an engineering design with the diameter of the trunk and branches tapering gradually along their length as the stresses diminish. The structure must also be sufficiently pliant to minimise the buffeting of wind.

By contrast, the roots are supported by the soil so that gravitational effects are of no significance beyond the main structural roots around the base of the trunk. These structural roots must support the load of the tree and anchor it into the soil, but the rest of the root system is adapted primarily to absorb water and dissolved nutrients. As water can only move slowly through the soil towards the root, the root system must actively explore the soil in search of moisture; it is this exploration of the soil which determines the overall shape of the system.

Although the factors influencing the crown and roots are so different, there is a widespread and popular misconception that the shape of the root system mirrors the aerial parts. A tree growing in an unexposed open site will develop a symmetrical crown (Figure 3.1.a) and, if soil conditions are similarly uniform, the root systems may show similar symmetry. However, this is rarely the case. Just as the aerial parts will respond to external influences, such as exposure or competition from other trees, to produce an irregular crown shape (Figure 3.1.b), so will the root system respond to variation in soil conditions. As soil conditions are far more variable than the air, the shape of the root system is also far more variable.

Figure 3.1

a)   The crown is usually symmetrical, which fosters the idea that the root system has a similar and regular shape.

b)   However, just as the crown will produce an eccentric shape if it is subject to an irregular external influence such as the extreme exposure of this olive tree on Lesbos, so can the root system develop with a very irregular shape.

Although the crown and root systems are so different, it is important that they are not considered in isolation. Together they form an integrated whole, mutually inter-dependent and linked by a common conducting system, relying on the roots for the supply of water and nutrients, and on the leaves for the synthesis of carbohydrates. The interaction of plant growth hormones provides the control for this system.

This book can only provide a brief summary of the complex nature of the root system. For further information, the reader should refer to the references and to suggested additional reading on page 32. The following sections describe the development of the root system, factors controlling the overall shape, and the mechanisms of water uptake.

Overall shape of root system

The popular image of the root system being a mirror image of the crown foster the concept that roots grow to considerable depth. Diagrams of root systems usually show the roots penetrating below ground almost as far as the crown extends above, and even the Countryside Commission depicted this concept in their literature (Figure 3.2).

Using this diagram as an example, if the height of the tree is 20m, large roots (of a thickness comparable to the branches) are shown to a depth of about 5.0m and radially for 7.5m. Occasional very fine roots might extend to such depth, but roots of the thickness shown are unlikely to extend more than 1m, either downwards or laterally. The great majority of the roots will be within 0.5m of the surface, with very few extending to a depth of more than 1.0m. Whilst the depth in this diagram is overestimated, the radial spread is underestimated. This radial spread is very variable in distribution, but a typical average spread for roots near the surface might be a distance equal to the height of the tree. If conditions are conducive to growth, either near the surface or at greater depth, a radial spread equal to twice the height of the tree would not be uncommon.

The survey of root systems undertaken by the Royal Botanic Gardens at Kew and elsewhere (Cutler and Richardson, 1989) (see also Chapter 9, page 141) provides information based on root samples taken from variable depths in foundation trenches, but as there is no information on how far the roots extend beyond the sampling point, it does not indicate the full extent of the root system. Stone and Kalisz (1991) also provide details on the maximum depth and radial extent of a wide variety of species.

If one draws the root system of a 20m high tree to scale on a diagram such as Figure 3.2, where the tree height is shown as 60mm (i.e. 1:333), and uses a very fine pen with a line width of 0.1mm, the smallest root one can draw will be 33mm diameter. Roots of this size are likely to be restricted to the close proximity of the trunk; for a tree of this size, few are likely to extend more than 2m from the trunk. The majority of roots will be 10mm or less in diameter and far too fine to draw. If one wishes to depict the overall mass, rather than individual roots, it is best represented by a horizontal line, with a maximum thickness of 4.5mm beneath the trunk (i.e. 1.5m deep), and tapering outwards to a distance of 60mm or more. Beneath this

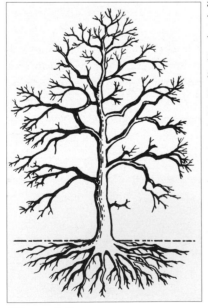

Figure 3.2

Popular concept of tree root system.

(as shown by Countryside Commission in Task Force Trees Information pack, 1987).

Figure 3.3

A more appropriate representation of a root system. At this scale individual roots would be too small to depict, but the overall root mass would be very shallow but extensive.

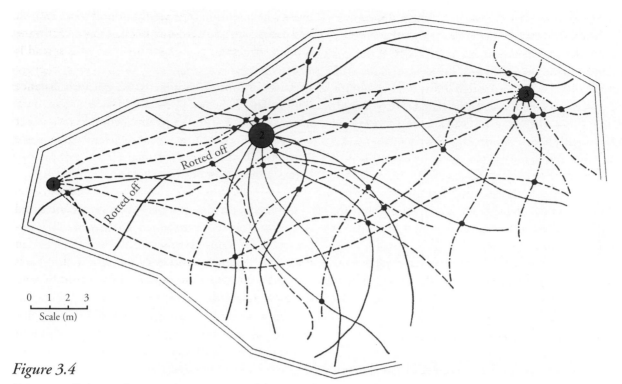

Figure 3.4

Diagram of the partly exposed root systems of three northern pin oak trees. Small solid black circles indicate 28 graft unions between roots of different trees; the numerous grafts between roots of the same tree are not shown.

(from Kuntz and Riker, 1956)

horizontal mass will be the occasional sinker roots penetrating to greater depth, and a low density of fine roots which are too small to draw to scale (Figure 3.3).

A simple analogy for the shape of a tree is a wine glass, with the cup as the crown and base as the roots. This is appropriate for the general shape, except that it implies a regular radial spread for the roots; in practice they are likely to be very irregular.

Any general description of the root system must recognise that it is very dependent on the soil conditions. A deep well-drained soil will encourage a deep root system, whereas a shallow soil over rock or over a waterlogged subsoil can produce a root system which is virtually restricted to the surface 200mm or less.

Where trees of the same species are growing close together, the root systems are usually extensively grafted (Figure 3.4). Grafts tend to develop wherever two roots have grown across each and come into contact. As the roots are held by the soil, any subsequent expansion growth pushes them together, eventually leading to the tissue of the two roots fusing together. Many coniferous species are particularly prone to grafting. Grafts provide a link between the trees and have implications for water and nutrient uptake, as well as for the transmission of disease and for the stability of the trees.

The root:shoot ratio

The overall size of the root system depends on the shoots, and vice versa. The ratio of the dry weights of the two parts, known as the root:shoot ratio, only varies to a limited extent. For most species of tree, it is within the range 1:10 to 1:3 (Figure 3.5), but for some plants with specialised root systems, such as sugar beet, it can be as high as 3:1. The ratio is dependent on the state of maturity of the plant, generally decreasing with

Tree species	Below ground	Above ground	Total	Root:shoot ratio
Beech (Germany)	1.6	8.2	9.3	1 : 5.1
Birch	2.2	6.7	8.9	1 : 3.0
Scots pine (mean)	1.6	8.9	9.3	1 : 5.6
Norway spruce (Ger.)	2.1	11.9	13.5	1 : 5.7
Rain forest (Ghana)	2.6	21.7	24.3	1 : 8.3
Herbaceous species				
Vetch (U.S.A.)	0.7	4.7	5.4	1 : 6.7
Wheat (mean)	2.0	6.8	8.8	1 : 3.4
Trefoil (mean)	2.9	6.1	9.0	1 : 2.1
Maize (U.S.A.)	4.5	8.7	13.2	1 : 1.9
Meadow fescue	5.9	4.1	10.0	1.4 : 1
Potato (mean)	4.0	2.6	6.6	1.5 : 1
Beet (mean)	9.5	3.1	12.6	3.0 : 1

Figure 3.5

Yearly production of organic matter (oven-dry weight, tonnes/ hectare).   *(derived from Bray, 1962).*

25

age from seedling stage onwards, i.e. the proportion of roots to crown of a tree decreases as the tree matures. It is also dependent on the soil conditions; if water is readily available there will be a lower root:shoot ratio than for a similar tree in a soil of low water availability. The concept of root:shoot ratio is based on dry weight, but in terms of the volume of soil encompassed by the roots, initially root volume is greater than the crown volume but this is reversed as the tree grows.

Although the ratio varies through the life of a tree and can be influenced by a change in conditions, for any individual it is a very fundamental value which is under tight control in the allocation of carbon resources. If the ratio is upset for any reason, for instance by damage or pruning either the root or shoots, the tree will seek to readjust back to the original relationship, either by enhanced growth if this can be achieved, or by dieback of tissue which is in surplus.

A clear indication of the significance of the root system in controlling the size of the crown is provided by many fruit trees, particularly apples. These trees are routinely grafted, with different scions used to produce the many different varieties of apple. There has been very extensive research into the root system of these trees which has shown that, by using different root stocks for this graft, one can control the size to which the scion (crown) will grow. Dwarfing root stocks will produce a very small tree whereas other root stocks will produce a large tree, all regardless of the type of scion which is used. There has been no similar work with amenity trees, but many species are routinely grafted and it is reasonable to assume that the root system of these will exert an influence on the size of the crown.

Initial root growth

Although the initial root growth is of negligible relevance to the problems of structural damage, it is helpful to consider the early growth as this forms the framework of the future root system.

The first root produced by a seedling, known as the radicle, shows strong positive geotropism, i.e. it grows straight downwards. If this root persists, it ultimately forms a tap root. In some plants, like the dandelion, this tap root is highly developed as the main root system. However, in most plants and virtually all trees, it usually dies, either as a result of natural causes (from adverse soil conditions, disease, fluctuations in water table etc.) or from human intervention (undercutting in the seed beds, root pruning when transplant-

ing). The retention of a tap root on a tree is an unusual exception, and certainly not a common feature as is often suggested.

Early in root development, lateral roots form on the primary radicle. These are known as first order laterals. Off these grow further laterals, known as second order laterals. Further subdivisions will produce third, fourth or fifth order laterals, but the distinction between these is of limited relevance.

All these developing roots have a similar structure. At the tip is the root cap, which is a mass of cells which protect the root tip as it thrusts through the soil. It is often mucilaginous, and cells are constantly being sloughed off as new cells are produced from within. Behind the root cap is the meristematic region, where the cells are rapidly dividing. Some of these form new cells in the root cap but most pass into the zone of elongation a few millimetres behind the root tip where the cells increase in size, particularly in length. This pushes the root cap and meristematic zone forward into the soil. Elongation of the cells is caused by the turgor of the cells, which is maintained by osmotic pressure (see also Chapter 10, page 157). Biochemical changes in the cell wall allow it to stretch until full elongation is achieved, at which stage the turgor pressure is restrained by the cell wall. As the cells elongate, they also differentiate into the various cell types which form the root.

The length of this tip region, from root cap to full differentiation, depends on the rate of growth. With actively growing roots it can be more than 5mm, but once elongation ceases, it can drop to less than 0.5mm.

Time lapse photography has shown that the growing tips of apple roots follow a spiral movement (Figure 3.6). Other species are probably similar. If the tip

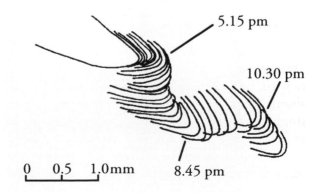

Figure 3.6

Variations in direction of growth of elongating root tip of apple. Outline drawings made at 15 minute intervals from time lapse photographs. *(from Head, 1965).*

encounters an obstacle it will be diverted, but the root will tend to curve back towards its original alignment once the obstacle is passed. The extent to which it curves back depends on the angle at which it strikes the obstacle. It straightens entirely from angles of less than 15°, but only partially if it strikes the obstacle at 90°. The ability to straighten also depends on the length of the barrier, but for distances up to 10cm there is little tendency for the root to become trained in the direction of the obstacle (Wilson, 1967).

The fine, moisture-absorbing, roots

Behind the root tip is the main zone of water uptake. This usually only extends for 5 to 10cm behind the tip, to a maximum of 20cm. These roots are fine, typically with a diameter of about 1mm, but with many species they are even thinner.

The surface area of this zone of water uptake is often greatly increased by root hairs, which are unicellular outgrowths from the outer cells of the epidermis. The size, distribution and persistence of these root hairs is very variable; they are typically less than 300µm long and 10µm diameter (1µm = 0.001mm) and therefore too small to see by naked eye. The combined surface area of the root hairs can more than double the effective surface area of the root. Fine roots are often described as "hair-like" as a convenient description of their diameter; this should not be confused with the unicellular root hairs.

The growing root tip is white but within a few weeks it starts to turn brown. This is caused by the cells of the cortex becoming lignified and suberised. The position of this transition from the white root tip to the brown suberised root depends on the rate of growth. A fast growing root can have a long white tip, but as it stops active elongation and becomes dormant, the zone of suberisation can extend right down to the root tip. It is the white unsuberised portion of the root which is most active in water uptake and usually only the unsuberised portion of the epidermis which produces root hairs. Once the cells are suberised, their ability to absorb water is reduced, but by no means entirely stopped. Some water can still pass through the suberised cells, and it can also be absorbed through lenticels (the areas on the root surface where the normal structure is disrupted to allow gaseous diffusion into the root). However, as the soil dries near the root, contact is lost between the root and the moist soil, and it is this lack of effective contact which becomes the main deterrent to water uptake by suberised roots. This applies particularly in clay soils which tend to shrink away from the root as the clay dries. Clay soils also have very low permeability which restricts the migration of water to the root surface.

For these reasons, the root tip must be constantly growing to exploit fresh areas. Straight elongation would be very ineffective at exploiting the soil volume; for this reason the root is constantly branching, with the lateral branches growing out to exploit the surrounding soil. Two types of root may be distinguished; short lateral roots, often heavily branched, which only grow for a single season or less, and extension roots which grow more actively through the soil.

Extension growth of the fine roots can be rapid. Poplar roots have been recorded as growing up to 50mm per day, birch at 15mm/day, oak at 12mm/day and false acacia at up to 56mm/day (Hoffmann, 1966). These rates were recorded in good soil but would be slower in dense soil. 3m growth can occur in a season.

Any description of the fine roots would not be complete without mention of mycorrhizal roots. These are fine roots which grow in symbiotic association with a fungus which is either predominantly internal (endomycorrhizal) or external (ectomycorrhizal). These fungi are highly efficient at the absorption of nutrients, particularly in soils of low nutrient status. These nutrients are made available to the tree, in return for starch, to the mutual benefit of the two organisms. This association is essential for the survival of trees in many situations. The sporophores (toadstools) of these mycorrhizal fungi are often seen growing around the base of trees in woodlands.

Factors affecting root growth

The development of fine roots is opportunistic, with roots proliferating where conditions are conducive to growth. As might be expected, there are many factors which influence this growth. The main requirements are the availability of water, an adequate supply of oxygen for respiration, other soil gases below their toxic levels, suitable soil temperature and absence of mechanical impedance.

In their search for water, roots will tend to follow moisture gradients, i.e. growth will be favoured in the direction of maximum water potential. If there is a zone of very dry soil, they cannot "sniff out" water beyond and go in search of it. For this reason they will not enter a drain, unless there is already a defect allowing water to leak, but they may proliferate on the surface of the drain, exploiting water which condenses if the drain is cooler than the surrounding soil. Where water is abundant, roots will proliferate to exploit that source: conversely root branching and elongation are inhibited by low water potential.

Optimum root growth requires oxygen levels in excess of 15%. Root initiation requires oxygen in excess of 12%, and growth of existing root tips requires in excess of 5 - 10%. Below 1% the root loses weight (Carson, 1974). Roots will be in competition with other soil micro-organisms for this oxygen. In the field, optimum oxygen levels are seldom achieved for the development of an extensive and effective root system. An important factor controlling the oxygen concentration is the rate of oxygen diffusion. In a uniform clay soil this will be very low; it is only if the clay dries and cracks that the necessary rates of gaseous diffusion will be achieved. Diffusion rates of oxygen through water are even lower, so if the soil is saturated all root growth is inhibited, except in those species which can utilise anaerobic respiration.

Mechanical impedance is also an important factor. For a root to elongate, the mechanical impedance of the soil acting against the cross-section of the root tip must be less than the pressure exerted by the root tip itself. The axial pressure exerted by the root tip is related to the osmotic pressure and turgor of the cells; this pressure can be very variable (see Chapter 10, page 158) but in many situations is insufficient for unrestricted root growth. In coarse soils the root tip can penetrate between the soil particles, but in fine soils, including clay and silt, the particles must be moved aside if the root is to penetrate. Pore size and the porosity of a soil is a function of the bulk density. In general terms root growth is likely to be significantly reduced by bulk density in excess of $1.2g/cm^2$ and to cease above $1.8g/cm^2$. The resistance of the soil to root growth is usually measured by a penetrometer (the constant rate penetrometer is recommended), as this instrument is similar to a root in that it measures the pressure required to push a steel probe into a soil. Different soils can exert a very different resistance and produce a different relationship between penetrometer readings and growth. In non cohesive soils the rate of root elongation will diminish at penetrometer resistance in excess of a value between 0.8 to 1.2Mpa, with little or no growth occurring above 4MPa. In clay soils growth will be restricted at substantially lower values than these, but few experiments have been made on these soils (Bengough and Mullins, 1990).

In practice, many clay soils have a bulk density in excess of $1.8g/cm^2$. Furthermore, their penetrometer resistance increases markedly as the soil dries (see Chapter 13, page 210) with readings in excess of 6MPa occurring in severely desiccated soils. Under these conditions it is unlikely that roots would be able to penetrate through the soil. Instead they will exploit macropores within the soil, created by soil cracking as it dries and shrinks, or biopores produced by previous root growth or the tunnelling activity of invertebrates.

It should be apparent from this that some soils, particularly clay soils, are relatively hostile for roots. By comparison, a soil with a well developed structure, a varied particle size, well aerated and with abundant supplies of available water, will provide favourable conditions for roots. These conditions can occur anywhere within the soil volume but are most usually found near the soil surface. It is for this reason that the great majority of roots are found in the surface 600mm. However, if the opportunistic exploitation of the soil encounters favourable conditions at any location, roots will proliferate.

Although other factors are also important, it is the search for water which is by far the dominant factor in determining the scope of the root system. The internal resistance of roots to water flow is very low. For this reason it can be more efficient for a tree to allocate carbon reserves to an extensive root system exploiting the optimal conditions wherever these are encountered, rather than expending energy on growth in adverse conditions closer to the tree.

Depending on the shape of the crown, there is often an abundance of roots beneath the trunk exploiting the rainfall which tends to run down the trunk of the tree (stemflow), or beneath the drip line on the outer periphery of the crown. By contrast, the crown may intercept rainfall and produce a rainshadow beneath, thereby encouraging a wider spread. Roots will also proliferate near any natural water source, and, if they encounter them, will exploit deep aquifers such as bands of sand within an otherwise hostile clay soil, particularly if there is lateral inflow to replenish the source. In the same way they will exploit artificial sources of water, such as leaking drains.

It should be appreciated from this that, unlike the leaves which are concentrated on the periphery of the crown, the fine roots will develop in whichever part of the root mass is most suitable. They can develop off roots of any size; they are not restricted to the ends of the roots in a similar manner to the leaves on the ends of branches. If soil and moisture conditions are uniform around the tree there will be uniform exploitation and root growth, but if there is any variation, the root system will be equally variable.

Control of root growth

The rate and duration of root growth varies between years, between seasons and diurnally, adjusting to a complex of constantly varying factors. The soil environment changes rapidly with depth, and in each soil layer it varies from day to day, especially in response to moisture, temperature and aeration. In very general terms, roots usually start growth shortly prior to shoot elongation, and to continue for a longer time than the aerial parts, but the time of elongation of existing roots will be different from initiation of new roots, and individual roots or different parts of the system can show completely different patterns to the rest. The period of maximum growth is usually in the early summer, and root growth may cease at times of water stress (contrary to the popular concept that root growth is stimulated by drought conditions).

Root growth is regulated to a large degree by the supply of photosynthetic products and hormonal control from the leaves and shoots. As a result, root growth is strongly influenced by the environment of the crown, with many examples to illustrate this relationship (see Kozlowski 1971 for review). It is known that defoliation of fir trees by budworm causes root mortality (Redmond, 1959). When defoliation destroyed more than 70% of the new foliage, rootlet mortality exceeded 30%, and with 100% defoliation, more than 75% of the rootlets died. Under artificial conditions, defoliation of apple trees 4 - 6 weeks before natural leaf fall greatly reduced root growth for the remainder of the year (Head, 1969). It is commonly recognized that severe pruning can greatly stimulate subsequent shoot growth. This does not imply corresponding stimulation of root growth; to the contrary, Head (1967) has shown that the more intense the shoot growth, the greater and more prolonged the reduction in growth of white roots, probably because of competition between the shoots and roots for nutrients at times of year when reserves are being utilised and are depleted.

Root growth will differ between species, but these differences are greatly subordinate to the influence of soil and site conditions.

Conducting roots

A proportion of the fine extension roots develop secondary thickening, with a central core of xylem and peripheral phloem in a manner similar to twigs and branches. These roots serve to conduct the water and nutrients from the zone of uptake to the main roots and thence to the trunk. Unlike the twigs and branches, these roots are supported by the soil and so do not need to resist gravity. They do not therefore require a regular taper along their length nor do they need to increase in diameter each year to support their additional weight. Increase in diameter is only necessary to enhance water conduction. These roots can therefore be very long and slender, and their diameter often varies along their length. The size of the root does not provide any indication of its age or position within the hierarchy of the root system.

It is usually the conducting roots which are taken for root identification purposes. Unlike the aerial parts of a tree which have a well-defined structure, root structure can be very variable, reflecting the conditions in which the root is growing. The shape of the root system and macroscopic features of roots are of no value for identification. Likewise, the proportion of the various cell types within the xylem can vary; for instance some roots will have a high proportion of vessels of large diameter while in others the vessels will be few, scattered, and of small diameter.

Other characteristics need to be used for identification of roots. In particular, the intervascular wall pitting which provides the link between adjacent vessels, and the wall pitting between vessels and ray cells, are of high diagnostic value. Other features such as the perforation plates between vessels, the helical thickening of the cell walls, crystalline cell inclusions and the structure of the phloem are also of diagnostic value. These features can only be distinguished by high-power microscopic examination of root sections (see Chapter 14, page 221). As so many of the features can be variable, identification must rely on comparing these sections with reference sections of known identification. The book 'Root Identification Manual of Trees and Shrubs' by Cutler *et al.* (1981) provides valuable guidance.

Sections of roots may reveal distinct growth rings, but these are not necessarily produced on an annual basis. They do not therefore provide a reliable measure of the age of the root.

Structural roots

Structural roots develop from the first and second order laterals which differentiate early in the life of the seedling. They grow on to serve two main functions:

 i) to support the weight of the aerial parts;

 ii) to anchor the tree into the soil.

The need to support the weight of the aerial parts is similar to the function of a house foundation, requiring the load to be spread over a wide area. At the base of the trunk the tree sub-divides into large buttress roots which usually turn at right angles to the trunk to extend out radially, thereby spreading the load. These buttress roots need to be stiff, and for this reason they are very thick, and are usually either oval or figure-of-eight shaped in cross-section, as these shapes will be more effective for supporting the vertical load. Severance or damage to any of these roots can have serious implications for the stability of a tree.

Hardwoods	Alder	32
	Birch	37
	False acacia	68
	Hybrid poplar	32-46
	Oak	32
	Willow	36
	Sallow	11
Conifers	Douglas fir	19-61
	Monterey pine	18
	Sitka spruce	23

Figure 3.8

Tensile strength of roots (MN/m².

(from Coppin and Richards, 1990)

Figure 3.7

Horizontally spreading structural roots of a mature beech exposed by erosion. These roots have probably increased abnormally in diameter as a result of their exposure.

As well as supporting the trunk, the large diameter buttress roots will provide some anchorage into the soil. However, efficient anchorage requires the tree to bind to a large volume of soil around the base of the trunk and for this purpose it is most effective to have a large number of small diameter roots which increase the surface contact with the surrounding soil. The root systems of most trees reflect these requirements, with the main buttress roots rapidly subdividing into a mass of smaller roots, so that even a large tree may have few roots in excess of 20mm diameter at a distance of 3m from the trunk (Figure 3.7). These roots are only subject to tensile forces directly along their length; they do not have to support the load of the trunk and so do not require lateral stiffening. For this reason they are pliant, but with high tensile strength (Figure 3.8). This strength can be of great value in soil stabilisation.

All of these roots combine to anchor the tree into the soil. The mass of roots and surrounding soil is normally referred to as the root plate, and it is this which is exposed if a tree is up-rooted. Observation on uprooted trees, especially following the Great Storm of October 1987, has provided extensive data on the shape of the roots within the root plate. A questionnaire sent out by Task Force Trees after this storm defined 6 main shapes of root system. Figure 3.9 shows these shapes and the relative frequency of the responses (Cutler *et al.* 1990). Many of the roots described as laterals would probably have been described as laterals with droppers if greater portions had been examined. This survey confirmed the rarity of tap roots, which were only found in 2% of the sample. A more detailed appraisal of the shape of the root plate of different species is provided by Gasson and Cutler (1990), although it must again be emphasised that root plate morphology, like all other parts of the root system, is influenced more by the environmental conditions than by the differences between species.

This survey also emphasized how shallow the roots are, even within the root plate directly beneath the trunk. In 50% of cases the depth of the plate was less than 1.0m, with it exceeding 2.0m in less than 4% of cases. Depths were especially shallow over chalk soils.

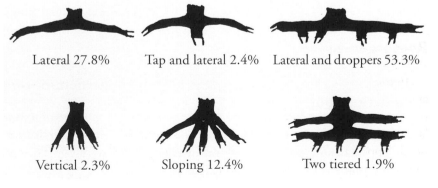

Lateral 27.8% Tap and lateral 2.4% Lateral and droppers 53.3%

Vertical 2.3% Sloping 12.4% Two tiered 1.9%

Figure 3.9

The distinction in previous sections between the fine, conducting and structural roots might imply that the sole function of these types of root are for water absorption, conduction and for anchoring the tree respectively. In practice all these roots are binding to the soil and helping to anchor the tree, regardless of their size.

Although there is a margin of safety against failure, damage to roots within the root plate area, either from natural causes such as decay or from severance by man, can affect the stability of a tree.

Root mortality

At all stages in root development, there is a high mortality (Head, 1965). The short lateral roots may only live a few weeks, and at most for a single season. Similarly, the majority of extension roots do not develop secondary thickening but die within one or two years. Most of this root death occurs in the winter, when the aerial parts are dormant. For instance, it was estimated (Bode, 1959) that 90% of the absorbing roots of walnut died during the winter. This shedding of roots can be considered analogous to the annual leaf drop. It is known from studies on fruit trees that the extent and timing of root death can be very variable, but there is very little information on amenity trees.

The greatest mortality occurs in the fine lateral and extension roots, but roots of any size are liable to die. For instance, a young tree seedling will have many lateral supporting roots, but by the time the tree matures, this has been reduced to only a few main laterals.

It must therefore be recognised that the root system is dynamic, with a mass of new roots being produced, living for variable times and growing to varying extent before they die. The root system is not immutable, but will respond to changing conditions.

Root regeneration

In most cases roots which are severed will regenerate. The severed root may dieback by a few centimetres, but new roots will be initiated from the cambial layer near the end of the root, producing a 'bottlebrush' appearance (Figure 3.10). These regenerated roots can grow rapidly to re-exploit the soil volume previously occupied by the severed root. There is probably considerable variation between species and individuals in their ability to regenerate, but there is inadequate data on the scope of this variation. It is known that the root system of a vigorous young tree, with good starch reserves, will regenerate more readily.

Figure 3.10
Regeneration of roots from a severed structural root.

The root as a storage organ

The roots of all perennial plants are used for storage, with parts of the roots of some plants, such as sugar beet or potato, specialised as storage organs. During the summer, sugar from the leaves is conducted in the phloem down to the roots, where it is polymerised into starch for storage. The cells throughout the xylem tissue of the roots are filled with starch grains, the concentration typically reaching a maximum in late summer. In trees, all of the perennial roots, i.e. the conducting and structural roots, are used for this purpose.

During the winter the reserves are slightly depleted, but the main use is in the spring when the starch is reconverted to sugar and then used for the initial burst of growth, while the leaves flush and new wood tissue is laid down by the cambium. The sugar moves up in the vessels from the roots to the leaves and cambial cells as a dilute syrupy solution. This sap can be tapped in trees such as maple to make maple syrup. The surge of spring growth will reduce the reserves, but these are again replenished in the summer.

A vigorous tree will maintain high reserves, but if a tree goes under stress for any reason it will utilise and deplete the reserves. In a reasonably vigorous tree the reserves are sufficient to maintain the root system and the first flush of growth for about a year. For this reason, if a tree is ring-barked so as to destroy the phloem connection down to the roots, the roots can carry on functioning and absorbing water until the reserves are exhausted. Thereafter the root system will die.

Summary

1. The root system has four main functions:

    i) to support and anchor the tree in the soil;

    ii) to absorb and conduct water;

    iii) to absorb and conduct nutrients required for growth;

    iv) to store starch reserves.

2. Support and anchorage is provided by the main buttress roots and main roots radiating from the base of the trunk. The growth and strength of these will respond to the stresses imposed by the crown of the tree.

3. Growth of the more distal parts of the root system is controlled by a complex of interacting factors. Root growth, like other aspects of plant growth, is seasonal. Roots will usually start growing before leaves expand and continue some growth after leaf fall.

4. Roots start as fine white roots extending through the soil. The majority of these fine white roots only live for a few weeks and all die during the inactive winter period.

5. All water and nutrient uptake occurs in this network of fine roots. These fine roots will develop each year throughout the zone of soil being exploited by the root system. If other factors are equal, the greatest development will be close to the base of the trunk and diminishing with radial distance and depth. Fine roots are not restricted to the ends of the root system.

6. A few of the fine white roots produce a brown suberised bark, and continue growth in both length and diameter. They become inactive for water and nutrient uptake, but instead function to conduct the water from the fine roots to the main root system. Many of these smaller roots will also die back each year.

7. Rates of extension growth vary greatly between species, and with the time of year. The roots of some species can grow more than 50mm per day. Annual extension growth can be in excess of 2 metres.

8. Root growth is favoured by readily available water and nutrients. Development is opportunistic; where suitable conditions exist, roots will proliferate, in preference to less favourable areas. The majority of root growth usually occurs in the surface 50cm of soil, but a proportion of roots will extend to deeper levels, particularly in search of water.

9. Mechanical impedance poses limits to root growth, particularly in a clay soil with a bulk density in excess of $1.8g/cm^2$.

10. Oxygen is essential for the respiration and growth of roots. Its inability to diffuse easily through the soil is a major factor controlling root growth. Some species are specially adapted to low oxygen levels, for instance by switching to anaerobic respiration, or using air channels through their roots.

11. Water is more freely available from sand or loam soils than it is from clay (see also Chapter 4). Roots will tend to favour these soils where water remains available at lower suctions than in clay.

12. As water uptake occurs preferentially from the most readily available sources, some parts of the root system may be become inactive and remain dormant for many years. This will only apply to thicker parts of the root system which are less prone to dieback. A root taken for sampling, even if still alive, does not establish that water uptake is occurring; it merely indicates that at some time in the past water has been conducted from more distant areas and such conduction may, or may not, be continuing.

13. There are many factors which control the direction and extent of root growth, and as these factors are not uniformly distributed in the soil, the shape of a root system will be very irregular. It is a common fallacy to think of the root system as being a mirror image of the aerial parts of the tree or being symmetrical around the trunk. The shape of the aerial parts is largely governed by support against gravitational forces; as the roots are supported by the soil, similar constraints do not apply to their shape.

Additional reading

Kramer, P.J. and J.S. Boyer (1995). Water relations of plants and soils. Academic Press. 495pp.

Helliwell, D.R. and S.J. Fordham (1992). Tree roots and tree growth. Reading Agricultural Consultants. 18pp.

Kozlowski, T.T. (1971). Root growth. Ch. 5 of Growth and development of trees. Academic Press. 196-305

Mature oak tree 1.5m from building on London Clay – No external damage and no movement – Water requirements of tree provided from within bands of sand – Settlement of floor slab unrelated to tree.

Background

The site is in south east London. The property was built as a detached bungalow in about 1950. In 1970 a substantial single-storey extension with flat roof was added to the east end. In 1975/76 rooms with dormer windows were opened in the roof of the original bungalow, and a pitched roof added to the previous extension to provide an additional room.

In the late 1970's damage developed in the partition wall between the kitchen and living room in the extension. This was investigated by an engineer who noted that the floor which supported this partition had settled and dished, with the centre of the floor approximately 25mm lower than the perimeter. Inspection of a surface water drain from the original house, which passed beneath the floor of this extension, revealed extensive cracking with some root penetration. The engineer also recorded that the strip foundations of the extension were at a depth of 1.3m and bearing on clay. He noted the close proximity of trees and expressed concern about the adequacy of the foundations.

In January 1983 I was instructed by the owner to advise whether the trees were the cause of the structural damage, and the possible implication if the trees were to be either retained or felled.

The trees

Three oak trees (*Quercus robur*) were growing in close proximity to the property; their location is shown on the site plan in CS Figure 3.1. The centre of the largest of these oak trees was only 1.5m from the rear corner of the extension (CS Figure 3.2). This was a large tree with a height of 22m and trunk diameter of 85cm. The engineer's investigations had shown that a substantial root from this tree had been severed when the extension was built, but despite this the tree was in good condition, with an attractive and well-shaped branch structure spreading over the extension. A short core of wood was taken from the trunk of this tree with an increment borer to record recent growth rate; the widths of the annual growth rings are shown as a histogram in CS Figure 3.3.

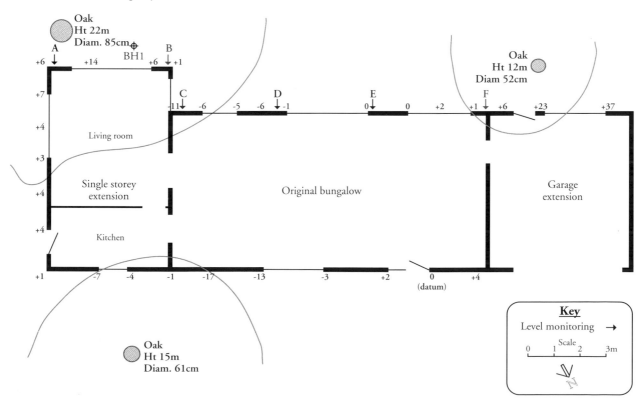

Case Study Figure 3.1

Site plan including location of level monitoring markers, and level distortion survey (mm) relative to arbitrary datum adjacent to front door.

Case Study Figure 3.2

Oak tree 1.5m from rear corner of extension.

A second oak tree was growing 3.5m from the front of the extension. This was a smaller tree, with a height of only 15m and trunk diameter of 61cm and it was not growing vigorously, probably as a result of disturbance and the raising of soil levels around the base during construction. A third oak tree was growing 2.2m from the rear corner of the original bungalow. It was a poor quality tree with a height of 12m and with extensive decay in the base. Felling of this tree was essential for safety reasons.

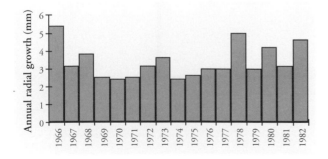

Case Study Figure 3.3

Histogram showing recent annual radial growth of oak tree adjacent to rear of extension.

Site investigations

The Geological Survey map showed the site to be on London Clay. The site was on a gentle slope, with the Claygate Beds and a capping of Glacial Gravel outcropping 300m away up this slope.

In order to check on subsoil conditions I drilled a borehole (in January) just to the rear of the extension, at the location shown in CS Figure 3.1. This borehole encountered:-

0	- 0.4m	Fill
0.4	- 0.8m	Original topsoil
0.8	- 1.0m	Sandy loam
1.0	- 1.6m	Sand
1.6	- 1.9m	Stiff slightly silty clay
1.9	- 2.0m	Sand
2.0	- 3.0m	Stiff silty clay, with some sand and stones near base.

The sand between 1 - 1.6m was running with water.

The results of a level distortion survey around the property are shown in CS Figure 3.1. Results are presented relative to an arbitrary zero datum adjacent to the front door, and include the corresponding brickcourse around the extension.

On 9th March I attached level monitoring markers at six locations across the rear elevation. Three subsequent sets of measurements were taken during that summer. The results are presented relative to station E as an assumed stable datum (this is the point furthest from significant trees, and also provides plausible results).

DISCUSSION

Damage was restricted to the floor slab of the extension and the partition wall resting thereon. This damage had developed progressively, without any relationship to periods of dry weather. There was no damage to external walls.

The level distortion survey shows some minor variations, but no significant trend.

Most importantly, the level monitoring demonstrated no significant movements. The greatest movement was only 1.1mm at station B on the extension, with 0.8mm of upward movement at station F close to the oak which had been felled for safety reasons. These directions are consistent with an influence of the adjacent trees, but their magnitude is negligible and totally insignificant. Movements of this sort would not cause any damage.

The explanation for this lack of movement is almost certainly the presence of the running water within the bands of sand. It is understood that even during the extreme drought conditions of 1975/76, a small stream at the bottom of the slope continued to flow. It is relevant to note

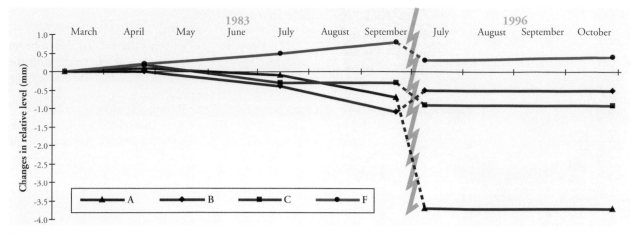

Case Study Figure 3.4

Level monitoring results in 1983, and continued in 1996, relative to station E as arbitrary datum.

that the annual growth rings of the oak showed no reduction in width in 1976; by contrast most oak trees in clay soils showed a distinct drop in growth rate during that year as a result of water stress.

In the light of this information it was concluded that the settlement of the floor slab was caused either by washout of fines by the foul water drain passing beneath the slab or by settlement of the fill. Subsequent investigation during re-laying of the floor slab confirmed that the fill was inadequate.

An oak tree only 1.5m from a building might be thought to pose a threat of direct damage. The root which had been severed would have regenerated from the cut ends, but the growth of these would not cause significant lateral pressure. Any lateral pressure developing from the growth of the base of the trunk would be in direct line with the flank wall of the extension, and would not be capable of pushing aside that structure. The additional weight of the roof should be sufficient to prevent any risk of the foundations being lifted by any large roots which pass beneath the foundations.

The tree was structurally in good condition. Despite the close proximity of the tree it did not appear unduly oppressive, and as all of the branches were carried well above the roof level, it did not obstruct the light to the lounge. It was greatly valued by the owner.

It was concluded that the oak tree did not pose any threat to the building, and could be retained.

Recent events

In 1996 I was again contacted by the owner in anticipation of selling the property.

Although the floor slab of the kitchen had been repaired in 1984, it had failed again. Further investigation of the adequacy of the previous repairs have not yet been undertaken.

Original monitoring markers were still in position so that further readings could be taken. Using station E as the datum (as in CS Figure 3.4), station A had subsided by 3.7mm on 9/7/96. All of the other stations were within 0.6mm of the previous readings in 1983. A further set of readings on 22/10/96 again recorded no movement during the summer (all readings within 0.1mm of those in July). The only exception to this was a new marker on the floor of the kitchen which showed 0.2mm of subsidence, but movements of this magnitude are within the accuracy of instrumentation.

The 3.7mm subsidence of station A suggests that the very slight seasonal movements had gradually accumulated by dynamic settlement, but the extent of this over the 13 year period was very small and had not caused any damage.

Lessons to be learnt

• A massive oak tree, even if only 1.5m distant and apparently on London Clay, will not necessarily cause damage.

• Bands of water-filled sand within the clay can be sufficient to provide all of the water requirements, provided this source of water does not dry up during drought conditions.

• Level monitoring was able to demonstrate that foundation movements were negligible.

• The level monitoring markers could again be used 13 years later to demonstrate that there had been negligible movement during the intervening period.

Introduction

Soil particles are only a part of the overall structure of a soil. They form a matrix, but between the particles there is a network of spaces or pores, correctly known as voids, which may be filled either with water or air. The relative proportions of voids to solid particles, which is known as the voids ratio (e), can vary, and it is this variation which is associated with volumetric change in the soil. As it is this volumetric change which can cause problems of foundation movement and damage, an understanding of the interaction of solids and voids is fundamental.

The voids may be filled with either air or water, or with any mixture of air and water. In some situations it can be a simple two phase system. For instance, an oven-dried soil consists of only soil particles and air. Likewise, below the water table (see page 44) a soil is saturated and again comprises only two phases, in this case soil particles and water.

However, the soils with which we are concerned are usually unsaturated and include all three phases, soil particles, water and air. Indeed, as noted in Chapter 3, the presence of oxygen is essential for root growth of most species. Such oxygen can exist dissolved within soil water but the slow rate of diffusion of water in most soils limits this source, so that roots will only survive in a fully saturated soil for a limited period.

Many of the concepts of soil mechanics, such as the principles of effective stress, the determination of shear strength, consolidation and settlement, and the concepts of permeability, are intended only for fully saturated soils where air, and its influence on the system, is excluded. These engineering concepts will require modification if applied to unsaturated soils.

This Chapter considers the nature of the solid particles, how these particles influence the proportions of the other two components, and the critical dimensional changes which can occur as a result. The concept of the three phases and the derivation of some of the common soil relationships is shown in Figure 4.1.

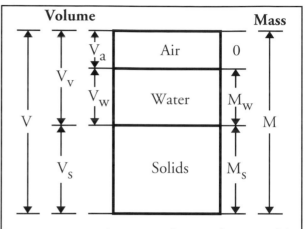

Moisture content (gravimetric), **m**, is the ratio of the mass of water to the mass of solids, usually expressed as a percentage:

$$m = \frac{M_w}{M_s} \times 100$$

Moisture volume (or volumetric moisture content), **m_v**, is the ratio of the volume of water to the total volume, also usually expressed as a percentage:

$$m_v = \frac{V_w}{V} \times 100$$

Voids ratio, **e**, is the ratio of the volume of voids to the volume of soil:

$$e = \frac{V_v}{V_s} = \frac{V_w + V_a}{V_s}$$

Bulk density, ρ, of a soil is the ratio of the total mass to the total volume:

$$\rho = \frac{M}{V}$$

and dry density, ρ_d, is the mass of the dry material to total volume:

$$\rho_d = \frac{M_s}{V}$$

The specific gravity of the soil particles, G_s, is:

$$G_s = \frac{M_s}{V_s \rho_w} = \frac{\rho_s}{\rho_w}$$

where ρ_s is the particle density and ρ_w is the density of water.

The degree of saturation, **S**, is the ratio of the volume of water to the total voids volume:

$$S = \frac{V_w}{V_w + V_a}$$

Figure 4.1

Soil phase diagram, and derivation of expressions of soil relationships.

The origin of soils

Soils originate from the destruction of rock, either by physical or chemical means. The physical processes are most commonly erosion, either by air, water or ice (glaciers), or disintegration caused either by thermal changes or by the expansive force of ice forming within cracks in the rock. Whatever the means of destruction, the resultant material retains the original composition of the parent material, but with a smaller particle size. The size may vary from that of a boulder (in excess of 200mm) down to very fine clay flour which is formed by glacial abrasion and can involve particles less than 0.001mm (1μm). The size of the soil particles is a basis for soil classification, and is considered in further detail on page 40.

Unlike the physical destruction of rock which involves no change in the parent material, the chemical formation of soil involves chemical change of the parent material, usually by hydrolysis (i.e. involving water) or oxidation (oxygen). The action of water may be aided by solutions of carbon dioxide or other materials which make it acidic or alkaline. Chemical weathering of rocks in this way produces material of crystalline structure which are collectively known as clay minerals. The type and composition of the crystalline structure is dependent on the type of parent material and the type of chemical action; for instance the breakdown of feldspar, which is a common component of granite rocks, by the action of water and carbon dioxide produces the clay mineral kaolinite, whereas the breakdown of basaltic rocks can form montmorillonite. The structure and significance of the different clay minerals is considered on page 43.

In practice these clay minerals only very rarely exist in pure form, but rather as a mixture of different clay minerals. These are aggregated together, typically with the flat plate-like crystals layered into particles like the pages of a book. In turn these particles may all be in similar or random alignment, dependent on their depositional history.

A few of the soils in Britain, for instance the china clay (which is predominantly kaolinite) in Cornwall, have been formed in their present location. However most have been transported from their place of origin, by the action of water, wind or gravity, and deposited elsewhere. In England this process has been occurring over a period in excess of 300 million years; some of the principal deposits laid down during this period are summarised in Figure 4.3.

The type of deposit is determined by the mode of movement and the conditions at the time they are laid down is crucial. Moving water can carry comparatively large particles such as sand, but as the water slows, the particles will fall under gravity. By contrast, the very fine clay minerals will only be deposited under very still, usually marine, conditions. If conditions remain constant, a great thickness of material can be deposited, whether of sand or clay.

This situation can be illustrated by the Eocene deposits, laid down over a period of 25 million years. At that time there was a mighty river (the "Eocene Mississippi") draining to the east over the area of southern England, with a massive delta in the general area of London and a shelf sea stretching far into France. A traverse from east to west would pass from aeolian conditions, through the fluviatile and deltaic environment, and out to the shelf sea. The shoreline was not stable, but fluctuating so that there were successive cycles of sedimentation as the sea invaded and retreated. This produced wedge-shaped deposits, thinning to the west, but with different conditions of overlap or lateral succession, depending on the movement of the shoreline.

Eocene deposits start with the marine Thanet Sands, restricted to the east of the area, with these becoming the Woolwich and Reading Beds as the seas shallowed into deltaic conditions. A second inundation laid down the Blackheath Beds to the east, but as the seas deepened the London Clay was deposited, reaching a maximum thickness of about 180m near Southend, tapering to zero around Hungerford. Further to the south, in the present-day Hampshire basin, the seas were shallower, producing more silty and sandy conditions. The depth of the shelf sea at that time has been estimated at 180m, with warm water and plants on the adjacent land which are now found in tropical climes. As the seas shallowed again, the London Clay grades into the sandier Claygate Beds, above which the very variable fluviatile Bagshot Beds were deposited. Around London these are predominantly sand but in the Hamp-

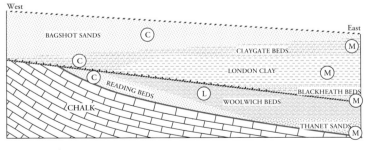

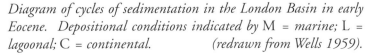

Figure 4.2

Diagram of cycles of sedimentation in the London Basin in early Eocene. Depositional conditions indicated by M = *marine;* L = *lagoonal;* C = *continental.* (*redrawn from Wells 1959*).

Principal Strata	System *Principal minerals*	Age(x10^6) (years)	Per- iod
Drift (**Boulder Clay**, Plateau Gravel, **Clay with Flints**, etc.) Crag (Red Crag, **Norwich Crag, Chillesford Crag**)	Pleistocene	1	Quat- ernary
Coralline Crag	Pliocene	25	Tertiary
Headon, Osborne, Bembridge, Hampstead Beds	Oligocene	35	
Barton (**Barton Clay**, Barton Sand) **Bracklesham Beds** **Claygate Beds** **London Clay** Oldhaven, Blackheath, Woolwich and **Reading Beds** Thanet Beds	Eocene *Smectitic*	 60	
Chalk (Upper with flints, Middle, **Lower**) **Gault** and Upper Greensand Lower Greensand (**Atherfield Clay**, Hythe, Sandgate and Folkestone Beds) **Weald Clay** Hastings Beds (Ashdown Sand, **Wadhurst Clay**, Tunbridge Wells Sand)	Cretaceous *Smectitic*	 120	Mesozoic
Purbeck Beds Portland Beds **Kimmeridge Clay** **Corallian Beds** **Oxford Clay** and Kellaway Beds **Cornbrash** Great Oolite (Upper Estuarine, Blisworth Limestone, **Blisworth Clay**) Inferior Oolite **Upper Lias** **Middle Lias** Lower Lias (White Lias, **Blue Lias**)	Jurassic *Smectitic / mixed*	 145	
Rhaetic **Keuper Marl** Keuper Sandstone Bunter	Triassic *Micaceous / mixed*	 170	
Permian Sandstones Upper Permian Marl Magnesian Limestone Middle and Lower Permian Marl	Permian *Micaceous*	 210	
Coal Measures Millstone Grit Carboniferous Limestone	Carboniferous *Micaceous / mixed*	 280	Palaeozoic
Old Red Sandstone (Upper, Lower)	Devonian *Micaceous*	320	
	Silurian	350	
	Ordovician	410	
	Cambrian	500	

Figure 4.3

Principal Geological Strata, indicating strata which often comprise **highly shrinkable** *and* shrinkable *clays.*

39

shire basin can include fine pipe clays (used in Poole Pottery), or coarse gravels. In the Hampshire basin there were additional periods of inundation, creating the Bracklesham and Barton deposits.

As clay deposits are usually laid down under marine conditions, it is difficult to see comparable conditions at the present time. However, under some estuarine conditions alluvial silty clay may be deposited, for instance the alluvial warp clay which is found around Hull and Canvey Island. These soils are extremely soft, with a very low bearing capacity which creates particular problems in foundation design.

Most of the clay deposits in Britain laid down in the geological past were then covered by a great thickness of subsequent strata which consolidated the clay. More recently, in geological terms, these various deposits have been lifted by earth movements, and re-exposed by erosion of the overlying strata which has removed the previous load. Clays which have been subject at some time in the past to greater effective stress than at present are said to be overconsolidated. The degree of the overconsolidation has a considerable influence on their current behaviour.

In recent geological time glaciation has had a major influence on the exposure of soils in Britain. The period from about 60,000 to 10,000 years ago was marked by a general lowering of temperatures and the formation of vast snowfields and subsequent growth of ice-caps and glaciers. During this Great Ice-Age there were slow fluctuations in the conditions, with periods of warmer climate intervening, so that the ice-caps continuously advanced and retreated producing glacial and inter-glacial phases. The furthest south that these ice-sheets extended roughly corresponds to the existing Thames valley, with much of the high ground of the Chilterns forming a barrier to the ice cap.

Where the ice extended, the extreme temperatures shattered the exposed deposits, and the advancing ice-sheet incorporated these deposits and carried them across the country. The thickness and weight of the ice-caps subjected the underlying soils to enormous stress, once again overconsolidating clays which had been left exposed. Eventually in the interglacial periods the unsorted material within the ice was deposited as boulder clay or till, the thickness of which is very variable dependent on the local conditions. Streams of melt water carried these materials for redeposition into areas extending beyond the ice caps as far as the present south coast. These conditions of deposition mean that most of the glacial deposits are very mixed in their composition. All of these deposits which origi-nate from the Ice-Age, and more recent times, go under the generic name of 'Drift', as opposed to the earlier 'Solid' deposits on which they rest.

The Ice Ages not only redeposited previous strata, but also influenced the solid deposits which remained *in situ*. These were subject to permafrost which caused the formation of extensive ice lenses to considerable depth within the clay. When these lenses subsequently melted, they could be filled with other materials carried in the melt water; often these were sand or silt.

The soils which have been left exposed by these geological events have been subject to further developmental processes, which are the particular interest of the soil scientist. Many factors influence the existing condition of the soil in the surface few metres. They have been subject to vegetational changes, particularly with the natural forest conditions which once covered Britain, as well as the more recent patterns of agriculture. Earthworms and other invertebrates move through and disturb the soil. Different drainage patterns also have a strong influence on the formation of the natural soil profile. All of these factors go to produce and influence the soil structure within a few metres of the existing soil surface.

Particle size

The main basis for the classification of soils is on the particle size. This applies regardless of whether the soil particle has developed from physical erosion or chemical degradation of the parent rock. These sizes are defined in Figure 4.4:

Boulders	Greater than 200mm		
Cobbles	200 - 60mm		
Gravel	60-2mm, subdivided into:		
	Coarse gravel	60	- 20mm
	Medium gravel	20	- 6mm
	Fine gravel	6	- 2mm
Sand	2.0 - 0.06mm, subdivided into:		
	Coarse sand	2.0	- 0.6mm
	Medium sand	0.6	- 0.2mm
	Fine sand	0.2	- 0.06mm
Silt	0.06 - 0.002mm, subdivided into:		
	Coarse silt	0.06	- 0.02mm
	Medium silt	0.02	- 0.006mm
	Fine silt	0.006	- 0.002mm
Clay	Particles smaller than 0.002mm (2μm)		

Figure 4.4

Soil particle sizes, in descending order of size.

This range of scale is difficult to envisage. Gravel particles can be seen, and the subdivisions can be readily appreciated. Similarly, particles of coarse and medium sand can be individually distinguished, but fine sand particles are too small for the eye to resolve. Figure 4.5 illustrates to scale the size of particles which are smaller than medium sand (0.6mm). At the same scale, a medium sand particle would be the size of this book, and coarse gravel would be the size of a house. In terms of actual size, a human red blood corpuscle, with a diameter of about 7.5μm, is the same size as a medium silt particle.

This emphasises the exceedingly small size of clay particles, and it must be realised that the 2μm size is the maximum; much clay will be appreciably finer. If fine clays of less than about 1μm are brought into suspension in water, they form a colloid, and exhibit typical colloidal properties. Such particles are so small that they are kept in constant movement in water by the impact of water molecules, which will prevent them from settling out under the action of gravity.

In practice, any soil contains a variety of particle sizes. The proportion of different sized particles can be determined by tests, such as those defined in British Standard BS 1377:1990. Different tests are required for the different size ranges of particles. Wet sieving is used to determine the proportion of parti-

cles larger than 60μm (i.e. to include fine sand), using a variety of sieve sizes dependent on the particular soil and the desired accuracy (BS 1377 section 9.2). The combined silt and clay fraction which passes the finest sieve can be deduced from the original weight. In practice, the nearest standard sieve size to 60μm is the 63μm sieve; for this reason the proportion of silt and clay in a soil is usually expressed as the percentage passing the 63μm sieve.

Sieving is not suitable for determining the proportions of silts and clay which pass the 63μm sieve. These must be distinguished by other tests, involving either taking pipette samples from the soil as it sediments (BS 1377 section 9.4) or by determining the influence of the suspended soil particles on the specific gravity of a solution by use of a hydrometer (BS 1377, section 9.5).

The results of particle size determination are usually shown as a distribution chart which uses a semilogarithmic scale (Figure 4.6). This plots the percentage of particles which pass specified sieve sizes, and the percentage of particles of specified size as determined by the pipette or hydrometer tests. Curves 'a', 'b' and 'c' on Figure 4.6 are examples of particle size distribution diagrams. Curve 'a' is typical for a soil such as London Clay. It shows very little variation in particle size, and has been formed by the slow deposi-

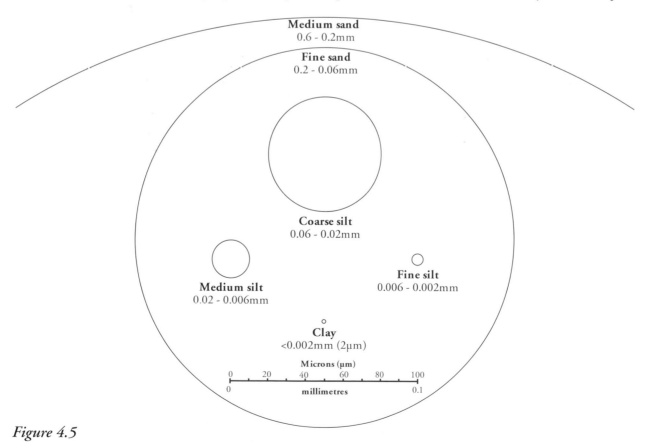

Figure 4.5

The comparative size of soil particles, at the maximum end of their size range, magnified x 500.

41

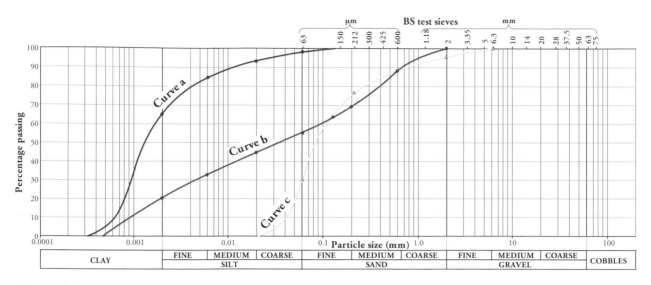

Figure 4.6

Particle size distribution curves, typical for London Clay (curve a), a clay loam such as Boulder Clay (curve b) and a sandy loam (curve c).

tion of very fine particles, under marine conditions. Curve 'b' shows a wide range of particle size, from clay to fine gravel and is typical of Boulder Clay soils produced under glacial conditions. Curve 'c' shows a similar range of particle size to curve 'a', but with only 30% silt present.

The correct terminology for soils depends on the proportions of clay, silt or sand which are present. The proportions of these three can be shown in the form of a triangular table, with each side showing the percentage of each constituent (Figure 4.7). Descriptive names are given to the textural classes of the soil depending on the proportion of each material present.

For instance, the soil depicted on curve 'a' of Figure 4.6 has 65% clay, 35% silt and 2% sand. The location of this point is shown (by an 'a') on Figure 4.7, and falls within the textural class of 'clay'. By contrast, curve 'b' has 20% clay, 36% silt and 44% sand, which is shown by point 'b' on Figure 4.7. This soil is in the textural class of a 'clay loam'. Curve 'c' consisting of 0% clay, 32% silt and 68% sand would be described as a 'sandy loam'.

With practice it becomes possible to assign a soil to a textural class on the basis of its feel. Certain characteristics of the soil are of assistance in assessing this feel. For instance, appreciable quantities of sand in a soil can be gauged by rubbing between the fingers, but smaller quantities are more easily

recognised by the teeth. Silt can also feel slightly gritty, particularly to the teeth. It can be rolled in a thread between the fingers, but this crumbles as it dries. A characteristic of silt is the phenomenon of dilitancy. This occurs if a pat of wet silt is shaken in the hand; this causes water to appear on the surface. If the pat is

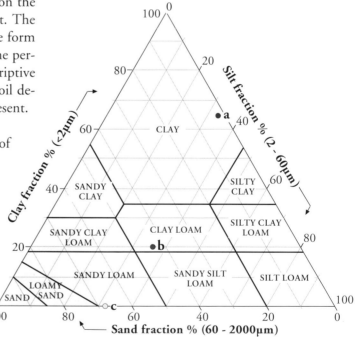

Figure 4.7

Soil textural classification, based on proportions of clay, silt and sand. Shaded area shows soil with less than 35% clay or silt, which will be non-shrinkable. Note that a "clay" soil may contain as little as 35% particles of clay size. This classification provides no information on the shrinkage characteristics, which will depend on the mineralogy of the clay. For instance, clay-size particles could be non-shrinkable rock flour rather than clay minerals.

then pressed, the water retreats into the silt, leaving a matt surface. Clay soils will have a smoother, greasier feel. They retain their cohesion and strength if dried, and if wetted merely become greasier without breaking down and losing cohesion in the manner of a silt.

Mineralogy of clay

The physical attribute of particle size is only one distinguishing feature of clay. Of potentially greater relevance is the chemical composition of the clay which depends on the chemical derivation of the clay from its parent material. This varies considerably and has a very important bearing on the behaviour and properties of the soil.

Chemically all clays have some similarities, consisting of a lattice structure of hydrated alumino-silicates. There are two basic molecular structures, both of which form as flat, plate-like sheets. One of these molecular structures is formed principally of silicon atoms, surrounded tetrahedrally by four oxygen ions. The other molecular structure consists principally of aluminium ions surrounded octahedrally by six hydroxy ions.

These sheets combine in varying proportions. The simplest consist of a single sheet of silica tetrahedra combined with a single octahedral alumina sheet, producing a 1:1 lattice structure. Hydrogen bonds form between adjacent sheets which allows these sheets to stack together in a regular form. Clays of this type are known as **kaolinites**.

Other clays are formed of a 2:1 lattice structure, comprising a single octahedral alumina sheet, sandwiched between two tetrahedral silica sheets. The sheets can be bonded by different ions, producing structures with different properties. The **mica** group are bonded by interlayer potassium ions. These provide a very tight bond which prevents any movement of the lattice, and make this clay non expansible. **Illites** are similar, but some of the potassium is replaced by hydroxy interlayers, or hydrated exchangeable cations. These hydroxy (water) molecules in the lattice make the clay potentially expansible. **Vermiculites** lack all interlayer potassium, but contain interlayers of hydrated calcium or magnesium ions. **Smectites** are similar, but have a smaller layer charge so that the layers are less tightly bonded and are therefore able to absorb more water. **Montmorillonite** is an example of a smectitic clay. Other clays with different structures can occur, and also composites with more than one type of clay mineral.

A mass of sheets are aggregated into a 'book' of clay which is smaller than 2μm. Other particles of non-clay minerals less than 2μm can also occur. For instance, quartz, calcite, feldspars and other minerals of this size are common in some soils, particularly those of glacial origin where they form a clay flour.

Distinguishing the different clay minerals requires complicated x-ray diffraction procedures, and would not form part of any normal investigation. However, it is important to appreciate that these differences occur, as they have an important influence on the properties of clay. The occurrence of the principal minerals in geological systems is included in Figure 4.3.

Water and clay minerals

Water is absorbed onto the molecular sheets within the clay crystal and held in place by hydrogen bonding. The stacking of the sheets in the 1:1 crystal lattice structure of kaolinite limits the amount of water absorbed in this way. The particles which have the greatest ability to absorb water, and to swell and shrink with changes in moisture content, are those clay minerals with the 2:1 lattice structure, such as smectites, but the rigid structure of micas make them unable to absorb water and swell. Similarly, non-clay minerals without a lattice structure are unable to absorb water.

The thickness of the layer of absorbed water depends not only on the crystal structure, but also on the concentration of ions dissolved in the soil water; the higher the concentration the less the thickness of the absorbed water. Equally important is the type of cation absorbed within the crystal structure; monovalent cations (e.g. sodium, Na^+) will allow a thicker layer than divalent cations (e.g. calcium, Ca^{2+}). The cation within the crystal may be exchangeable with cations in the soil water. Kaolinites have few exchangeable cations of this type, but smectites and vermiculites have a high exchange capacity. Exchange of cations between the clay particle and the soil water can alter the property of the clay. For instance, a smectitic clay with a high lime content will be saturated with Ca^{2+}, will be able to absorb less water and therefore be less shrinkable.

The water which is absorbed within the molecular structure of the clay tries to force the sheets apart but it is held in equilibrium by complex electrostatic and osmotic forces which hold the sheets together. This equilibrium can be affected by pressure. If external pressure is applied to a clay particle with an open laminated lattice structure, the distance between the sheets will decrease and water will be squeezed out. This increases the ion concentration, which in turn increases the osmotic pressure. A new equilibrium will be reached between the osmotic pressure within the particle and the external pressure. Conversely, a decrease in external pressure reduces the osmotic pressure and allows water to be sucked into the particle. These changes in the amount of water absorbed within the clay are accompanied by shrinking or swelling of the sheets as the water is squeezed out or re-absorbed.

Although some types of clay particles are unable to a*bs*orb water within the molecular structure, they are able to a*ds*orb it onto the surface by capillary action. As the particles are so small, they have a very large surface area per unit volume, and the ability to adsorb considerable volumes. Just as the water within the lattice structure is held in equilibrium between the osmotic pressure and external pressure, so is the water adsorbed by capillary action held in equilibrium with the external pressure.

Behaviour of water in sandy soils

Before considering the more complex behaviour of clay soils, it is helpful to consider the behaviour of water and air in the voids of a sandy soil. Figure 4.8a depicts a sandy soil which is fully saturated, with the voids entirely filled with water and the particles in contact. In Figure 4.8b a very slight suction has been applied to the soil. Water has been drawn out and air has entered. There is some scope for changing the contact between particles, which can allow some variation in their packing and thereby alter the density of the soil. However, assuming that particle contact does not change so that the packing density remains the same, the overall volume of the soil is unaltered.

The suction which is required to remove the water from the sandy soil is in balance with the soil water potential. This soil water potential is made up of two components:

  i) the matric potential, which is a function of the porous soil matrix in which the water is held by capillary effect.

  ii) the solute potential, which is the osmotic effect of dissolved salts.

Of these, the matric potential is by far the more important, with the solute potential being very small. The soil water potential is therefore determined mainly by the physical properties of the soil. By definition, water potential will be at zero at the depth of the water table; Figure 4.8a represents the conditions at or below the water table. Below the level of the water table the potential will increase in proportion to the weight of a column of water between the observed depth and the water table i.e. hydrostatic pressure. Above the water table there will be a negative potential (suction). A soil above the level of the water table which has been allowed to drain naturally is described as being at **field capacity**; this is normally taken to be equivalent to a suction of 5kPa (as shown by Figure 4.8b). As noted in Chapter 2, the maximum suction which can be exerted by the roots of most plants at their wilting point is about 1500kPa. Vegetation can therefore cause the suction to vary over the range from field capacity to wilting, i.e. from 5 - 1500kPa. At field capacity those structural voids larger than about 60μm will be drained. Even a very slight further increase in suction (to 10kPa) will remove all the water, except that in the finest capillary contacts (Figure 4.8c).

Figure 4.8

Water and air in the voids of a fine sand (diagrammatic x100).

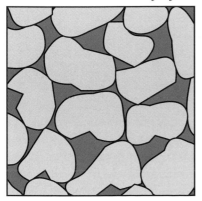
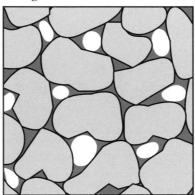
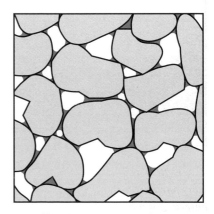

a) Fully saturated (suction 1kPa). All voids filled with water.

b) At field capacity (5kPa). Voids larger than 60μm drained, and air entering.

c) Still at low suction (10kPa). Capillary action now only holds water in the finest voids.

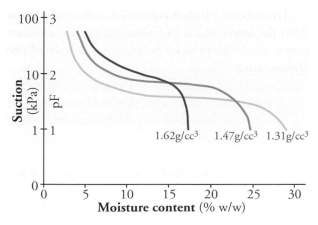

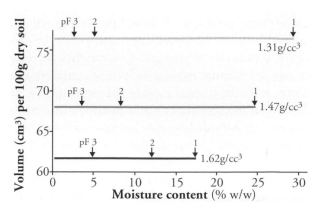

Figure 4.9

Moisture release curves for fine sand of differing densities. (derived from Croney, 1977).

Figure 4.10

Volume/moisture content relationship for fine sand of differing density over range of pF values from 1 to 3.

Figure 4.9 shows how a uniform fine sandy soil will release the water as the suction is increased. The water is held onto the fine particles up to a suction of about 1kPa, but there is then a rapid release with most of the water lost even below a suction of 10kPa. This water is therefore very readily available to plants. Figure 4.9 shows three curves, representing differing packing densities for the soil. These lines cross because at a low suction the pore space will dictate the volume of water which can be held, whereas at a higher suction the smaller pores associated with the high density will have greater matric potential (capillary attraction) and therefore remain full. At lower packing densities the water is more easily lost, and likewise it will be more easily lost from the larger pores of a coarser sand. Conversely it will be held to a higher suction in a finer soil (i.e. in a silt).

As sand particles are not compressible, the changes in moisture content will not produce any volumetric change. Figure 4.10 shows this relationship; with this non-compressible sandy soil it is of limited interest, but is included to allow comparison with the situation in silt and clay soils, shown in Figure 4.20. The small arrows indicate the pF values appropriate to the moisture content, again showing how a sand at a lower density will loose its moisture very easily at a low suction.

Behaviour of clay soils;
a) moisture release

A previous section (page 43) has described how water can be absorbed into the molecular lattice structure of clay particles, and how the types of clay and absorbed cations can influence this behaviour. These changes are occurring at the molecular level, and so can only be shown in highly diagrammatic form in Figure 4.11. This shows the "particles" of smectite as

Figure 4.11

Air and water in clay soil (diagrammatic representation of clay particles; smectite 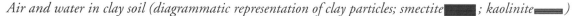 ; kaolinite ⬛⬛)

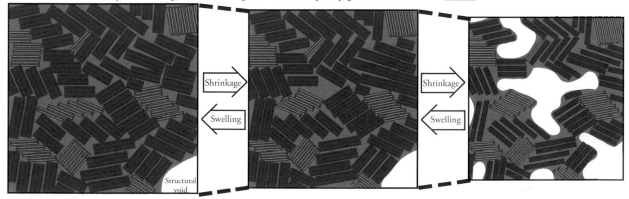

a) At field capacity (suction 5Kpa). Clay particles fully saturated, with air entering structural void, i.e. in the structural shrinkage range. (See page 49 for description of shrinkage ranges)

b) At moderate suction (500kPa). The clay particles lose water from their structure, and the volume decreases. Air is not entering the soil, therefore $\Delta W = \Delta V$, i.e. in normal shrinkage range.

c) At high suction (1500kPa). Further shrinkage has occurred to below the shrinkage limit, so that air has entered the soil. Soil is in the residual shrinkage range ($\Delta W > \Delta V$).

a triple sandwich, representing the three sheets of the lattice, and kaolinite as a double sheet, with the absorbed water within the lattices.

Figure 4.11a represents a clay soil in its natural condition at field moisture capacity, i.e. at a suction of 5kPa. It includes a structural void which is of sufficient size to drain even at this low suction. If the volume and weight of a small clod of soil in this condition is determined and this clod is then dried, either in air, or in the laboratory by using a suction plate, it will lose water from within the molecular lattice structure and from the water adsorbed onto the surface of the very fine clay particles. This loss of water will be accompanied by reduction in volume which will be in direct proportion to the volume of water which is lost (note that the diagrammatic box has shrunk). This stage is indicated diagrammatically by Figure 4.11b.

If this clod is further dried, a point will be reached where the matric and solute potential are insufficient to maintain the clod in a saturated condition, so that air is able to enter the minute pores (Figure 4.11c). Once this stage is reached, the loss of volume will become less than the loss of moisture. Eventually the point will be reached when the particles are in contact and unable to contract further, so that any further reduction in moisture content will not be accompanied by any shrinkage.

This process of drying of a clay soil can be related to the suction required to produce the drying, and thus to the potential effects of root activity. Research by Croney (1977) demonstrated typical moisture release curves for a heavy clay (Figure 4.12, and compare this with Figure 4.9 which shows the similar curves for a fine sand). Curve A of Figure 4.12 shows the drying of an undisturbed sample taken from the ground when saturated, and then dried to near zero moisture content. With this soil there is negligible loss of water below a suction of about 10kPa; by contrast the sandy soil in Figure 4.9 has lost most of its water below this suction. Within the range of suction which can be produced by plants (i.e. up to 1500kPa), the moisture content only drops from an initial 33% down to about 20%; these are the limits within which water is available to a plant.

If this soil is allowed to rewet, there is a hysteresis effect so that it follows a slightly different curve (curve B). The water is unable to re-enter the soil at suctions corresponding to those in the drying curve and the soil has a lower moisture content (and volume) when the rewetting is complete. This process is therefore increasing the density of the soil. Curve C shows a further cycle of drying.

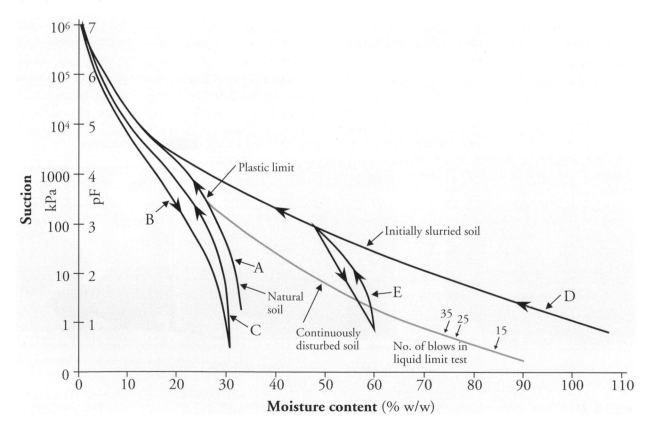

Figure 4.12
Moisture release curves for a heavy clay soil.

(from Croney 1977).

While curve A shows the drying from the natural state, curve D shows the relationship if the soil has been slurried. The slurrying destroys the structure of the clod and creates a far lower bulk density for the soil. Under these conditions a heavy clay is able to absorb far more moisture into its structure, and this water will then be released at comparatively low suctions. If a slurried soil which has partially dried is then allowed to rewet, or if a soil is slurried to an intermediate moisture content, it will follow the relevant parts of the loop of curve E. Slurrying of the soil in this way can occur naturally at the soil surface where it can be subject to disturbance, but does not occur at depth. At depth, the initial density and moisture content are related to the past history of the clay, particularly with regard to consolidation in geological time and the influence of vegetation in post-glacial times.

Croney (1977) also noted that if a clay is sheared at constant moisture content, its suction will change to the value on the dotted curve in Figure 4.12, which is a unique line for any particular soil. Thus, a naturally occurring soil such as shown by curve A would increase in suction on shearing, whilst unconsolidated clay such as shown by curve D would decrease in suction. The suction / moisture content condition of a soil during any test involving shearing will lie on this dotted curve; care must taken in any suction tests to avoid influencing the value as a result of disturbance in this way. It follows that the soil plasticity tests including plastic and liquid limit values, which are described further on page 54, will lie on this curve.

Croney (1977) also provides typical moisture release curves for a number of clay deposits from south east England. Figure 4.13 shows these curves, obtained from undisturbed samples and showing only the initial drying sequence.

He also suggested that tests on several heavy clay soils indicated a suction of about pF 3.4 (250kPa) for the plastic limit. This relationship is shown in Figure 4.14 for those clays listed in Figure 4.13, and confirms this relationship for these soils.

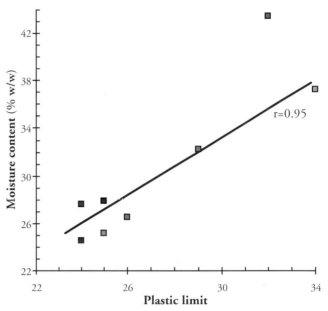

Figure 4.14

Relationship between the plastic limit and the moisture content of the soils in Figure 4.13, at a suction of pF 3.4 (250 kPa).

Driscoll (1983) has used this same data to show a close relationship between the index properties, particularly the liquid limit, and the suction values, as shown on Figure 4.15. He has suggested that, for these heavy clay soils, the moisture content at a suction of 10kPa is about 0.5 times liquid limit, and at 100kPa it is about 0.4 times liquid limit. This latter value is particularly relevant as 100kPa is the approximate load imposed by typical low-rise building. The release of suctions in excess of this value would cause uplift of a building which exerts such load. As shown by Figure 4.15, there is a very close correlation, particularly at the very high values of liquid limit provided by two of the samples of Gault clay. However, if these two samples of Gault clay with these exceptionally high values of liquid limit are excluded, the statistical correlation (r) drops (r= 0.64 at 10kPa (pF2), and r=0.71 at 100kPa (pF3)) and is not statistically

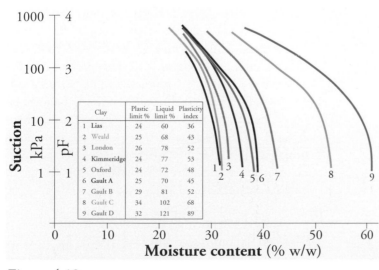

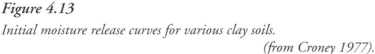

Figure 4.13

Initial moisture release curves for various clay soils.

(from Croney 1977).

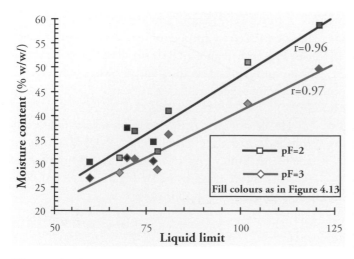

Figure 4.15

Relationship between the liquid limit and the moisture content of a soil at different suctions. *(from Driscoll, 1983).*

significant. This demonstrates that this relationship may be valid for overconsolidated clays with high values of liquid limit, but that it may break down at lower values. Whilst there is very limited published data on moisture release for clays of lower plasticity, theoretical considerations suggest that this relationship would not be valid for such soils.

Behaviour of clay soils;
b) shrinkage

The previous section has considered how a clay soil will lose water if it is subjected to suction, but the important and relevant factor is how this affects the volume of the clay. Figure 4.8 has shown that, with a sand soil, there is no change in volume and that air

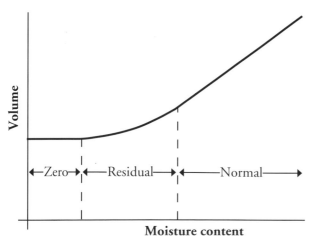

Figure 4.16

Simplified diagram showing the shrinkage phases in the relationship between moisture content and volume of a clay soil.

merely replaces the water as it is lost. By contrast, as shown in highly diagrammatic form in Figure 4.11, with a clay soil the loss of water is accompanied by volumetric reduction.

Figure 4.16 shows, in simplified form, the relationship between moisture content and volume for a clay soil (contrast with Figure 4.10 showing the relationship for sands). It identifies three shrinkage phases. In the normal shrinkage phase the soil remains fully saturated and the volume decrease is equal to the moisture loss. A stage is reached in this process where air starts to enter the pores and so the rate of volume reduction becomes less than the moisture loss; this is the residual phase. In the zero shrinkage phase the soil has reached its densest configuration and so the volume remains constant; the moisture loss is therefore equal to increase in air volume.

The majority of texts (e.g. Building Research Establishment (BRE) Digest 240, 1993) imply that a curve of this sort is generally applicable to typical clay soils. Whilst it is correct that a soil which has been artificially slurried or denatured and then allowed to dry may follow a simple curve, in practice the system is far more complex, but unfortunately there is a dearth of practical and relevant research to demonstrate the actual relationship. The most relevant information comes from soil science research, but this is normally concerned with soil horizons near the surface. However, it has the advantage that it is usually concerned with the effects of soil drying by vegetation and describes the actual changes which occur. Interpretation of this information is complicated by the many different ways used by different authors for showing the relationship between moisture content and volume; different variables such as porosity, volume change ratio, bulk density and specific volume have all been used. The system which is now generally preferred, and which is adopted in Figure 4.17, is to present it as the curve of void ratio, e (volume of voids per unit volume of soil) against the moisture ratio, ϑ (volume of water per unit volume of solids). This method, which is based on the volume of water and soil, provides a straight line relationship; methods based on gravimetric moisture content are influenced by the change in bulk density of the soil as it dries.

Figure 4.17 shows an actual curve of this sort; it is based on data of Reeve and Hall (1978) for a highly shrinkable alluvial clay soil from a depth of between 0.6 - 0.8m (Wyre series, Bg horizon). The replicated measurements were taken on undisturbed clods of between 100 - 200g.

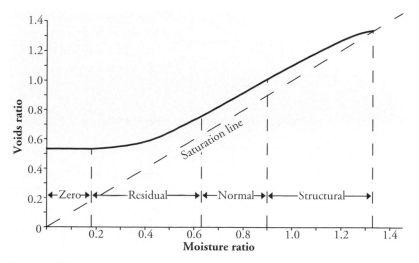

Figure 4.17

Soil shrinkage curve for a typical clay soil with well developed structure.

(Derived from data of Reeve and Hall (1978), as presented by Tariq and Durnford (1993)).

Four stages can recognised in this curve:-

i) Structural shrinkage - this is an additional stage which is not recognized in Figure 4.16. In this stage, as the soil dries from saturation, large water-filled pores will empty and fill with air without accompanying volume change, $\Delta W > \Delta V$ (see also Figure 4.11a).

ii) Normal shrinkage - the volume decrease of the soil is equal to water loss $\Delta W = \Delta V$. The soil remains fully saturated (Figure 4.11b).

iii) Residual shrinkage - as the soil dries, air starts to enter the pores and the soil cracks. As a result, although there is further reduction in volume, the rate of water loss exceeds the volume loss, $\Delta W > \Delta V$ (Figure 4.11c).

iv) Zero shrinkage. The soil particles have reached their densest configuration, and there is no further volume loss. Further loss of water produces a corresponding increase in the air volume within the soil aggregate.

Appreciation of the structural shrinkage phase is very important. It is in this phase that air can start to enter the soil. Without this air, roots will be unable to obtain the oxygen which is essential for their growth and activity. Part of the drying which occurs in this phase is associated with the natural cracks and fissures which open between the fine peds as the soil dries (peds are the fine aggregates of soil which make up a clod). For this reason the structural shrinkage phase is especially evident in those soils with a well developed fine ped structure and is less obvious in coarse structured soil. Although soil structure of this sort is most apparent near the surface, any soil which has been subject to root activity, even if only in the past, will have developed some structure. Drying in the structural phase is also associated with drainage around any larger soil particles which may be present; the erosion of fine clay particles from within cracks can leave these larger particles concentrated in such cracks, thereby further aiding the development of soil structure. Drying in the structural phase can also be caused by pores or fissures which are present for any other reason. This can include old root channels, or voids from the tunnelling or burrowing of animals (worms etc.).

Although Figure 4.17 shows the overall shrinkage which can occur if the soil is dried to zero moisture content, it is more relevant to consider this in relation to the actual suctions which can be produced by vegetation. In the case of the Wyre series clay shown in Figure 4.17, the maximum suction of 1500kPa will fall within the structural shrinkage phase, thus restricting the amount of shrinkage which can occur. With other clay soils, suction by roots may extend through the normal shrinkage phase.

The relative importance of the different shrinkage stages is very dependent on the proportion of clay in the soil, its mineralogy, and the degree of structural development. Clays with a high smectite content will show normal shrinkage over a wide range of moisture contents and have considerable potential for shrinkage. By contrast, clays with a predominantly illite or mica structure will show mostly residual shrinkage.

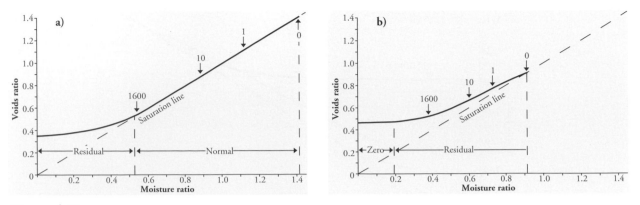

Figure 4.18

Contrasting shrinkage curves for undisturbed clods of two clay soils from the Netherlands. a) Oosterend Marine clay with 41% particles <2μm. b) Kats Marine Clay with 31% particles <2μm. Arrows show corresponding suctions in kPa.
(from Bronswijk, 1988).

Figure 4.18 shows two clay soils with very contrasting shrinkage curves, and also relates these to the range of suctions which can be produced by roots.

Information of this sort, relevant to the range of clay soils encountered in Britain and relevant to the soil structures which occur below foundation level, is at present non-existent, but needed.

Behaviour of soils of intermediate structure

The previous sections have considered the extreme conditions of soils with no shrinkage potential (i.e. non-cohesive sandy soils) and those with the greatest shrinkage potential (i.e. heavy clay with a wide range of moisture change in the normal shrinkage range). Most soils will fall into intermediate categories, and will exhibit varying intermediate degrees of shrinkage with change in moisture content.

Figure 4.7 (page 42) presented a diagram showing the soil textural classification based on the proportion of clay, silt and sand. It is generally considered (and defined by BS 5930:1981) that 'fine' soils, which are capable of shrinking, will contain less than 35% sand. Thus, only those soils within the area shown shaded on Figure 4.7 will be non shrinkable. The remainder, which covers the great majority of soils, will have varying degrees of shrinkage potential.

Figure 4.19 provides a phase diagram for all of these soils. It shows the relative proportions of clay, silt and sand for a representative sample from the mid-range of each of the textural classes. It also shows the proportions of air and water which are typical for these subsoils textures when they are at field capacity. This water is further sub-divided to show the proportion which is available to plants at a suction of less than 1500kPa.

If one considers the clay loam shown in Figure 4.19 as an example, a soil at full saturation would have a volumetric moisture content of 46%. This would reduce to 35% at field capacity with the entry of air into the soil. This entry of air indicates that this change in moisture content would fall within the structural shrinkage range with no volumetric loss. There is the potential for drying by roots to cause a further 14% reduction in moisture content. Part of this is likely to be accommodated by the entry of further air without any shrinkage, particularly as about 31% of the soil particles are sand. However, drying of the clay frac-

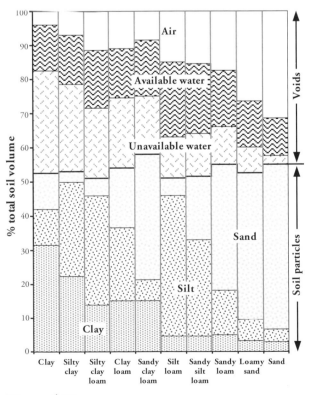

Figure 4.19

Phase diagram of soil textural classes, showing components of the soil particles and composition of the voids at field capacity.   *(derived from Hall et al. 1977)*

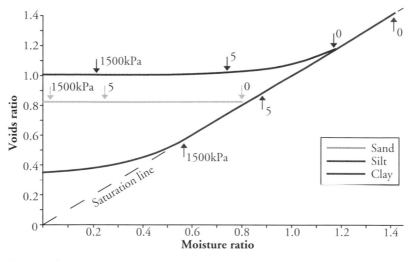

Figure 4.20

Typical shrinkage curves for clay, silt and sand soils, including corresponding suction values from 0 to 1500kPa. A composite soil is likely to contain elements from each of these curves, dependent on the relative proportions of the different particles.

tion, and to a much lesser extent the silt fraction, will produce some volumetric loss. The exact shape of this curve cannot be defined, nor are there published examples which might be relevant to the typical soil structure encountered below foundation level.

Figure 4.20 shows typical curves which might be expected for a heavy clay, a silt and a sand soil. As shown in Figure 4.18, the curve for the clay can be very variable, and the curves for the silt and sand will also be variable depending on their packing density. A composite soil with a mixture of clay, silt and sand can be expected to combine elements from each, but once again there is virtually no information on the shape of the shrinkage curves, nor the factors which control this shape.

Soil moisture deficit

When considering the behaviour of any soil it is desirable to have a measure of how dry it is; the soil moisture deficit is the most helpful concept for this. Soil moisture deficit (SMD) may be defined as the amount of water which needs to be added to a soil, to the full depth of the profile, to bring it to its normal moisture content at field capacity.

Consider a cube of soil with 100mm sides, which is at field capacity with a volumetric moisture content of 0.435 (or 43.5%). This can be depicted by a 'water level' at 43.5mm (Figure 4.21). In a similar cube of drier soil at a moisture content of 0.30 (30.0%), the 'water level' will be at 30.mm, i.e.13.5mm less water.

This sample would require 13.5mm of water to bring it back to field capacity; the 100mm thickness of the dry soil therefore has a soil moisture deficit of 13.5mm (note that the area of the soil cube is immaterial; a moisture deficit is measured in terms of depth of water in a manner comparable to rainfall).

A soil profile can be considered as a series of layers of convenient thickness, with representative measurements of moisture volume for each layer. Figure 4.22 illustrates this, using a layer thickness of 100mm, and plotting the moisture volume for a desiccated soil and for a soil at field capacity (from a control borehole). Note that for these calculations it is preferable to use the moisture volume fraction (rather than percentage). Multiplying this value by the layer thickness (in millimetres) will show the soil moisture deficit (also in millimetres) for that layer. By summing the deficit in each layer, the total soil moisture deficit for the whole desiccated profile can be obtained. However, it is often desirable to know the deficit below a certain depth, for instance below foundation level. For this reason it

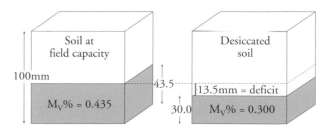

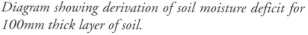

Figure 4.21

Diagram showing derivation of soil moisture deficit for 100mm thick layer of soil.

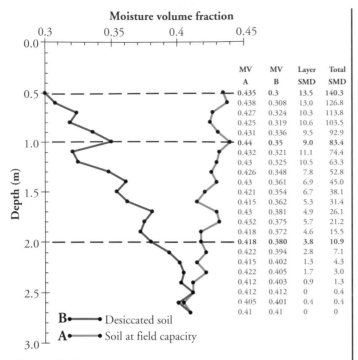

Moisture volume fraction

	MV A	MV B	Layer SMD	Total SMD
	0.435	0.3	13.5	140.3
	0.438	0.308	13.0	126.8
	0.427	0.324	10.3	113.8
	0.425	0.319	10.6	103.5
	0.431	0.336	9.5	92.9
	0.44	0.35	9.0	83.4
	0.432	0.321	11.1	74.4
	0.43	0.325	10.5	63.3
	0.426	0.348	7.8	52.8
	0.43	0.361	6.9	45.0
	0.421	0.354	6.7	38.1
	0.415	0.362	5.3	31.4
	0.43	0.381	4.9	26.1
	0.432	0.375	5.7	21.2
	0.418	0.372	4.6	15.5
	0.418	0.380	3.8	10.9
	0.422	0.394	2.8	7.1
	0.415	0.402	1.3	4.3
	0.422	0.405	1.7	3.0
	0.412	0.403	0.9	1.3
	0.412	0.412	0	0.4
	0.405	0.401	0.4	0.4
	0.41	0.41	0	0

B ●——● Desiccated soil
A ●——● Soil at field capacity

Figure 4.22

Moisture volume profiles for a soil at field capacity and when desiccated, showing method of calculation of soil moisture deficit below any depth.

is often easier to sum the layer values from the base of the profile to derive the deficit below any specified depth; these values are shown in the right hand column of Figure 4.22. From this it can be seen that the deficit below 2m is 11mm, below 1.0m it is 83mm, and the total deficit, below 0.5m, is 140mm.

These calculations of soil moisture deficit are using volumetric moisture content. The relationship between gravimetric and volumetric moisture content is considered at page 57, and the calculation of soil moisture deficit using gravimetric moisture content is described in Chapter 16, page 265.

Soil moisture deficits and soil shrinkage

Previous sections have considered the behaviour of sand, clay and intermediate soils, and the volumetric changes which occur in these soils at the particle and clod level. These need to be related to the gross soil movements which are occurring either at the soil surface or at the level of the base of the foundations.

Figure 4.21 depicted a soil cube subject to drying, to depict the soil moisture deficit, but does not consider the shrinkage which would occur. Figure 4.23 shows a similar 100mm cube of soil, which is subjected to drying and shrinkage in the normal shrink-

age phase. If the shrinkage is isotropic (i.e. equal in all directions), it will shrink to an equal extent vertically and also in both horizontal directions. As the total loss in soil volume is equal to the soil moisture deficit, it follows that the vertical component of the shrinkage will be equal to 1/3rd of the soil moisture deficit.

This ratio between the soil moisture deficit and vertical soil shrinkage is known as the water shrinkage factor (or WSF). A soil which is showing isotropic shrinkage in the normal shrinkage phase will have a WSF = 3. If the drying is accompanied by air entering the soil, as occurs in the structural and residual phases, the WSF will be greater than 3. It will be infinite in the zero shrinkage phase and also for a non-shrinkable sand. If shrinkage is non-isotropic, the factor may be more or less than 3, dependent on whether horizontal or vertical component predominates.

If the soil moisture deficit and the WSF for a soil are known, it should be possible to determine the extent of associated soil shrinkage. General guidance such as that contained in BRE Digests 298 (1985) and 412 (1996) proposes that WSF = 4 should be assumed for highly shrinkable clays (i.e. it accepts that shrinkage is not normal or isotropic). More recently Crilly, Driscoll and Chandler (1992) have measured actual ground movements on a very highly shrinkable London Clay soil at a site in Chattenden, Kent. These movements have been correlated with soil moisture deficits measured by neutron probe. These measurements were being made in the proximity of poplars during the period from 1988 to 1990

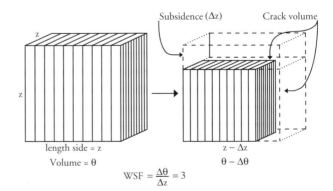

$$WSF = \frac{\Delta\theta}{\Delta z} = 3$$

Figure 4.23

Diagram showing relationship between vertical subsidence and crack volume for clay soil with isotropic shrinkage in the normal shrinkage phase.

with desiccation extending to below 3m. On average over the full depth of the profile they found WSF = 4. However they also showed that this value is not constant with depth. In the surface metre it was in excess of 5, reducing to less than 3 between 1 - 2m depth, and approaching unity below 2m. This indicates that at depth the soil is not behaving isotropically and that the majority of shrinkage is vertical. Furthermore they showed that the value is variable during the winter when the soil swelling is dependent on the condition of cracks in the soil, whereas it is more constant when shrinking.

The scant information which is available on soil shrinkage is restricted to heavy highly shrinkable clays. There is no comparable data to enable estimation of vertical movement of other soils where shrinkage is restricted and occurs primarily in the residual or structural phases, but with these soils the values of WSF are likely to be substantially greater than 3.

Soil cracking

Where horizontal shrinkage occurs it will be accompanied by a reduction in any horizontal stresses within the soil; once these fall to zero, vertical cracks will develop along pre-existing planes of weakness, so that the horizontal stress remains at zero. Similar cracks will have almost invariably developed in the past, either as a result of the existing pattern of soil drying or from similar historical drying. It is these cracks which provide a soil with its structural identity and create the peds and clods which are present in a structured soil.

One can often see the effects of this horizontal shrinkage in the development of cracking of the soil surface (Figure 4.24). If there are no predetermined planes of weakness, for instance in a slurried soil where all previous structure has been destroyed, this horizontal shrinkage produces a characteristic hexagonal pattern. The development of this can be particularly noticeable where a soil has been slurried so that it can dry over an abnormally wide range of moisture content. Sometimes wide cracks at the soil surface can extend deep into the soil, but more usually the cracks at greater depth are far narrower and more frequent and provide much of the fine structure of the soil peds and clods. If, as implied in the previous section, soil shrinkage at depth becomes anisotropic and predominantly vertical, it implies that these vertical cracks do not develop.

Figure 4.24

Vertical cracks developing as a clay soil dries. Cracks are larger where the soil structure has been damaged by tractor movements and there are fewer roots to bind the soil.

In most situations any vertical shrinkage produces a corresponding lowering of the soil surface; there is no need for cracks to develop. However, with some soils, particularly those with strong horizontal laminations such as many examples of Lias Clay, the vertical stresses can be relieved entirely by development of horizontal cracking without any overall shrinkage of the soil mass.

The development of cracks within the soil has many important implications. In particular vertical cracks provide a rapid pathway for rainwater to enter the soil. They will massively increase the permeability of a soil, particularly a clay soil which will have exceedingly low permeability if it is structureless (see also page 56). The cracks also enable oxygen to diffuse into the soil, and thus provide the conditions which are essential for root growth.

Soil shrinkage and cracking can be damaging to roots. As a soil is dried and shrinks, it can break the intimate contact between root and soil so that further direct moisture uptake cannot occur. Although roots can help to bind the soil, the shrinkage can be sufficient to break the roots.

53

Shrinkage and swelling potential

Although the shrinkage behaviour of different clay soils is inadequately researched and poorly understood, it is desirable to be able to make at least a qualitative assessment of their behaviour. Many factors will influence this behaviour, in particular the particle size distribution, the mineralogy of the clay, and the past history of soil structure development. Some aspects, particularly structural development, are best assessed in the field, but other factors are difficult to assess. Laboratory analyses can define particle size and clay mineralogy, but these are complicated and still do not define the swelling and shrinkage characteristics of the soil.

One simple test of swelling potential is the 'free swell test', in which a known volume of dried soil is put in water and allowed to settle, without any surcharge, to the bottom of a graduated cylinder. The difference between final and initial volume of the soil, expressed as a percentage of initial volume, is the free swell value. This test is crude and of limited value, but illustrates the considerable swelling which can occur when there is no imposed load. Other tests introduce the complication of a load applied to the soil while it is swelling or shrinking.

The most direct method of measuring the swelling involves the oedometer (derived from the Greek word, *oedos*, meaning swelling), otherwise known as the one-dimensional consolidometer (see also Chapter 16, page 267). In this equipment the soil is confined in a metal cylinder which prevents lateral swelling (hence the one-dimensional nature of the test) with porous plates at top and bottom. The soil sample can be wetted via the porous plates, allowing the soil to swell. Vertical expansion can be recorded by a micrometer gauge and is expressed as a percentage of the initial height. The initial and final moisture content of the sample is then determined. There are other variables which influence this test, most notably the pressure exerted on the sample, indeed the equipment is basically designed for determining the load:volume relationship of the soil. There are also practical problems in testing the soil in this way, and so this test, although the most direct, is very rarely used (see also Chapter 16, page 267).

Although these direct methods of measuring swelling are problematical, there are other measures of the property of the soil which provide a qualitative assessment of the swelling or shrinkage potential. The most commonly used soil classification tests are the Atterberg limits, otherwise known as the Index properties.

The Atterberg limits consist of the liquid and plastic limits. **Liquid limit** is determined by progressively adding water to the soil and mixing to a smooth paste. As more water is added, the soil becomes weaker and less plastic until it reaches a point, defined by mechanical apparatus, at which it is defined as 'liquid'. The moisture content of the soil at this point is the liquid limit. There are two alternative apparatus for determining the point; either the cone penetrometer or the Casagrande apparatus. The methods are defined in BS 1377:1990, sections 4.3 and 4.5 respectively. The higher the value of liquid limit, the more clay-like is the behaviour of the soil. Some authors favour this value, on its own, as the most appropriate measure of the swelling potential of the clay.

For determination of the **plastic limit**, the moisture content is progressively reduced, until the point is reached where the soil loses its plastic condition, air starts to enter the spaces between the soil particles and it breaks up. This is determined by a simple test in which the soil is rolled into a thread beneath the hand on a glass plate until it shears and breaks up (BS 1377:1990, section 5.3). The Standard defines precise conditions, and although the test might appear crude, it does provide remarkably consistent results.

The difference between the plastic and liquid limit is known as the **plasticity index**. Over the range of moisture contents between these limits, the soil is behaving in a plastic condition with the moisture lubricating the soil particles. It is over this range that shrinkage will be directly proportional to the amount of water which is being removed (assuming shrinkage is normal, rather than structural). For this reason soils with a high plasticity index will usually have a high shrinkage potential and vice versa.

Plasticity index, or in some cases liquid limit, are the most commonly used methods for defining shrinkage potential. Thus the initial edition of BRE Digest 240 1980 used a four-stage classification of "clay shrinkage potential" based on both plasticity index and clay fraction:

Plasticity Index %	Clay fraction %	Shrinkage potential
>35	>95	Very high
22-48	60-95	High
12-32	30-60	Medium
<18	<30	Low

The overlaps between stages and the use of two different criteria creates potential ambiguity in this classification. For this reason the National House-Building Council, in the 1985 revision of Practice Note 3, adopted a simplified, three-stage, non-overlapping classification based on plasticity index; this is also used in BS 5837:1991.

More recently BRE Digest 240 has been revised (1993). The overlapping classification and inclusion of the clay fraction has been dropped, but an additional stage of "very high" has been added to the NHBC system. This provides a useful refinement, and should be preferred. The classification is:

Plasticity index	Shrinkage Potential
>60%	Very high
40 – 60%	High
20 – 40%	Medium
10 – 20%	Low

An alternative system is used in BS 5930:1981 as the basis for its soil classification system for fine soils. This defines the plasticity of the soil (plasticity is the ability of the soil to undergo unrecoverable deformation at constant volume without cracking) rather than the shrinkage potential, and utilises the values of both the liquid limit and plasticity index (Figure 4.25). The 5-stage classification from low to extremely high plasticity depends on the value of the liquid limit. The A-line on this figure provides the distinction between silts and clays; soils which plot above the A-line are considered to be clays, while those below the line are defined as silts. This definition therefore ignores the usual basis of using particle size for distinguishing between clay and silts, but in practice the majority of genuine clay soils will plot above the line and silts below. One advantage of this system is that it provides the means for distinguishing whether a fine soil is predominantly clay or silt, which can provide some indication of the likely shrinkage behaviour.

Plasticity index is influenced by many factors, particularly the clay mineralogy but also the particle size distribution. Soils with a high smectite content remain plastic over a very wide range and therefore have a high index. As noted in an earlier section of this chapter, the cations absorbed into the molecular lattice structure of the clay can also influence the plasticity index. The presence of non-shrinkable materials will also have an influence on the plasticity index. The test require that, before determining the plastic and liquid limits, materials which do not pass the 425μm sieve should be removed. However, this can still leave fine sand and a proportion of medium sand particles as well as silt, all of which will reduce the plasticity index and have an influence on the shrinkage behaviour.

Relevance of plasticity index to soil shrinkage in the field

Although clays with a high plasticity index have the potential to absorb a lot of water and achieve very high values of moisture content, in practice these values do not occur. For instance, Figure 4.12 has shown the relationship between suction and moisture content, and includes the values for a continuously disturbed soil such as occurs in the plasticity tests. The soil shown in that example has a liquid limit of 76 and plastic limit of 26 (plasticity index 50). However, as shown in that figure, the normal range of variation of moisture content of the soil in its natural state would be only about 10%, the exact values depending on the previous history of the clay and the range of suction. Most over-consolidated clays have a very limited range of moisture content change even if they have a large plastic limit.

Work by Reeve, Hall and Bullock (1980) included measuring actual shrinkage of clods of clayey soils taken from various soil horizons over a range of fourteen commonly occurring soil series. These were coated in a solution of Saran resin which, when dry, allows the passage of water vapour out during drying while maintaining close contact with the soil, but acts as a barrier to liquid water when the volume is being determined by water displacement. The samples were suspended in the air and slowly dried from field capacity (5kPa suction) with a regular record of their volume and their weight, for determination of the corresponding moisture content. When negligible further air drying was

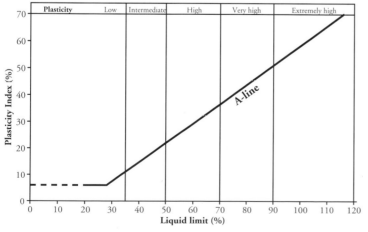

Figure 4.25
Classification of plasticity of fine soils, as defined in BS 5930:1981.

achieved, they were finally oven dried (at 105°) and the weight determined. Cores of samples from the same profiles were also used for moisture release measurements to establish the moisture content which corresponded to a suction of 1500kPa. Samples were also used for determination of Atterberg limits, particle size and various clay mineralogical analyses. They found highly significant correlation coefficients between total volume reduction from 5kPa suction to air dried and a variety of soil parameters including Atterberg limits, particularly liquid limit and plasticity index (Figure 4.26).

Parameter	Range	r*
Bulk density at 5kPa	0.68 - 1.74	-0.86
Clay (<2µm)	26 - 89	0.64
Fine clay (<0.2µm)	4 - 59	0.56
Plastic limit (%)	19 - 72	0.61
Liquid limit (%)	38 - 144	0.83
Plasticity index	19 - 78	0.83
Organic carbon	0.4 - 11	0.56
Cation exchange capacity (meq/100g)	20.4 - 59.2	0.63
CEC x clay/100	8.3 - 50.7	0.80
* all results significant at 1% probability level.		

Figure 4.26

Correlation coefficients (r) for 42 subsoil samples between total volume reduction (from 5kPa to air dried, expressed as percentage of volume at 5kPa), and various soil parameters. (from Reeve, Hall and Bullock, 1980).

Although these good correlations were obtained when the soil was taken all the way to air-dry, when they attempted correlations with these same variables but only over the available water range (i.e. drying from 5kPa to 1500kPa), they generally gave low correlation coefficients which were not significant at the 5% probability level.

This work illustrates that the plasticity index, or any of the other readily available parameters, does not give an indication of the actual shrinkage which may occur over the range of moisture content change which can be produced by root activity. Furthermore, the plasticity index does not indicate whether shrinkage will occur in the structural, normal, or residual range. High values of plasticity index do not necessarily equate to low values of the water shrinkage factor, nor vice versa. In addition, account should always be taken of the proportion of material which is greater than 425µ and thus excluded from plasticity tests.

Soil permeability

The permeability of the soil is of crucial importance as it is this which controls the rate at which the soil can recover following desiccation.

There are detailed theorems for water flow through a fully saturated soil under a hydraulic gradient. The coefficient of permeability of soils can be determined, and there are tables of typical values (Figure 4.27). For sand, and to a lesser extent silt, the coefficient can be related to the particle size, but this relationship breaks down with the finer grained soils and clay. In these fine grained soils the existence of fissures, even if these are effectively closed and water filled, is of crucial importance, This is recognized in Figure 4.2 which shows that desiccated and fissured clays can have a permeability as high as sand. However, structureless clays can be practically impervious. In general, the higher the clay content and the greater the plasticity index, the lower the permeability.

Where clay has been desiccated and open cracks have developed, these cracks can provide an in immediate flow path for water into deeper soil layers. However, the shape, magnitude and pattern of the shrinkage cracks is changing constantly, which makes it very difficult to estimate the rates of water movement. Computer simulation models have been devised for soils near the surface which provide reasonable predictions down to about 1m (Bronswijk, 1988), but the accuracy of these for deeper soils is unproven. Even if

Coefficient of permeability k (m/s)	1	10^{-1}	10^{-2}	10^{-3}	10^{-4}	10^{-5}	10^{-6}	10^{-7}	10^{-8}	10^{-9}	10^{-10}
Permeability	High				Medium		Low		Very low		Practically impermeable
Type of soil	Clean gravels		Clean sands and sand-gravel mixtures			Very fine sands, silts and clay-silt laminates			Unfissured clays and well-mixed clay silts containing more than 20% clay		
			Desiccated and fissured clays								

Figure 4.27

Permeability characteristics of soils (Based on BS 8004:1986, with permeability descriptions from Carter and Bentley, 1991)

a model did exist, detailed measurements of crack dimensions, which would be essential for this, are not usually available.

In these circumstances, any estimation of the rates of recovery of moisture by a desiccated clay soil will inevitably be liable to considerable inaccuracy.

Not only is it difficult to predict the rate of movement through a fairly uniform clay soil, but also any large scale features such as bands of gravel or sand can have a major influence. If such bands are continuous with adjacent areas of saturated soil and there is a slope or hydraulic gradient to allow this water to move, it can radically alter the water movements in the soil. Extensive shallow bands of sand are often present near the surface of clay soils as a result of solifluction deposits into ice lenses during the Ice Ages.

The low permeability of clay soils is also an important consideration when they are being dried by root activity. Roots will favour growing through the natural fine cracks and fissures on the surface of the peds, indeed they may be physically incapable of penetrating into a ped as it dries and hardens. As the surface of a ped dries, it will set up a hydraulic gradient within the ped but the low permeability will restrict the rate of any water movement. As roots only remain active for a limited time, the amount of moisture which can diffuse to the surface will be limited. When a soil cracks as it dries, the crack will break any hydraulic gradient. This, combined with the low permeability of structureless clay, means that the influence of roots in clay soils is restricted to their immediate vicinity. The root must grow through the soil to find the moisture, rather than the moisture diffusing to the root. By contrast, sandy soils have high permeability so that water can move rapidly. This, combined with capillary action, can allow the roots to obtain moisture from well beyond and below the root.

Relationship between gravimetric and volumetric moisture content

Figure 4.1 (page 37) has provided the definition and formulae for deriving volumetric and gravimetric moisture content. When soils are sampled, it is usually gravimetric moisture content which is determined. However, the research described in Volume 2 used the neutron probe, which measures volumetric moisture content. Calculation of soil moisture deficit (page 51) requires volumetric moisture content. To allow comparison of these methods and calculation of soil moisture deficit, it is desirable to be able to relate these values to each other.

The relationship between the two is:

$$\text{Volumetric moisture content} = m_v = \frac{m}{\frac{1}{G_s} + \frac{m}{S}}$$

$$\text{Gravimetric moisture content} = m = \frac{m_v}{G_s(1 - \frac{m_v}{S})}$$

(see Figure 4.1 for explanation of symbols)

The degree of saturation is not usually known, but for a clay soil in the normal shrinkage range, it is often assumed to approach unity. G_s will usually have a value of about 2.75. This allows the derivation of volumetric moisture content to be simplified so that:

$$m_v = \frac{m}{\frac{1}{G_s} + m} \quad \text{or} \quad m_v = \frac{m}{0.3636 + m}$$

For a sand soil, the overall volume remains constant, but the saturation is variable, depending on the moisture content. This allows volumetric moisture content to be expressed in terms of the dry density:

$$m_v = m\,\rho_d$$

The relationship between gravimetric and volumetric moisture content using the calculations for a fully saturated clay and for a sand soil are shown graphically in Figure 4.28. In practice, a clay soil will not remain fully saturated, with air entering to varying extent in all shrinkage phases so that the actual relationship will lie between the extremes. Figure 4.28 includes an example, derived from the shrinkage curve shown in Figure 4.17.

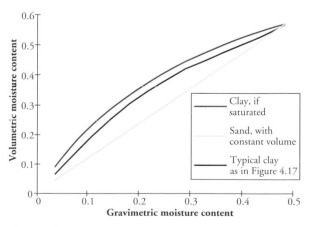

Figure 4.28

Relationship between gravimetric and volumetric moisture content (assuming G_s = 2.75).

Water potential and moisture content

Water potential provides a unifying concept for considering the stresses within the continuum of soil/tree/atmosphere. This Chapter has considered the negative values as a result of suction induced by root activity. Positive values of water potential from imposed stresses are also used in engineering; for instance the foundation load is supported by, and equal to, the matric and solute potential within the soil voids (see Chapter 7, page 106). For theoretical work there are major advantages in the use of the concept of water potential.

However, there are, or have been, major problems in the practical application because of the difficulty of field determination of negative water potential (or suction) in the soil, or for the measurement of water potential in the plant. In soil the traditional method of measuring suction has been by tensiometer, but these are difficult to use and can only record over a limited range (up to suctions of about 100KPa). This situation is now changing, with alternative techniques becoming available (e.g. the filter paper technique for determining soil suction - see Chapter 13, page 207) but this technique is slow and laborious. New designs of tensiometer are capable of measuring suctions as great as 1500KPa (Ridley and Burland, 1995), and may in due course provide a practical means for the rapid measurement of suction in boreholes. Recent developments in biological research now allows the measurement of water potential within parts of the plant, for instance within the xylem, or even within individual cells, and is providing major advances in the understanding of physiological processes (Steudle, 1993).

Where actual suctions of clay soils are being measured in the vicinity of trees, it is interesting to note that the maximum values are usually less than about 500kPa (e.g. Chandler *et al.*, 1992). They certainly fall far short of the potential maximum of 1500kPa which can be achieved by other vegetation at shallow depths. This may relate to the inability of roots to penetrate the peds in a clay soil as it dries, particularly the larger peds which occur at depth. It implies that roots in a clay soil are unable to exploit much of the available water from inside a ped, and that the low permeability of clay restricts the moisture from diffusing to the roots.

Even when suctions are known, there are still problems in relating these to vertical soil movements. Page 52 has noted the difficulties which are inherent when changes in moisture content are related to soil movement; similar difficulties will be encountered if attempts are made to relate changes in suction to soil movements (see also Chapter 16, page 267).

At present, while determination of soil suction remains essentially a research tool, it is necessary to continue to measure the behaviour of the water phase using cruder methods, such as the simple but practical determination of the moisture content. However, it should be borne in mind that eventually water potential will provide a more effective means for determining the water regime of the soil and for predicting water movements between plant and soil.

Summary

1.   Soil is formed of a matrix of particles of different size between which is a network of voids.

2.   In a saturated soil these voids are filled with water. Under negative potentials, i.e. suction, which are induced by root activity, they are usually at least partially filled with air.

3.   The clay particles have a sheet-like crystalline molecular structure which is capable of absorbing water between the sheets. The amount of water which can be absorbed in this way depends on details of the molecular structure.

4.   Water is also adsorbed onto the surface of all soil particles (sand, silt and clay).

5.   If a sand soil is dried, the water in the voids and on the surface of the particles will be replaced by air, with no volumetric change.

6.   If a clay soil is dried, it can loose some of the water from within the molecular structure. This causes the plate-like sheets to move closer together so that the volume reduces.

7.   Provided a clay soil remains saturated, the volumetric reduction is directly proportional to the loss of water (normal shrinkage).

8.   In practice, when a soil is under suction, air enters the soil to a varying degree either in the structural or residual shrinkage phases. This entry of air reduces the extent of soil shrinkage.

9.   The entry of some air in this way is essential if there is to be sufficient oxygen in the soil to sustain root growth.

10.	Clay soils which are, or have been, subjected to drying, develop a network of fine cracks so as to form structural peds of varying size. Horizontal shrinkage is bound to induce such cracking; the vertical component of shrinkage may either cause horizontal cracking (laminations), or cause the soil surface to subside.

11.	Even with a clay soil it is difficult to predict the amount of air which will enter, and thus the pattern of shrinkage which will occur, as the peds dry. Furthermore, the behaviour varies at differing depths.

12.	With soils containing a greater proportion of silt or sand, the amount of shrinkage will be less, and the behaviour even less predictable.

13.	There is negligible practical information on the shrinkage behaviour of the wide range of different clay soils which occur in Britain.

14.	The plasticity index of the soil provides an indication of the magnitude of the normal shrinkage phase and thus a qualitative guide to the total amount of shrinkage which can occur. However, estimation of the actual shrinkage requires information on the range of moisture content change which can occur and also the pattern of structural, normal and residual shrinkage which can occur across this range of moisture content. As these aspects of soil behaviour have little relationship to plasticity index, it should be recognized that **plasticity index is of limited value for predicting actual shrinkage behaviour.**

15. The development of cracks in a clay soil as it dries has a major influence on its permeability, and can greatly increase the rate at which a desiccated soil can recover moisture.

Bungalow underpinned after subsidence in 1976 – Cypress trees felled –
Subsequent damage diagnosed as settlement of underpinning caused by softening of soil –
Such explanation inconsistent with damage – Monitoring demonstrates heave –
Engineers negligent and liable – Heave continuing and bungalow demolished.

Background

The subject property was a bungalow, located on Bembridge Marls towards the eastern end of the Isle of Wight. It was built in 1934, with standard cavity brick walls under a gable end tiled roof (CS Figure 4.1). Two small bays project on the south elevation. In 1973 it was purchased by builders and extensively renovated, including rendering all external walls (to mask damage ?). A garage was built, necessitating the felling of two Monterey cypress trees.

It was sold on, and in 1976 suffered extensive damage and was underpinned in 1977/78. This underpinning comprised 17 piers, generally taken to a depth of about 1.5m below external ground level. These piers were linked by reinforced beams which were cast within the brickwork directly above the original strip foundations, the underside of which were at 630mm depth. An unusual feature of the underpinning was the use of short discontinuous beams, with approximately 250mm support at each end on the piers. The layout of the piers and beams is shown in CS Figure 4.2.

While the underpinning works were in progress the owner took the opportunity to remove a partition wall to provide a larger lounge and also to open up rooms in the roof. To improve light to the new window in the west facing gable, he felled a large Monterey cypress which was growing opposite this wall.

Within a few months of repairs being completed, damage started to reappear and became progressively worse. Insurers were notified and those responsible for the underpinning, together with engineers for the insurers, carried out further investigations in 1981.

Case Study Figure 4.1
South elevation of bungalow.

On the basis of the pattern of cracking they concluded that the south west corner was continuing to subside and so they excavated a trial hole adjacent to the underpinning pier W in this south west corner. This demonstrated that the base of this pier was 1.5m below existing ground level, the soil was very wet and it was softened beneath the pier. They also recorded that beam PW (between piers P and W) had lost its contact on pier W and the bricks on this pier were loose. They lifted floor boards to inspect the underfloor area, and noted that the oversite concrete which had been laid on completion of the underpinning was extensively cracked in the area of the south west bay, with a gap between the sides of pier W and the edge of this concrete. They concluded:-

> "From the evidence so far seen, it is our considered opinion that, for reasons as yet unknown, pier W has subsided, probably with some vertical rotation resulting in the rotation of beams PW and XW about piers P and X respectively. In fact the apparent loss of contact of the bearing of beam PW on pier W indicates that the beam is now taking secondary bearing along its length off the original footing."

At a further meeting in autumn 1981 it was noted:-

> "There is considerable water in this subsoil clay strata round and to well below the base of the pier [W]. Due to the waterlogged nature of the subsoil and that the pier base appears to have acted as a sump, the clay soil beneath the pier has washed away, possibly resulting in further settlement as noted in the main structure."

It was considered that this waterlogged condition and softening of the soil was caused by cutting down the trees. Settlement, as opposed to subsidence, was not an insured peril, and so the insurance company rejected the claim. The matter was referred to the Insurance Ombudsman who instructed me in April 1982 to investigate. My initial investigations during 1982 were on the basis of these instructions; after these revealed that the insurance claim should be accepted, I subsequently acted for the building insurers.

The trees

The tree which was felled in 1978 was a Monterey cypress (*Cupressus macrocarpa*). It had stood 6.5m from the south west corner (CS Figure 4.2). I was advised that it had been a substantial tree with branches extending close to the gable wall. There were also the stumps of the two other Monterey cypress which had been felled in 1974 beside the front of the garage. There was no information on the size of these, but the stumps were smaller.

Still present on site was a 12m high Monterey cypress on the western boundary, 13.2m from the corner of the building, plus a second smaller suppressed specimen.

7m to the north of the bungalow were two oak trees. These were compact specimens with a height of only 12m.

Site investigations (1982)

Damage to the property was extensive and can only be briefly summarised in this Case Study. There was very extensive cracking through the render, particularly around the south west corner, including a vertical crack 10mm wide below the left side of the French windows on the south elevation. Internally the study in the south west corner was the worst damaged room. This had a 10mm wide diagonal crack in the partition wall between it and the hall (CS Figure 4.3) and extensive cracks around the bay.

Inspection of the sub-floor area showed an 8mm wide crack at the end of beam SY where it rested on pier S. There was a similar 8mm wide crack at the end of beam VX where it rested on pier X. Associated with this were cracks in the oversite concrete which indicated that piers X and Y had moved to the south by about 8mm. Pier Y had dragged beam SY with it, creating a gap at the far end, whereas pier

X had moved on its own, creating the gap where it supported beam VX. Pier W had similarly moved 10mm south westerly, and also rotated slightly about its vertical axis.

Overall I assessed the damage as BRE Category 3, or Category 4 in the study area.

The render on the building and re-laying of the suspended floors following the underpinning work prevented a detailed level distortion survey. However, measurements across the window sills of the bay showed the western bay to tilt down at its west end by 24mm, and with a total difference in level between the two bays of 79mm, confirming apparent subsidence of the south west corner.

I drilled a borehole adjacent to the south west corner. This hole encountered a soft topsoil and backfill to a depth of 0.6m overlying sandy clay. This sandy clay continued to 1.9m, where there was a thin layer of sandy gravel. Below this, to the base of the hole at 3m, there was a stiff grey clay. Samples were taken from 1.5 and 3.0m for soil classification tests. The results were:-

Depth (m)	Plastic limit (%)	Liquid limit (%)	Plasticity index (%)	% Linear Shrinkage
1.5	20	53	33	7.4
3.0	32	91	59	19.1

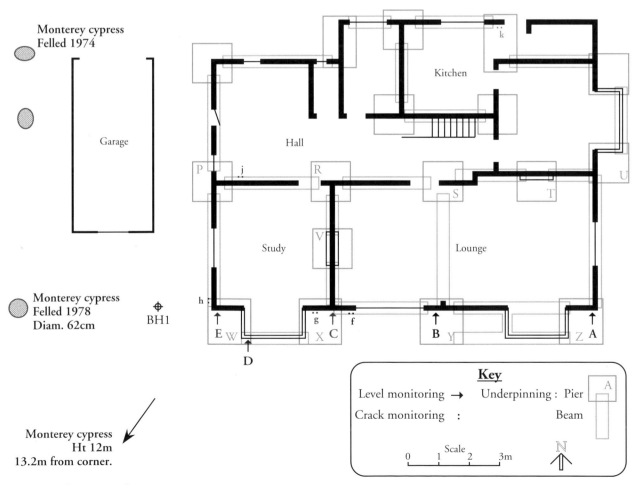

Case Study Figure 4.2
Site plan, including 1977 underpinning scheme and location of monitoring stations.

Case Study Figure 4.3

Crack in partition wall between study and hall (viewed from hall)

While drilling the hole no free water was encountered, even in the band of sandy gravel at 2.0m. I noted occasional fine moisture-absorbing roots throughout the full depth of the profile at the bottom of the hole at 3.0m. These roots were all too small for identification.

On 10th May 1982 I attached level monitoring markers at five locations across the south elevation, as shown on CS Figure 4.2. Changes in level recorded during subsequent readings are shown in graphical form in CS Figure 4.4. For the presentation of these results, I have assumed that station A at the east end of the south elevation has remained stable.

I also attached demec strain gauge markers across a selection of the cracks, with further readings taken during the next 12 months. The location of these stations are shown in CS Figure 4.2 and the results presented graphically in Figure 4.5.

DISCUSSION

Cause of damage

The suggestion that pier W in the south west corner had subsided leaving the building supported on its original foundations defies logic. It would mean that this pier had subsided under its own weight. The density of concrete is only slightly greater than that of soil, and so the load which it imposes on its own, without the weight of the building, would be negligible. There was no reason to suspect that, when the pier was laid, the base of the excavation had not been dry and firm.

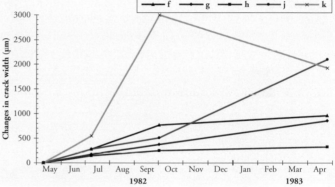

Case Study Figure 4.5

Results of crack monitoring.

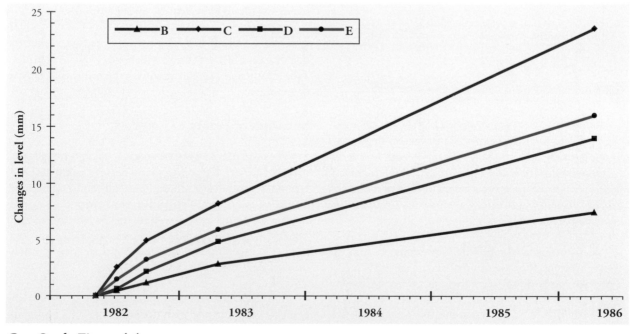

Case Study Figure 4.4

Results of level monitoring, presented relative to station A at south east corner.

A far more logical explanation was that the south western corner of the building was subject to progressive heave. As illustrated by Figure 4.6, this would account for:

i)   Beam PW losing its contact on pier W. This beam was cast direct into the original foundations; soil swelling in the zone between the underside of foundations and base of the pier would lift the foundations off the pier.

ii)   Lateral swelling of the soil adjacent to the piers would produce a lateral thrust. When these piers were concreted, shuttering was used on the outer faces, and this area subsequently backfilled. This fill offered no restraint to the lateral thrust, thus allowing the piers to move. This created the horizontal gap between the piers and the oversite concrete, and also at the ends of some beams.

iii) The softening of the soil beneath pier W is probably explained by this pier, which was no longer supporting any load, being lifted by the swelling soil. This created a gap underneath, allowing water to enter and to soften the underlying clay.

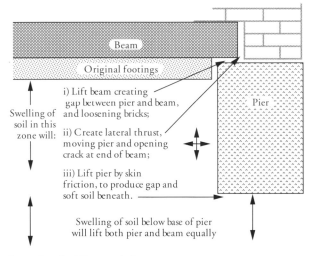

Case Study Figure 4.6
Diagram illustrating effects of heave on underpinning.

Although the piers were founded in a soil of only moderate swelling potential, below the piers at 2m there was a soil of extremely high shrinkage potential, with root activity, undoubtedly from the cypress trees, observed within this soil. Felling of the cypress would have allowed this soil to rehydrate, causing differential movement of the whole underpinning system.

The distortion in the building (as estimated from the window sills) and the development of damage in 1976 provided strong circumstantial evidence that the original damage was caused by subsidence. Furthermore, the extent of this distortion implied that a considerable persistent deficit could have been present when it was underpinned.

Based on this information I reached the preliminary conclusion that the damage subsequent to underpinning must be caused by heave.

This was further confirmed by the level monitoring. The first set of results from this monitoring were obtained in July 1982, only two months after the markers were attached. Even within that brief period station C had moved up relative to station A by 2.5mm, with slightly lesser movements (1.4mm) at station E. These movements continued progressively through the winter, with station C 8.2mm higher than A by April 1983. This direction and progressive movement was not compatible with any possible influence of the remaining cypress or of other vegetation. Although there was no stable datum, as all of the damage was at the western end around stations C, D and E, it was logical that it was this area suffering heave, rather than the eastern end suffering subsidence or settlement. Furthermore, there was no potential cause for movement of the eastern end.

The crack monitoring at most of the stations showed a similar pattern of progressive movement. The exception to this was station k on a crack on the north elevation, which showed seasonal movement. This was probably caused by the root activity of the remaining oak trees 7m to the north of the building. The underpinning was apparently to an inadequate depth to prevent such movement. Although the crack monitoring at station k recorded the greatest movement, it was seasonal rather than progressive and so the damage in this area was generally minor.

The level monitoring provided a logical explanation for the apparent subsidence of the south west corner. Heave was occurring at the corner (station E), but was occurring at an even faster rate at station C (CS Figure 4.7). This gave a misleading impression of subsidence in the corner. Other aspects of the cracking, such as the wide crack adjacent to the base of the French windows were consistent with damage was caused by heave, centred around station C.

On the basis of this information I confirmed that the damage was caused by heave which was likely to continue. This information was sufficient for the insurance claim to be reinstated.

Subsequent events

The owner, faced with the prospect of continuing movement or further massive disruption, decided to sell the property and settle the claim on the basis of diminution in value. The sale took place in November 1982, with the sale particulars supported by a copy of my report, which had been updated with further monitoring readings taken in October. The building was purchased by a builder who subdivided it into two flats, and re-decorated.

The insurance company pursued a claim against the engineers, alleging negligent design in the 1977 underpinning. A secondary issue was whether the underpinning had been executed in accordance with the design. The case even-

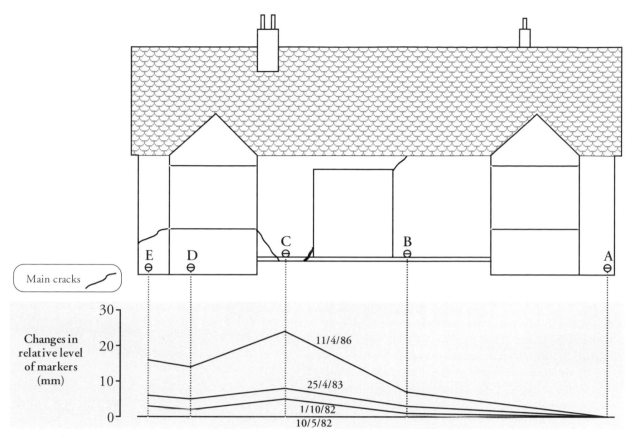

Case Study Figure 4.7

Diagram of south elevation showing how the angular distortion at various dates, as revealed by the level monitoring, can account for the misleading impression of subsidence of the western corner (left end of diagram).

tually came to trial in 1986. A further set of monitoring readings was taken at that time and showed that, over the four year period, station C had heaved by 23.5mm. Examination of the building at that time showed that many of the original cracks had reappeared; this was not surprising as it had only been cosmetically decorated.

The report produced for trial by the engineer acting for the defendant engineers concluded:-

> i) From my investigations I consider that, with the exception of the SW corner of the building in the area of pier W (see paragraph vii below), *the underpinning appears to have satisfactorily stabilised the foundations* [my italics].

> ii) I have obviously not had the opportunity of monitoring the building as has Dr. Biddle. However from careful investigation of the internal oversite, external paving and crack patterns, *there is no sign of heave* (upward movement).

> iii) Unfortunately, experience has shown that once cracking develops, from whatever source, it is likely that movements due to other sources will be concentrated at these areas of weakness. This is borne out by the fact that most of the present cracking occurs at similar locations to the original cracks.

> iv) Generally the fabric of the superstructure is in poor condition due to original poor construction and materials, possible lack of maintenance and movement prior to 1977. This would certainly not be enhanced by the following alterations carried out on the instructions of the owner since the underpinning:-

>> a) The removal of main internal walls reducing the 'box like' integrity of the overall building.

>> b) The cutting out of additional windows in the west and east gables creating additional stresses in the walls.

>> c) The additional loadings imposed at roof ceiling level by the inclusion of living areas in the roof space.

>> d) The rendering over of the damp proof course, encouraging damp to travel up and past the damp proof course into the outer skin brickwork behind the render which will cause damage due to freezing and temperature change.

> v) The original roof construction was suspect - lacking ties at eaves/ceiling level - allowing roof spread which in itself will cause cracks. The roof may well have been further weakened by opening up the roof areas.

> vi) Whilst from my inspection of the subfloor area, the underpinning appears generally to be carried out in a satisfactory and workmanlike manner, this is not the case at pier W.

> vii) Having carefully considered all the foregoing, it is my opinion, that while an extent of the moderate cracking of the west wall and further movement of the SW bay window is *due to further subsidence at pier W since the underpinning*, generally the cracking around the building can be accounted for due to reasons stated in clauses iii), iv) and v).

> viii) The *further subsidence of the south west corner* and the adjacent cracking is clearly due to bad workmanship at this corner culminating in a lack of 'pinning up' between the top of the pad and the brickwork and beams it supports.

These opinions, particularly those highlighted in italics, clearly fly in the face of the observed facts, and in particular the level monitoring. Judgement was given to the plaintiff.

Although the engineer was found liable, I wonder whether there would have been a different outcome if he had accepted that heave was occurring, but had argued that the underpinning was to an appropriate and reasonable design and that he could not have foreseen the potential for heave. Such arguments could have emphasised that the underpinning was placed in soil of only moderate shrinkage potential, with much of the subsequent movement probably developing within the underlying highly shrinkable soil, whose existence was not known during the underpinning work. However, even with these arguments the design should have taken account of the swelling potential of the soil adjacent to the piers and included anti-heave precautions to prevent the upthrust on the underside of the beams and the lateral movement of the piers.

The tenants who lived in the house after it was sold in 1982 had accepted that cracks would be appearing. They had tolerated the damage, albeit with increasing disquiet as it gradually increased. However, by 1986 the builder who purchased decided that the situation was not going to stabilise within a reasonable period and that, as the building was so badly damaged, it was better to demolish and rebuild, particularly as there was scope for additional development within the plot.

Lessons to be learnt

- The bungalow and trees were of similar age. The persistent deficit and associated subsidence must have developed early in the life of the bungalow, and have been masked by the repairs in 1973.

- The underpinning to correct this subsidence in 1976 did not include any anti-heave precautions, and the short discontinuous beams made it particularly prone to differential movement and to accentuate any angular distortion.

- The subsequent felling of the Monterey cypress allowed the persistent deficit to rehydrate and heave to occur. Strictly speaking this was recovery as far as the bungalow was concerned. However, in respect of the underpinning which was founded into the desiccated soil, it is appropriate to refer to heave.

- Experience has shown that this species of tree can cause extreme soil desiccation. In this case the heave movements were recorded up to 14m away.

- Diagnosis based on crack pattern analysis would imply that the corner was subsiding, but this was misleading. There was no other evidence for subsidence.

- The level monitoring demonstrated that the areas showing maximum damage were moving upwards relative to the rest of the house, and that heave must be involved.

- Heave provides an entirely logical explanation for the history and pattern of damage.

- Any assessment of the risk of heave based on the relative ages of the bungalow and trees would have been misleading.

- Proper site investigations should have established the full depth and extent of desiccation to ensure that the underpinning went deep enough, and the underpinning should have included anti-heave precautions against the soil swelling.

- The level monitoring provided essential evidence in a successful claim against the engineer for negligent design of the underpinning.

CHAPTER 5

SEASONAL CHANGES IN SOIL MOISTURE CONTENT

Introduction

Chapter 4 has described how changes in moisture content of a clay soil will cause it to swell or shrink. If a building is founded on soil which is subject to such swelling or shrinkage, it will move and be vulnerable to damage. Before considering this interaction between the building and the soil, it is necessary to have a clear understanding of the changes which are occurring within the soil; the seasonal changes are described in this chapter and persistent moisture deficits in Chapter 6. Chapter 7 then considers how these can be modified by the building and how the soil movements which occur as a result of these changes in moisture content will affect the building.

The term "**seasonal changes**" is used for those changes in moisture content which generally follow an annual cyclical pattern, with the soil drying during the summer and rehydrating during the winter. Various factors can cause this change, particularly:

i) evaporation from the soil surface;

ii) transpiration by vegetation. This covers all vegetation, including trees, shrubs, herbaceous plants, grass, etc.;

iii) natural drainage of water within the soil.

The factors which control the rates of both evaporation and transpiration are similar (temperature, humidity, radiation and wind speed) and in the strict sense, transpiration is evaporation from the internal surface area of the leaf. For this reason the terms are often combined as "evapotranspiration", but it is the transpiration element of this which predominates. As this book is primarily concerned with the effects of trees, it concentrates on the drying caused by the transpiration of trees. However, when analysing these effects, it is important to bear in mind and contrast the influence of all types of vegetation, including grass, shrubs, etc., with the effects of trees. The chapter is illustrated by examples taken from the results which are described in Volume 2 of this book; see the introduction to Volume 2 for further details of the methods. In all cases

the most suitable examples have been selected, but study of all of the research results should demonstrate that these principles have widespread application.

Seasonal development of soil drying

During the winter a deciduous tree has no leaves and so there is no photosynthesis and no loss of water by transpiration. Evaporation loss from the bare twigs and branches is negligible. As there is no water loss, there is no water uptake by the roots (although some root growth may be occurring). As a result, rainfall during the winter allows replenishment of moisture resources in the soil, so that the soil is characteristically at its wettest just as the tree comes into leaf. With most species of tree, this is in late April or early May.

The initial flush of growth involves expansion and growth of the leaves and shoot which were pre-formed within the buds. At the same time the cambium becomes active, particularly in ring-porous species, starting to lay down new water-conducting vessels and the annual growth ring of xylem. To aid in this initial rapid growth, starch reserves in the roots are mobilised by being converted to sugar and carried up to the growing points where it is converted to cellulose and laid down in the cell walls. The moisture requirements for this are still insignificant, so that water uptake remains low.

As the leaves unfold and expand, photosynthesis can start. As soon as there is photosynthesis there will be loss of water by transpiration, so water uptake by the roots will start in earnest. This water will be taken from the most readily available source, where least energy is required. Usually this is close to the tree (to minimise the frictional resistance of the roots) and from sandier soils where water is less tightly bound to the soil and therefore more available. Top soil and Head-derived soils overlying clay will usually have sandier conditions of this sort, and so the zone of soil drying typically spreads downwards. Figure 5.1 shows this progressive soil drying in the very close proximity (2.8m) to a lime tree on Boulder Clay soil (tree 15) during the prolonged dry summer of 1984.

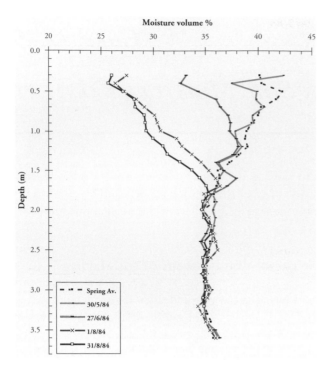

Figure 5.1

Progressive development of soil drying during 1984, 2.8m from lime tree on Boulder Clay (tree 15).

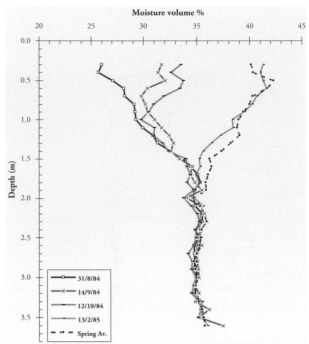

Figure 5.2

Progressive rewetting of soil during winter 1984, 2.8m from lime tree on Boulder Clay (tree 15).

In this example there is a slight reduction in moisture content to a depth of 0.7m by 30th May. This has extended to 1.0m by 27th June and to 1.7m by 1st August. Between the 1st and 31st August there is only a slight further increase in depth of drying to about 1.8m. 1984 was an unusual year with a long dry summer broken by heavy rain at the beginning of September. This rain was sufficient to allow the soil moisture content to begin recovery, with the profile significantly wetter by mid-September and even more so by October (Figure 5.2). In most years soil drying will continue until later in the autumn, particularly if there is a dry "Indian summer". However, regardless of the amount of rainfall, as the temperatures fall and day lengths shorten, the tree prepares to shed its leaves. The chlorophyll within the leaf is broken down, producing the characteristic autumn leaf colours, and an abscission layer starts to form at the base of the leaf petiole (stalk) at the position where it later falls off. This abscission layer cuts water supply to the leaf and with the chloroplasts becoming inactive, photosynthesis and transpiration slows and stops. As water uptake ceases, any rainfall will allow the soil to start to rehydrate. This balance between diminishing water uptake by the tree and input by rainfall can produce some variation in the date of maximum soil drying, but with most species it is usually in mid-September.

The process of rewetting during the winter usually allows the soil to reach its maximum potential value (field capacity or equilibrium moisture content) some-

time in the late winter or spring. There are important exceptions to this, considered in detail in Chapter 6, but typically values each spring are very similar; Figure 5.3 shows the profiles in various years close to this same tree (tree 15). The profiles are essentially identical, the slight differences being no more than the random counting error of the neutron probe and the slightly late initial reading in 1984.

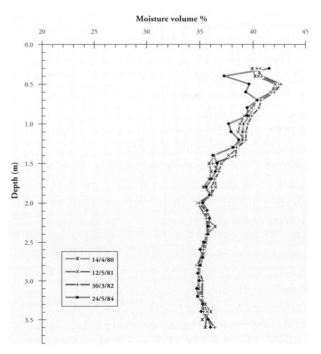
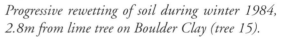

Figure 5.3

The soil returns to near identical moisture content each spring. 2.8m from lime tree on Boulder Clay (tree 15).

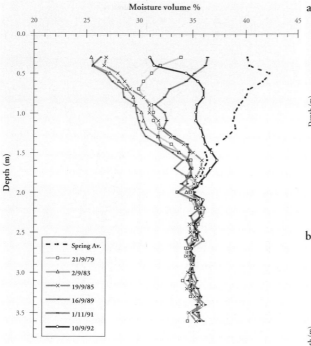

Moisture volume %

Figure 5.4

The driest profiles recorded in various years between 1979 - 1992, 2.8m from lime tree on Boulder Clay (tree 15).

This cycle of the soil drying each summer and rehydrating each winter repeats every year. The extent of drying which develops each year is dependent on the weather conditions during the summer, dry years such as 1984 and 1989 producing greater drying. Figure 5.4 shows the driest profiles recorded in various years near the same lime tree on Boulder Clay (tree 15). The intensity of drying differs, but the depth remains essentially similar in both wet and dry years.

These graphs only show the development of the soil drying at one of the closest access tubes. Figure 5.5 shows the overall pattern of the development of soil drying through the very dry summer of 1984, including information from all of the access tubes. (For further details on the method of presentation of these diagrams, see page 11 of Volume 2). At the control access tubes beyond the influence of the tree (to the extreme right of the diagrams), the deficit caused by the grass already extends to 0.8m by 24/5/84, increasing in depth and intensity through the reading on 27/6/84 and reaching to 1.2m by 1/8/84. There is very little further drying at this position on 14/9/84. At the access tubes close to the tree there is a similar gradual development with the greatest drying at 5.6m from the tree. The intensity of drying is no greater, but it extends deeper. At the access tube 11.2m from the tree there is less drying than at the control.

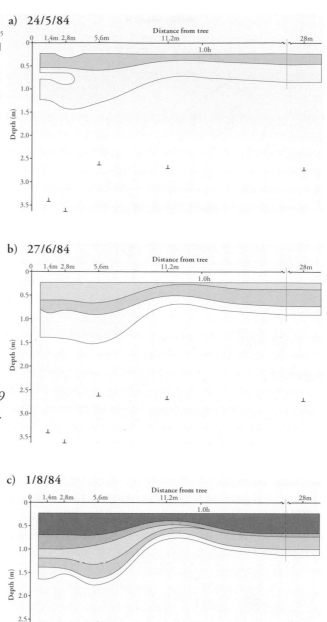

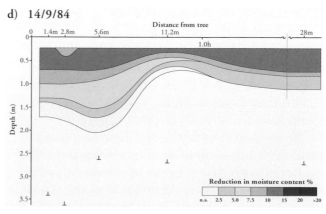

Figure 5.5

Development of soil drying during the very dry summer of 1984, in proximity of lime tree on Boulder Clay (tree 15).

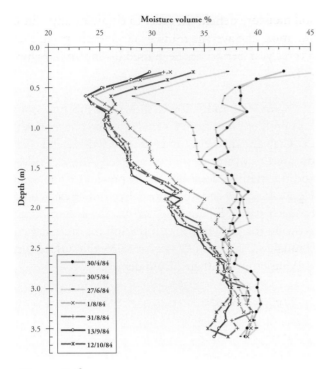

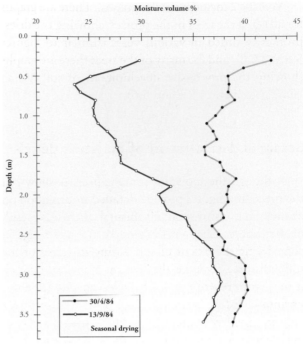

Figure 5.6

Progressive development of soil drying during 1984, 5.0m from poplar tree on Boulder Clay (tree 33).

Figure 5.7

The wettest and driest profiles from Figure 5.6 used to show the overall extent of seasonal soil drying.

The previous examples have shown the effect of a lime tree on Boulder Clay. Figure 5.6 shows the seasonal development of soil drying occurring in close proximity (5.0m) to a poplar, also on Boulder Clay soil (tree 33), during the same season of 1984. Compare this with Figure 5.1 which shows the comparable profiles for a lime on Boulder Clay. The poplar would have come into leaf in late April, but even by 30/5/84 there was negligible change in moisture content. By 27/6/84 drying had extended to 1.4m, by 1/8/84 to 2.3m and by 31/8/84 to the base of the neutron probe access tube at 3.6m. Throughout this period the moisture content diminished throughout the full depth of root activity. After 31/8/84 there was very little further change in the surface 3m, probably because the suction within the soil was reaching limiting values for root activity. However, further soil drying occurred below 3.0m and clearly extended to below the depth of the access hole. By 12/10/84 the soil was beginning to rehydrate near the surface, although there was slight further drying at depth.

The overall extent of seasonal drying between the wettest profile (on 30/4/84) and the driest (on 13/9/84) can be conveniently shown by shading, as in Figure 5.7. Similar yellow shading is used throughout the examples in Volume 2 to indicate the extent of seasonal soil drying.

Similar seasonal soil drying developed each year; Figure 5.8 shows the driest profiles at the end of the summer in various years. The driest of these were recorded in particularly dry years such as 1984 and 1989. By comparison, comparatively wet years such as 1985 and 1982 produced significantly less drying, although the overall pattern remains essentially similar.

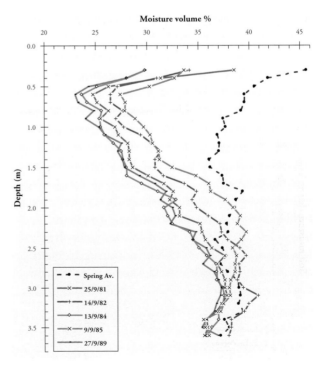

Figure 5.8

The driest profiles recorded in various years between 1981 - 1989, 5.0m from poplar tree on Boulder Clay (tree 33).

Volume 2 includes similar graphs. There are graphs for all 60 of the trees in the project, showing the driest profiles recorded in various years (similar to Figures 5.4 and 5.8), and for many of the trees there are graphs showing the progressive development of soil drying (similar to Figures 5.1 and 5.6).

Seasonal development of moisture deficit

Although the moisture content profiles shown in the preceding figures provide detailed information on changes in moisture content through the whole depth of the profile, Chapter 4 has noted the advantage in considering the extent of soil drying in terms of the soil moisture deficit, i.e. the amount of moisture which is needed to return the soil to field capacity (or equilibrium moisture content). Not only does this provide an easy way of quantifying the extent of soil drying but also, and more importantly, if the water shrinkage factor is constant at all depths, it provides an indication of the amount of soil shrinkage. Even if the value of the water shrinkage factor is not known, the pattern of changes of moisture deficit occurring over a period of time will produce a corresponding pattern of soil movement. These soil movements can then be related to building movement.

Calculation of soil moisture deficit requires knowledge of the moisture content at field capacity. Typically the soil in the spring is at about field capacity and for this reason the spring readings have been used throughout Volume 2 as the basis for calculation of

soil moisture deficit. In order to eliminate any minor variation, the average readings taken each spring over a three year period has been used (as shown in Figure 5.3).

Figures 5.1 and 5.2 have shown the moisture content profiles 2.8m from a 14m high lime tree on Boulder Clay during the summer as the soil dries, and then during the winter as it rewets. Using these profiles, and the method described in the previous Chapter in Figure 4.22, the soil moisture deficit can be calculated for each date. Figure 5.9 presents this information, showing the development of the soil moisture deficit throughout the year (1984) just below the surface (i.e. at 0.3m) and at 1.0 and 2.0m depths.

Just below the surface the maximum deficit (138mm) was recorded on 31/8/84, with the subsequent rain saturating the surface layers and preventing any further increase in the overall deficit at that level. However this rainfall only penetrated to a limited extent so that at 1.0m depth the maximum deficit (109mm) was recorded on 12/10/84. At 2.0m depth there was negligible change, with the maximum deficit of only 6mm being recorded on 12/10/84. Almost full recovery had occurred at all depths by 13/2/85.

The poplar on Boulder Clay (tree 33) produced a generally similar pattern (Figure 5.10), although at all depths the maximum deficits were recorded on the same date (13/9/84), and were far greater than those produced by the lime tree, (236mm at 0.3m, 144mm at 1.0m and 54mm at 2.0m depth).

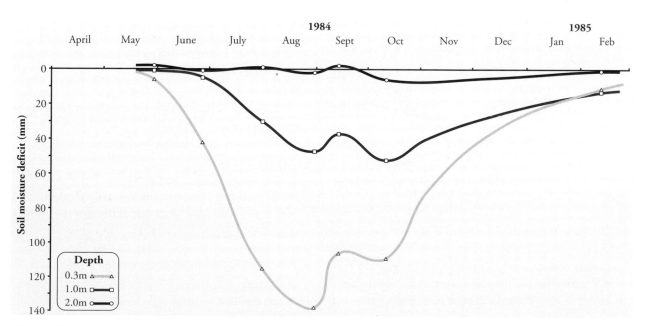

Figure 5.9

Development of soil moisture deficit at varying depths during summer of 1984 and recovery during winter, 2.8m from lime tree on Boulder Clay (tree 15).

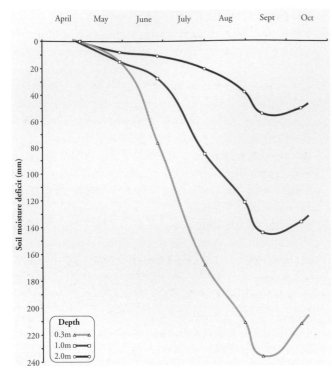

Figure 5.10

Development of soil moisture deficit at various depths during 1984, 5.0m from poplar on Boulder Clay (tree 33).

This seasonal development of the moisture deficit provides a convenient method for comparing the effects of different tree species. Figure 5.11 presents the results from a selection of the trees on Boulder Clay, in each case using the data from the access tube closest to the tree, and calculating the deficit at 1.0m depth. The massively greater effect of the poplar is immediately apparent. These differences between species are considered in further detail in Chapter 9.

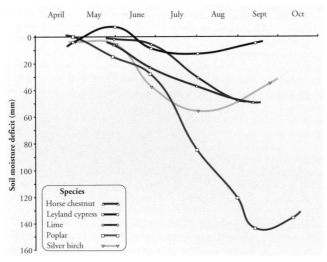

Figure 5.11

Development of soil moisture deficit below 1.0m at closest access tube to various tree species on Boulder Clay in 1984

The results in Volume 2 include similar diagrams to show the seasonal development of soil moisture deficit for all of the trees on which measurements were taken periodically during 1984 and other years.

Seasonal fluctuations of soil moisture deficit

Whilst it is interesting to see how the soil moisture deficit develops through the summer, the information which is most relevant to problems of damage to buildings is the amount of soil moisture deficit which develops each autumn. It is the difference between the readings taken in the spring (when any soil moisture deficit is at a minimum) and in the autumn (when it is at its maximum) which indicates the full extent of the seasonal fluctuation in the soil moisture deficit.

The lime tree on Boulder Clay which has featured earlier in this chapter (tree 15), is used to illustrate this annual fluctuation in soil moisture deficit in Figure 5.12. This shows the maximum and minimum soil moisture deficits recorded at a depth of 1.0m throughout the period of the research project. A depth of 1.0m was chosen as it is the normal minimum depth for foundations on clay soil; it therefore shows the extent of seasonal soil drying which would occur below such foundations. The main period of the readings was from 1979 to 1984, with subsequent readings in 1986 and 1989 and then regular readings again since 1991. The years when no readings were taken are indicated by a zig-zag line, and when readings have been not been taken in the spring or autumn the line is dotted with an estimated value for the missing result.

This figure includes the results from each of the five access tubes, and thus shows the difference in amplitude of the fluctuation in moisture deficit at varying distances from the tree. At the control tube 28m from the tree (the green line), there is negligible fluctuation except in the very dry years of 1984 and 1989, when the grass was sufficient to produce this slight deficit below 1.0m. Likewise the fluctuations for the access tube 11.2m from the tree shows negligible fluctuation similar to the control, indicating that there is no significant influence of the tree at this position. By contrast, at each of the three access tubes nearest to the tree (at 1.4m, 2.8m and 5.6m), there is considerably greater amplitude of fluctuation, with this essentially similar at each of these tubes.

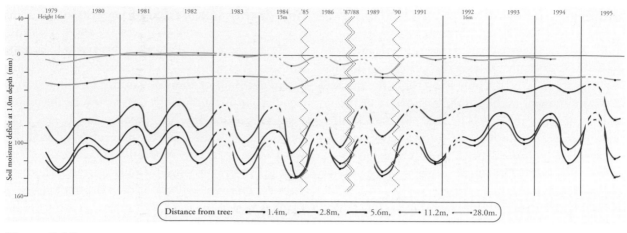

Figure 5.12

Seasonal fluctuations in soil moisture deficit at each of the 5 access tubes in proximity of lime tree on Boulder Clay (tree 15) during the period from 1979 to 1995. Note that the deficit in this, and all similar figures, is calculated at 1.0m.

It will be noted in Figure 5.12 that the line for the control access tube generally fluctuates along the line of zero soil moisture deficit, whereas the other lines are at a lower level. The significance of this is considered in further detail in the next Chapter. The next Chapter also considers the trend towards diminishing values of the deficit during the period from 1992 to 1994.

Volume 2 includes similar diagrams for all of the trees. During the main period of the research through to 1985, readings were taken each autumn for all of the trees and at all of the access tubes . They were also taken every spring over a 3 or 4 year period. On a selection of the trees, further readings have been taken in the autumn and in the spring in subsequent years.

The extent of the deficit, as demonstrated by the amplitude of the cycle of seasonal drying, generally reflects the weather conditions during the summer, with maximum deficits recorded in dry years such as 1984, 1989 and 1995 (see also Chapter 8, page 126).

All of these diagrams also demonstrate the considerable variation in effects of different individuals of the same species, and between species. This aspect is considered in further detail in Chapter 9.

Soil drying by evergreen vegetation

Soil drying by deciduous vegetation cannot start until after the plant comes into leaf in the spring, and stops in the autumn with the formation of the abscission layer and leaf fall. There are no such restrictions for evergreen vegetation. However, other factors, particularly low temperature, short day length and low light levels, restrict photosynthesis and transpirational water loss during the winter period. As a result, any drying during the winter is very slight and usually far less than the input from rainfall.

However, some influence during the winter can be demonstrated. For instance, Figure 5.13 shows a zone of soil drying which developed between 1/11/91 and 15/4/92 close to a Leyland cypress on Gault Clay (tree 45). Readings were not taken during this winter period to determine exactly when this drying occurred, but at this depth it was probably in the late autumn rather than early spring (when moisture was again available near the surface).

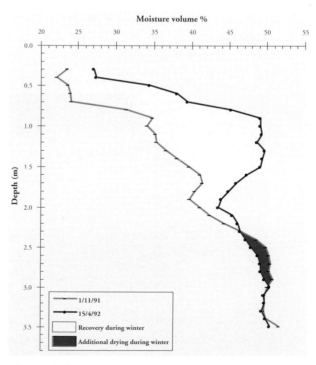

Figure 5.13

Additional soil drying developing during winter period at access tube 1.5m from Leyland cypress on Gault Clay (Tree 45).

Soil drying by grass

Grass is an evergreen which starts growth and transpiration significantly earlier in the spring than deciduous vegetation. One has only to consider the need to start lawn mowing as soon as the weather warms up in March and April to appreciate this! By the time deciduous trees have flushed and started active growth, considerable moisture deficits have often already been produced by grass. The deficits in early spring are usually restricted to near the surface, usually not extending more than 0.5m, but the moisture reserves in these surface layers are already denied to the tree.

Competition between grass and trees will continue throughout the year. In this respect, grass is fiercely competitive and capable of creating far greater soil suctions than those produced by most tree species, particularly near the soil surface. This effect of grass must not be under-estimated. It can cause significant soil drying in a dry summer extending down to depths of at least 1.2m. Within this zone, the roots of the grass will be competing with tree roots. Consideration of the patterns of soil drying in the vicinity of trees growing in grass shows that the grass can mask the effects of tree roots except in the close proximity to the tree (Figure 5.5 on page 69 and also Figure 5.14), as well as many examples in Volume 2.)

Although grass can cause this intense soil drying near the surface, its effects do not extend laterally in a manner comparable to the wide-spreading lateral root system of a tree.

Soil drying in absence of vegetation

Even if there is no vegetation, there can still be some soil drying as a result of evaporation of water. The extreme surface of the soil can dry in this way very rapidly, but this surface layer then protects the underlying soil so that any further water loss is very slow. There will be some capillary movement of water towards the surface, but evaporation from a bare soil surface, even after prolonged drought, is unlikely to reduce the moisture content below a depth of 0.3m. It requires vegetation and a root system to extract moisture from any greater depth.

The potential depth for evaporative drying may be increased if it is a clay soil which cracks and opens the internal surface of the cracks to further evaporation. However, deep cracks will usually develop only if there are roots, and it will be transpiration by the vegetation, rather than evaporation, which predominates.

Any form of hard surface, such as tarmac or paving slabs, will reduce, or virtually eliminate, any evaporation and drying from the soil surface. A totally impermeable surface would also prevent any ingress of water from rainfall, but few surfaces are entirely impermeable. There are usually cracks, joints between slabs or at the junction between tarmac and kerbs etc., which allow water to penetrate. Once beneath the surface, the water can usually move laterally, particularly if there is a permeable layer such as the sub-base to a road or paving overlying an impermeable clay soil. For this

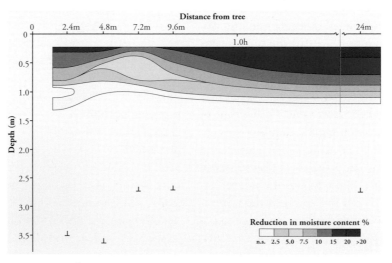

Figure 5.14

Pattern of soil drying in proximity to horse chestnut tree on London Clay (tree 2) on 19/9/89. The access tubes are all located in similar close-mown grass. At the control tube the deficit as a result of this grass is greater than at any of the tubes close to the tree. Overall the grass totally masks any effects of the tree. (See also the contours of soil moisture deficit for this, and other trees in Volume 2.)

reason, in the absence of vegetation, a clay soil beneath hard paving usually maintains its maximum field capacity, even after prolonged drought.

A surface covered with a material such as gravel or any other form of surface mulch can be particularly effective for maintaining maximum moisture content. It can allow rainfall to penetrate direct into the underlying soil with minimal loss onto the surface of the stones, and can then protect the soil from evaporative loss.

Seasonal fluctuations in water table

The water table is defined as the upper surface of the groundwater. In a reasonably permeable soil this is readily observed - it is the level to which water will equilibrate in a borehole. However, in a clay soil the rates of water movement may be very slow, so that it is difficult to establish this equilibrium. For this reason, in all soils, it is better to define the water table as being that level in the soil where the water is at atmospheric pressure. Water below this level will be at a positive pressure, and water above this level will be at a negative pressure (suction). Under some circumstances there can be a water table in a saturated layer of soil near the surface, with this separated from an underlying saturated layer by an unsaturated layer. Under these circumstances the upper water table is described as a perched water table.

Under vegetation there can be a marked fluctuation in the level of the water table, with the table being lowered during the summer as a result of the drying effect of the vegetation. During the winter the water table will return to, or near to, the soil surface. These fluctuations are the direct effect of the vegetation, and should be recognised as such. The next chapter (Chapter 6) describes how the seasonal fluctuations may be affecting a perched water table, with a zone of persistently desiccated soil at greater depth.

Under some circumstances there can also be a fluctuation in the water table irrespective of any local effects of vegetation. This can only occur if the water is moving through the soil so as to allow drainage to occur. Drainage requires high hydraulic conductivity, which implies large pore size and therefore large particle size, or else a well-developed soil structure. As discussed in Chapter 4, these conditions will occur in sandy soils, but are less applicable to clay soils. Under most circumstances there will be little or no fluctuation in the water table of a clay soil in the absence of vegetation, except possibly on steeply sloping sites (Case Study 19, page 343).

An exception to this can occur in heterogeneous soils where bands of permeable soil are mixed with clay or underlie it. During the winter the permeable soil may be saturated and applying a positive water potential to the clay, but in the summer the permeable layers of this soil may be able to drain and apply a negative potential, or suction, to the clay. The pattern of drainage of the permeable soil is clearly dependent on the overall hydrology of the site, which makes it difficult to predict the behaviour of the overall soil mass. If drainage is uniform over the whole site, any suction and shrinkage of the clay will be fairly uniform, but if conditions allow differential drainage and suction, it could induce seasonal movements irrespective of any effects of vegetation.

Although these conditions do occasionally occur, experience suggests they are unusual. For instance, the moisture content in almost all of the control boreholes in the research described in Volume 2 remains very constant; some slight exceptions to this are seen, for instance trees 39 and 47 (Volume 2, pages 209 and 249) which show layers of soil drying associated with bands of sand. The possibility of changes due to this effect should be considered whenever there is a heterogeneous soil mass.

Influence of soil type on seasonal moisture deficits

The extent of soil drying which can develop during the summer will be influenced by many factors. Figure 4.19 has shown the variation in available water between different soil textural classes; in general, the greatest available water is associated with loam soils, which have a broad mix of sand, silt and clay. The porosity of the soil and the packing density of the soil particles, both of which influence the bulk density, are crucial in determining the amount of water which can be held at available suctions. Sandy soils will generally increase their available water with an increase in bulk density, and for this reason will generally benefit from rolling and trafficking. By contrast clay soils will benefit from a reduction in bulk density, achieved by techniques such as subsoiling (Hall *et al.*, 1977).

These factors of bulk density, porosity and air capacity also influence the ability of the roots to penetrate and exploit the available water. A heavy clay soil, with a high bulk density and less than 10% air, provides a very hostile growing medium which is less likely to be exploited, even though it may contain available water. The extent of root penetration into a soil of this sort may be very limited. By contrast, a light loam soil provides an ideal rooting medium, and may be exploited to very great depth.

The permeability of the clay is also important. A soil of low permeability may be unable to recover to its field capacity during the winter, leaving it in a persistently desiccated condition; this is considered in further detail in the next Chapter. The extent of seasonal drying of a soil of this sort will be governed by the amount of recovery which can occur during the winter months.

For all of these reasons the greatest extent of seasonal soil drying will usually occur with soils of comparatively low clay content. Soils of this sort will tend to have limited shrinkage potential. The combination (of a large change in moisture content acting on a soil of low shrinkage potential) may be capable of producing as much soil movement as can occur with a soil of high shrinkage potential which is subjected to only a limited change of moisture content.

The results presented in Volume 2 confirm that it was generally the Boulder Clay soils, or other clays with significant bands of permeable sand or silt near the surface, which showed the greatest range of fluctuation in soil moisture deficit.

Effect of pruning on seasonal changes

Pruning reduces the leaf area of a tree. The amount of water lost from the leaves in transpiration is related to the leaf area. Reducing the leaf area by pruning should therefore reduce the amount of water which is taken from the soil, and thus the amplitude of the cycle of seasonal development of soil moisture deficit.

Although there is this relationship between transpiration and leaf area, a reduction in leaf area will not necessarily produce a corresponding reduction in the amount of water which is transpired. There are various reasons for this. Not all leaves will be transpiring at the same rate; in particular, leaves in the inner crown which are shaded are usually working less efficiently with lower rates of photosynthesis and transpiration. If these leaves are exposed by the pruning, they can work with greater efficiency. In addition, the increased exposure of the leaves to the sun will produce higher leaf temperatures, whilst a more open canopy will allow more rapid windflow and thus lower relative humidity. The large leaves which develop after pruning often have juvenile characteristics, and may have less efficient stomatal control. All of these features will tend to increase the rate of transpiration. In addition, the rate of transpiration of a tree with a full canopy is often limited by the availability of water, with the tree frequently going into water stress so that the stomata close, and photosynthesis and transpiration cease. However, if the overall rate of transpiration is reduced by pruning, there will be a reduced likelihood that the remaining leaves will be stressed in this way, and so they should be able to maintain a full rate of photosynthesis and transpiration for longer. For all of these reasons the rate of transpiration will tend to be higher on those leaves which remain after pruning.

Although the reduction in transpiration will not be directly proportional to the reduction in leaf area, theoretical considerations indicate that pruning should reduce the extent of soil drying. The experimental pruning of plane trees provides clear evidence of the practical benefits (Volume 2, pages 274 to 297). These trees were pruned to varying degrees (light, moderate and heavy), approximately corresponding to a 25%, 50% and 75% crown reduction, with some left untreated as controls. Figure 5.15 shows the spatial pattern of reduction of soil moisture content in the autumn following this treatment (September 1984). There appears to be little benefit with the light pruning, but an obvious pattern of diminishing soil drying with the increased severity of pruning. The pruning was repeated in 1986, and again shows a similar pattern (Figure 17.5 and Volume 2, pages 280 to 283). A very similar pattern was demonstrated by a second group of plane trees subjected to similar pruning regimes (Volume 2, page 290 to 297).

Another example of the benefits of pruning is provided by the pollarding in 1995 of the plane trees used previously as the untreated controls; this drastic treatment virtually eliminated all soil drying by these trees during the subsequent summer (Figure 17.6). Some of the other trees described in Volume 2 were pruned (as part of management by the owners, rather than at my request); a poplar (tree 32, page 172) and a whitebeam (tree 41, page 214) both showed a reduced amplitude of soil drying following this treatment. Storm damage to an oak (tree 22, page 116) provided a natural form of pruning, with the same result.

Chapter 17 considers in detail the different methods of pruning and the practical implications of tree pruning as a remedial measure if damage to buildings has occurred.

Pruning a tree upsets the root:shoot ratio. After pruning, the tree will endeavour to restore the original ratio, either by enhanced shoot growth to restore the

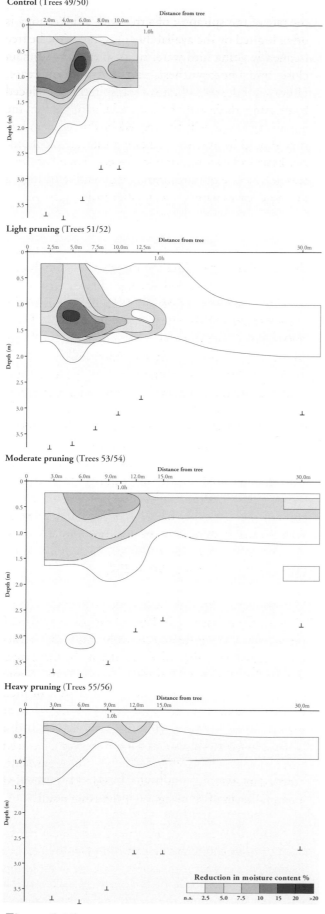

Control (Trees 49/50)

Light pruning (Trees 51/52)

Moderate pruning (Trees 53/54)

Heavy pruning (Trees 55/56)

Reduction in moisture content %

n.s. 2.5 5.0 7.5 10 15 20 >20

Figure 5.15

Effect of different severity of pruning on patterns of soil drying by plane trees (1984).

previous leaf area, or by dieback of the root system. Where possible the tree will prefer the former strategy, and it is commonly observed that there can be very vigorous regrowth after pruning, with the tree producing shoots which are often longer and thicker than normal shoot growth, with these bearing larger leaves. This does not necessarily indicate that the amount of wood tissue which is produced is greater; the available resources may be concentrated in a few very vigorous shoots rather than being disseminated into a mass of twigs throughout the whole of the previous crown. Furthermore, as described in Chapter 2, page 17, regrowth can be achieved at the expense of mobilisation and utilisation of carbon (starch) reserves, and by the allocation of available photosynthates to the crown rather than root system. However, as the number of leaves and leaf area will have been reduced, the total water use will be less. For these reasons, even if there is very rapid regrowth, it does not indicate an increased rate of photosynthesis and transpiration.

A tree which is in good health, with abundant starch reserves, can recover very rapidly and can soon restore the original leaf area and return to its the original water uptake. As a result, pruning will only provide a temporary benefit. The duration of this restoration process will depend on the severity of pruning, the availability of carbon reserves and also on the species of tree. If the tree had not reached its full size prior to the pruning, it will still be capable of growing to its original potential, so that under these circumstances the water uptake may ultimately increase. However, unless it achieves additional growth, there is no evidence to indicate that water uptake is ever increased by pruning.

Regrowth of shoots after pruning will deplete starch reserves. If the pruning is repeated, it will progressively deplete reserves, and so the tree will be less capable of shoot regrowth, and root mortality will increase. Provided a regular cycle of pruning is maintained, the correct root:shoot ratio will be restored, but with the mass of both roots and shoots reduced in proportion.

Although a tree will seek to allocate reserves to enhance shoot growth and thereby restore the original root:shoot, this will not be possible if its reserves are inadequate. In these circumstances the ratio must be restored either by a reduced rate of new root development or by increased root mortality. Initially this will usually only affect the abundance of fine roots. However, if there is a continuing imbalance, superfluous conducting roots are also likely

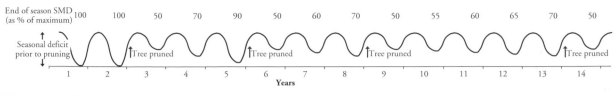

Figure 5.16

Diagrammatic representation of effect of repeated pruning (for simplicity, variation in amplitude of seasonal cycle from climatic conditions has been ignored). In years 1 and 2, prior to pruning, there is a full cycle of seasonal drying and recovery (100% SMD). At the start of year 3 the tree is pruned, sufficient to reduce the SMD to 50%. There is rapid recovery in the two following years (SMD 70% and 90 % of maximum). At the start of year 6 the tree is again pruned to reduce SMD to 50%. After this second pruning, recovery will be slightly slower (SMD 60% and 70% in years 7 and 8). After another 3 years the tree is again pruned to reduce the SMD to 50% (start of year 9). After this repeated pruning the recovery will be even slower, allowing the interval before the next pruning to be increased to 5 years (start of year 14).

to die back. A tree will not continue to expend energy on the maintenance of conducting roots which are serving no useful function.

Figure 5.16 provides a diagrammatic representation of the effect of pruning on the amplitude of the seasonal cycle of soil drying, but it must again be emphasised that the extent to which it reduces the amplitude will depend on the severity of pruning.

Summary

1.   During the summer the rate of transpiration from leaves, or evaporation from a soil surface, is usually far greater than the input of water from rainfall. As a result a soil will dry out progressively, with a temporary reversal after rain. The soil is typically at its wettest in late spring (April), and at its driest in the autumn (September), the exact time depending on weather conditions.

2.   The extent of this **seasonal drying is negligible in the absence of vegetation.** With grass, or other herbaceous vegetation, there can be intense drying, but usually restricted to within about 1.2m of the soil surface, i.e. having little influence below the level of normal foundations.

3.   The root activity of a tree can extend to greater depth and can also extend a considerable distance laterally. This allows the tree to exploit a far greater soil volume and have a greater ability to influence the soil below the foundations of adjacent buildings.

4.   The root activity will create a cycle of seasonal soil drying during the summer and recovery during the winter. **In the great majority of situations, any influence of trees is entirely seasonal; they create an enhanced seasonal effect compared with other vegetation.**

5.   With clay soils this seasonal cycle will cause a corresponding seasonal cycle of shrinkage and swelling.

6.   In some situations, considered in detail in the next Chapter, the soil is unable to recover its moisture fully during a single winter, allowing the development of a persistent moisture deficit. This is particularly applicable to soils of low permeability. However, even these soils will also show a seasonal cycle of drying and recovery, with associated shrinkage and swelling.

7.   The amplitude of the seasonal cycle of soil movement will depend on:

    i)   the species of tree involved;

    ii) the condition and water requirements of the tree;

    iii) the water availability, shrinkage characteristics and permeability of the soil;

    iv) the weather conditions during the summer, as affecting the rate of transpiration and the input of water from rainfall;

    v)   other factors such as site topography.

8.   The amplitude of this seasonal cycle can be restricted by pruning the tree to reduce its leaf area and ability to transpire. As the tree recovers from such treatment, it will recover the previous amplitude, unless further pruning is applied.

CASE STUDY 5

*Single storey school building on Boulder Clay – Damage caused by various adjacent poplars –
Initial tree felling stabilised parts of building – Additional felling and eventually hedge removal
required for complete stability – Level monitoring essential to demonstrate effects of tree removal.*

Background

The site is a school in Bletchley, Buckinghamshire, located in an area of Boulder Clay. In about 1970/71 a purpose-built single storey extension with a flat roof was added to provide classrooms and changing facilities. This extension is 'U' shape in plan, open on the south side and enclosing a central grassed quadrangle (CS Figure 5.1). External walls are 28cm cavity construction, and it is sub-divided into classrooms partially by brick partition walls and partially by flexible sliding screens. All internal brickwork is unplastered and exposed. CS Figure 5.1 shows the internal layout of the eastern wing and outline of the north and west wings.

In 1979 damage occurred, and repairs were undertaken in 1981. This included relaying the floor slab in the east wing, and increasing the depth of the internal foundations to about 1m, which was comparable to the depth of external foundations.

Damage re-occurred in 1984, with further development of damage each subsequent summer. In 1988 I was instructed by the owners of the school to advise on the involvement of trees as a cause of damage, and on the remedial works. By that time the east wing was severely damaged, particularly at the south end. There were cracks in the internal and external brickwork. At the French door openings near the south end of the east wing there was a pronounced step of about 25mm between the floor slab and the adjacent walls, and the movement of the floor slab was breaking the central heating pipes on a regular basis.

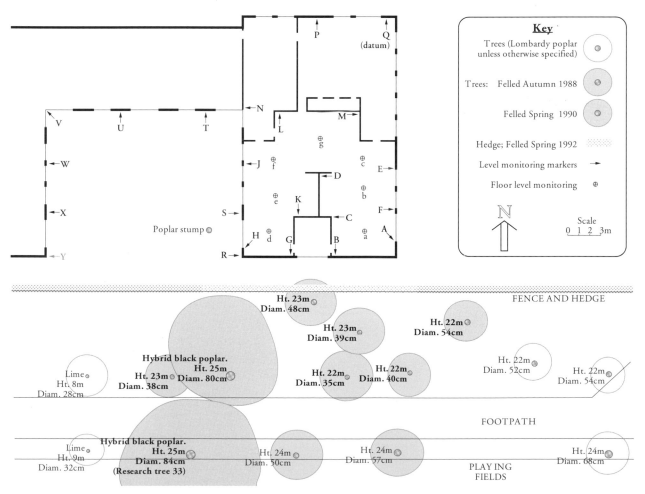

Case Study Figure 5.1

Site plan, including location of level monitoring stations and adjacent trees.

79

The trees

The boundary with an adjacent park and playing fields was only 3m from the south end of the two wings. Along this boundary was a hawthorn hedge, kept regularly trimmed to a height of 2.5m.

In the adjacent area of the park was a group of mature Lombardy poplars (*Populus nigra* 'Italica'), the nearest of which was 4m from the east wing. At distances of 10.9 and 18.7m from the east wing were two large mature hybrid black poplars (*P.* x *euramericana*). The further of these two trees was one of the poplar trees used in the research project (tree 33); the five neutron probe access tubes were aligned away from the school to the south of this tree.

Soon after the extension was built a poplar tree had been removed from the grass quadrangle, from a point approximately 3m from the west wing.

The location of all of these trees, the hedge and stump are shown on the plan in CS Figure 5.1.

Initial recommendation

It was known that the damage was associated with significant seasonal movement. This, combined with my experience from the research readings of changes in soil moisture content near tree 33, suggested that movements were primarily seasonal and that there would not be a significant persistent deficit. I therefore recommended felling the adjacent poplars which were most likely to be contributing to

the movement. This included the six Lombardy poplars closest to the east wing (identified by bold type on CS Figure 5.1) and also the two hybrid black poplars.

As I only received my instructions in August 1988, not surprisingly no action was taken with the trees prior to that autumn. Indeed, the owners of the trees were denying their involvement, but in October a gale blew down a similar Lombardy poplar on an adjacent part of the playing fields. All of the trees were inspected, and on safety grounds five of the Lombardy poplars were felled (and also two others to the south of the footpath, whose removal I had not requested). At the same time the nearer of the two hybrid black poplars was crown-reduced by about 25%. This left one of the Lombardy poplars, the pruned hybrid poplar, and also the hybrid poplar (tree 33) still at its original size.

Level monitoring

In August 1988 I started level monitoring, at the same time as recommending the removal of the trees. Level monitoring markers were installed at 23 stations on the internal and external walls. In addition, indelible marks were made on the tiles on the floor slab of the east wing to allow monitoring movements of this slab. The location of all of these stations is shown in CS Figure 5.1.

It is relevant to note that the open-plan layout of the classrooms made it easy to set up the markers on the inner face of the external walls; this allowed observation of all of the markers in the east wing with only a single transfer of the tripod and level. At station J there were marker screws

	30/8/88	4/10/88	18/11/88	24/1/89	16/6/89	27/9/89	26/3/90	1/5/90	26/10/90	22/4/91	2/1/92	10/9/92
A	-9.1	-12.5	-11.9	-10.7	0	-8.1	2.1	3.0	-1.6	6.0	6.4	7.0
B	-9.4	-12.0	-11.2	-9.9	0	-1.3	3.8	2.7	2.3	5.3	4.7	4.5
C	-2.1	-3.1	-1.2	-1.4	0	1.0	0.4	0.4	0.9	1.3	0.7	0.8
D	-2.1	-1.4	-0.7	-	0	0.8	-0.2	0	0.2	0.7	-0.5	-0.1
E	-9.1	-11.2	-6.6	-3.6	0	0.6	0.4	0.5	0.3	0.5	0.6	0.7
F	-13.1	-16.9	-15.0	-11.1	0	-1.7	1.1	1.5	-0.1	2.8	3.3	3.0
G	-12.7	-15.6	-14.3	-11.9	0	-7.6	2.5	3.1	0.9	5.1	4.8	4.3
H	-10.3	-14.0	-12.4	-9.5	0	-11.8	1.2	1.6	-5.8	1.9	0.7	-
J	-4.7	-6.7	-4.1	-2.6	0	-2.4	-0.6	-0.2	-1.1	-0.8	-0.7	-0.7
K	-4.0	-4.7	-3.2	-2.5	0	-0.7	0.5	0.6	0.2	1.0	0.8	0.8
L	-3.4	-5.0	-3.5	-2.9	0	-0.8	-0.5	-0.3	-1.1	-0.9	-0.4	-0.2
M	-2.8	-3.3	-1.9	-1.8	0	-	-	-	-0.7	-0.5	-0.5	-
N	-3.5	-5.3	-3.2	-2.0	0	-1.6	-0.6	-0.5	-1.2	-0.9	-1.1	-1.4
P	-1.5	-1.4	-1.5	-1.0	0	-0.7	-0.3	-0.3	-0.3	-0.3	-0.1	0
Q	Datum	Datum	Datum	Datum	Datum	Datum	Datum	Datum	Datum	Datum	Datum	Datum
R	-11.3	-15.6	-13.8	-11.4	0	-13.0	0.4	0.9	-7.8	0.5	0.7	1.1
S	-6.8	-9.7	-6.1	-4.2	0	-3.7	-0.6	0	-0.5	0.3	0.6	0.4
T	-2.5	-3.7	-1.9	-1.6	0	-1.4	-0.6	-0.6	-0.3	-0.1	-0.3	-0.2
U	-2.3	-2.4	-1.4	-1.6	0	-0.7	-0.7	-0.4	-0.4	-0.1	-0.7	-0.7
V	-2.3	-2.2	-0.9	-1.7	0	-1.1	-1.4	-0.7	-1.2	0.1	-0.4	0.1
W	-2.3	-3.8	-2.2	-2.4	0	-2.4	-1	-0.9	-0.8	-0.2	-1.1	-1
X	-3.3	-5.7	-3.9	-2.8	0	-3.0	-1.5	-1.1	-1.7	-0.8	-1.0	-0.8
Y	-3.9	-7.1	-5.7	-2.9	0	-6.2	-1.3	-1.5	-4.0	-1.0	-1.0	-1.4
a			-2.7	-3.2	0	0.8	1.6	1.8	2.0	2.8	3.8	
b			-1.6	-1.9	0	0.7	0.2	0.2	1.1	0.4	1.1	
c			-1.6	-2.3	0	0.7	0.2	-0.3	0.4	0.3	0.7	
d			-5.6	-4.5	0	-3.1	0.9	1.7	1.3	1.9	-	
e			-3.4	-2.7	0	-0.9	0.2	0.3	-0.5	-0.3	0.9	
f			-3.5	-2.7	0	-0.7	-0.2	0	-1.0	-0.9	0.2	
g			-3.3	-2.6	0	-0.5	-0.2	0.3	-0.5	-0.5	0.4	

Case Study Figure 5.2

Results of level monitoring (mm), presented relative to station Q as arbitrary datum, and to readings on 16/6/89.

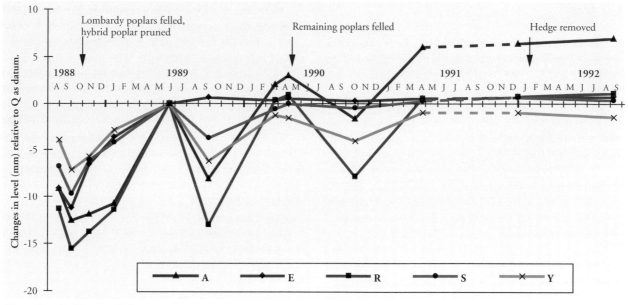

Case Study Figure 5.3

Results of the level monitoring for selected representative stations (location of these stations only is included in Figure 5.4 below).

on both the internal and external face of the wall, and a third tripod set up was used for readings on the markers on the external walls around the quadrangle. This extensive monitoring therefore only required two transfers.

The tabulated results for all of the readings are presented in CS Figure 5.2, and CS Figure 5.3 provides a graphical presentation for a selection of these stations.

For the presentation of these results I have assumed an arbitrary zero datum at station Q on the north wall of the north wing. It will be noted that the other stations in the

locality show negligible differential movement relative to this station. For ease of interpretation of the results, they have been presented relative to the readings taken on 16th June 1989, as these record the recovery which had occurred during the first winter of monitoring.

Level distortion survey

It was not until May 1990, when I was first advised of the existence of the poplar stump, that I undertook a level distortion survey. The results are shown in CS Figure 5.4.

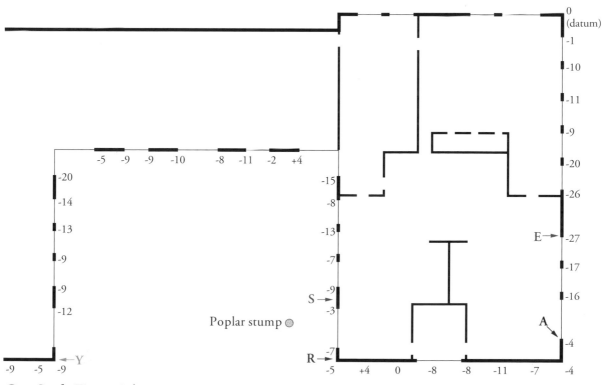

Case Study Figure 5.4

Results of the level distortion survey (mm) in May 1990, relative to arbitrary datum in north east corner.

81

DISCUSSION

The level monitoring provides an excellent demonstration of the influence of vegetation on different parts of the building.

The monitoring did not start until August 1988. At that time much of that summer's subsidence had already occurred, but slight further downward movements were recorded until 4/10/88.

Recovery during the winter 1988/89 demonstrated the amplitude of the seasonal movements which were affecting the different parts of the building. As might be expected, large movements were recorded on the south flank wall of the east wing (stations A, B, G, H and R), all of which showed movements of between 11 to 15mm. However the greatest movement was at station F (16.9mm). Significant movements extended throughout the southern half of the east wing, slight movements in the south wall of the north wing, and with increasing movements as one moves south along the west wing (stations V, W, X, Y). In the east wing, the western half of the floor slab showed some movement (stations d, e and f), but there was surprisingly little movement in the eastern half (stations a, b and c), particularly in comparison with the far greater movements recorded on the adjacent walls. The differential movement between the walls and slab explained the severe damage to the slab in that locality.

The removal of some of the trees during the winter 1988/89 produced some benefit the following summer, as demonstrated by the further set of monitoring readings at the end of that summer (27/9/89). The most dramatic benefits were at station F, where the seasonal movements reduced from 16.9mm in 1988 to only 1.7mm in 1989, and at station E (reduction from 11.2mm to 0.6mm).

CS Figure 5.5 compares the seasonal movements in 1988 with those in 1989 after this initial felling, and distinguishes, by the coloured background, the amount of reduction in movement which occurred. Bearing in mind the drier weather conditions of 1989 which would be expected to increase the amplitude of movement, all of the stations show a significant benefit, but this was only marginal at the south west corner of the east wing (stations H and R) and at the south east corner of the west wing (station Y).

In the light of this evidence I expressed the opinion that the extent of tree felling which had occurred in 1988 was still inadequate. The remaining Lombardy poplar near the south east corner probably accounted for the continuing movements of station A, with the two hybrid black poplars causing continued movements of the walls which faced onto the quadrangle.

Legal proceedings were started for an Injunction for the removal of these trees, but eventually in April and May 1990 these three remaining poplars were felled.

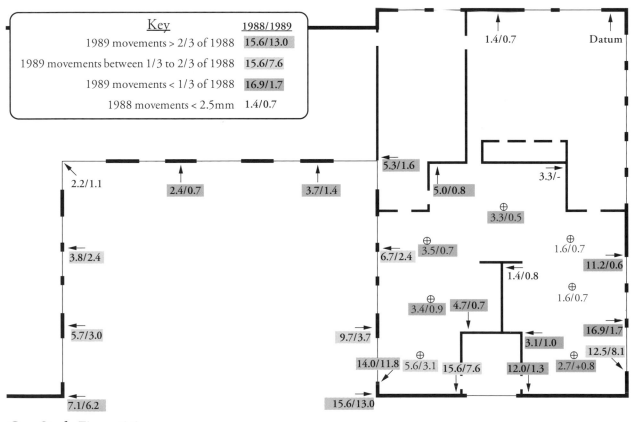

Case Study Figure 5.5

Comparison of seasonal movements in 1988 with 1989 after initial felling of poplars. Stability achieved at stations highlighted in green; continuing movements (at pink or brown stations) attributable either to remaining poplars or hedge.

In the meantime, the monitoring during the winter 1989/90 showed that station E, which had been subject to the greatest seasonal movement, had completely stabilised. Likewise, other stations did not show evidence of heave following the initial tree removal. This helped to demonstrate that there would not be significant long-term recovery following the felling of the remaining trees.

This stabilisation of station E helped to disprove the claim made by an arboricultural consultant acting for the tree owners in respect of the Injunction proceedings. He alleged that much of the damage was caused by heave occurring as a result of the earlier felling of the poplar in the quadrangle, and that any additional tree felling would cause further long-term heave. In response to these claims, I undertook the level distortion survey; this showed no evidence of heave in the locality of the stump. Indeed, the only significant departure from level is on the east wall of the east wing, particularly in the region of stations E and F which had been showing the greatest seasonal movement. As the monitoring demonstrated that station E was already stable and that further recovery would not occur, the distortion in this area can probably be attributed to dynamic settlement.

I had hoped that the removal of the final poplars would result in complete restability. However, further level monitoring in autumn 1990 (26/10/90) showed significant con-tinuing movements, particularly in the south west corner of the east wing (stations H and R, showing 7.4 and 8.7mm of continued movement). During that summer movements in excess of 2mm also continued at stations A, G and Y (CS Figure 5.6). These movements were therefore occurring in those parts of the building closest to the hedge, and it was apparent that this was continuing to have a minor influence.

As these small movements were continuing to cause minor damage in the east wing, it was recommended that the section of hedge adjacent to this wing should be removed. The smaller movements in the west wing were not causing damage, and it was therefore considered that this section of hedge could be retained. The hedge adjacent to the east wing was eventually removed in spring 1992, and readings that autumn showed that stability of the remaining stations had been achieved (CS Figure 5.3). Although the hedge had not been removed from beside the west wing, station Y showed negligible movement during 1992. This was probably partially a reflection of the wetter weather during that summer, but may also have been aided by the hedge no longer having to compete with the poplars for water.

In the meantime, the building had been refurbished during the 1992 summer holiday.

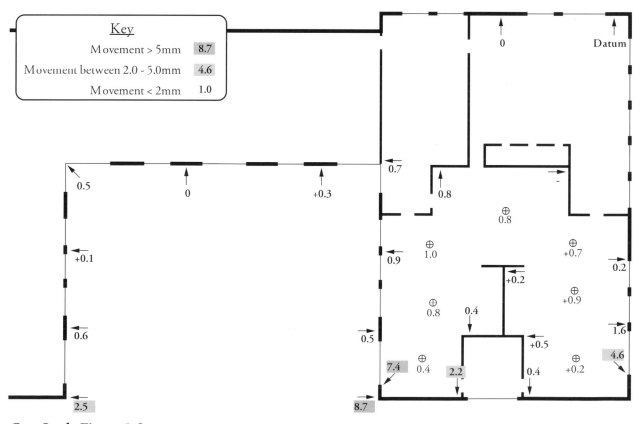

Case Study Figure 5.6

Continuing seasonal movements in 1990 after felling final poplars, attributable to hawthorn hedge (movements ceased after removal of adjacent section of hedge).

Lessons to be learnt

- The level monitoring was invaluable in demonstrating the involvement of the different trees and the role of the hedge.

- If my recommendations had been followed during the first winter and all of the relevant trees removed, a further annual cycle of movement would have been prevented.

- In my initial recommendations I had not thought that the hedge was involved. Subsequent monitoring showed that the hedge was a minor contributing factor to the south flank wall. Removal of the hedge stabilised that wall.

- As anticipated, despite the close proximity of the poplars, on this Boulder Clay soil there was negligible persistent deficit. Only stations A, B and G showed recovery movements in excess of 5mm after the first winter (6.0mm at station A on 22/4/91, increasing by only another 1mm to 7.0mm by 10/9/92).

CHAPTER 6

PERSISTENT MOISTURE DEFICITS

The previous Chapter (Chapter 5) has described the seasonal fluctuations in soil moisture content caused by evapotranspiration, and has shown how these can be enhanced in the proximity of trees. The soil undergoes an annual cycle, drying during each summer and rewetting during each winter. However, in some circumstances the process of rewetting may not be complete during a single winter, and the soil may still be in a partially desiccated condition at the time that the cycle of drying recommences. In those situations where there is still a soil moisture deficit present in the spring, I suggest that the term "**persistent moisture deficit**" should be applied to distinguish such deficit from those associated with the cycle of seasonal change. The term "permanent moisture deficit" is used by some authors (e.g. Institution of Structural Engineers, 1994), usually, but not always, to describe a similar concept. However, as described in this Chapter, these deficits are not permanent - they can increase or diminish. The adjective 'persistent' is more appropriate, and should be preferred.

As shall be described in later Chapters (Chapters 7 and 15), the problems of heave or long-term recovery can only occur if there is a persistent moisture deficit.

As heave and long-term recovery impose special requirements for remedial action, an understanding of persistent deficits and their correct identification is of fundamental importance.

The long-term monitoring of changes in soil moisture content described in Volume 2 provide some clear examples of the development of a persistent deficit. The best example is provided by tree 26 (one of the poplars on London Clay). Figure 6.1 reproduces the diagram which shows the annual fluctuation in the soil moisture deficit. At the two access tubes closest to the tree, there was an underlying trend of an increase in the soil moisture deficit throughout the whole period of the project, with the seasonal effects superimposed. Thus, at the access tube 4.5m from the tree there was a soil moisture deficit below 1.0m depth of 24mm in spring 1982, but this had increased to 176mm by spring 1992. At the access tube 18.0m from the tree there were slight seasonal fluctuations during the period from 1981 to 1985. After 1989 the amplitude of these seasonal fluctuations increased dramatically, and this was accompanied by the development of a slight persistent moisture deficit, increasing from 26mm in spring 1982 to 63mm in spring 1992.

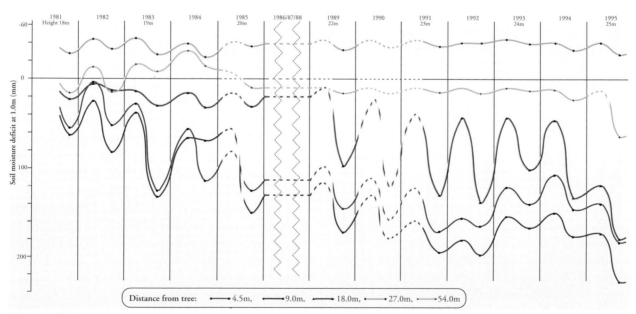

Figure 6.1

Seasonal fluctuations in soil moisture deficit, with underlying trend from development of a persistent moisture deficit. (Poplar on London Clay, tree 26).

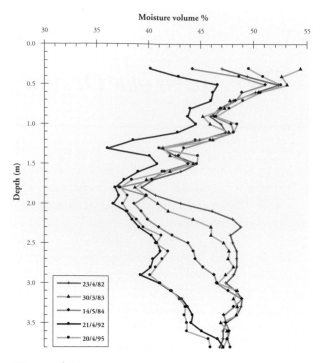

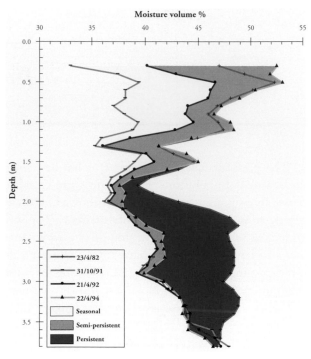

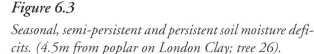

Figure 6.2

Spring soil moisture content profiles, showing progressive development of persistent deficit (4.5m from poplar on London Clay; tree 26).

Figure 6.3

Seasonal, semi-persistent and persistent soil moisture deficits. (4.5m from poplar on London Clay; tree 26).

As a persistent deficit is, by definition, still present in the spring after winter recovery, it is the readings which are taken in the spring which are most relevant for showing these deficits. The way in which the persistent deficit established for this poplar tree is therefore best shown by the spring moisture content profiles from spring 1982 to 1992 (Figure 6.2). Above a depth of about 1.8m, all of the profiles are essentially similar except for that of 1992 (which is drier because of the abnormally dry preceding winter, which restricted the amount of seasonal recovery). The really significant changes were those below 1.8m. In spring 1983 there was additional drying down to 2.9m, with further drying in spring 1984 down to 3.1m. Unfortunately there were no further spring readings taken until 1992, by which time there was a further reduction in moisture content and the drying had extended to the base of the access tube at 3.6m. By 1995 there was very slight additional drying below 3.2m, but slightly less drying at shallower depths than in 1992.

In the previous chapter the extent of the seasonal soil drying, determined from the difference between the moisture content profiles in the spring and autumn, was depicted by yellow shading between these profiles (Figure 5.7). In similar fashion Figure 6.3 shows the extent of the persistent deficit by red shading; in this case derived from the difference between the moisture content profiles in the spring at the start and end of the project (1982 and 1995). The yellow shading on this Figure shows the extent of seasonal drying in 1991.

As noted from Figure 6.2, the recovery during the winter of 1991/92 was restricted by the comparatively dry conditions of that winter. During the subsequent winters (1992/3, 1993/4) there was some further recovery, showing that part of the deficit which was present in spring 1992 was only "**semi-persistent**"; this term is proposed for a persistent deficit which develops during a dry period but which cannot be sustained during subsequent more normal weather conditions. The extent of this semi-persistent deficit is shown on Figure 6.3 by the orange shading.

Figures 6.2 and 6.3 only are only concerned with the access tube closest to the tree (4.5m distant). Figure 6.4 shows the spatial pattern of reduction in soil moisture content derived from all of the access tubes. Like Figure 6.2, these diagrams are based on the spring readings so that they show only the persistent deficit. They indicate how this has gradually extended and intensified over the period from 1982 to 1995.

Although tree 26 provides this good example of the development of a persistent deficit, it must not be thought that this is a typical result. Of the 60 trees investigated in the research project, **only 3 trees showed an increase in the persistent deficit during the period of the readings.** One of the others was tree 25, an identical poplar on the same site as tree 26 (Volume 2 page 130); the other was tree 1; a horse chestnut also on London Clay (Volume 2, page 14).

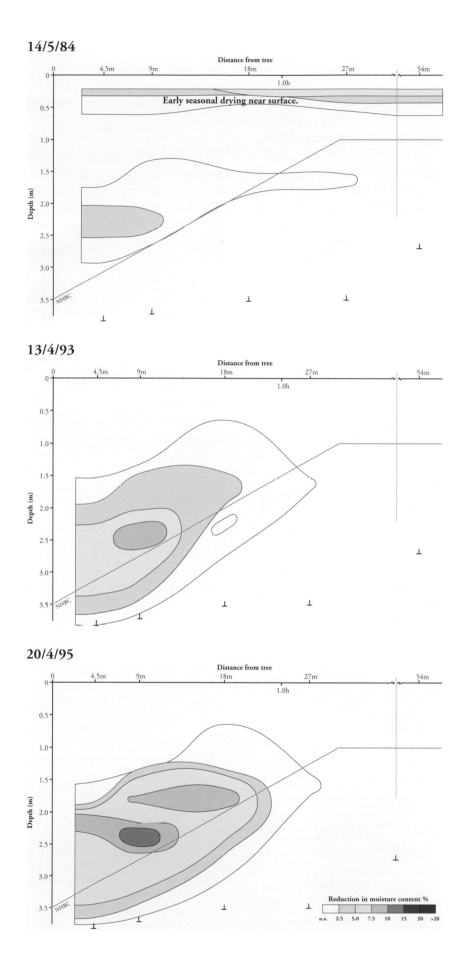

Figure 6.4

Gradual development of persistent moisture deficit in proximity to poplar on London Clay (tree 26), as shown by the reduction in soil moisture content in the spring. In each case the reduction in soil moisture content has been calculated by comparison with the readings at the start of the project on 23/4/82.

Assumed persistent deficits

The long-term monitoring shown in Figure 6.1 allows comparison of the moisture content profiles over a long period and shows how the persistent deficit develops progressively year on year. However, it is possible in this example, and in all of the other examples in Volume 2, that a persistent deficit was already present at the start of the project. One way to check on this is to assume that the soil conditions across the site are uniform, so that the profile for the most distant access tube from the tree (i.e. the control tube) in the spring will indicate the normal moisture content at field capacity for all of the other access tubes. If a comparison in the spring between the control profile and the profile at any of the other locations shows any reduction in moisture content, it would indicate a persistent deficit. Figure 6.5 is similar to Figure 6.3 but also includes the profile for the control hole. This shows that at the control tube the soil is wetter than at the hole closest to the tree between 1.2 and 2.1m. This might be an indication of a persistent deficit; this assumed persistent deficit is indicated by the pink shading. Calculation of the deficit represented by this pink area indicates a deficit of 46mm. However, Figure 6.6 also shows that the control profile includes a single far drier reading at 2.2m. This drier reading is associated with a narrow band of sand at this depth which is not present at the other access tubes close to the tree. In addition, the control profile below 2.2m is generally

drier than the profile for the closest access tube at the start of the project. If account is taken of the whole of the control profile below 1.0m, including these drier readings, the assumed persistent deficit is only 22mm.

Figure 6.1, and all of the similar diagrams which show the seasonal and long-term fluctuations in soil moisture deficit below 1.0m, are based on comparison of the profiles close to the tree with the control profile. For this reason the average soil moisture deficit value in the spring for the control access tube will be zero. If the other fluctuating lines are generally displaced below the zero line (e.g. the lines on Figure 6.1 for the access tubes at 4.5m, 9.0m, and 18.0m) it indicates that on average they are drier than the control, which might be an indication of a persistent deficit. Conversely, if the fluctuating line is displaced above the zero (e.g. the line on Figure 6.1 for the access tube 27.0m from the tree) it indicates that the profile is wetter than the control.

However, it must be strongly emphasised that any calculation of a persistent deficit based on a comparison of the profiles close to the tree with the control is based on the assumption that the soil across the site would be uniform in the absence of a tree. Experience shows that such assumption is frequently invalid. For instance, Figures 6.1 and 6.5 (and all of the other preceding Figures in this Chapter) are based on tree 26, which is a poplar on London Clay. Tree 25 is a closely adjacent poplar, and the two control access tubes are located in apparently similar conditions within 30m of each other. These two control tubes are therefore closer to each other than they are to the trees. Figure 6.6 shows the profiles for these two holes, and shows that there are significant differences. The control for tree 25 does not have the band of sand (and low readings) at 2.2m, and is generally wetter between 1.7 and 2.1m. It has been noted that the assumed persistent deficit for tree 26 (i.e. the area shown pink in Figure 6.5) would be 46mm if one ignores the band of sand, or 22mm if one takes account of all of the readings below 1.0m depth. However, if one makes the same calculations but using the control for tree 25, these values become 29mm and 13mm respectively. As these two access tubes are almost equidistant from tree 26, the use of either would be valid, with the choice making a slight but significant difference to the result.

Trees 25 and 26 are on London Clay, which is normally noted for its uniformity. Examination of the results in Volume 2 for the spring average moisture content profiles for all of the other trees on London Clay shows that variation of this sort is not atypical. On less uniform clay, for instance Boulder Clay, even

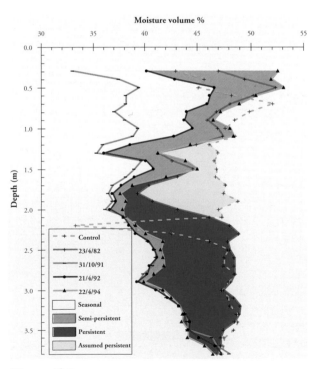

Figure 6.5

Inclusion of the profile for the control tube 54.0m from the tree shows the assumed persistent deficit 4.5m from poplar on London Clay (tree 26).

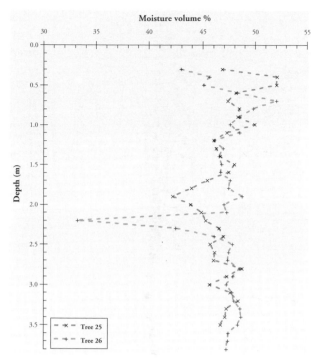

Figure 6.6

Control profiles for trees 25 and 26, showing the inherent variability in soil conditions, even in London Clay, for access tubes only 30m apart.

greater variation will occur. Figure 6.7 shows the spring profiles for the control access tubes for trees 32 and 33, both of which are poplars on Boulder Clay. Like trees 25 and 26, these two are on the same site, with the control tubes in the proximity of each other (38m apart). The profiles are similar down to 1.7m, but below this they diverge considerably. In contrast to this, the access tubes closest to these two trees have fairly similar spring average profiles, both of which are noticeably drier than either of the control tubes. On this basis one would assume that there was a persistent deficit in the proximity of both of these trees (the assumed persistent deficits being 64mm and 155mm for trees 32 and 33 respectively). However, both of these trees have been felled (in 1985 and 1990 respectively) but neither site has shown any significant recovery of moisture content. Figure 6.8 shows the negligible recovery for tree 32. The diagrams in Volume 2 showing the long-term fluctuations of soil moisture deficit for these two trees (page 173 and 179), further illustrate the stability in moisture content after these trees were felled. As the soil is capable of rapid seasonal recovery, it is clear that no further recovery will occur, and that any assumption that there was a persistent deficit would be incorrect.

Chapter 13 (page 209) provides further examples of differences between closely adjacent control tubes, and that assumptions of uniformity of soil conditions can be unreliable.

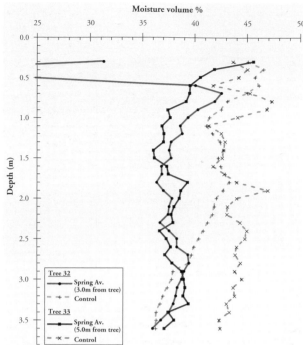

Figure 6.7

Control profiles (dotted lines) for trees 32 and 33 (poplars on Boulder Clay), showing major difference (below 1.7m) despite tubes being only 38m apart. Also included are the spring average profiles for the access tubes closest to these trees; these are far drier than the controls, thus implying persistent deficits.

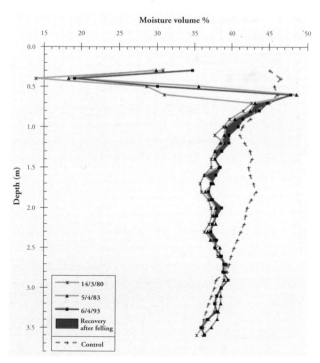

Figure 6.8

Recovery of moisture content at the access tube closest to tree 32 during the 8 year period after the tree was felled. The lack of recovery demonstrates that it would have been erroneous to assume a persistent deficit on the basis of the control profile.

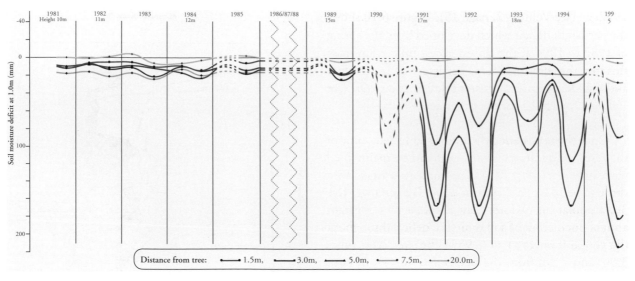

Figure 6.9

The development of a persistent deficit at the three access tubes closest to a Leyland cypress on Gault Clay (tree 45) prior to 1992. During the preceding period the tree had been growing rapidly to 17m. There was partial recovery in 1993 and 1994, showing that the deficit was only semi-persistent.

Development and maintenance of persistent deficit

It has been noted that only three of the trees in the research project showed a significant increase in persistent deficit during the course of the project. In addition, the two Leyland cypress trees on Gault Clay (trees 45 and 46) developed a persistent deficit in 1992, but this was not maintained through the subsequent wetter winters of 1992/93 and 93/94; i.e. it was a semi-persistent deficit (Figure 6.10, and see also Volume 2, page 235 and 241). With the exception of tree 1, all of these trees were in the early stages of maturity so that they were still growing rapidly and had not reached their full height or crown development. Thus tree 26, whose soil drying is illustrated in Figure 6.1, grew from a height of 18m in 1981 to 24m in 1993. Tree 25, a similar poplar on the same site, showed the same growth, but with less development of a persistent deficit. The two Leyland cypresses showed negligible influence on the soil from 1981 to 1989 while they grew from 10m to 15m height (from 12m to 15m for tree 46), but then produced a dramatic change and increase in soil drying while their height was increasing further to 18m.

Other observations, not in the research, also support the concept that, where conditions are conducive to a persistent deficit, they develop early in the life of the tree. Case Study 6 (page 99) describes a considerable persistent deficit which had developed adjacent to a Turkey oak which was only 38 years old, but which had reached a height of 15m and trunk diameter of 60cm in those years.

An exception to this concept is provided by tree 1. This horse chestnut growing on London Clay had already reached its full mature size at the start of the project and showed no significant further growth. However, it showed a steady slow increase in persistent deficit at the three access tubes closest to the tree during the period from 1981 to 1991, but again this diminished during the subsequent wetter period of

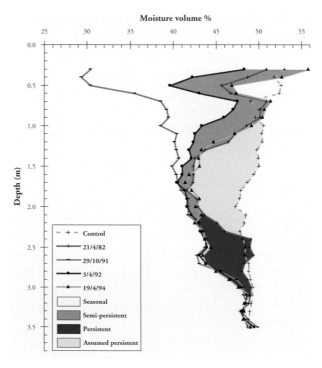

Figure 6.10

Development of a persistent deficit 2.8m from a horse chestnut on London Clay (tree 1) during the period from 1982 to 1994. This was not accompanied by any significant increase in size of the tree.

1992/93 (see Volume 2, page 15). Figure 6.10 shows the persistent deficit which developed from the spring of 1982 to 1994 at the closest access tube 2.8m from this tree, the additional semi-persistent deficit in 1991 and also the assumed persistent deficit at the start (see Volume 2, page 18 for the other access tubes).

Once the persistent deficit has established, some of the research results suggest that it can be maintained with little variation over a prolonged period, even through periods of extreme drought. For instance, Tree 30, a poplar on Oxford Clay, shows a very constant annual fluctuation of soil moisture deficit throughout the period from 1981 to 1993 at the two access tubes 3.8m and 7.5m from the tree (Figure 6.11); in both cases they are fluctuating below the zero line, indicating an assumed persistent deficit. Figure 6.12 shows moisture content profiles for the tube 3.8m from the tree and for the control tube, to show the seasonal effects, the assumed persistent deficit, and the negligible change in persistent deficit during this period. In this case it seems probable that the assumption of a persistent deficit is valid, and that it has remained constant over the 13 year period. This poplar grew significantly during the 13 years (from 15m to 22m), but the persistent deficit had already established and did not increase during this period at these access tubes closest to the tree. By contrast, at the access tube 15.0m from the tree, conditions changed, with a sudden increase in seasonal effects from 1989 onwards, indicating that root activity had reached this location. However, these effects were seasonal (or semi-persistent in 1992) and did not produce a persistent deficit.

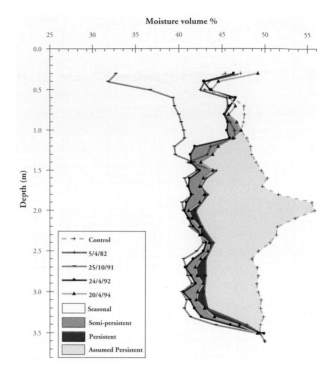

Figure 6.12

Negligible increase in persistent deficit between 1982 and 1994, despite apparent previous development of a massive assumed persistent deficit (3.8m from poplar on Oxford Clay, tree 30).

Some of the other trees show a similar pattern with regular seasonal fluctuations superimposed on a constant assumed persistent deficit (e.g. trees 3, 5, 13, 27, 28, 29), but in all these examples it must be remembered that the assumption of a persistent deficit will not be valid if conditions at the control are not comparable.

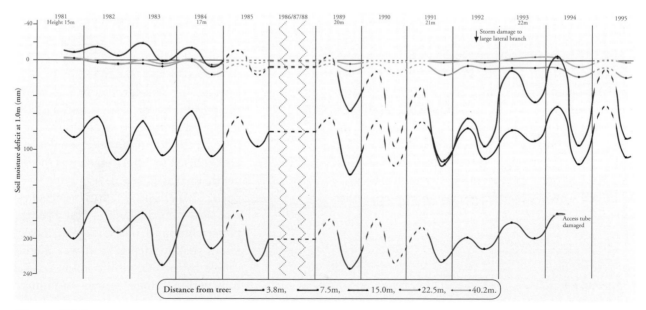

Figure 6.11

A persistent deficit appears to have developed prior to 1981 at the two access tubes closest to the tree. Since then there have been regular seasonal fluctuations of soil moisture deficit, but no further increase in the persistent deficit. At 15.0m, seasonal effects only develop after 1989. (Poplar tree on Oxford Clay, tree 30).

Recovery from persistent deficit

If a tree is felled there will be no further water up-take. If a persistent deficit has established, the soil can now rehydrate and eventually eliminate the deficit. The duration of this recovery depends on the permeability of the clay and on the depth and extent of soil drying. As noted in Chapter 4, the permeability of clay is very difficult to predict and can be influenced by many factors. However, a high plasticity index is generally associated with low permeability.

The rehydration and associated swelling of a previously desiccated clay can cause heave of a building founded on such soil; this is considered in further detail in Chapter 7 and practical implications in Chapter 16. However, as an example of the potential duration of the process of rehydration, a classic and oft-quoted case concerns a terrace of cottages at Windsor. These were built on a site which had recently been cleared of large elm trees. About 6 years after construction the Building Research Station was asked to investigate cracks which had started to appear about 2 years after completion (Samuels and Cheney, 1974). The soil, which was London Clay and generally with a liquid limit of about 80, was considered to be still desiccated to a depth of at least 4.5m. On the basis of a distortion survey it was estimated that, at a point virtually over the site of two of the former trees, about 100mm of heave movement had already occurred, and monitoring the building during the subsequent period

recorded a further nearly 50mm of movement in the next 14 years (Figure 6.13). Slight movements were still continuing 25 years after the trees were felled (Cheney, 1989).

This example illustrates one extreme of the potential duration for soil recovery. At the other extreme, rehydration of a permeable soil can be virtually instantaneous, depending only on the availability of water. Persistent deficits are no more than an extension of a seasonal deficit; these seasonal deficits recover in a single winter. In practice, cases can fall anywhere between the extremes of many years or a single winter, with the duration dependent on the permeability of the clay and the depth of desiccation.

Although a number of trees included in the research were felled for various reasons during the project, none of those on which monitoring was continued was associated with a significant persistent deficit. This research therefore provides no examples of the duration of recovery. However, the significance of the permeability of the soil can be seen in many examples. For instance, Figure 6.3 shows the extent of seasonal drying in 1991 and the persistent deficit which had developed during the previous decade at the access tube 4.5m from tree 26 (poplar on London Clay). At this position the seasonal recovery in a single winter was restricted to within 2.0m of the surface, with negligible change below this level. By spring 1994 there was slight further recovery (of a semi-persistent deficit).

In numerical terms, the soil moisture deficit below 2.0m was 112mm in September 1991, reducing to only 108mm by April 1994, despite the previous two wet winters. Clearly in this situation the considerable persistent deficit which had developed would take many years to rehydrate. By contrast, Figure 6.14 shows the profiles for the corresponding dates for the access tube 18.0m from the same tree. At this location the seasonal recovery occurred to 3.0m, which was the full depth to which any drying had developed. A slight persistent deficit had established compared with the start of the project, but much of this was at comparatively shallow depth, and was merely caused by inability of the soil to recover fully within a single winter. In numerical terms, the soil moisture deficit below 2.0m depth in September 1991 was 33mm, but this had reduced to only 7mm within a single winter (i.e. it is seasonal recovery). In this situation, with

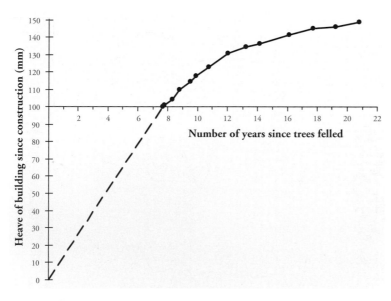

Figure 6.13

Long-term heave of a building caused by exceptionally slow recovery of a persistent deficit. Monitoring the building did not start until about 7 years after the trees were felled, and was still continuing more than 25 years after felling.

Derived from Samuels and Cheney (1974)

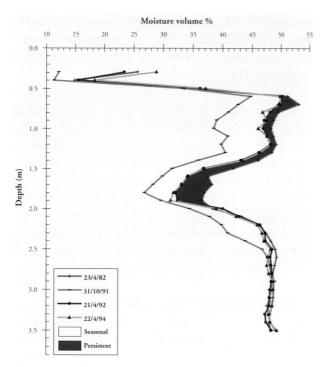

Moisture volume %

Figure 6.14

Seasonal and persistent soil moisture deficits developing 18.0m from poplar on London Clay (tree 26); contrast with Figure 6.3.

about 80% recovery occurring in a single winter, it can be anticipated that any remaining recovery of the persistent deficit would be a rapid process (provided there was no further annual cycle of soil drying).

The different behaviour of the soil at these two locations is probably a result of the slightly sandy conditions between 1.5 and 1.8m at the access tube 18.0m from the tree (as indicated by the lower moisture content values, and by the soil description (see Volume 2, page 138). It illustrates the potential variation which can occur, even on closely adjacent sites with apparently similar conditions.

The difficulty of predicting the rate of recovery is further illustrated in Figure 6.15, which shows the profiles close to tree 46 (Leyland cypress on Gault Clay). Figure 6.15a shows the profiles for the access tube 1.8m from the tree, and 6.15b for the access tube 3.6m from the tree (i.e. these tubes are only 1.8m apart). The spring average profiles for both of these tubes are very similar, with low values of moisture content down to about 1.0m as a result of the sandy Head soil at shallow depth, but they have virtually identical profiles in the underlying uniform Gault clay. The plasticity index of this clay at 1.5m depth in the tube 3.6m from the tree was 56. Despite the similarity in soil conditions and close proximity of the two tubes, the extent of recovery in the winter 1991/92 was very different. At 1.8m from the tree there was only very slight recovery, with this not extending below 2.1m. Below this is a zone where the soil became drier during the winter period, presumably as a result of continued transpiration by this evergreen tree in the late autumn. Overall the deficit below 1.0m only recovered during the win-

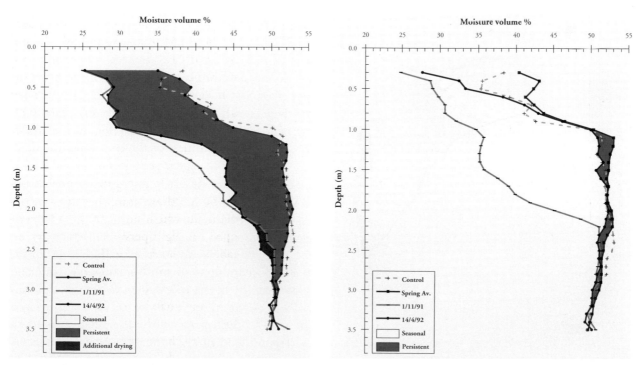

Figure 6.15

a) *1.8m from Leyland cypress on Gault Clay (tree 46)* **b)** *3.6m from Leyland cypress on Gault Clay (tree 46)*
Contrasting extent of seasonal and persistent deficits at two access tubes in close proximity on similar soil.

93

ter by 21mm, leaving a persistent deficit of 129mm. In complete contrast to the behaviour at 1.8m, at 3.6m from the tree there was virtually complete recovery, with the deficit below 1.0m reducing from 172mm to only 19mm.

Although there was negligible recovery in the winter of 1991/92 at the access tube 1.8m from the tree, leaving a deficit at the end of that winter of 129mm, the behaviour in the following wetter winter of 1992/93 was very different; there was virtually full recovery, leaving a persistent deficit below 1.0m of only 19mm (Figure 6.16).

It is difficult to explain this difference in behaviour at the two closely adjacent positions in the winter of 1991/92, and also the contrast in the extent of recovery during the two winters at the closest access tube. It may be because the access tube 1.8m from the tree is beneath the dense canopy, whereas the access tube 3.6m from the tree is clear of the canopy and in open grass. The canopy could have intercepted much of the rainfall during the dry winter of 1991/92, but in the subsequent wetter winter there could have been sufficient rainfall for there to be lateral run-off into the soil beneath the tree. It is also interesting to note that, in the winter of 1991/92 at the tube 3.6m from the tree, the recovery penetrated vertically into the soil to a depth of 2.3m, but seemed unable to spread laterally by 1.8m to the adjacent access tube. This is prob-

ably the result of the vertical development of soil cracking which enabled the water to penetrate so deep into this high plasticity soil.

Recovery from persistent deficit as result of overmaturity

It does not necessarily require a tree to be felled for recovery to occur. If the water uptake diminishes, for whatever reason, it can reduce the amount of seasonal drying in the summer to below the amount of recovery in the winter, so as to allow a gradual increase in moisture content. This is illustrated by various trees in the research project.

Figure 6.17 shows the long-term fluctuations of soil moisture deficit near tree 8 (horse chestnut on Oxford Clay). During the initial three years of the project the three access tubes nearest to the tree show a progressive reduction in the persistent deficit, with seasonal effects barely detectable at 1.0m depth. Unfortunately at this stage the associated soil movements were sufficient to bend the access tube 1.8m from the tree, so that no further readings were possible at this position. At the other tubes there was increased drying in the dry summer of 1984, but a gradual further recovery in subsequent years. Overall, at the access tube 3.8m from the tree, there was a 34mm reduction in the persistent deficit between the spring of 1980 and 1994.

Tree 21 (oak on London Clay, Volume 2, page 111) appears to show a similar gradual reduction. It is surprising that this oak did not have a far greater assumed persistent deficit, as this species has a reputation for soil drying, and the clay on this site is uniform and of high plasticity. It is probable that the persistent deficit had been slowly diminishing over many years, with the period of monitoring coming right at the end of this phase.

Both of the examples referred to above (Trees 8 and 21) appeared to be healthy mature specimens at the start of the project. However, during the next 10 years dieback started to become apparent in the twigs on the periphery of the upper crowns. This is indicative of a tree becoming overmature and deteriorating, and of an inability of the root system to obtain sufficient water to sustain those leaves which are under greatest stress. The dieback in the twigs probably reflects a corresponding dieback in the root system, so that the tree maintains a constant root:shoot ratio. With both trees it is apparent that there is negligible drying during the summer; in effect the soil is recovering as if the tree had been felled.

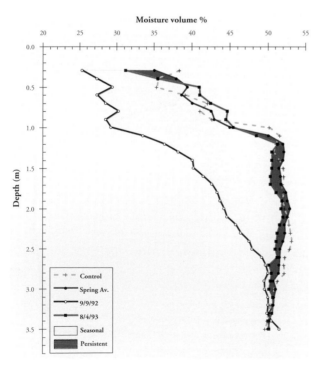

Figure 6.16

Leyland cypress on Gault Clay (tree 46). In the winter of 1992/93, there was virtual full recovery (compare with Figure 6.15.a).

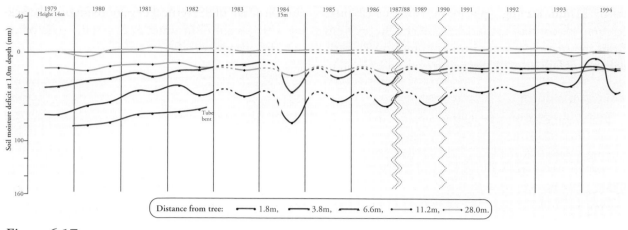

Figure 6.17

Progressive diminution in soil moisture deficit for tree 8. (Horse chestnut on Gault Clay).

Another example of a reducing deficit is provided by tree 5 (horse chestnut on Gault Clay, Volume 2, page 35). This shows considerable seasonal fluctuation, with this superimposed on a gradual reduction in soil moisture deficit at the access tube closest to the trees during the period 1981 to 1984. This trend was reversed in the drier summer of 1984 and the persistent deficit had increased again by 1991, but there was a further gradual reduction in this persistent deficit from 1992 to 1994. In the previous chapter it was noted that tree 15 also shows seasonal movements superimposed on a progressive reduction in the period from 1991 to 1994. Both of these trees still appear healthy, but it might be anticipated that twig dieback will become apparent if there is any further reduction in the persistent deficit.

Factors conducive to development of persistent deficit

The previous sections have emphasised the importance of the permeability of the soil in the development of a persistent deficit. It is only with soils of low permeability that any significant deficit is likely to establish; with more permeable soils there is likely to be full recovery during each winter, with any deficit being entirely seasonal. Any features of the soil which aid permeability, such as bands of sand or gravel or the development of soil cracking, can help to ensure full recovery each winter.

The amount of water taken by the tree is not directly relevant as there is usually sufficient rainfall during the winter to correct any deficit which has developed during the summer, provided the soil is sufficiently permeable. Thus, the maximum deficits to develop during a summer, as recorded in the research, were 363mm in 1989 at the access tube closest to tree

29 (poplar on Gault Clay), and 266mm in 1991 at the access tube 3.6m from tree 45 (Leyland cypress on Gault Clay, although there may have already been a persistent deficit at the start of that year) (see also Figure 8.13). For practical reasons these deficits were being recorded below 0.3m depth; under drought conditions there may be an additional deficit of 45mm in this surface 0.3m. The maximum deficit to develop during a dry summer was therefore about 300mm. Average rainfall during the winter, even in dry parts of the country, is in excess of this (for instance the average for the nineteen year period at the meteorological station at Stock in Essex (Grid ref. TQ 693986) for the months October to April inclusive is 333mm). Occasionally there will be dry winters when the rainfall is significantly below average, and if this follows a dry summer when high deficits have developed, there might be inadequate rainfall to correct such deficit. However, provided the soil is permeable, any such deficit would only be semi-persistent, and would disappear with the resumption of more average conditions. The research results include several examples of semi-persistent deficits of this sort (e.g. trees 6, 15, 31, 41, 43).

If water is freely available, rates of photosynthesis are fairly similar for most plant species (Chapter 2); the limiting factors are energy input and leaf area. However, water is not usually freely available, and plants differ significantly in their ability to obtain and utilise the water. One of the features of trees is their ability to obtain water from greater depth than other vegetation. Observations indicate that different species of tree differ in their ability to overcome adverse conditions such as high soil suctions, low oxygen availability or resistance of the soil to penetration, and to utilise these water reserves. Chapter 9 considers these differences between species, and recognises that some species are particularly efficient in this regard. It will be these species, which are capable of exploiting the soil to greater depth, particularly soils of low permeability where rates of oxygen diffusion are very low, which are most likely to be associated with persistent deficits. Persistent deficits are far less likely with species which cannot exploit these adverse conditions, or which can only grow a deep root system in very permeable and freely drained soils.

Where conditions are conducive, the persistent deficit appears to establish during early maturity when the tree is growing actively, and this is followed by a long period of maintenance of this *status quo*. This pattern might be anticipated, as it is during the period of early growth that the water requirements are increasing most rapidly, and the root system will be increasing the zone of exploitation.

If the species is capable of growing into a soil of low permeability, it can exploit the moisture reserves in this soil. However, once this water supply has been used, it will not be readily replaced. The desiccated soil will not be conducive to further exploitation; further reserves of water would only be found by growing ever-deeper into ever-more hostile conditions, or alternatively by further lateral growth. Growth to greater depth may provide a short-term benefit, but once this soil has been exploited, the roots which have developed through this soil will be of no further value. In terms of efficient utilisation of the carbon resources of the plant, the exploitation of water which is not going to be replenished provides a poor return on investment. It is much more efficient for the tree to extend the roots further near the surface where there is an-

nual replenishment of the moisture reserves. This strategy ensures that these roots are able to continue to function throughout the life of the tree.

The popular concept of a root system developing ever-deeper, with a year-on-year increase in the persistent deficit, is certainly erroneous. Indeed, as shown in Figure 6.18, there is almost as much likelihood that the persistent deficit will be decreasing, rather than increasing, especially with trees which are becoming overmature.

Details of the pattern through the life cycle of a tree will obviously vary greatly depending on the local soil conditions and on the species and condition of the tree involved, but a typical situation for a tree such as poplar on a clay of low permeability is shown diagrammatically in Figure 6.19. The initial effects are close to the tree, but extend into additional areas as the tree grows. At each location the persistent deficit develops over a short period, particularly during dry weather, and thereafter remains fairly constant, with the surface seasonal effects superimposed. As the tree reaches maturity, the influence of the roots stabilizes with no further lateral spread nor increase in depth. With a long-lived species this situation may be maintained for many decades. As the tree becomes overmature the efficiency of the roots diminishes and the soil will start to rehydrate even while the tree is still present. Unless a tree is felled or blown over, full recovery of any persistent deficit may have occurred long before it finally dies, unless the soil is of exceptionally low permeability.

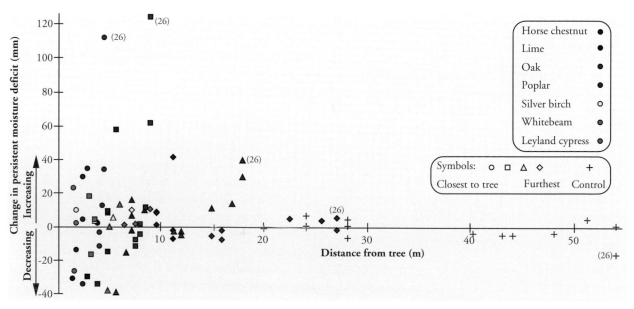

Figure 6.18

Change in persistent moisture deficit for all trees in the research project for which records are available over period of at least 10 years. The deficit decreases (i.e. rehydrates) in almost as many cases as it increases. The exceptional values for tree 26 are identified.

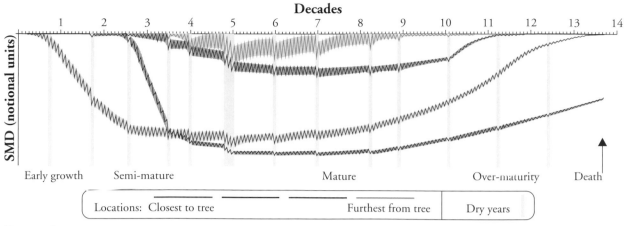

Figure 6.19

Diagram of long-term variations in the persistent moisture deficit which might occur through the life of a tree which is capable of causing deep-seated soil drying (such as poplar). The four different coloured lines represent the pattern at four locations at different distances from the tree. They also indicate the amplitude of seasonal movement which is superimposed on the changes in persistent deficit. The amplitude of the red and blue lines would be applicable to a soil of low permeability. By contrast, the amplitude of the purple line would be applicable to a soil of exceptionally low permeability with negligible seasonal fluctuation, whereas the green line would be soil of higher permeability allowing greater seasonal fluctuation.

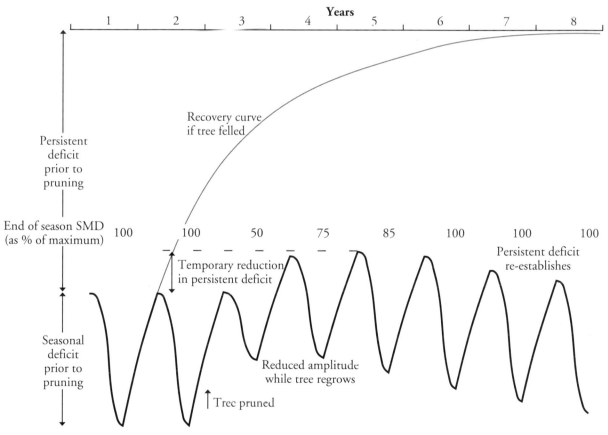

Figure 6.20

Diagrammatic representation of effect of pruning on a persistent deficit. Years 1 and 2 depict the seasonal amplitude of the deficit, with the dotted line at the end of year 1 indicating the recovery curve if the tree was felled. At the start of year 3 the tree is pruned, sufficient to reduce the extent of seasonal deficit by 50%. By year 4 the tree is starting to recover so that the seasonal deficit is only reduced by 75%, and in year 5 by 85%. In subsequent years the deficit is shown as back to the original level of years 1 and 2. This scenario would produce a slight reduction in the persistent deficit by year 5, but with it increasing again in subsequent years.

Effect of pruning on persistent deficit

Chapter 5 has considered the effect of pruning on the seasonal pattern of soil drying, and shown how it can reduce the extent of drying and thereby reduce the amplitude of the seasonal cycle. If there is a persistent deficit, pruning will have the same effect of reducing the extent of drying and should allow extra recovery to occur in the following winter. There will therefore be a gradual reduction of a persistent deficit, with a seasonal cycle of reduced amplitude superimposed. As the tree recovers from the effects of the pruning, it can be expected that the amplitude of seasonal movement will increase until the drying again exceeds the recovery so as to reverse this process and again increase the persistent deficit. A pattern of this sort is shown diagrammatically in Figure 6.20 (previous page). It can be seen that, over a period of several years, the pruning produces a greater range of moisture deficit. For this reason, where there is a persistent moisture deficit, pruning will not be effective in reducing changes in soil moisture content nor preventing movement of a clay soil.

If further pruning was to be applied, the gradual reduction in persistent deficit would continue, but the on-going cycle of seasonal drying would greatly extend the period until full rehydration and recovery is achieved.

Although no trees which had developed major persistent deficits were pruned as part of the research project, the somewhat anomalous results produced by tree 41 (Volume 2, page 214) illustrate this effect. This whitebeam on Boulder Clay showed considerable reduction in moisture deficit after a heavy crown reduction, but the effect was only short-term. The persistent deficit near this tree increased considerably during the period 1989 - 1991, particularly at the access tubes 4.8m and 6.4m from the tree. This was followed by negligible recovery in the dry winter of 1991/92. The tree was then heavily reduced in the early spring of 1992, removing about 40% of the crown. Apparently in response to this treatment, and to the wetter conditions of the summer of 1992, there was a massive reduction in the persistent deficit, with the soil becoming wetter even during the summer months. However, the benefits of this were short-lived, with the amplitude of the seasonal fluctuations of the soil moisture deficit again increasing in 1993 and subsequent years.

Summary

1.   Under some circumstances a soil which has been dried during the summer is unable to recover to normal moisture content in a single winter, so that there is still a deficit in the spring. A deficit of this sort is best described as a persistent moisture deficit, to distinguish it from the cycle of seasonal soil drying and recovery described in Chapter 5.

2.   Over a period of years, if seasonal recovery is less than the drying, a persistent deficit can gradually accumulate. This typically occurs over a comparatively short period, particularly during years of below average rainfall, and during the stage of rapid growth prior to a tree reaching maturity.

3.   The most important factor for determining whether a persistent deficit will develop is the permeability of the clay. Only clays of very low permeability are unable to recover fully in a single winter. The development of a persistent deficit also requires a tree which is capable of causing soil drying to a sufficient depth where recovery cannot occur in a single winter.

4.   Once a persistent deficit has established, it can be maintained for many decades through maturity.

5.   As a tree becomes overmature and its water uptake starts to reduce, a persistent deficit can gradually diminish. It does not require a tree to be felled for this to occur.

6.   If a persistent deficit has established, and the tree is then felled (or its water uptake reduced), the soil will be able to gradually rehydrate and swell. This can cause either recovery or heave of foundations (considered in further detail in Chapter 7); a persistent deficit is an essential prerequisite for heave to occur.

7.   The length of time that it takes for a persistent deficit to rehydrate (and thus for heave to occur) is dependent on the permeability of the clay, and the depth and intensity of soil drying. In may take more than a decade, or alternatively be little more than a slight extension of seasonal recovery over a single winter.

8.   **In the majority of situations the influence of a tree is predominantly seasonal; the development of a significant persistent deficit only occurs in extreme cases.**

9.   Pruning a tree which has produced a persistent moisture deficit will not be effective in preventing changes in moisture content and associated damage.

*Extensive damage to old house near horse chestnuts and vigorous young Turkey oak tree –
Persistent deficit from oak tree allowed to develop – TPO imposed – Trees felled –
Monitoring shows long-term recovery from effect of oak tree, but rapid recovery from horse chestnuts.*

Background

The subject property is a two-storey detached house located in West London. It was architect-designed and built in about 1910. External walls are of solid brickwork and mainly pebble-dash rendered. It has a suspended timber floor at ground floor level and conventional timber floor at first floor level. Ground floor layout is shown in CS Figure 6.1.

The property has a concrete drive adjacent to the west flank wall, and extensive areas of crazy paving to front (south) and rear. There is a thick stone mulch adjacent to the east flank and around the front bay window. These areas of paving and gravel exclude all vegetation, except around the front bay where there is grass within about 0.5m.

The current owner purchased in 1968 and recorded minor damage in 1976. Further damage occurred in 1981 and by 1983 he submitted a claim on insurers. Structural engineers (Hurst Peirce & Malcolm) investigated and dug trial holes. These showed that the walls had two brick steppings resting upon a concrete strip of nominal 150mm thickness, cast upon a bed of loose uncemented clinker approximately 300mm thick. This clinker bed rested upon a stiff sandy silty clay at depth of 700mm. Various root samples were taken and underpinning was recommended.

I was instructed by the loss adjusters acting for insurers, and was requested to advise on the options for tree removal and on the engineer's recommendations for underpinning. At that stage there were no detailed site investigations, but I expressed the opinion that a persistent deficit was likely to be present and that underpinning would be required to restabilise the foundations. The depth of this underpinning would depend on whether the adjacent trees were felled or retained. I advised that any detailed recommendations would require proper site investigations.

I heard nothing further of the matter until 1986 when I was instructed by solicitors acting for the insurers to carry out further site investigations. It transpired that no further action had been taken by the owner since my preliminary report in 1984.

The trees

The following trees were of potential relevance:-

i) Turkey oak (*Quercus cerris*), height 15m, diameter 60cm, located 7.2m from south west corner (CS Figure 6.2). This tree was growing very vigorously. A core of wood was taken from the trunk but did not penetrate to the centre, and so a complete

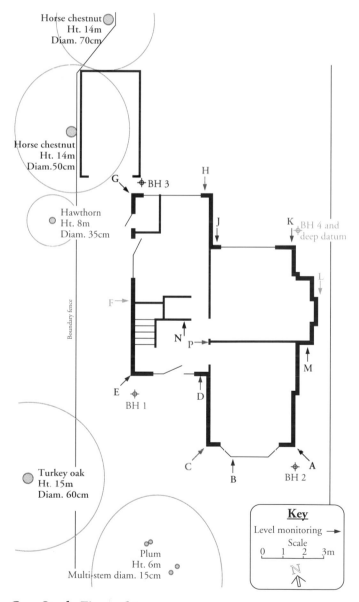

Case Study Figure 6.1

Site plan, showing location of trees, boreholes and level monitoring stations.

Case Study Figure 6.2
Turkey oak adjacent to front corner of building.

analysis of the annual growth rings was obtained off the surface of the stump after the tree was felled; the width of these rings is shown in CS Figure 6.3. It indicated that the tree was 40 years old when it was felled in 1988. It had probably grown from seed off another Turkey oak growing about 40m further away, this other tree being a mature specimen 24m high and with a trunk diameter of 1.1m.

ii) Horse chestnut (*Aesculus hippocastanum*), height 14m, diameter 50cm, located 4.25m from the rear left corner of the building beyond the detached garage (CS Figure 6.4). This tree had been pollarded periodically in the past to a height of about 7m, most recently in the mid-1950's. I estimated the tree to be between 80 and 100 years old.

iii) Horse chestnut, height 14m, diameter 70cm, located 8.4m to the rear of the north west corner of the building. This tree had a similar history of pollarding as the tree referred to in para. ii).

iv) Hawthorn (*Crataegus monogyna*), height 8m, diameter 35cm, located 4m from the left flank wall. In 1984 many of the branches of this tree overhung the boundary and driveway and were cut back soon after. By 1986 the tree was heavily enveloped in ivy, with only the ends of a few branches projecting.

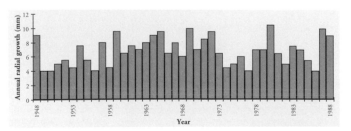

Case Study Figure 6.3
Width of annual growth rings of Turkey oak, measured off the cut surface of the stump.

Case Study Figure 6.4
Horse chestnut adjacent to rear corner of building.

v) Plum (*Prunus domestica*), height 6m, multi-stemmed with diameters up to 15cm, located 5.5m to south of building.

With the exception of the plum, all of the above trees were located in the adjacent property. The Turkey oak and both horse chestnut trees were felled in mid-September 1988.

Soil investigations

The Geological Survey map indicates that the subsoil in the immediate locality should be Taplow Gravel, which is one of the River Terraces of the Thames, associated with an adjacent tributary of the Thames. The Taplow Gravel is shown to overlie London Clay.

In June/July 1987 I drilled four boreholes using a 50mm diameter hand auger. The location of these boreholes is shown on the site plan in CS Figure 6.1. Each of these holes was to a depth of 5.0m. All of the holes encountered a loamy clay Head soil to depths varying 0.6 - 1.1m with typical London Clay below this level; there was no evidence of the Taplow Gravel. Although it was London Clay, it was fairly variable, with occasional bands of silty sand (for instance between 2.85 - 3.05m in borehole 1, and 2.7 - 2.8m in borehole 2), and with increasing sand content towards the base of all of the holes.

Soil samples were taken at 0.25m intervals for moisture content determination, and soil classification tests undertaken on representative samples from three depths in each hole. The results of the moisture content are shown as profiles in CS Figure 6.5, and the soil classification tests are tabulated in CS Figure 6.6.

When drilling borehole 1 abundant root activity was recorded down to 1.5m, with occasional fine roots below this level. At 4.6m there was a 2.5mm diameter root, and at 4.95m there were several 2mm diameter roots. These larger roots were sectioned for microscopic examination, which showed that they were oak.

In borehole 2 there were frequent fine roots to 1.6m and occasional fine roots to 3.0m. Roots of 1mm and 1.5mm taken at depths of 4.1 and 4.6m were sectioned and identified as oak.

Borehole 3 was adjacent to a large horse chestnut root, with several roots up to 10mm diameter in the surface 1.0m. Very frequent fine root activity was observed to 2m, with occasional fine roots to 3m and very occasional fine root activity to 4.25m. None of these fine roots were large enough for identification, but their macroscopic features suggested that they were from horse chestnut rather than oak.

No significant root activity was observed in borehole 4.

Depth (m)	Plastic limit	Liquid limit	Plasticity index	% linear shrinkage	Moisture content %
Borehole 1					
1.5	20	58	38	15.2	18.5
3.0	21	55	34	13.9	19.0
4.5	19	52	33	12.5	16.1
Borehole 2					
1.5	26	64	38	14.6	24.6
3.0	27	72	45	12.9	24.7
4.5	22	45	23	12.0	14.4
Borehole 3					
1.5	21	54	33	13.9	17.2
3.0	22	51	29	12.9	15.7
4.5	21	51	30	11.8	20.5
Borehole 4					
1.5	32	88	56	15.0	39.9
3.0	26	54	28	12.1	24.4
4.5	22	52	30	12.5	24.4

Case Study Figure 6.6
Soil classification tests.

Subsequent sets of readings were taken in autumn and spring of 1987 and 1988 to record the seasonal movements which were occurring (although note that the readings in autumn 1988 were not taken until mid-November, by which time some recovery had probably occurred). Further readings were then taken in 1991, 1992, and 1993 to record the recovery movements after the felling of the trees. The results of the level monitoring for the stations on the front half of the building are shown in CS Figure 6.8, for the rear half in CS Figure 6.9, and for the internal stations (and adjacent external station F) in CS Figure 6.10.

Damage to building

The initial damage was a near vertical crack running the full height of the west flank wall. At first the owner tried to repair this by stitching the base of the crack; not surprisingly this was not effective. The appearance of this crack in 1983 is shown in CS Figure 6.7a.

After these initial attempts at repair the owner was remarkably tolerant (or apparently unconcerned) at the gradual development of damage throughout the property. The felling of the trees in 1988 halted further development of most of the cracks, but by that time there was extensive damage throughout the property, the overall assessment being BRE Category 3 to 4. CS Figures 6.7b and c show some of the cracks on the rear elevation.

The engineers who were instructed in 1983 (Hurst Peirce & Malcolm) took photographs of the damage at that time, and again 10 years later when legal proceedings were imminent. CS Figures 6.7d - i compare the damage on the front bay and at two internal locations over this period. Both of the internal locations show considerable development of the cracking; these are at the junction of the projecting front section with the rest of the building and became gradually worse subsequent to the felling of the trees. The extensive cracking elsewhere throughout the building generally stabilised after the trees were felled.

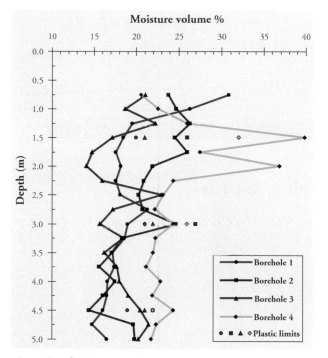

Case Study Figure 6.5
Moisture content profiles of the 4 boreholes (boreholes 1 and 4 drilled on 23/6/87, 2 and 3 on 8/7/87)

Level monitoring

On 23/6/87 I attached level monitoring markers at 12 locations around the periphery of the building and on two internal partition walls. The location of these stations is shown on the plan in CS Figure 6.1.

A deep datum was installed in borehole 4. This consisted of a 6m long steel reinforcing rod, driven 1m into the base of the borehole, and with the basal metre embedded in concrete. The upper sections were sleeved, and the top of the rod concealed beneath a paving slab.

Case Study Figure 6.7

*Aspects of the damage. **a)** initial damage to left flank wall; **b,c)** Rear elevation; **d,e)** front bay window; **f,g)** dining room in front projecting section, with ceiling supported by acrow prop in 1993; **h,i)** Bedroom in front projecting section.*

DISCUSSION

There was agreement between all parties that the trees, particularly the Turkey oak and the two horse chestnuts, were the prime cause of the damage. Discussion centred on the appropriate remedial action.

Interpretation of the moisture content profiles from the four boreholes was complicated by the dissimilarity in conditions at these four locations. Varying quantities of sand and silt were present at different levels, and as a result the soil classification tests gave significantly different results. However, if borehole 4 which is remote from all of the trees is taken as a control, it is apparent that the soil at all of the other holes was significantly drier (soil moisture deficit below the underside of foundations was 503mm at borehole 1, 335mm at borehole 2 and 542mm at borehole 3).

Even at the base of the boreholes at 5m depth, the moisture content in borehole 1 was 5.3% lower than the control. This, combined with the abundant and large roots found near the base of that borehole, suggested that the deficit extended to even greater depth.

As all of these boreholes were drilled in early summer, the deficits which were present must have been persistent. This indicated a considerable heave potential. However, it was anticipated that the sand and silt within the soil should improve the permeability and allow reasonably rapid recovery. It is particularly notable that the Turkey oak adjacent to the south west corner was a comparatively young but very vigorous tree. The rapid escalation of damage during the 1980's suggested that this was caused by the development of the persistent deficit during this period. This illustrates the ability of a persistent deficit to establish comparatively early in the life of a tree.

The Turkey oak had the potential to grow far larger, as demonstrated by the massive specimen nearby. It was growing very rapidly and it could be anticipated that its influence and associated damage would increase still more.

For this reason I recommended the felling of this tree but also advised that, as there was considerable persistent deficit, there would be considerable recovery with this likely to continue for many years. For this reason, it was considered that underpinning, with full anti-heave precautions, would be required.

If such underpinning was implemented, it was considered that the two horse chestnut trees could be retained as these trees were near maturity and their influence was unlikely to increase. If these trees were removed, it was anticipated that they would also cause some recovery, but such movements should be of shorter duration.

The owners of the trees, faced by a substantial claim for continuing nuisance, decided in 1987 to fell all three trees. At this stage (September 1987) the local authority imposed a Tree Preservation Order. Despite objections to the Order it was confirmed, and faced by this Order the owners were unwilling to fell the trees. In May 1988 I produced a report presenting the full results of the investigations including the results of the level monitoring to date. These showed the extent of seasonal recovery during the previous winter. The greatest movements (of about 17mm) were occurring on the projecting front section of the building, with 12mm on the projecting rear section. Despite my recommendation that these trees were creating a nuisance and that felling was therefore exempt, the owners insisted on waiting until consent was eventually granted. As a result the trees were not felled until mid-September 1988, by which time a further cycle of subsidence had occurred.

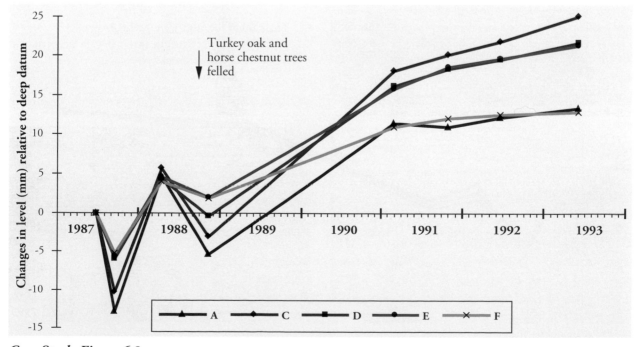

Case Study Figure 6.8

Results of level monitoring for selected stations on front (south) part of building (relative to deep datum).

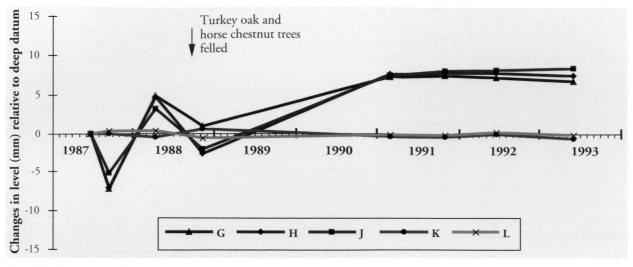

Case Study Figure 6.9

Results of level monitoring for selected stations on rear (north) part of building (relative to deep datum).

Although it was predicted that heave movements would continue for a number of years, the house owner was strongly averse to any underpinning and decided to allow natural recovery to occur. No monitoring readings were taken initially (through 1989 and 1990). However, at that stage the insurers decided to proceed with a recovery action against the neighbouring tree owners. Further monitoring readings were therefore taken during the period from 1991 to 1993 until the claim was eventually settled.

This monitoring demonstrates that by 1991 the rear half of the building had restabilised (CS Figure 6.9). Likewise, the front elevation of the main body of the building had also virtually stabilised (stations E and F in CS Figure 6.8). The internal monitoring stations showed that the rate of recovery of these was virtually identical to station F (CS Figure 6.10). It is probable that the clinker footings would be particularly effective in allowing rapid movement of water to beneath the building. Although all of the main building had stabilised, the projecting front section was continuing to heave progressively. As a result, the cracks in that section were particularly active (CS Figure 6.7e, g and i).

Lessons to be learnt

- The house owner took little action initially, allowing a persistent deficit to develop.

- This persistent deficit developed during the period of rapid early growth of the Turkey oak. There was negligible persistent deficit associated with the older and mature horse chestnuts.

- The TPO should not, and need not, have been allowed to delay the felling by 12 months, as consent was not required where it was necessary to abate the nuisance.

- Level monitoring demonstrated that felling the trees allowed the main building to restabilise, but with ongoing recovery of the front section associated with the persistent deficit produced by the Turkey oak.

- The clinker footings were particularly effective in ensuring that recovery of the internal walls proceeded at the same rate as external walls.

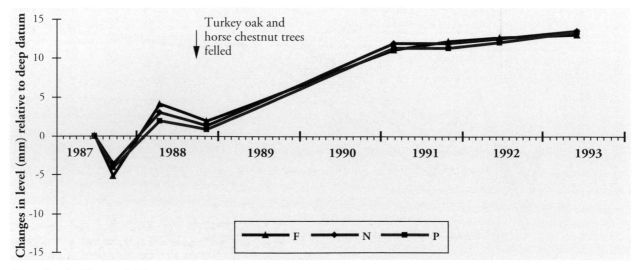

Case Study Figure 6.10

Results of level monitoring of internal stations and adjacent external station (F) (relative to deep datum).

CHAPTER 7

INTERACTION BETWEEN TREES AND BUILDINGS

"Whoever expects from soil mechanics a set of simple, hard-and-fast rules for settlement computation will be deeply disappointed. He might as well expect a simple rule for constructing a geological profile from a single test boring record. The nature of the problem strictly precludes the possibility of establishing such rules."   *Terzaghi (1936)*

A quotation which is still applicable today, and just as applicable to subsidence as it is to settlement.

Introduction

Virtually all descriptions of the way trees cause damage to buildings refer to the roots drying a clay soil so that it shrinks, with this causing subsidence [1] of the foundations. This gives rise to the very common misconception that root activity is progressively increasing and extending and that this causes the building to gradually subside. There is often no clear concept of what this "subsidence" involves, and a failure to appreciate that the predominant, and by far the most important, movement caused by tree root activity is seasonal. It may be recognized that cracks in a building will open and close seasonally, but this concept is subordinate to the idea of subsidence. If anything it is often implied that seasonal movements are caused by weather conditions, and should be distinguished from the effects of root activity as if there is a different cause (e.g. Institution of Structural Engineers, 1994).

Misunderstanding and misconceptions of this sort will inevitably give rise to incorrect diagnosis where damage has occurred, failure to apply the most appropriate remedy, or inadequate provision to prevent damage developing in the first place. To avoid such pitfalls it is essential to have a detailed understanding of exactly what soil and building movements are occurring.

---

[1]   Subsidence is defined as the downward movement of a structure caused by loss of support of the site beneath the foundations. It usually involves volumetric change of the subsoil and must be caused by a factor external to the structure. Examples are the influence of trees on clay, collapse of mine workings or slope instability.

Settlement is the downward movement of a structure caused by its own load and the re-distribution of stresses to the soil.

Soil movements

Chapter 4 has described the soil and the relationship between soil moisture deficits and vertical soil shrinkage. Under some circumstances shrinkage will be in the normal range and directly proportional to the deficit, but in the structural or residual phases it will be less. In addition, the pattern of soil cracking can influence the amount of vertical shrinkage. The plasticity index allows some qualitative assessment of shrinkage potential, but this is of limited relevance over the range of moisture variation induced by root activity. For all of these reasons it is not possible to predict, in accurate quantitative terms, the amount of movement which will occur even when there is information on the moisture deficit or soil suction.

It is, of course, only soil movements which are occurring below the level where the structure is supported which are relevant to problems of structural damage. The relevant depth will depend on the type of structure; for most buildings it is the underside of the foundations but this is less definable for piled foundations. Paths, drains and other structures can also be subject to movement.

Damage will occur if these movements are excessive. This depends on the angular distortions which are occurring within the structure - this aspect is considered in further detail on page 112.

Seasonal movements

Chapter 5 has described the patterns of seasonal changes in moisture content, and emphasised that in most circumstances the influence of trees is predominantly seasonal. The way in which the soil is dried is the same for trees as it is for any other vegetation. The

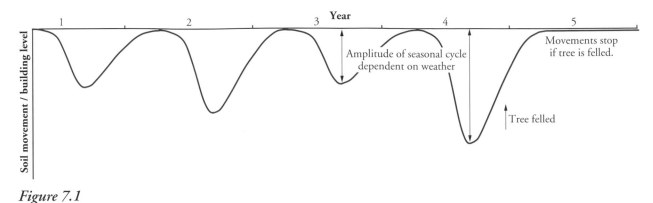

Figure 7.1

Theoretical pattern of seasonal foundation movement, if influence of building load is ignored.

only difference is that trees have the ability to dry the soil to greater depth and are therefore more likely to influence the soil below foundation level. They can also extend laterally and thus influence a structure which is at some distance from the tree. However, in most situations the deficits which develop each summer, even at depth and close to large trees, will recover fully each winter.

The patterns of seasonal change in soil moisture deficit which are described in Chapter 5 can be approximately converted to soil movements within the limitations of estimating soil movement. During the summer the soil will be drying and shrinking. Unless the foundations are able to cantilever or bridge over the area where the soil has shrunk, the withdrawal of support from beneath the foundations will cause the foundations to subside.

In the winter the reverse situation will apply. The soil will rehydrate and swell. The swelling forces which are generated are typically far greater than the load imposed by the foundations of the building, and so the building will move upwards, or recover.

The influence of foundation load on this process is considered in further detail in the next section, but in theory, if the soil recovers to its original moisture content, it should return to its original level. There will therefore be a cycle of **seasonal movement**, with the building subsiding each summer and then recovering in the following winter. The amplitude of this cycle of movement will depend on the extent of soil drying (soil moisture deficit) and on the shrinkage characteristics of the clay. As long as the soil returns to its original moisture content each winter, there is no volumetric change and therefore no overall subsidence, as shown diagrammatically in Figure 7.1.

Influence of foundation load

The load of a building is transmitted to the soil by the foundations. These foundations must satisfy two criteria:

i)   the amount of settlement from consolidation of the soil should be tolerable, and in particular differential settlement should not cause unacceptable damage;

ii) the factor of safety against shear failure must be adequate, a factor of at least 2.5 normally being specified.

The details of the methods for satisfying these requirements are outside the scope of this book, but it is relevant to consider some details which can be influenced by root activity.

The load transmitted into the soil produces an increase in effective stress. A frequently used and useful analogy for considering the effects of this stress on the soil is that of a spring in a cylinder filled with water and fitted with a piston and valve (Figure 7.2a). The spring represents the compressible soil skeleton, the water in the cylinder is the pore water and the diam-

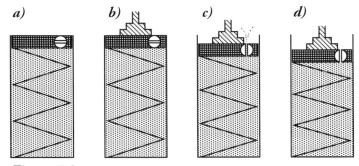

Figure 7.2

Analogy for consolidation of soil under load, with the spring representing the soil, the water in the cylinder representing the pore water, and the bore size of the valve the permeability of the soil.

eter of the valve is the permeability of the soil. If a load is now placed on the piston with the valve kept closed, as water is effectively incompressible the piston cannot move (Figure 7.2b). There is therefore no load transmitted onto the spring but all this extra load is carried by the water, the increase in pressure being equal to the load divided by the piston area. This situation, with the valve closed, corresponds to what is termed the undrained condition of the soil. If the valve is now opened, the water will be forced out at a rate governed by the diameter of the valve, i.e. governed by the permeability of the soil (Figure 7.2c). As it does so, the spring will start to be compressed and start to carry some load. As the load on the spring increases it will cause a corresponding decrease in the pressure of the water. Eventually a stage is reached where all of the load is carried by the spring and the excess pressure in the water has been entirely dissipated. At this stage, with no excess pressure in the water, there will be no further drainage and the piston will come to rest (Figure 7.2d). This situation represents the drained condition of the soil. Using this analogy, the movement of the piston represents the change in volume of the soil; this is governed by the compressibility of the spring which is equivalent to the compressibility of the soil skeleton.

Sandy soils have a comparatively high permeability; by analogy the valve has a large diameter, so that as a load of a building is applied, it is immediately carried on the soil skeleton. These soil particles themselves are incompressible, but may be subject to rearrangement, so that there is some movement and a corresponding increase in the packing density.

By contrast, clay soils have a low permeability. As a result, as the load is applied it is carried by an increase in the pore water pressure. The risk of shear failure is increased by high pore water pressure, and therefore the greatest risk of shear failure is immediately after construction. The allowable bearing pressures of foundations are designed on this basis. As the pore pressures dissipate, the factor of safety against shear failure will increase, but there can be a long period of consolidation of the soil while it drains.

One can extend the analogy of the water filled cylinder and spring by inserting a root into the cylinder, with the fine roots distributed throughout (Figure 7.3a). The initial pore pressure at the level of the water table will be zero. If the root is connected to vegetation which is transpiring and applying a suction (or negative potential), it will draw water out of the cylinder (Figure 7.3b). Chapter 2 has described the suctions which can be generated, with peak values of 1500 kPa, and sustained values which are frequently as great as 1000 kPa. Water will try to enter the cylinder through the piston valve (analogous to water moving from adjacent areas) but, except with soils of high permeability, the rate of this will be far less than the rate of transpiration. Using this analogy, as the water is drawn out of the soil, the stress will be transmitted to the soil particles which, if they are clay, will be compressed, i.e. the clay will shrink. If this shrinkage stays within the normal range, the voids will stay water-filled, although in practice air will start to enter, associated either with structural or residual shrinkage (Figure 7.3c). If the suction applied by the root is constant, an equilibrium would be established between the suction applied by the root, the negative stress within the soil particles, and an equal negative stress within the voids.

If a foundation load is now applied (Figure 7.3d), for a low rise building the effective stress is typically about 100 kPa and thus considerably less than the suction induced by the vegetation. If this suction is stopped, either by removing the vegetation or because it becomes inactive in the winter, water can enter and the soil will swell until it again reaches an equilibrium. Full equilibrium would be the same state as that depicted in Figure 7.2d. If the soil is reasonably permeable so that drying is seasonal, this state will be achieved

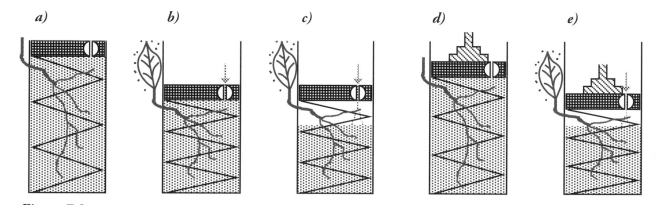

Figure 7.3
Analogy used in Figure 7.2, extended to include influence of soil drying by vegetation.

during the first winter, but if the soil has low permeability, long term swelling (heave) can occur. If the movements are seasonal and the vegetation again becomes active, the soil will shrink again under the influence of the combined stresses of the foundation load and the suction (Figure 7.3e).

The stresses beneath the foundations diminish with depth. This is shown in Figure 7.4 as a pressure bulb, which shows contours of equal vertical stress beneath a foundation. The shape of the pressure bulb is dependent on the plan shape of the foundations; that shown in Figure 7.4 is applicable to a strip, such as a typical strip footing, where the length of the foundation is more than 5 times the width. It will be seen from this diagram that the vertical stress (q) beneath a foundation is about 0.2 times foundation pressure at a depth of 3 times foundation width (B), i.e. for a 1.0m deep strip foundation which is 0.6m wide, the stress will be 0.2 times foundation pressure at a depth of 2.8m. Some root activity can go considerably deeper. The interaction between roots and foundation load will be occurring to varying extent throughout this zone.

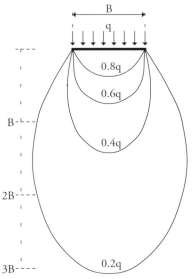

Figure 7.4

Contours of equal vertical stress under a strip area.

Effect of dynamic foundation movement

The consolidation of soil under foundation load is well known, and described in any standard textbook on foundation design. It can generally be predicted with reasonable accuracy, and foundation design aims to ensure that differential settlement movements caused by such consolidation of the soil are not excessive and can be tolerated. It is these movements which account for much of the cracking in new housing.

Once these consolidation movements have ceased, the foundations should be in a stable equilibrium, as depicted in Figure 7.2d. The soil mass below foundation level will have lost water in accordance with the imposed load (Figure 7.4), and the pore water pressure should be in equilibrium with the foundation load. Provided nothing happens to change this equilibrium, the foundations should remain static.

However, if root activity is present below foundation level, any changes in moisture content will affect this equilibrium, as depicted in Figure 7.3. When the soil dries it will shrink and the foundations will subside. Conversely when it rehydrates, the clay will generate swelling forces which will lift the foundation load. In theory, after a single cycle of seasonal movement, if the soil returns to its original moisture content, the level of the building should be restored as suggested by Figure 7.1.

In practice, simple observation clearly indicates that full recovery does not occur and that the building does not return to the level of the previous spring. This lack of full recovery after the initial cycles of movement of this sort is recognized and described in standard textbooks. It is caused by the hysteresis effect which was described in relation to Figure 4.12 (page 46) and which prevents the soil from returning to its original moisture content. This is accompanied by an increase in the bulk density of the clay. This hysteresis effect provides a potential explanation for the lack of recovery in the first few cycles of movement, but any increase in bulk density should be complete after a few cycles of seasonal movement. Observation shows that the distortion continues to accumulate as long as the seasonal cycle continues and that other factors must be involved.

The development of irreversible distortion of this sort, caused by the seasonal movement of the foundation, appears to be inadequately recognised or explained. I do not propose any definitive explanation of the cause, but observations suggest that the distortion accumulates most rapidly in any situation where:

a) the soil has a low margin of safety against shear failure;

b) foundations are shallow or there is poor lateral restraint, e.g. on slopes.

This suggests that shear failure may be involved, even though the bearing capacity of the soil should in theory be adequate for the imposed loads. A possible explanation is shown diagrammatically in Figure 7.5;

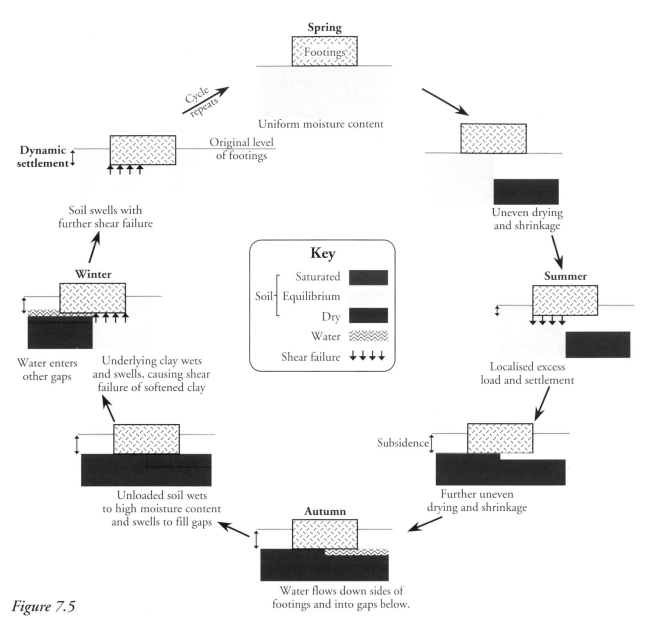

Spring

Footings

Uniform moisture content

Cycle repeats

Dynamic settlement

Original level of footings

Soil swells with further shear failure

Uneven drying and shrinkage

Key

Soil — Saturated

Equilibrium

Dry

Water

Shear failure

Winter

Water enters other gaps

Underlying clay wets and swells, causing shear failure of softened clay

Summer

Localised excess load and settlement

Subsidence

Unloaded soil wets to high moisture content and swells to fill gaps

Autumn

Further uneven drying and shrinkage

Water flows down sides of footings and into gaps below.

Figure 7.5

Diagrammatic representation of cycle of seasonal movement and the potential mechanism for dynamic settlement.

this postulates that the soil movements, and thus the loads, beneath the foundations are not uniform. If the soil below one part of the foundations shrinks slightly more than the adjacent areas, these adjacent areas will take the extra load (and suffer extra consolidation). At the same time a gap will develop below the foundations as a result of the extra shrinkage. In the winter, rain will run into the foundation trench and into the gap below the foundations, wetting this soil. In any areas where the clay has shrunk away from beneath the foundations it is under no load, it will swell easily, softening in the process. Observation of clay under the foundations in these conditions often shows that it is very soft. As it swells, this softened clay will again come into contact with the underside of foundations and start to come under load. As the moisture permeates to deeper layers of desiccated clay, this whole mass of soil will swell. If the swelling in this locality is greater than in the adjacent areas, it will

start to take the full load of the building rather than this being distributed over the whole of the foundations. As a result, excess load will act on the very soft clay directly below foundation level. This softened clay will be much more vulnerable to shear failure. Once it has failed, its load will be transferred to adjacent sections of the foundation which will then be liable to similar failure.

Similar localised variations in the rate of swelling and shrinking below foundation level will produce constantly varying stress within the soil. The localised loads to which the soil is subjected could therefore be many times greater than those predicted by simple calculation of foundation area and building mass.

This irreversible distortion is clearly distinct from the reversible effects of soil shrinkage. As the load of the building is involved, it should be defined as settle-

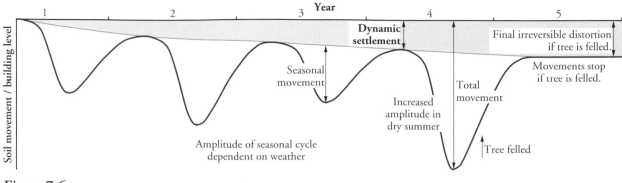

Figure 7.6

Diagram showing development of dynamic settlement associated with repeated cycles of seasonal movement.

ment, rather than subsidence. As it is caused by the constant movement and change of stress within the soil as a result of the fluctuations in moisture content, I would suggest the term **"dynamic settlement"** to describe the progressive downward ratcheting movement of this sort. The existence of irreversible distortion of this sort is apparent in many of the Case Studies (Case Studies 3, 7, 15, 17, 19). The details of the explanation must be left to Engineers.

Where damage occurs to a building, there is almost always considerable accumulated distortion of this sort. When this accumulative distortion, combined with distortion from the seasonal shrinkage (which will be increased in a dry year), becomes too much for the structure, damage occurs (Figure 7.6).

If the distortion was caused solely by drying and shrinkage of the clay, removal of the tree and allowing the soil to rehydrate and swell would eliminate the distortion. It must be emphasised that full recovery does not occur, and that distortion of this type is irreversible.

Movements caused by persistent deficits

In those situations where a persistent deficit establishes, there is a progressive reduction in the moisture content and associated shrinkage of the soil. This shrinkage is reversible if the soil drying ceases and the soil is allowed to rehydrate. It is caused by the external influence of a tree, and therefore it is **subsidence** within the correct definition of this term. It is preferable to restrict the term subsidence to these situations, and to use seasonal movement, or seasonal subsidence, when referring to the effects of seasonal changes in moisture content.

A persistent deficit can only increase, or be maintained, if soil drying is being maintained. In these situations there must also be a cycle of seasonal drying in summer with recovery each winter. This cycle of seasonal movements will be superimposed on subsidence caused by any underlying changes in the persistent deficit, and will also create the normal irreversible effects of dynamic settlement.

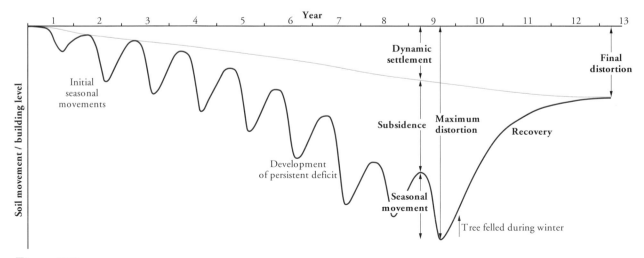

Figure 7.7

Diagram of movements associated with development of a persistent deficit, with associated seasonal movements and dynamic settlement (individual years are symbolic - actual time scales could be longer).

For this reason, while a persistent deficit is establishing, a building will be subject to subsidence, seasonal movement, and dynamic settlement. These different influences are shown in diagrammatic form in Figure 7.7.

Where a persistent deficit is present, it implies a soil of low permeability. Such soils will normally have a high plasticity index and therefore be more prone to shrinkage within the normal range. For this reason the soil movements, whether caused by the persistent deficit or by the superimposed seasonal deficits, are usually greater than those associated with deficits which are exclusively seasonal.

The effect of the development of a persistent deficit on a building

Under most circumstances, if the species of tree and soil conditions are conducive to the development of a persistent deficit, damage will have occurred and remedial action will have been taken as a result of seasonal movements long before any persistent deficit starts to develop. For instance, if a building exists at year 1 in figure 7.7, it is probable that damage will have started to appear as a result of the increasing amplitude of seasonal movements by year 4. At this stage the movements are still predominantly seasonal. However, the exceptions will occasionally occur where the increasing growth of a tree is sufficient to allow a persistent deficit to develop. Case Studies 4, 6 and 17 provide examples. In all these cases there were considerable seasonal movements occurring, with the subsidence caused by the persistent deficit superimposed on these seasonal effects. In all these cases the situation was allowed to develop (or deteriorate) to the point where a persistent deficit had established. In Case Study 6 the owner of the property remained remarkably unconcerned and allowed the damage to gradually develop; in Case Study 4 the early damage was masked by unscrupulous repairs; in Case Study 17 the rapid growth of the trees and unusual foundations allowed a slight persistent deficit to develop very rapidly (while the owner of the trees prevaricated about their involvement).

It must be emphasised that these Cases Studies provide the exceptions. If damage has only recently started on an established building, it is probably caused by seasonal movement, and it is very unlikely that there will be a persistent deficit. The converse situation does not necessarily apply. Thus, if there is an established building with a history of damage, the movement and damage may be entirely seasonal with any distortion due solely to dynamic settlement rather than subsidence, or it may be due to a persistent deficit and subsidence.

Heave as result of building on a pre-existing persistent deficit

If a building is constructed on soil which already has a persistent deficit, and if inadequate precautions are taken in foundation design, it is inevitable that at some stage the soil drying will cease and the soil will rehydrate and swell. The swelling pressure which is generated will be equal to the suction, and is usually many times greater than the typical 100 kPa load of a two storey building. The swelling of the soil will therefore lift the foundations; this upward (and sometimes lateral) movement of the foundations is known as **heave**. Heave movements will continue until the soil has been able to rehydrate to the point where the soil suction is equal to the foundation load.

The development of heave is entirely dependent on when the persistent deficit is allowed to rehydrate. It is sometimes mistakenly thought that this can only occur after a tree has been felled (i.e. at year 10 in Figure 7.7). Certainly the majority of cases of heave occur in this situation. This is because, if a tree has to be felled to make room for a building, it is very likely that the new foundations will be very close to the former location of the tree. It is in this position, close to the tree, that the greatest persistent deficits are usually present.

However, a persistent deficit can be present even at some distance from a tree. In these circumstance heave can, and often will, develop even if the tree is retained. On most building sites there is extensive damage to the root system, either by severance of the roots for the foundations and the underground services, or by compaction and disturbance of the ground which leads to die back of the fine roots. As a result of this damage the persistent deficit will usually start to recover. This recovery will not be sustained if the root system manages to regenerate sufficiently so that the persistent deficit can start to re-establish. However, before the roots can regenerate in this way, structural damage is often apparent. Just because the tree is still present, this is often incorrectly diagnosed as being caused by subsidence, but damage in the early life of a building is far more likely to be due to heave (Case Studies 1, 13 and 14 provide examples).

Even if significant heave does not develop soon after construction, if a building is constructed on a significant persistent deficit (i.e. at the start of year 8 in Figure 7.7) there will almost inevitably be significant seasonal movements occurring. These seasonal movements will usually be sufficient to indicate a potential problem and the need for investigations.

For all of the reasons described in this and the previous section, it is very unusual to encounter a significant persistent deficit beneath any existing building unless there is clear evidence of long-term movement. If there is evidence of long-term movement, it is necessary to determine whether this is due solely to seasonal movement and dynamic settlement, or whether there is a persistent deficit and a risk of heave. Chapters 11 and 16 consider the methods of diagnosis.

Angular distortion and damage

Considerable foundation movements can occur as a result of tree root activity without damage necessarily occurring. It is not the absolute amount of movement which causes damage, but rather the amount of differential movement and angular distortion. For instance, the level monitoring described in Case Study 15 recorded seasonal movements during 1983 of 35mm at the front of the building and 23mm at the rear. These were being caused by a large oak, 12.5m from the front and 21.5m from the rear, which was mature and must have been having a similar influence for many years. Prior to 1976 any problems had been very slight and ignored; the slightly greater seasonal movements of that year resulted in some damage and a rash decision to underpin half of the building. As a result, the movements which had previously been affecting the whole building fairly uniformly were now restricted to those parts which had not been underpinned. This created far greater angular distortion along the party wall and the development of far worse damage.

For this reason it is preferable to consider movement in terms of the angular distortion. Angular distortion is defined as the vertical displacement recorded as a fraction of the horizontal distance over which this displacement is occurring, i.e. h/AB.

For these results to be meaningful, it is necessary for measurements of movement to be taken at fairly close intervals so as to define both the horizontal and vertical measurements. For instance, if measurements show that one corner of a 12m wide building is moving by 15mm, one must have measurements at other points to determine whether this is a general movement affecting all parts of the building with no differential movement (Figure 7.8a), whether it is a uniform slope to the opposite corner of the building (Figure 7.8b), or just restricted to the corner (Figure 7.8c). Expressing movement in this way should provide a more rational way of determining whether it is cause for concern or can reasonably be tolerated.

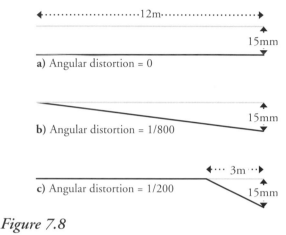

Figure 7.8
Diagrams of angular distortion
(original level _____, Present level _____)

There is scant information on the tolerance of building materials and the angular distortions which are associated with the onset of cracking. BRE Digest 63 quoted 1/300 for the onset of cracking in brickwork and plaster, and 1/150 for buildings with a frame construction (factories etc.). However, different types of brickwork have a different response to a bending moment and can be expected to have different critical values of angular distortion.

If the depth of the foundations around a building vary, it is likely that the extent of moisture deficit below foundation level (and the associated movement) will also vary. The shallower parts of the foundations will also be more vulnerable to dynamic settlement. Any abrupt change in depth is therefore more likely to create angular distortion and increase the risk of damage.

Angular distortion is also relevant when considering the ability of different species of tree to cause damage. For instance, species such as Leyland cypress may not produce a large soil moisture deficit, but their influence is very localised and so, if they are close to a building, they can produce a large, although localised, distortion. By contrast, the oak tree referred to earlier in this section (Case Study 15), although producing 35mm of seasonal movement, was only producing an angular distortion of (35-22)/9000 = 1/690 between the front and rear. After one half of the building was underpinned, the continuing movements created a maximum differential across the front of 1:195, with damage re-occurring after this exceeded 1:315.

Influence of building on soil permeability

Chapters 5 and 6 have emphasised the importance of soil permeability; it is this which controls the ability of the soil to recover either by lateral ingress of water from adjacent areas, by vertical penetration of rainfall, or occasionally from a rising water table. Structureless clay soils have exceedingly low permeability and so drying of such soil would quickly lead to the development of a persistent deficit. However, in practice most clay soils have a well defined structure which improves the permeability. In addition, as seen in many of the examples in Volume 2, soils often have gross features, such as bands of sand or sandier clay, which improve the overall permeability. However, even where boreholes have shown the presence of these features, it is not easy to predict their influence on the patterns of soil drying and recovery.

If soil conditions at an undisturbed site can be variable, the situation in the built environment where there is extensive disturbance will be even more variable. There is a network of underground services, often extending to considerable depth, with these usually partially backfilled with granular materials, or with unconsolidated soil. In addition, the foundations provide a series of deep trenches both around the periphery of a building and usually beneath internal partition walls. These trenches may be partially filled with concrete, but observation of any such trench in winter shows how rapidly they can fill with water and also allow lateral water flow, either through shrinkage cracks in the soil along their edges or through gaps left at the time of construction between soil and concrete.

These service and foundation trenches can be expected to have a major influence on soil permeability. Not only do they provide their own interconnecting network through the soil, but they will also link with any naturally occurring permeable bands to further aid the gross permeability of the soil. In particular, they provide a rapid means of access for water down to at least the soil at foundation level, thereby bypassing the

need to permeate through the surface layers. For this reason, even if there is a deficit below deep foundations in fairly homogeneous clay of low permeability, it can normally be anticipated that there will be significant seasonal recovery.

An exception to this normal behaviour is provided by Case Study 17. In that case the 2.4m deep foundation trench had been double lined with polythene sheeting before the foundations were laid. This provided an effective and tight seal to the soil. A trial hole in winter showed that water was trapped between the polythene and the foundations, literally in a polythene bag so that it could not get into the soil below foundation level. As a result of these unusual features, natural recovery during the winter was restricted and in that situation a persistent deficit had developed. Even in these conditions some seasonal movement occurred.

It is sometimes suggested that a network of trenches provides a means for draining away water which would otherwise be available, and that this therefore increases the propensity for soil drying. However, such drainage will be from areas where moisture is in surplus to those of deficit, i.e. overall it will be towards the tree and will therefore aid the moisture availability.

Influence of building on root growth

Just as foundations improve the permeability of the soil, they also improve the conditions for root growth. As described in Chapter 3, roots need oxygen for their respiration and growth and they will favour soil where water is more readily available. The disturbed backfill of service trenches is less compacted and provides just these conditions, and the permeability of foundation trenches also provides oxygen and water. For these reasons enhanced root growth can be expected in and adjacent to trenches and other areas of disturbed ground. As the resistance to water flow along a root is low, there is no disadvantage to the tree in exploiting a long length of trench. The tree will exploit these areas in preference to the more hostile conditions within the main body of undisturbed soil.

This enhanced root activity has important implications on the overall patterns of soil drying. Volume 2 shows that the patterns of soil drying, even in undisturbed conditions, are variable and unpredictable. In disturbed conditions they will be even more variable. Even if there is information on which areas have been disturbed, it does not improve the predictability.

Although details of the pattern of drying in areas of built development are unpredictable, overall it can be expected that deficits are even more likely to be seasonal and that there is reduced likelihood of the development of a persistent deficit compared with an undisturbed site. Root activity will favour areas where seasonal recovery can occur most easily.

Exclusion of rainfall by buildings and other impermeable surfaces

In the urban environment much of the rainfall is intercepted and removed by the drains, without ever coming in contact with the soil or roots. Such water is lost from the system. Inevitably this must suggest that soils in this situation will be more susceptible to moisture depletion. Whilst undoubtedly hard surfaces and drains increase water loss in this way, it must also be noted that annual rainfall is in excess of the water used, even by tree root activity, and that there will always be considerable run-off of surplus water in all situations, both urban and rural.

However, there is another compensating effect. Wherever impermeable surfaces are present, they will be excluding other vegetation such as grass. Chapter 5 has emphasised the considerable effects of such vegetation, particularly within the surface 1.2m of soil where it can produce more intense soil drying than that of other root activity. When this surface vegetation is excluded, the roots of a tree can still extend into this soil and exploit the available water, with the added advantage that there is no competition. Few surfaces are entirely impermeable, so that water can penetrate through cracks and gaps, or alternatively water can still get under these surfaces by lateral flow in the permeable base which normally exists.

A building will provide a totally impermeable surface and also includes special provision for disposing of water through the gutters. However, as noted earlier in this chapter, foundation trenches provide an enhanced pathway for water to get back into the soil.

Overall there appears to be no evidence that deficits, whether seasonal or persistent, are more likely to develop beneath the normal range of impermeable surfaces as compared with the deficits under grass. However, if surfaces are used which exclude vegetation but allow free entry for water, for instance a mulch of coarse gravel or open jointed paving, it will enhance the water availability and can significantly reduce the extent of soil drying.

Summary

1.   The most common type of soil movements which can result in damage to foundations are **seasonal movements**, caused by the annual cycle of drying and rehydration. This causes **seasonal subsidence** and **seasonal recovery**. The amplitude of this cycle is dependent on the annual changes in the soil moisture deficit and the shrinkage potential of the soil.

2.   Localised variations in the extent of seasonal soil movements cause constant variation in the foundation load. This produces an irreversible and load-dependent settlement, for which the term **dynamic settlement** is proposed.

3.   If moisture deficits extend below the depth to which moisture can penetrate in a single winter, a **persistent deficit** establishes. Shrinkage of the soil as a result of this deficit causes **subsidence**.

4.   Dynamic settlement and subsidence produce similar distortion, but the former is irreversible, whereas subsidence will be reversed if a tree is felled or if water uptake diminishes for any other reason.

5.   Experience from monitoring buildings indicates that, in almost all circumstances, **seasonal movements are the most significant**. It also indicates that the majority of distortion observed in buildings (in the spring, after seasonal recovery has occurred) is caused by dynamic settlement, and that subsidence (in its strict sense, associated with a persistent deficit) only occurs in a small proportion of cases (probably less than 10% of insurance subsidence claims).

6.   Damage to a building normally occurs when the **angular distortion** caused by dynamic settlement (or subsidence) is combined with the additional distortion caused by seasonal subsidence which builds up to a peak in late summer. If the stress associated with this distortion is excessive, damage occurs.

7.   If a persistent deficit has developed, subsequent restriction of water uptake (i.e. by felling the tree, damaging roots, heavy pruning or overmaturity) will allow the soil to rehydrate and swell. If buildings are constructed on desiccated clay, this process lifts the foundations to above their original level, and is referred to as **heave**. This can be the cause of serious progressive foundation movements and damage. If the soil has been desiccated after the house was built (causing subsidence), subsequent rehydration will cause **long-term recovery**.

Terrace of 3 properties – Central one underpinned – 28mm seasonal movements continue – Damage exacerbated – Dynamic settlement – Level monitoring essential for diagnosis – Oak tree felled to restabilise most of building – Minor continuing predicted recovery.

The site is located in East Wiltshire on Kimmeridge Clay, close to the interface with the underlying Red Down Sand. The subject property was originally built in the 1920's as the left hand half of a pair of semi-detached cottages. Soon after it was built an additional cottage was added to the left hand side, making the subject property the centre of a terrace of three. In the late 1960's extensive alterations were undertaken to all three, with the addition of a two-storey extension to the rear. All external walls were rendered. The ground floor plan is shown in CS Figure 7.1

In 1976 various cracks started to appear; initially they were made good and re-decorated but they kept re-appearing. This damage was investigated by engineers who concluded that there was old subsidence damage on the right hand party wall, but more recent damage around the stair-

well which was consistent with tree root activity. They were also concerned about possible fill material below the site, changes of geology and of water table. They recommended underpinning, and that study of the soil should be undertaken during this work. The underpinning was carried out in 1984, using a continuous strip to a depth of 1.5m. This underpinning did not encounter any of the anticipated problems from fill or ground water. The engineers noted:-

> The amount, type and timing of the damage in the building is not totally consistent with tree root activity in the heavy clay. The main indicator against this solution is that, as far as we know, no recent cracks have developed in the two properties to either side. The spread of tree roots from the group of trees would have been expected to affect all three properties fairly equally. It appears that the main damage is confined to the centre (subject) building of the terrace.

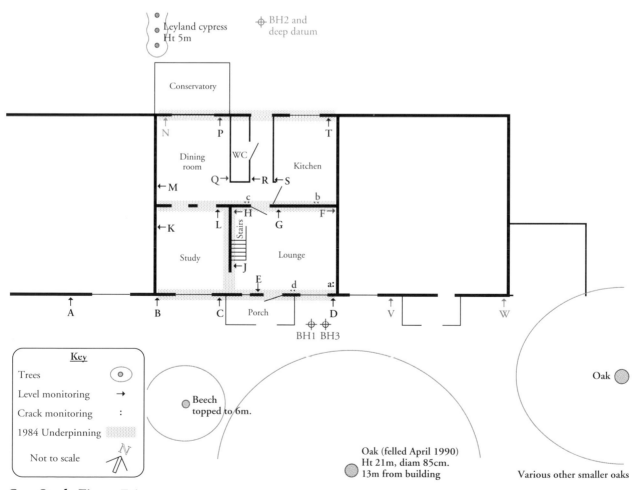

Case Study Figure 7.1
Site plan showing location of significant trees, boreholes, and level and crack monitoring stations.

In 1987 the owner became aware of renewed damage, and following further movement the same engineer was recalled in September 1988. At that stage the damage was comparatively minor and the problems were attributed to root activity of two beech trees in the front garden and the cypress hedge in the rear. Recommendations were made for these trees to be felled. The tree surgeon questioned their recommendation and (quite correctly) suggested that the beech trees were unlikely to be having any influence but that the adjacent oak might be involved. As a result, I was instructed by the loss adjusters, and inspected for the first time in January 1989.

Damage to property

At the time of my initial inspection in January 1989 the damage was comparatively minor, with slight cracking on the front elevation and some internal movement, particularly in the rear wall of the original cottage. In June 1989 there was slight further deterioration, and by late July the cracks on the front elevation had opened considerably, a 5mm crack had opened internally on the original rear wall (now the central spine wall), and there was additional cracking on the front wall adjacent to the right hand party wall. Between July and October the situation continued to deteriorate with the cracks gradually becoming worse, particularly in the region of the central spine wall and adjacent to the right hand party wall. By October 1989 I assessed the overall condition as Category 3 "Moderate".

The external render prevented a level distortion survey, but it was apparent that there was considerable distortion throughout the building.

Monitoring of building level

On 17th June 1989 I attached level monitoring markers both internally and externally at the locations shown in CS Figure 7.1. This included a single marker (station A) on the left hand property; the owner of the right hand property declined to co-operate.

Although it was intended to use station A as a datum, there were suspicions that this station was moving and so in November 1989 I installed a deep datum in the borehole drilled at that time to the rear. The datum rod was driven into the base of the borehole to 5.5m, and backfilled with concrete to 3m. Subsequent readings suggested that station A had been moving slightly; the results shown in CS Figure 7.2 are adjusted to reflect these probable movements (of up to 2mm).

Although the owner of the right hand property was unwilling to co-operate, by 1990 it became apparent that it was very desirable to have information on the movement of that property. The problem was overcome by observing two definable marks (a fine paint splodge and an irregularity on a brick) to provide two accurately defined points which could be observed with the optic level. When readings were taken, the height of the optic level was carefully adjusted to coincide with these marks, and this was then compared with the level of station D in order to determine the differential movements which were occurring.

The results for all of the stations are shown in CS Figure 7.2, and are shown graphically for selected stations in CS Figure 7.3.

Changes in level (mm) relative to deep datum, compared to initial readings on 17/6/89:									
Station	17/6/89	27/7/89	6/10/89	14/11/89	13/2/90	23/3/90	7/5/90	16/7/90	16/10/90	16/4/91
A	0	-1.0*	-2.0*	0*	+0.6	-0.4	-0.5	-0.7	-2.9	-0.9
B	0	-2.6	-8.3	-6.8	-3.6	-3.6	-3.6	-2.9	-3.2	-1.5
C	0	-2.1	-4.5	-2.8	-1.1	-1.3	-1.4	-1.0	-0.7	+1.3
D	0	-15.1	-28.2	-25.4	-14.5	-12.2	-11.1	-9.3	-9.3	-2.2
E	0	-3.2	-6.2	-3.7	-2.5	-2.9	-2.8	-2.5	-2.2	-0.9
F	0	-11.9	-24.1	-21.2	-14.1	-12.4	-11.4	-10.3	-9.4	-5.6
G	0	-7.2	-13.8	-11.1	-7.7	-7.3	-7.9	-6.5	-6.1	-3.8
H	0	-2.0	-2.5	0	+1.1	+0.5	+0.3	+0.5	+0.4	+1.5
J	0	-2.5	-4.1	-2.0	-0.3	-0.8	-0.8	-0.7	-0.6	+1.2
K	0	-2.8	-6.0	-4.1	-2.9	-2.7	-2.8	-2.7	-3.7	-2.2
L	0	-3.1	-5.9	-3.9	-3.0	-3.1	-3.1	-3.1	-3	-2.4
M	0	-2.8	-7.4	-3.4	-2.5	-2.6	-2.6	-2.7	-2.7	-2.9
N	0	-2.2	-5.6	-1.5	-0.7	-1.4	-0.5	-2.0	-1.9	-2.6
P	0	-2.6	-6.7	-2.4	-1.7	-2.3	-2.4	-2.7	-2.4	-2.9
Q	0	-3.5	-9.0	-4.7	-3.1	-3.4	-3.5	-3.5	-3.3	-2.9
R	0	-4.1	-10.0	-4.7	-2.8	-3.3	-4.4	-3.8	-3.7	-2.4
S	0	-5.7	-10.2	-7.8	-5.0	-5.2	-6.2	-5.4	-5.5	-3.4
T	0	-6.5	-13.3	-10.7	-9.2	-8.1	-8.6	-7.9	-7.0	-5.8
Adjacent building compared to initial readings on 7/5/90:									
V							0	+0.8	-3.3	+8.5
W							0	-2.1	-15.5	+0.8
(*assumed movements prior to installation of deep datum)									

Case Study Figure 7.2

Results of level monitoring.

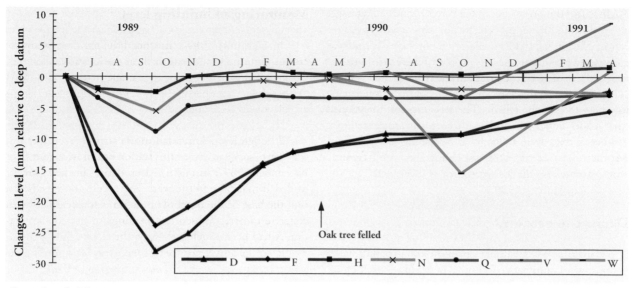

Case Study Figure 7.3

Results of level monitoring for selected stations relative to deep datum (readings for station V and W commenced 23/3/90).

Crack monitoring

Monitoring some of the main cracks was started in November 1989 and continued until the property was re-instated in summer 1991. The location of stations is shown in CS Figure 7.1, and results shown in CS Figure 7.4.

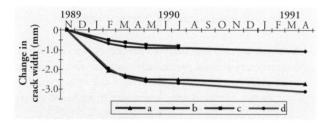

Case Study Figure 7.4

Results of crack monitoring

Condition of underpinning

In view of the pronounced movements recorded at level station D, a trial hole was excavated in August 1989 to inspect the underpinning at this location. Although this hole was dug during a period of drought, at the base of the underpinning water was encountered flowing out from adjacent to the underpinning. The conditions encountered in the trial hole are illustrated in CS Figure 7.5 It shows that the original foundations were to a depth of 0.57m, with the underpinning taken to 1.5m, founded on stiff brown, slightly sandy clay. The underpinning works had been carried out from inside the building, and it was apparent that the quality of the workmanship for the insertion of the dry pack between the underpinning and original footings was very poor. Soil had been left beneath the original footings, and in addition there was a 200mm wide gap between this soil and the dry pack. Probing showed that elsewhere the dry pack was more extensive, but in the area under inspection it was clear that it had not been driven to the full width of the gap between the underpinning and footings.

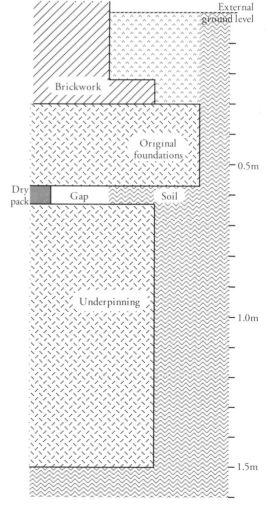

Case Study Figure 7.5

Diagram of original foundations and defective underpinning.

117

Soil conditions

In November 1989 I drilled two boreholes at the locations shown in CS Figure 7.1. Both boreholes encountered grey clay, typical of the Kimmeridge clay in that locality. Slight variations in colour and texture were recorded at the same depth in both holes, and both holes encountered marl and stones at 4.75m. In borehole 1 the stone was penetrated, with a brown silty sand beneath. The similarity between the two boreholes suggested that similar conditions extend beneath the whole site.

The moisture content profiles are shown in CS Figure 7.6, and the results for the soil classification tests are shown in CS Figure 7.7. The results of the soil classification tests show broadly similar values from comparable depths which again suggests uniform conditions beneath the site.

Calculation based on comparison of the two profiles indicate a soil moisture deficit of 202mm between 1.5m (underside of underpinning) and 4.3m (where the two profiles cross).

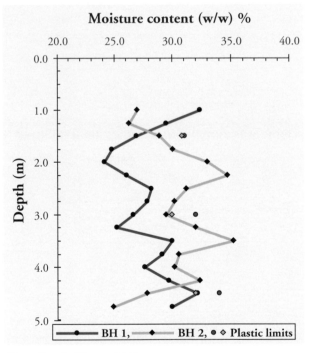

Case Study Figure 7.6

Soil moisture content profiles in November 1989.

Depth (m)	m.c. (% w/w)	Plastic limit	Liquid limit	Plasticity index	% linear shrinkage
Borehole 1					
1.5	26.9	31	73	42	11.8
3.0	26.7	32	68	36	11.4
4.5	32.1	34	76	42	13.2
Borehole 2					
1.5	29.0	31	65	34	10.0
3.0	29.5	30	65	34	10.4
4.5	27.8	32	73	41	11.4

Case Study Figure 7.7

Soil classification tests.

While drilling these holes I noted fine root activity to the full depth of borehole 1. These roots were too small for identification, with the exception of one of 2mm diameter in the silty sand at the base of this borehole which was oak.

The trees

The location of the significant trees is shown in CS Figure 7.1. The most important was a large mature and very vigorous oak (*Quercus robur*) with a height of about 21m, and diameter of 85cm (CS Figure 7.8). This was growing in the front garden of the adjacent property to the right, at a distance of 13.0m from the front of the party wall. It was felled (on my recommendation) on 23/4/90.

There remain a number of oak trees within the front garden of the adjacent property to the right. The location of the nearest, and probably most significant, is shown in CS Figure 7.1. The owner was not prepared to co-operate to allow me to obtain details of these trees.

There were various small trees in the front garden of the subject property. The closest was a beech tree, about 6.0m from the building. This had been topped to a height of 6m prior to my involvement. This had left only a few lateral branches and had virtually killed the tree. There were some small ash trees in the front garden to the left.

In the rear garden, on the left boundary, was row of Leyland cypress which had been topped to a height of 5m. The nearest of these was in very close proximity to the conservatory extension and was felled to prevent further movement of that structure.

Case Study Figure 7.8

Offending oak (and other smaller oaks) in adjacent garden.

DISCUSSION

Cause of damage

Whilst it is not possible to prove the cause of the original (1976 - 1984) damage, there can be little doubt that it must have been caused by tree root activity. There was no evidence, either during the underpinning or during my investigations, of the various other possible causes which had been postulated by the engineers.

The extent of movements which were occurring prior to 1984 are not known, but the underpinning was totally ineffective. My monitoring during the summer of 1989 demonstrated up to 28mm of downward movement occurring at the front of the party wall, despite the underpinning. It also showed that parts of the building, particularly stations H and J adjacent to the stairwell, had virtually stabilised. It will be recalled that the engineers had concluded that subsidence was centred in this area, whereas the monitoring shows that this was acting as a 'hard-spot' with differential movement occurring around this area.

Monitoring of the recovery movements during the subsequent winter showed only partial recovery. For instance, station D which had subsided by 28mm during the summer, had only recovered by 17mm by the following May, leaving a net downward movement of 11mm. It seems probable that this can be attributed to increased dynamic settlement during the first few cycles of seasonal movement of the new underpinning. As this underpinning had been completed 5 years previously, it is probable that considerable distortion must have been accumulating during this period; this would help to account for the extent of damage. Despite the poor quality of the underpinning, there is no reason to suspect that this contributed to the movement.

Despite the underpinning, the seasonal movements extended throughout the property, including station N on the corner diagonally opposite to the tree, which subsided by 5.6mm during the summer, and station T on the rear of the party wall which subsided by 13.3mm. This pattern of movement indicated that the oak tree was the prime cause.

As the adjacent property to the right had refused to co-operate in the monitoring, in the spring of 1990 there was no information on the extent of movement affecting that part of the building. However, it seemed reasonable to assume that similar, if not greater, movements must have been affecting it, particularly as it was still on its original foundations. Increased differential movement between the shallow foundations of that property and the underpinning of the subject property would account for the damage being worse than it had been in 1984.

Options for remedial action

It was clear that, unless the adjacent property was willing to co-operate, any form of further underpinning of the subject would be counterproductive. It might succeed in stopping the considerable seasonal movements which were occurring, but only at the expense of further exaggerating the differential movements between any such underpinning and the adjacent shallow foundations. Such movements would cause even worse damage to both properties. The adjacent owner was aware that his property was subject to some movement but was prepared to tolerate this. He was adamant in refusing any form of underpinning, but even without this attitude it was apparent that the expense of underpinning would have been prohibitive and not warranted for old cottages of this sort.

The alternative was to deal with the principal cause of the movements, i.e. the vigorous oak in front of the party wall. The owner was reluctant, but under threat of an injunction, agreed to felling the tree in April 1990.

It was recognised that, if a persistent deficit was present, any such action could cause problems of long-term recovery. The boreholes which had been drilled in November 1989 had indicated a soil moisture deficit of about 202mm adjacent to the front of the building. In order to determine whether this had diminished during the winter, I drilled a further hole in May 1990 (borehole 3) adjacent to my previous borehole 1. CS Figure 7.9 compares this profile with the earlier results. Although some recovery had occurred, a soil moisture deficit of 177mm was still present below 1.5m.

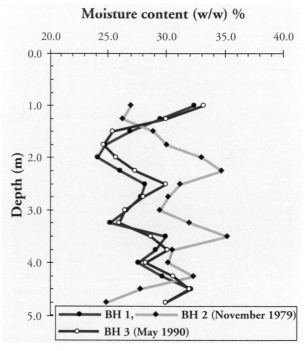

Case Study Figure 7.9
Soil moisture content profiles in May 1990.

On the basis of these results one might conclude that the 25mm reduction in soil moisture deficit had been accompanied by a 14.3mm recovery of the adjacent station D. This would imply a water shrinkage factor approaching 2, and, if this value was applied to the remaining deficit, would suggest a potential for a further 177 x 14.3/25 = 101mm recovery. Movements of this magnitude would be unacceptable and furthermore, as only 17mm of recovery had occurred during the winter, it suggested that movement would continue for many years.

However, other factors suggested that this was an unduly pessimistic prediction. In particular the level monitoring during the winter had shown a noticeable reduction in the rate of movement, implying that much of the recovery was already complete. In addition, the amount of recovery was being underestimated because of dynamic settlement, and it was likely that the boreholes, which were located 1.2m from the edge of the underpinning, were not representative of the conditions beneath the underpinning, as this provided an easy route for rapid access of water.

It was therefore decided to proceed with felling the tree, whilst recognizing that some long-term recovery was likely. It was anticipated that such movements would not be excessive or cause unacceptable damage.

Effect of tree removal

The level monitoring provided a clear indication of the effect of removing the oak tree. Movement of the foundations of most of the property ceased immediately (see CS Figures 7.2 and stations H, N and Q on CS Figure 7.3).

As anticipated, stations D and F continued to show recovery, associated with rehydration of the persistent deficit. At station F (at the middle of the party wall) the rate of these movements was virtually uniform throughout the year (at a rate of about 6.0mm per annum from May 1990). By comparison, station D at the front of the party wall showed a continuing seasonal influence, with recovery ceasing during the summer but accelerating during the winter so that the overall movement was about 9.0mm during the year.

The explanation for this can be seen from the monitoring of the adjacent property which was started when the tree was felled (stations V and W). Station W near the corner and near a remaining large oak tree showed continuing seasonal movement, subsiding by 15.5mm during the summer, with full recovery during the subsequent winter (note negligible dynamic settlement with these long-established foundations). Station V midway along the front elevation was clearly also under the influence of this tree, subsiding by 3.3mm during the summer. However, it was also subject to recovery as a result of felling the oak tree to the front, with upward movement of 11.8mm during the winter. It is reasonable to deduce that station D was also slightly under the influence of the remaining oak, but the amplitude of movement would be small and quite acceptable.

In spring 1991, after a winter for recovery, the property was fully repaired and redecorated. The render and areas of damaged plaster were stripped (revealing that the underlying cracking was considerable worse than the cracks visible at the surface) and the whole property redecorated. (Temporary cosmetic repairs had been applied a year earlier so that the owners did not have to live with the very unsightly damage during the initial recovery period).

The redecoration destroyed all of the monitoring markers, and this exercise ceased.

In spring 1995 the owners reported some further damage around the front of the right hand party wall. The worst was a crack which had developed slowly and progressively to a width of 3mm. Insurers accepted a claim for further redecoration of this, as part of the original claim. Ideally it would be advantageous to have continued to monitor the movements to determine whether they have now ceased. In the absence of this information there is a remaining possibility of slight further movement and damage, but it is clear that the property is now substantially stable and any movements which do continue are not unacceptable.

Lessons to be learnt

- The diagnosis of damage in 1984 was very inadequate. The pattern of movement was incorrectly diagnosed, and incorrect assumptions were made about subsoil conditions without the benefit of any site investigations.

- The underpinning applied at that time was ineffective in stopping the movements. If anything it made matters worse by increasing the differential movement across the party wall.

- The level monitoring during the summer of 1989 was very helpful in demonstrating the extent of movement, and indicating that the whole building was still subject to some movement, despite the underpinning. The relative stability of the central stairwell created differential movement and explained the concentration of damage in this area.

- The boreholes suggested a considerable persistent deficit and potential for long-term recovery. This contradicted information based on the level monitoring. Subsequent events indicate that the information from the boreholes was misleading, and that it was correct to rely on the level monitoring.

- Underpinning could not provide an effective remedy without co-operation of the adjacent house owner. Even if such co-operation had been forthcoming, the cost and disruption of work would have been excessive.

- Felling the large and vigorous oak was sufficient to immediately restabilise most of the building. Seasonal movements from other trees in the adjacent garden continued to affect the adjacent property, with very slight movements extending as far as the party wall.

- As anticipated, slight recovery movements continued, necessitating minor further repairs 4 years after the main repairs. However, felling the tree was substantially effective in restabilising the subject property. The adjacent owner can, if he desires, deal with the movements which continue to affect his part of the building.

- As there are other trees slightly further from the building, felling the large oak has caused negligible environmental damage.

Chapter 8

Introduction

Chapter 4 has considered the soil moisture deficit (SMD) within the soil and its relevance to soil shrinkage (page 52), and Chapters 5 and 6 have described the seasonal and persistent development of soil moisture deficits as a result of trees and other vegetation. Even if improved methods are developed for determining soil suction (Chapter 4, page 58), SMD will continue to provide a simple method for assessing and comparing desiccated soils.

In addition to deriving SMD from soil moisture content, it can also be derived using mathematical models based on data on the weather conditions. The weather has a fundamental influence on the extent of soil drying which develops each year, as it affects the balance between:

i)   the loss of water as a result of transpiration[1] and evaporation;

ii) the input of water from precipitation.

The method for calculating the evaporation was developed by Penman (1948) and has been subjected to various modifications, particularly by Montieth (1965). Details of the calculations (the Penman-Montieth equation) and its refinements are complex and need not be considered in this book, but they take account of all of the so-called Penman variables (sunshine, temperature, vapour pressure and wind speed), as well as relevant features of the crop or surface cover, to determine the daily water loss.

---

[1]   As noted in Chapter 2 (page 14), the evaporation of water from within the leaf is termed transpiration. The factors which govern the rate of transpiration are the same as those which influence the rate of evaporation, and for this reason the two terms are often combined as "evapotranspiration". However, throughout this chapter I have used the terminology preferred by hydrologists, and refer to both processes as evaporation, whether occurring from a water surface or from within the leaf.

Figure 8.1 shows (in red, below the horizontal axis) the potential evaporation determined in this way for a crop such as grass, during the hot and dry summer of 1976. Each bar of this histogram, and all similar figures in this Chapter, indicate the measurements over a 7 day (1 week) period. It is clear that the evaporation is closely linked to day length (and thus sunshine and temperature), reaching peak values in June.

Figure 8.1 also shows (in blue, above the horizontal axis), the rainfall recorded at the same location over the same period.

It should be apparent from Figure 8.1 that the extent of potential evaporation at any time is reasonably predictable, albeit varying considerably through the year. Across the country the annual total varies between about 600mm in south east England, to less than 300mm in the uplands of north west England, with a standard deviation between years of only about 25mm. By contrast, the amount of rainfall is very variable and unpredictable, with standard deviations usually greater than 100mm (Jones and Thomasson, 1985). This might suggest that rainfall is the only variable which is relevant if one wishes to compare the weather conditions in different years. This would be

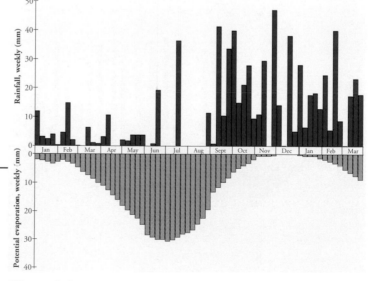

Figure 8.1

Weekly rates of potential evaporation from a grass crop during the period January 1976 to March 1977, and rainfall recorded in north London during the same period.   *Crown Copyright 1997.*

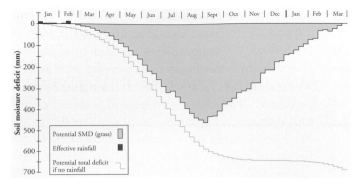

Figure 8.2

Theoretical maximum soil drying and soil moisture deficit for grass during 1976 (with no allowance made for available water). Crown Copyright 1997.

correct if one is interested solely in a general comparison of weather in different years. However, as evaporation varies through the year, if one wants information on the extent of soil drying (or SMD) throughout the year, it is essential to consider both rainfall and evaporation.

The pink line in Figure 8.2 sums the potential evaporation recorded in Figure 8.1 for each week, thus indicating the potential deficit which (theoretically) could occur over this period if there was no rainfall. This accumulates throughout the summer, reaches a plateau in the winter, and then again starts to accumulate in the spring of 1977. Figure 8.2 also shows (by the solid area, with green indicating grass) the balance between the evaporation loss and the input from rainfall, i.e. the amount of SMD, over this period. It shows how the low rainfall during the spring and summer of 1976 only reduces the SMD very

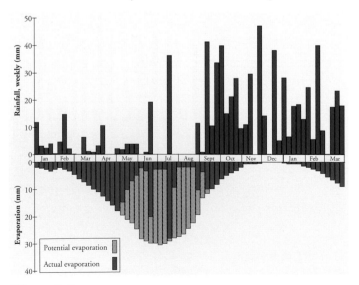

Figure 8.3

Rainfall, potential evaporation, and actual evaporation with allowance for available water for grass during 1976. Crown Copyright 1997.

slightly, but the heavier rainfall during the autumn was sufficient to eliminate the deficit, and get the soil back to field capacity, by the end of March 1977. Figure 8.2 also shows that during some weeks in January and February 1976, the rainfall was in excess of the deficit; it is assumed that this excess rainfall runs off and is available to fill aquifers or rivers. It is therefore termed "effective rainfall".

The extent of evaporation shown in Figures 8.1 and 8.2 assume that there is unlimited water available in the soil. In practice it is known that grass can only root to a limited depth and can therefore only exploit a limited volume of water. The model for calculating SMD makes allowance for this by assuming that grass is able to extract the first 95mm of water without hindrance. If further evaporation occurs, the availability of water is assumed to be limiting and increasingly difficult to extract, so that

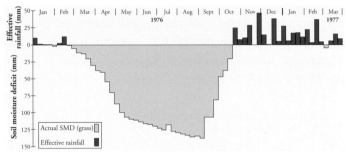

Figure 8.4

Calculated actual soil moisture deficit for grass and effective rainfall during 1976 (with allowance for available water). Crown Copyright 1997.

the actual rate of evaporation will fall progressively. Figure 8.3 shows the actual evaporation for grass calculated in this way, superimposed on the potential rate, showing that the availability of water was limiting to grass from May through to August. Note that the brief periods of rain in June and July partially replenish the available water and allow the rate of evaporation to increase temporarily.

Figure 8.4 shows the soil moisture deficit from grass with allowance for the actual, rather than potential, evaporation (contrast with Figure 8.2). It provides a good indication of how the soil moisture deficit might be expected to develop, with the grass starting to dry the soil in the early spring, but having diminishing effect as the availability of water becomes limiting to further growth. Different values of available water capacity can be used for different crops.

Evolution of MORECS Versions 1.0 and 2.0

The method described in the previous section is comparatively simple, but even this requires fairly complicated calculations to determine the SMD. However, since 1963 all of the necessary calculations of SMD have been undertaken routinely as one of the services provided by the Meteorological Office.

In 1978 this service was refined and greatly expanded, under the acronym **MORECS** (**M**eteorological **O**ffice **R**ainfall and **E**vaporation **C**alculation System). MORECS is intended primarily to provide up-to-date estimates of weekly and monthly soil moisture deficits to assist agriculturists and hydrologists in a variety of ways, particularly for irrigation requirements and for assessment of water catchment balance and river flow. The information is provided as the average over 40 x 40km grid squares covering England, Wales and Scotland (the service will extend to Northern Ireland in the near future), using daily synoptic weather data as its inputs. The essential purposes of this service are rapid provision of the information (it is calculated on the Tuesday of each week, using data up to the Monday, with the results available by facsimile on the Wednesday) and countrywide coverage.

Although it is intended primarily to provide a rapid response in real-time, it is recognised that it also has value as archive material, as a means of estimating the SMD at any location and any time in the past. It is this latter use which is of primary interest for assessing the influence of vegetation on buildings, as it provides a means for assessing and comparing conditions at any time in the past. I am not aware of anyone using the weekly release of data as an early-warning system that SMDs are becoming excessive with an associated risk of damage and possible need for preventative action, but the potential for this application must also exist.

The number of meteorological stations providing data are limited (only 56 reporting sunshine, and 131 reporting rainfall). This compares with a total of 190 40km squares, from which it is immediately apparent that the values for each square rely on interpolation of the data. Details of this interpolation, and of all other aspects of the MORECS system, are provided in Hydrological Memorandum No. 45 (Thompson *et al.* 1981).

In 1995 MORECS was updated, as version 2.0. Details of the changes, as well as a more comprehensive description of the whole system, are provided in an update to Hydrological Memorandum No. 45 (Hough *et al*, 1997). It is outside the scope of this book to consider the details of the MORECS systems 1.0 and 2.0; reference should be made to the relevant Hydrological Memorandum for this information. However, the following sections consider some aspects which are of particular relevance if requesting or interpreting MORECS data in respect of problems of tree root damage. They also identify some of the differences between the two versions of MORECS. In the figures, in order to distinguish the two versions, data derived from version 1.0 is shown against the normal yellow background   , while version 2.0 is distinguished by a green/yellow background shade   .

Available water content

Chapter 4 has considered the availability of water in sand, clay and other soils, with Figure 4.19 showing the amount of water which is available to plants (i.e. released at suctions between 5 and 1500kPa) within the different soil textural classes. MORECS 1.0 adopts a simpler model, defining only 3 classes; low, medium and high water availability. Figure 8.5 shows the seasonal development of soil moisture deficit for a crop of real land use (see next section) for each of these soil types. With the soil of low availability, the reserves were depleted by June, with a maximum deficit of 67mm; with medium availability reserves were greater but were depleted by mid July with a maximum deficit of 89mm, and with the high water availability reserves lasted until August, with a maximum of 111mm. The heavy rainfall in December was sufficient to replenish supplies in the low availability soil, but additional rain was required to replenish the other soils.

MORECS 2.0 provides considerable refinement. It is based on the LANDIS soils database, which provides information on the available water content of soils throughout the country, at a resolution of 1km. For each crop, the available water content is determined for each of the 1km squares. For each 40km MORECS square, this provides 1600 sets of data for each crop; these are used to determine the median, 10 percentile and 90 percentile values. These values of available water content now replace the previous MORECS 1.0 equivalents of 'medium', 'low' and 'high' available water content.

SMD modelling for different crops

MORECS calculates evaporation from 16 different crop types or surfaces. The majority are agricultural, reflecting the primary objective of the system for assessing agricultural irrigation needs. These agri-

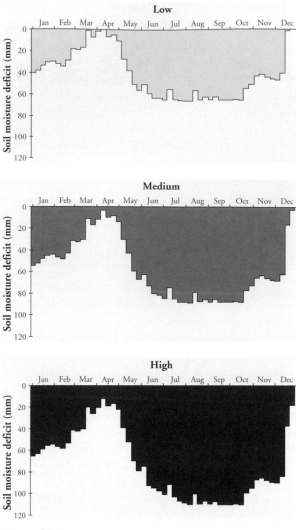

Figure 8.5

Comparison of soil moisture deficits for soils of low, medium and high available water content, for 1989 in MORECS square 161 with 'real land use' vegetation.

Crown Copyright 1997.

cultural crops include grass, winter wheat, winter and spring barley, oilseed rape, potatoes, sugar beet and upland grass (including set-aside). Three different tree crops are considered; orchard, deciduous, and coniferous. Other surfaces are bare soil, rock, urban and water. For each of these, the crop models describe aspects such as the growth and development, the leaf area index, crop height, surface resistance, and changes in availability of water as the root system develops.

'Deciduous trees' are potentially the most relevant crop for indicating the effect of trees, and warrant further description. All species are assumed to come into leaf at the same time, but this date is varied for the different 40km squares, ranging from 5th April in south west England, to 5th May in the Scottish highlands. From the date of bud burst it is assumed that 40 days elapse before full leaf cover is attained, providing a leaf

area index of 6 (i.e. leaf area grows to 6 times the ground area beneath the trees). Leaf fall is assumed to start on 17th October throughout the whole country, and to take 40 days to completion. During the winter a bare soil situation is assumed. Foliation is assumed to affect the wind profile, so the effective height is considered to be 2m at bud burst, increasing to 10m at full leaf cover. The values for median, 10%ile and 90%ile available water content are assumed to be 305mm, 262mm and 429mm respectively. This water is considered to be available to the root system throughout the year.

By contrast, permanent grass pasture is assumed to have a leaf area index which varies from month to month (2 in January, increasing to 5 from May to August, and diminishing to 2 by December). The median, 10%ile and 90%ile values for available water content are 133, 114, and 187mm.

Evaporation from bare soil is calculated (with no allowance for transpiration by vegetation), applying a leaf area index of 0. The median, 10%ile and 90%ile values for available water content are 36, 31, and 50mm.

In addition to the calculations of SMD for the various crops and soil surfaces, both versions of MORECS determine the area of each 40km square which are covered by each of the these crops or surfaces, expressed as a percentage of the total area. The calculated SMD for each individual crop can then be multiplied by its percentage area, and all of these values summed to give overall SMD for the whole square. This average value for the square is termed 'real land use'.

Figure 8.6 shows the development of SMD in 1989 (a comparatively dry year - see Figure 8.8) in square 161 (see Figure 8.9 for location of squares) for real land use, permanent grass, deciduous trees and bare soil, comparing the results for versions 1.0 and 2.0. Note that version 1.0 is calculated for high available water content, whereas version 2.0 uses median available water content. It might therefore be expected that the results for version 1.0 would be higher. This is correct for grass, but both trees and bare soil produce higher values with version 2.0. Likewise, the results for real land use, which provide an average for all crops, are higher with version 2.0, indicating that the modifications in 2.0 generally produce significantly higher values of SMD.

Comparison of the two versions in Figure 8.6 shows that the peak values of SMD can be achieved very rapidly in early summer with version 2.0, with these be-

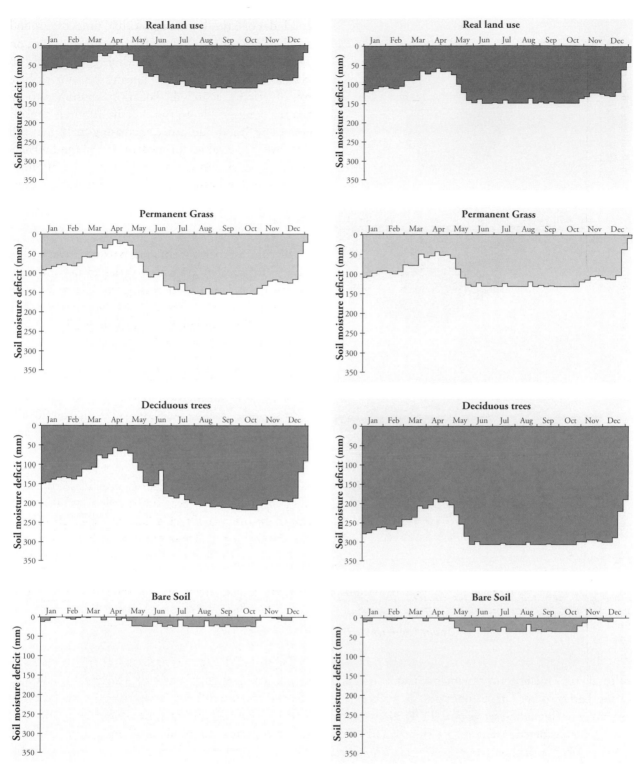

Figure 8.6

Comparison of soil moisture deficits for different types of land use, for 1989 in MORECS square 161. Results on left side are derived by version 1.0, using soils of high available water content. Those on the right side are derived by version 2.0, using soils of median available water content. Crown Copyright 1997.

ing maintained at a high plateau for much of the rest of the summer. By contrast, with version 1.0 the SMD continues to increase throughout the summer, albeit at a diminishing rate. This is most noticeable with the 'deciduous trees'. This continuing development of SMD throughout the season provides a more accurate reflection of the measurements of the seasonal development of SMD, as described in Chapter 5 (page 71), which suggests that version 1.0 is preferable in this respect.

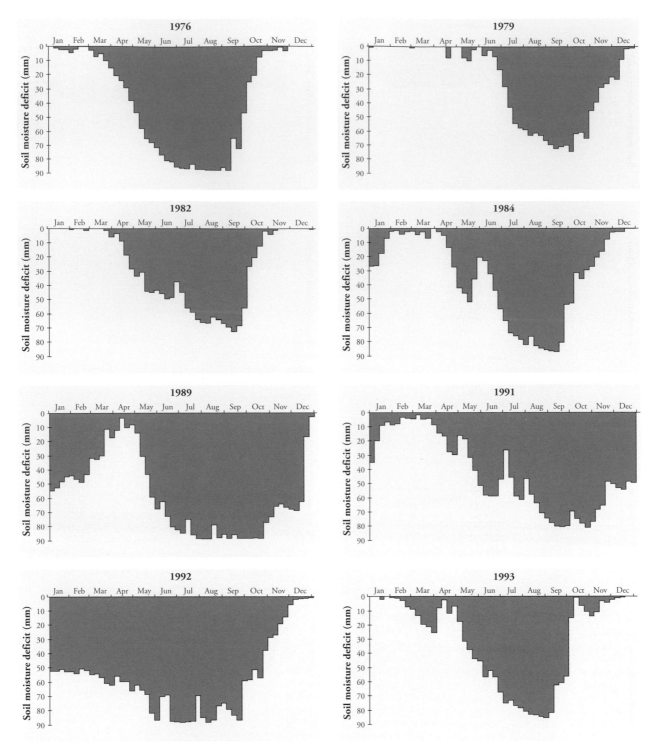

Figure 8.7

Development of SMD in square 161 in various recent years, derived with MORECS 1.0 for 'real land use' and medium available water content.   *Crown Copyright 1997.*

Comparison between years

Figure 8.7 shows the SMD for various recent years for square 161. It is derived using MORECS 1.0, for real land use and medium available water content. By contrast, Figure 8.8 shows the SMD for the same years (plus 1995 and 1996) within the same square, but derived using MORECS 2.0, for 'deciduous trees' and median available water content.

Attention is drawn to the following features:

i) Real land use in version 1.0 produces comparatively small deficits (maximum 89mm). Rainfall was able to produce full recovery in each subsequent winter, except for the extremely dry winter of 1991/92. This provides a reasonable likeness to the patterns of seasonal soil drying in proximity to trees, as described in Chapter 5.

126

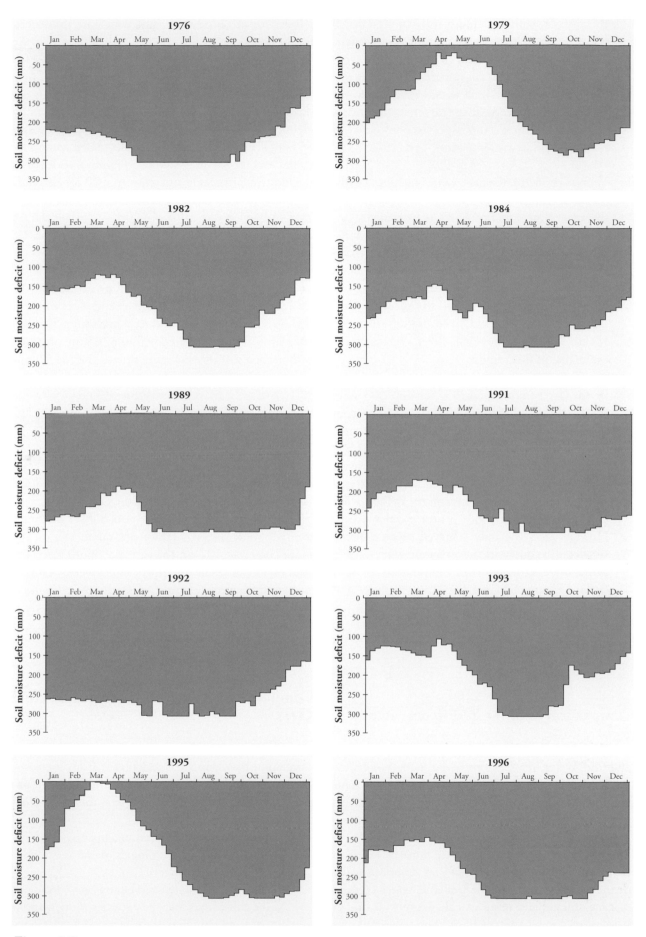

Figure 8.8

Development of SMD in square 161 in various recent years, derived with MORECS 2.0 for 'deciduous trees' and median available water content.   *Crown Copyright 1997.*

127

ii) By contrast, with 'deciduous trees' in version 2.0 the maximum deficit is 308mm. If this full deficit develops in the summer (which it did in every year which is shown, apart from 1979), it is unlikely that winter rainfall would be sufficient to produce full recovery. It appears to be producing a persistent deficit - this aspect is considered in further detail in a later section (page 132).

iii) With version 2.0, the peak value is achieved comparatively easily, with a pronounced plateau for the rest of the summer. This is particularly apparent in 1976, 1989 and 1996. Chapter 5 indicates that, in practice, the deficit continues to accumulate through the summer. It is this extra soil drying in a dry summer which is particularly relevant in causing additional soil shrinkage and damage, and it would be preferable for the MORECS data to show this effect. Version 1.0 is preferable in this respect.

iv) In the dry summer of 1995, version 2.0 shows the development of the full 308mm deficit (from 0 to 380mm), with this achieved by mid-August. This is an appropriate representation of the drought conditions during that year. However, it appears that 1996, which was a far less extreme summer, produced the maximum deficit at an earlier date and a more pronounced plateau. However, this was only achieved because of the restricted recovery in the previous winter. The actual increase in SMD in 1996 was only 155mm (from 153mm in March to 308mm by the end of June).

These problems are considered in further detail on page 131.

Comparison of SMD in different areas

Figure 8.9 identifies the MORECS squares in England and Wales; reference must be made to Hydrological Memorandum No. 45 for similar maps of Scotland and Northern Ireland.

If valid comparisons are to be made of the SMD in different parts of the country, care must be taken to define the method. MORECS 2.0 determines the median, 10%ile and 90%ile available water content for each square, and bases its calculations on one of these values (usually the median). This value will vary in the different squares, and this variation will confound any differences caused by weather conditions. Likewise, real land use, applied to either MORECS

1.0 or 2.0, will produce results which are influenced by the land use in the square, rather than just the weather conditions.

The results for the different squares which are shown in Figure 8.9 have therefore been obtained by identifying meteorological stations which provide data on rainfall and the Penman variables which are similar to the average for that square. Figure 8.9 identifies the location of the relevant stations used for this purpose, but in some cases additional stations have been used and an average value obtained. The calculation of SMD from site specific data of this sort is a service which can be provided by the Meteorological Office, but their calculations (at present) are based on MORECS 1.0. As a result, it will be noted that the 'deciduous trees' and medium available water content, as shown in Figure 8.9, produce a maximum SMD in 1989 of 175mm, compared with the 308mm obtained with version 2.0 for this same square and 'deciduous trees', and median available water content (see Figure 8.8). Not only are the peak values different with the two versions, but the whole shape of the curves in the histograms are radically different.

The results for the six locations shown in Figure 8.9 confirm the common observation that the driest weather, and greatest SMD, is likely in south east England; square 161 maintains the peak SMD of 175mm over a 7 week period. However, square 182 on the south coast and 101 on the east coast both reach the peak of 175mm, but only for a single week. The examples from north west and south west England (squares 97 and 189) have far lower peak values (123mm and 155mm respectively), with square 125 in Birmingham achieving a peak of 151mm.

Comparison between calculated and actual SMD

It should be anticipated that there will be a good correlation between SMD calculated from meteorological data and SMD measured in the field by neutron probe. Figure 8.10 demonstrates this, using lime tree 14 as an example. However, it must be appreciated that there are many limitations in correlating the research results with meteorological data.

For instance, calculated SMD gives no consideration to the differences between species, nor to variation between individuals of the same species (see Chapter 9, page 137 and 136). Different species or individuals would produce different correlation coefficients.

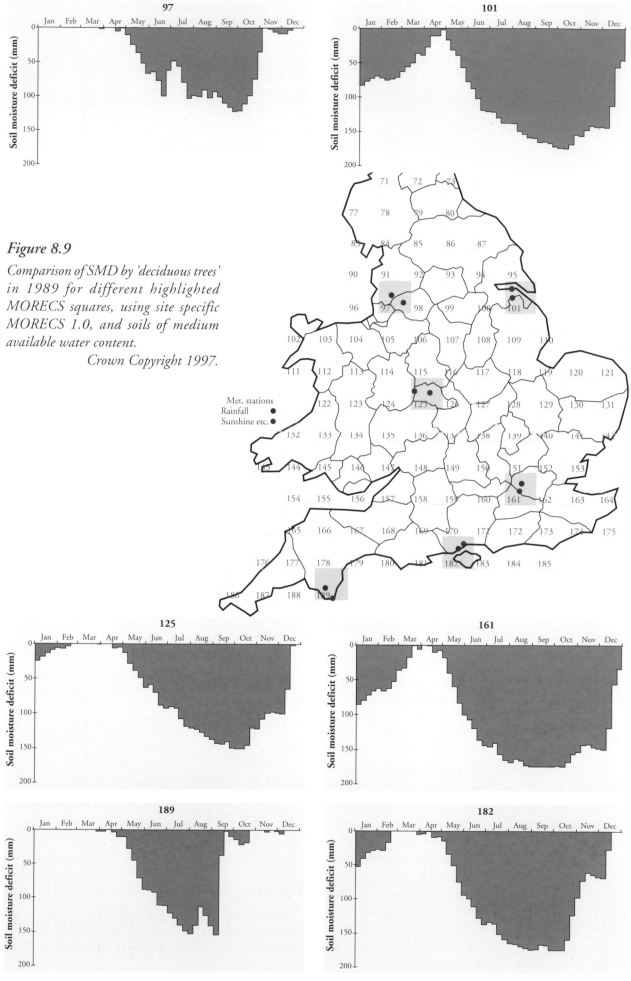

Figure 8.9

Comparison of SMD by 'deciduous trees' in 1989 for different highlighted MORECS squares, using site specific MORECS 1.0, and soils of medium available water content.

Crown Copyright 1997.

129

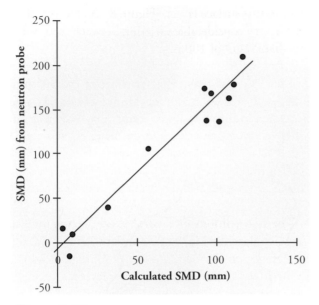

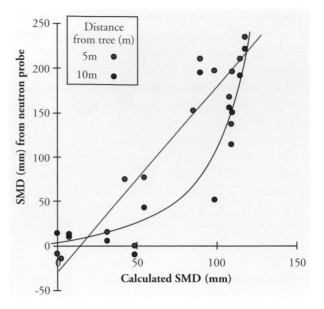

Figure 8.10

Correlation between SMD determined by calculation from meteorological data, and by neutron probe measurements (below 0.3m depth) at a distance of 2.4m from a lime tree on Oxford Clay (tree 14).

Figure 8.11

Correlation between SMD determined by calculation from meteorological data, and by neutron probe measurements (below 0.3m depth) at varying distance from a poplar tree on Boulder Clay (tree 33).

In addition, calculated SMD assumes that evaporation is uniform over the whole area. This is easy to appreciate for an extensive grass sward. The comparable conditions for calculating SMD for 'deciduous trees' implies a uniform woodland. It is probable that the neutron probe access tube closest to each tree should equate to these conditions, but the other more distant tubes are intended to show the diminishing effects with increasing distance from the tree, and should therefore correlate with a calculated SMD intermediate between trees and grass. Figure 8.11 shows this effect. At 5m from the tree there is a linear correlation, but at 10m the correlation is curvilinear, implying that the influence of the tree is less when the calculated SMD is small. This is consistent with the concept that soil drying by a tree starts in close proximity to the trunk and develops outwards and downwards. Although this example shows this effect, other trees produced different patterns.

For accurate correlations it would be desirable to have measurements over the full range of variation (for each tree and each access tube), distinguishing the development of the deficit during the summer from rehydration during the winter. This information is not available. For most trees, the only neutron probe measurements were in spring and autumn, providing only the minimum and maximum SMD. In only a few examples are there measurements showing the development of SMD thorough the season, and even these are at approximately monthly intervals; far shorter intervals would be preferable. Figures 8.10, 8.11 and 8.12 utilise the monthly readings taken on these trees in 1983 and 1984, but similar data is not available for most trees.

The neutron probe results were intended primarily to determine seasonal changes below foundation depth (most SMD results are calculated below 1.0m). Readings were taken to within 0.3m of the surface, but for practical reasons no attempt was made to record the

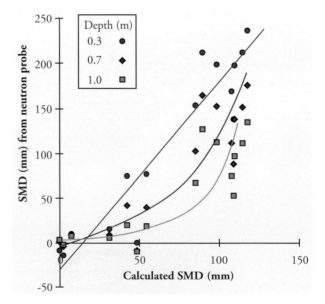

Figure 8.12

Correlation between SMD determined by calculation from meteorological data, and by neutron probe measurements below varying depths (at 5m from a poplar tree on Boulder Clay (tree 33).

moisture content and SMD from the surface down to 0.3m. It is this surface layer which will be particularly influenced by any small amounts of rainfall, and any correlation cannot take account of variation of the SMD within this layer. Figure 8.12 shows the correlation if the measured SMD readings are determined at different depths; as might be anticipated, the relationship becomes curvilinear with increasing depth. Figures 8.10 and 8.11 might provide an even better correlation if SMD could have been measured from the soil surface.

Limitations of calculated SMD

The introduction to this Chapter advocated the calculation of SMD from meteorological data as being the most relevant method if one wishes to compare the influence of a tree in different years or in different areas. The previous section has confirmed that there is a close correlation between calculated SMD and the determination of SMD by neutron probe. However, the previous section and other sections in this Chapter have drawn attention to various limitations in the use of calculated SMD. It is important that these limitations are appreciated.

Some of the differences between MORECS 1.0 and 2.0 have been described, particularly the very different peak values which are obtained for 'deciduous trees'. It has been noted that 'deciduous trees' embraces all species (except conifers and orchards), with no allowance for differences between species, nor variation between individuals. Figure 8.13 presents a frequency distribution diagram, recording the maximum SMD recorded by the neutron probe at the access tube closest to all of the trees in 1989 (or 1984 if readings for a tree were not taken in 1989). Allowance has been made for the lack of neutron probe readings in the surface 0.3m, by increasing the SMD for all of the trees by 45mm (i.e. it is assumed that there is 15% available

water in this surface layer). Figure 8.13 confirms that there is very considerable variation between trees, with a median SMD of 180mm.

This value of 180mm is far short of the 305mm used by MORECS 2.0 for 'deciduous trees' and a soil of median available water content. Likewise, it is far less than the 262mm for 'deciduous trees' and a soil with 10%ile available water content. It is, however, close to the MORECS 1.0 value of 175mm for 'deciduous trees' and medium available water capacity.

The two editions of Hydrological Memorandum 45 which describe MORECS versions 1.0 and 2.0 do not describe the basis for the values which they adopt for 'deciduous trees', nor the reason for the considerable increase in available water which is used in version 2.0. It is quite possible that 'deciduous trees' could produce an SMD of 305mm in a soil of median available water capacity, provided the soil conditions are conducive to root growth. However, as emphasised in Chapter 3 (page 28), clay soils tend to have low oxygen content and high mechanical impedance, making these soils hostile to root growth. These hostile conditions probably account for the modest values of soil suction which are recorded in clay soils (Chapter 4, page 58), reflecting the inability of roots to exploit all of the available water. However, it is not sufficient to overcome this problem by assuming that a clay soil has low available water content (in version 1.0) or the 10%ile value in version 2.0. The use of these values merely reduces the total available water, and allows the peak SMD to be reached even earlier (Figure 8.5). A better model might be achieved by reducing that percentage of the available water which is deemed to be 'easily available', but any such refinements of the MORECS model lie outside the scope of this book.

It is sufficient merely to note that the development of SMD through the season produced by MORECS 1.0 provides a better approximation to the seasonal development described in Chapter 5, (Figures 5.9, 5,10 and 5.11, pages 71 and 72). If requesting data from the Meteorological Office, under most circumstances the most useful results will be obtained by specifying SMD derived by MORECS 1.0, for 'deciduous trees', and either high or medium available water.

The previous section which contrasts the SMD in different years (page 126) has noted that, with version 2.0, if 'deciduous trees' achieve their maximum deficit in the summer, it is unlikely that winter rainfall will be sufficient to produce full recovery. In Figure

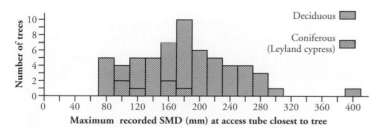

Figure 8.13

Frequency distribution of the maximum seasonal soil moisture deficit below the soil surface, as recorded in 1989 (or other driest year) by the access tubes closest to all 60 of the trees in the research project.

8.8, the only year to achieve full recovery of moisture content was 1995, with almost full recovery in 1979. By contrast, the dry winter of 1991/1992 meant that the deficit only reduced by 47mm, to a minimum of 261mm. This suggests the development of a persistent deficit. However, it would be incorrect to consider the residual deficit in the spring as a genuine persistent deficit. As emphasised in Chapter 6 (page 95), low soil permeability is the critical factor which governs the development of a persistent deficit; the MORECS model takes no account of this. Very few trees actually achieve the very large peak SMD postulated by MORECS 2.0; if a more appropriate peak SMD is used, such as the 180mm average shown in Figure 8.13, full recovery would be shown in most winters.

As well as rainfall figures, the Meteorological Office will provide most combinations of calculated data for any of the 40km squares, i.e. SMD, potential evaporation, actual evaporation and effective precipitation for any of the various crop types (or real land use) on any of the three soil types. Most of these calculations can also be provided for a single site, subject to availability of suitable rainfall records. Most calculations now use MORECS 2.0, but it should be possible to specify a preference for version 1.0. Their objective is to supply "what the customer wants and is prepared to pay for". Regrettably the cost of this information has risen dramatically in recent years.

As a *caveat*, it should be noted that each of the last four sets of data which I have obtained from the Meteorological Office have contained errors, either in some of the calculations or typographical, which were sufficiently obvious to spot. The possibility of other unseen errors cannot be discounted. It should also be noted that I have referred throughout to versions 1.0 and 2.0, implying that these are the only alterations. However, minor modifications have been made to each version, without this being apparent as an update to the decimal place. Similar modifications may occur in future, sufficient to invalidate comparison with results which have been obtained previously.

Global warming and climate change

The climate of a region is dynamic, and subject to constant change. The Ice Ages, which only finished about 10,000 years ago, caused a general lowering of temperature, and were also marked by extreme fluctuations associated with the advance and retreat of the ice-caps. Within a shorter period, historical records show lesser short-term fluctuations, whilst individual years can vary widely from the statistical average.

It is now recognized that, superimposed on these natural variations, the activities of man are beginning to alter the climate of the planet. The production of 'greenhouse' gases, primarily carbon dioxide, but also ozone, methane, nitrous oxide and halocarbons, is affecting the absorption and radiation of energy from the sun. It is predicted that this will cause an increase in global temperature, with consequential changes on many facets of the weather, including precipitation, humidity, radiation, and winds/storms.

The extent of these man-made changes, and their interaction with the unpredictable natural fluctuations, are very difficult to predict, and fall outside the scope of this book. Air and soil temperatures seem likely to rise, with the potential for increased evaporation. Rainfall may increase, but possibly with shorter heavier periods which may produce more run-off, and thus be less effective in replenishing moisture deficits.

There are obvious implications that the risks of tree root damage may increase, unless preventative action is taken (see Chapter 18). Altered conditions are also likely to increase the important benefit of trees in providing shade, as well as their minor but positive contribution to diminishing carbon dioxide levels.

Summary

1.   The extent of soil drying depends on the balance between input of water from rainfall, and extraction of water by evaporation from the soil and by vegetation. Rainfall is more variable than evaporation, but both must be considered.

2.   The factors which control evaporation can be modelled, based on meteorological data. Potential evaporation and rainfall data can be combined to estimate soil moisture deficit. This provides the best available model for comparing soil drying at different sites or times.

3.   The Meteorological Office can provide data for various crops type, including 'deciduous trees', using the MORECS system. The current version 2.0 provides a less satisfactory model for trees than the previous version 1.0. It should not be expected that the data will provide details of the spatial patterns of soil drying, but can be useful as a basis for comparisons.

4.   Long-term changes in weather patterns, either man-made or natural, can be expected to alter the patterns of soil drying, and the associated risks of tree root damage. The extent and timing of these changes are difficult to predict.

*Crack in flank wall allegedly consistent with involvement of adjacent lime tree -
Timing of crack movement inconsistent with seasonal soil movements - Gravel soil -
Level monitoring confirms no foundation movements occurring.*

The subject property forms the left hand end of a terrace of small two-storey houses with integral garages, built in 1978 (CS Figure 8.1). It is located in Hertfordshire. The Geological Survey map indicates that the subsoil in the locality should be Glacial Gravel overlying Upper Chalk, with Alluvial soils associated with a small stream outcropping to the south of the terrace. External layout is shown in CS Figure 8.2.

Previous history.

In 1981 a diagonal crack was first noted towards the front of the left hand flank wall, with this gradually increasing in width. In addition, there was cracking where the garage projected from the front of the house and in internal partition walls at first floor level, particularly those above a beam which spanned the full width of the house.

From May 1985 to May 1986 a surveyor acting for the owners monitored the building using Avonguard tell-tales, and alleged that these showed seasonal movement.

On the basis of this, a claim was submitted against the owner of the trees adjacent to the flank wall. In November 1986 I was instructed to act on behalf of the owner of the adjacent trees.

Case Study Figure 8.1

Lime tree adjacent to front corner of flank wall.

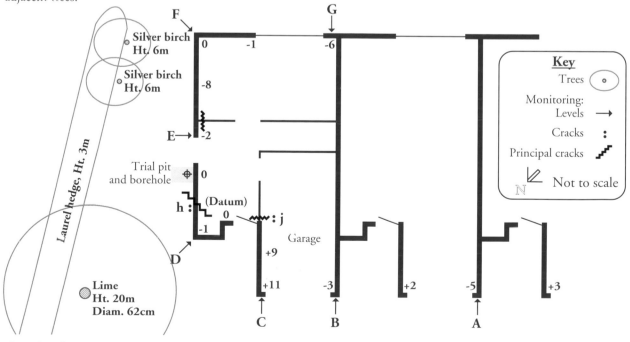

Case Study Figure 8.2

Site plan, including location of level monitoring stations and results of level distortion survey (mm), relative to arbitrary datum adjacent to the front door (for clarity levels are shown internally, although taken on external brickcourse).

The trees.

The most significant tree was a lime (*Tilia* x *europaea*) with a height of about 20m and diameter of 62cm, located 5.4m from the front corner of the flank wall.

In addition, there were two young small silver birch 3.2m from the rear of the flank wall and a 3m high laurel hedge parallel to the flank.

Level distortion survey.

Following my appointment I undertook a level distortion survey, the results of which are included in CS Figure 8.2. They show no significant trend in variation of level.

Foundation depth and soil conditions.

Following my appointment the owners excavated a trial pit adjacent to the flank wall. This showed that the brickwork extended to 1.95m below ground level, where it was supported on concrete footings which projected 0.5m from the wall. The trial pit was taken to a depth of 2.25m but did not expose the underside of the footings. The base of the hole was full of water in January.

The soil exposed in the trial pit was gravel. I extended the depth by hand auger to 2.65m where an impenetrable object, probably a large stone, was encountered which prevented further drilling.

Soil samples taken for particle size analysis by wet sieving gave the results shown in CS Figure 8.3.

Particle size	Depth	
	2.3 - 2.45m	2.45 - 2.65m
> 2000μm (gravel)	6.3%	33.8%
600-2000μm (coarse sand)	6.6%	8.8%
212-600μm (medium sand)	20.8%	18.9%
63-212μm (fine sand)	16.6%	10.1%
< 63μm (silt/clay)	49.8%	28.4%

Case Study Figure 8.3

Particle size analysis of soil samples from below trial pit.

Observation showed that the suspension of particles less than 63 μm settled very rapidly, indicating that the majority of these were silt rather than clay.

Monitoring.

On 3/11/86 I set up level monitoring around the periphery of the building, with an additional station on the front elevation of the adjacent block. I also set up crack monitoring on the main external cracks. The location of all of these stations is shown on CS Figure 8.2 and the results presented in CS Figure 8.4.

Changes in relative level (millimetres) between 3/11/86 and:-		
Station	12/1/87	7/5/87
A	Datum	Datum
B	-0.2	+0.1
C	-0.2	+0.1
D	-0.2	0
E	-0.2	+0.2
F	-0.2	+0.1
G	-0.4	0
Changes in crack width (μm), compared to 3/11/86:-		
h	+122	-170
j	+94	+76

Case Study Figure 8.4

Results of level and crack monitoring.

DISCUSSION.

Although the Surveyor had alleged seasonal movement during 1985/86, examination of his results showed no movement in the main crack in the flank wall prior to 2nd October with the crack then opening to 16th November and thereafter closing to 14th May. This opening of the crack was too late in the season to imply soil shrinkage.

It was apparent that the level distortion survey did not suggest any subsidence of the front corner and the gravel soil revealed by the trial hole and borehole also implied that soil shrinkage could not be occurring. However, the possibility remained that there could be a pocket of clay beneath the front of the flank with this causing the damage.

The level monitoring was able to show that no foundation movements were occurring. The recorded movements were all less than 0.4mm, and within the accuracy of the instrumentation. Furthermore, the minute apparent movement recorded between 3/11/86 and 12/1/87 was not consistent with the direction which could occur with seasonal soil drying. Likewise, the pattern of crack movement was not consistent with seasonal soil drying and rehydration.

On this basis the potential involvement of the tree was denied, and the claim was subsequently dropped. It was suggested that the damage to the internal wall could relate to the major beam supporting internal partition walls, but it was difficult to implicate this in the damage to the flank wall.

Subsequent to these events the owner extended the building, involving demolition of the flank wall. No further problems have occurred on the new foundations.

Lessons to be learnt.

- The legitimacy of claims that cracks movements are seasonal should always be carefully checked.

- The level monitoring was effective in showing that foundation movements were not occurring and that the tree could not be involved.

CHAPTER 9

COMPARATIVE EFFECTS OF DIFFERENT SPECIES, AND OF INDIVIDUAL TREES AND GROUPS

It is widely believed that a 'rank order' must exist, which indicates the ability of different species of tree to cause damage. Various lists of this sort have been produced, and are considered later in this Chapter.

Any such rank order can only be valid if species (or genera) differ in those parts of their genetic systems which control the patterns of soil drying, i.e. if there is inter-specific (or inter-generic) variation. If species differ as a result of their genetic systems, it must also be expected that individuals within the same species will vary (intra-specific variation). In addition to this variation which is under genetic control (genotypic variation), it can be expected that there will also be variation caused by differences in site conditions (phenotypic variation). The available evidence suggests that intra-specific variation and phenotypic variation are just as, if not more, significant than any inter-specific variation.

Phenotypic variation

Some trees are commonly grown as clones; that is they are vegetatively propagated and are genetically identical (i.e. akin to identical twins). Leyland cypress (X *Cupressocyparis leylandii*) is an example. This is an inter-generic hybrid between Monterey cypress (*Cupressus macrocarpa*) and Nootka cypress (*Chamaecyparis nootkatensis*). Although several different clones can be distinguished, the majority of trees are from one of two clones, 'Haggerston Grey' or 'Leighton Green'. These clones differ from each other genetically, but all of the individuals from the same clone will be identical. Any differences in the growth of individuals from the same clone must therefore be a result of any differences in site conditions, i.e. phenotypic variation.

The six Leyland cypress described in Volume 2 (trees 43 to 48) are all 'Haggerston Grey' and are therefore genetically identical. On the different soil types these identical trees produce very different patterns of soil drying (Figure 9.1); these differences illustrate the massive importance of site conditions in determining

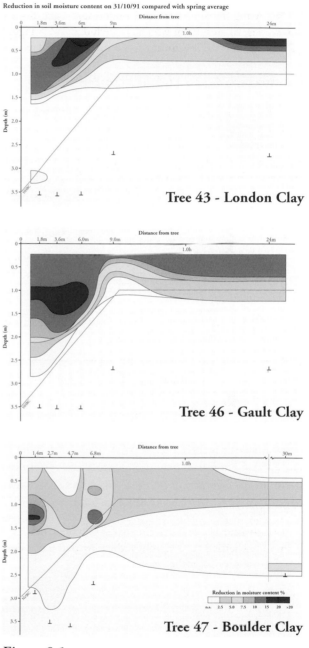

Figure 9.1

Genetically identical Leyland cypresses, growing on three different soil types, produce very different patterns of soil drying.

the patterns of soil drying. If examples were available from other soil types, there is no doubt that an even wider range would be apparent.

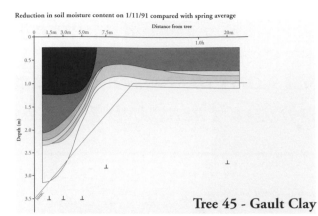

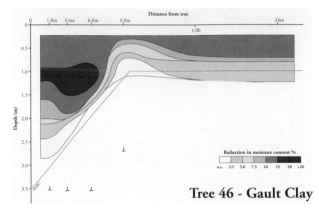

Figure 9.2

Even if genetically identical Leyland cypress are growing on an apparently very similar site (in this example only 30m apart on Gault Clay), they can produce different patterns of soil drying.

Even if soil conditions are apparently uniform, significant variation can occur. For instance, the two Leyland cypress on Gault Clay (trees 45 and 46), which are only 30m apart on a uniform site, produce patterns of soil drying which have some similarities but show important differences, particularly in the depth and lateral extent of drying (Figure 9.2). Volume 2 includes further details of these two trees (pages 234 to 245) which further illustrate their differences, in particular in the different patterns of persistent moisture deficit.

Plane trees are another species which are grown as clones. Although there are far more clones and it is difficult to distinguish between them, it is probable that all of the plane trees described in Volume 2 (Trees 49 - 60) are from the same clone. Prior to the different pruning regimes they were growing under very similar conditions, but despite this they produced different patterns of soil drying.

These examples, where any effects of genetic variation are eliminated, illustrate the extent of variation which occurs between individuals solely as a result of site conditions. They demonstrate that nurture, rather than nature, is a major factor in determining the variation which occurs. This phenotypic variation will be present whenever trees are being compared. It will therefore mask any attempts to identify the difference between individuals of the same species, or to compare different species.

Intra-specific variation

It is widely recognised that different clones of a species can differ in many of their physiological processes. For instance, Michael *et al.* (1990) demonstrated variation in whole tree photosynthetic production of two poplar clones, while Tang and Land (1995) showed differences in the timing of water uptake, xylem pressure potential, stomatal conductance and transpiration of different clones of plane trees. These differences between clones are a result of genetic differences.

The researchers used clonal stock for these experiments, as this allowed them to replicate the experiment and thereby distinguish whether differences were due to phenotypic variation or to differences between the clones. The clonal differences which they identified (as a result of genetic variation between the clones) will also be present between individuals of the same species which are grown from seed (i.e. they are examples of intra-specific variation). However, with seedling stock grown under field conditions, it is not possible to distinguish whether any variation which is revealed is a reflection of site or genetic differences.

Horse chestnut is a species which is commonly grown from seed, so that individuals will be subject to intra-specific variation. Figure 9.3 (overleaf) shows the diagrams of the seasonal fluctuations in soil moisture deficit at 1.0m depth for the four horse chestnuts on London Clay (trees 1 - 4), and also for the three horse chestnuts on Gault Clay (Trees 5 - 7). These soil conditions should be reasonably uniform, but this figure illustrates the considerable variation which can occur.

The other horse chestnuts on the Oxford and Boulder Clays show even greater variety. The diagrams in Volume 2 which show the spatial patterns of soil drying and soil moisture deficit for all of these trees further illustrate this variation.

Consideration of all of the other species in Volume 2 shows a similar variation between the individuals, but, as emphasized above, it is not possible to determine whether this variation should be attributed to site or to genetic differences between the individuals.

Is inter-specific variation to be expected?

The examples in the previous two sections illustrate the extent of phenotypic and intra-specific variation which can occur in the patterns of soil drying. Before going on to consider the potential difference between species (inter-specific variation), this section considers whether a reliable basis for identifying variation of this sort is likely to exist.

By definition, different species of tree (or indeed of any plants or animals) are normally unable to interbreed. The exact boundary between species or genera is often blurred, giving ample scope for a taxonomist to split or combine them, but the features which are used need to be clear cut and discreet. Characteristics of flower and fruit morphology are the most important for defining the species, but there are many other features which are linked to the evolutionary history, such as leaf shape or bud position, which are also relevant. Evolutionary history may also have involved development of special metabolic pathways, so that particular chemicals are present within related species. Details of this sort provide the definitive distinction between species, whereas more general differences exist between genera.

By contrast, there are many features which are of negligible value for identifying or distinguishing between species. These include some of the most obvious features of a tree, such as the general size and shape of the crown. Thus most species of tree, if growing in an open site, will develop with a compact and rounded crown because this is the most efficient shape for maximising the energy from sunlight. However, if the tree is growing in competition with others, it will grow with a taller and narrower crown. If this competition is on one side only, or if there is extreme and unilateral wind exposure, growth may be very asymmetric. If all conditions are optimum, growth may be very rapid, but if any factor is limiting, for instance a poor quality soil, it can reduce or even stop further growth. As a result there can be enormous variation in the size, shape and growth rate of a tree; for example, a mature oak may have a massive and broad crown or may be a stunted and etiolated object, or any other combination of size or shape.

Even if size and shape are ill-suited as a basis for classification, it might be suggested that, under a range of site conditions, different species will usually show a similar hierarchy in terms of their size and shape. For instance, oak or sycamore will usually be larger than birch or holly. However, under particular conditions this hierarchy may alter. For instance, in a dense wood-land site, oak may be larger than sycamore (although initial growth may be slower), and holly will flourish while birch may not tolerate the shade. By contrast on a cold exposed site, sycamore and possibly even birch will be larger than oak, whereas under conditions of heavy animal browsing only the holly may be able to survive.

This shows that these features of size and shape of the crown are determined primarily by site conditions rather than genetics. For this reason neither size nor general shape of a tree would provide a suitable basis for distinguishing between species. This is not to deny that there are also subtle differences in general shape which enable the practised eye to distinguish most species of tree at a distance, regardless of the conditions under which the tree has been growing. With some tree species these differences may not appear to be so subtle; for instance the tall fastigiate shape of the Lombardy poplar is widely recognised. However, this shape is not a reliable indicator of the species, as there are other species, such as Dawyck beech, which have a generally similar shape but which have no relationship to Lombardy poplars.

It is easy to see and appreciate that the size and shape of the crown is very variable and so does not provide a suitable basis for distinguishing between species. It is known that root growth is strongly influenced by environmental factors and so, even though the root system cannot be seen, it should be expected that the extent of the root system and the intensity of soil drying will be very variable. It can also be expected that much of this variation will be totally unrelated to species differences, and that different species will impose only minor and subtle variations, or with any such differences varying dependent on the site conditions.

Although site conditions, rather than species differences, are of paramount importance in determining the overall form of the crown and root system, there will be some aspects which are under tight genetic control and where clear species differences might exist. For instance, the tolerance of some species to anaerobic conditions is based on a metabolic pathway which enables the root to switch to anaerobic respiration. This pathway is likely to be under a simple genetic control, and so any species with the relevant genes will have this ability. In those situations where soil oxygen levels are the limiting factor for growth, these species should be able to maintain root activity and could therefore produce additional soil drying. However, this difference would only be apparent in those situations where it is oxygen, rather than some other

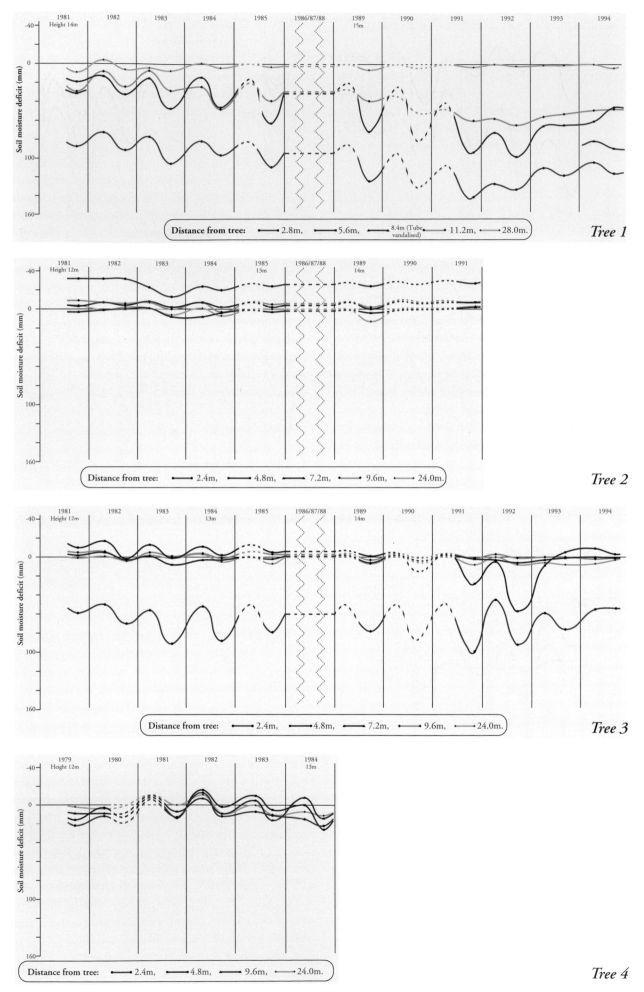

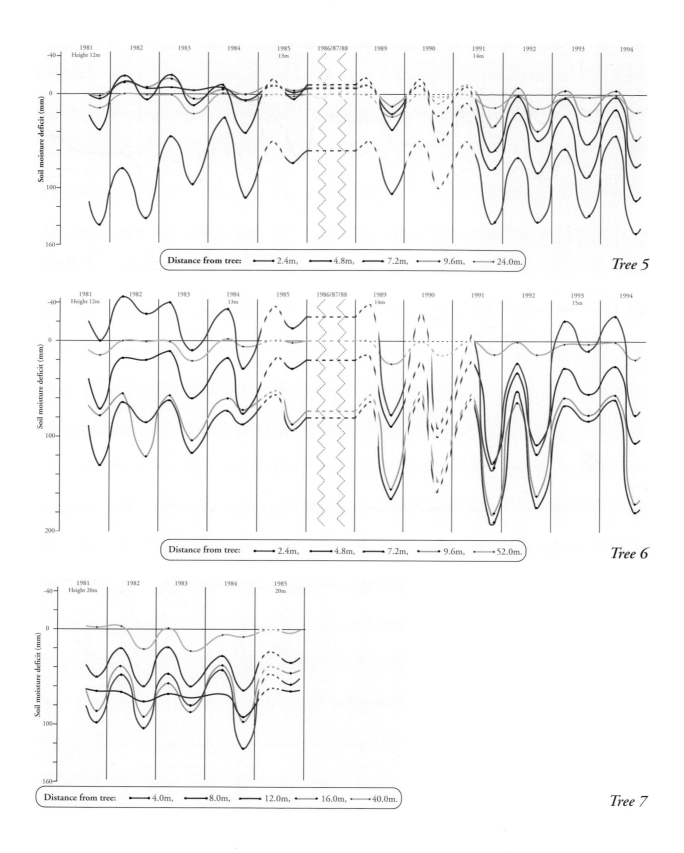

Figure 9.3

Seasonal fluctuation in soil moisture deficit at 1.0m depth for the four horse chestnuts growing on London clay (trees 1 - 4, opposite) and for the three horse chestnuts on Gault Clay (trees 5 - 7, above). These diagrams illustrate the very variable patterns of soil drying which can occur even with the same species on similar clay.

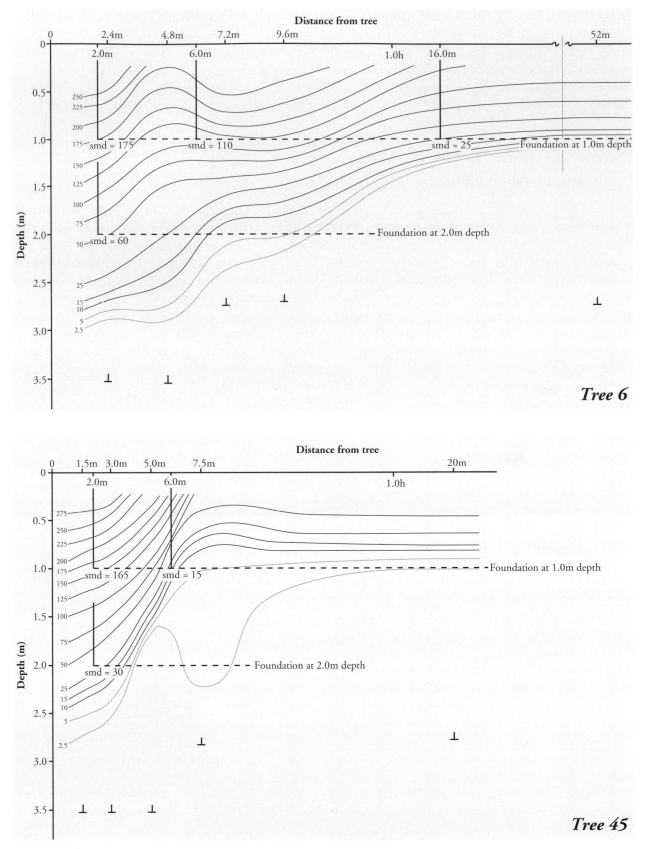

Figure 9.4

Contrasting patterns of soil drying in the proximity to two trees of different species on Gault Clay, demonstrating that angular distortion (caused by soil shrinkage induced by the soil moisture deficit) is dependent on the depth of the foundations and their proximity to the tree. Tree 6 is horse chestnut; Tree 45 is Leyland cypress.

factor, which is limiting. As there are many different factors which might be limiting, all of which will be under varying genetic control, it can be anticipated that any inter-specific differences which do exist may vary, depending on which factors are most relevant to the site.

Criteria for comparing effect of different species on soil and buildings

If different species of tree are to be compared, there must be suitable criteria on which to base such comparison. Volume 2 of this book describes the patterns of soil drying which can occur in the proximity of different species, which suggests that these patterns might provide a suitable criterion. If the patterns were of the same general shape but differed in magnitude, this might provide a suitable means of comparison.

However, comparison of the diagrams in Figure 9.4, which show the soil moisture deficit in autumn 1991 for a Leyland cypress (tree 45) and a horse chestnut (tree 6), both on Gault Clay, demonstrates the very different patterns which can occur. In both cases the deficits very close to the tree are similar, but the radial extent is totally different. These patterns would produce totally different risks of damage to a structure, depending on how close it is, on the depth of the foundations and on its vulnerability to angular distortion.

Thus, if a building with a 1.0m deep foundation extended to within 6m of tree 6, there would be a deficit of about 110mm below foundation level, reducing to 25mm at a distance of 16m. If the soil has a water shrinkage factor of 3, this would produce a differential movement of 28mm (between the foundations at 6m and 16m from the tree). Over the 10m length, this would create an angular distortion 1 : 357, which might be just within the tolerance of the building. If that same foundation was at the same distance from tree 45, it would be subject to only 15mm deficit, creating negligible angular distortion. However, if a 1.0m deep foundation extended to within 2m of these two trees, the deficits would be very similar for both (175mm for tree 6 and 165 for tree 45), but the angular distortion by tree 6 would only increase to 1 : 280, whereas near tree 45 it would be 1 : 80 with an attendant far higher risk of damage. By contrast, if the foundation was 2m deep, at a distance of 2m from tree 6 the deficit would be 60mm, compared to 30mm for tree 45; i.e. a lesser risk for tree 45.

This illustrates that the relative positions of these two species in a rank order would depend on the criteria which are used. It also suggests that potential criteria might be:

- radial extent of root influence;

- vertical extent of root influence;

- angular distortion as a result of root influence.

Simple criteria of this sort are being controlled by a whole variety of different and interacting factors, some of which may be under genotypic and others under phenotypic control. Thus, the vertical extent of root activity may depend on the requirement of the roots for oxygen, on their tolerance to carbon dioxide or waterlogging, on the interaction of the roots with the soil structure or soil temperature gradients, or on the ability of the root to penetrate the soil, with this being influenced by soil voids, etc.. The reaction of different species to all of these factors is likely to vary depending on the local soil conditions.

For these reasons it should be anticipated that, if we had the knowledge, very different hierarchy would be produced, dependent on the criteria adopted.

Despite these potential problems, attempts have been made to categorise species in various ways, in particular in respect of:

- radial extent of root influence;

- propensity to cause damage;

- "water demand".

These are considered in further detail in the following sections.

Rank order based on radial spread of roots

Since 1971, data have been collected by the Royal Botanic Gardens, Kew in association with root samples submitted for identification. This is commonly referred to as the Kew Tree Root Survey. The results were first published in 1981 in the book "Tree Roots and Buildings" (Cutler and Richardson, 1981). In 1989 this book was extensively revised to include additional data concerned with the spread of roots from trees reported as having caused or contributed to damage, and also to include additional data from Dr I.B.K. Richardson from his business practice of Richardson

Botanical Identifications (Cutler and Richardson, 1989). Reference should be made to this book for the full details of the survey.

The survey was based primarily on data supplied by loss adjusters, surveyors, structural engineers, arboriculturists, etc. who had sent in roots for identification. They were asked to complete a simple survey card giving details of the tree species, estimated tree height, root diameter, whether the tree was believed to be involved in damage to a building, drive or wall, together with the distance of the tree from that structure. Other details about where the tree was growing, the soil type and the shape of the root system were also sought.

The data which were collected provide valuable information, but have important limitations which must be recognised. In particular, completion of the survey cards could give rise to differences of interpretation, with this compounded by the large number of individuals who completed the cards. For instance, the survey card asked for the 'Distance [of the tree] from building drive or wall'. This was variously interpreted as being the distance from the tree to the trial hole from which the root was taken (which might be closer), the distance to the nearest part of the building (even if that part was not damaged, so that the relevant distance may be greater), or the distance to the furthest part of damage (which may be influenced more by a weak spot in the structure, rather than the maximum distance of root activity). Despite this variation in interpretation, it is this distance which was used as the basis for all of the calculations which relate distance of the tree to the incidence of damage.

The varying disciplines of the individuals who completed the cards also creates potential errors. In particular, many non-arboriculturists were unable to correctly identify trees in the vicinity, and even less able to identify stumps of trees removed in the past. For these reasons there is sometimes doubt whether the tree for which records were taken was necessarily the relevant individual. Estimates of tree height (which were requested but are not quoted in the results) were often subject to considerable error.

The survey did not seek any information on the depth of foundations, nor the depth from which the root samples were taken. Very often the roots which were taken for identification were from comparatively shallow depth, and may have been growing in the fill soil adjacent to the foundations, rather than below foundation level. Such roots are of dubious relevance. In addition, many of the buildings which suffered damage were older houses on shallow foundations; the results may not be relevant to modern properties with deeper foundations.

The results which they presented include:

- maximum tree-to-damage distance recorded for the species or genus. As the authors note, this is the extreme for the data, with only a very small proportion near this maximum;

- the distance which encompasses 90% of the recorded cases. This eliminates the extremes associated with the maximum distance, but is far greater than the average distance at which damage occurred;

- a table with the distances which encompass 90%, 75%, 50% and 25% of the recorded cases;

- a graph showing the accumulated percentage of cases with increasing proximity to the tree (see Figure 18.3, page 305). This graph also specifies the distance within which 50% of cases occurred.

Detailed results, including this and other data, are given for 17 different species or species groupings. Reference should be made to the book for the full details. Figure 9.5 summarises these results in graphical form, listing the trees in rank order to allow comparison of the different species. It clearly shows that the maximum distance is far greater, and also subject to far greater variance, than the distance which encompasses 90% of cases. By contrast, the distance within which 50% of cases occurred is very compact.

These criteria for determining a rank order show contrasting results. For instance, both willow and false acacia have 50% of their cases occurring within 8m of the tree. However, 90% of cases for willow are within 18m, whereas this distance has only increased to 10m for the false acacia. The difference between the maximum recorded distances is even greater (40m for willow compared to 12.4m for false acacia). Likewise, cypress appears in mid-table for the maximum recorded distance, but at the bottom of each of the other tables.

In addition to the 17 species which receive a detailed analysis, Cutler and Richardson (1989) also include brief entries for 13 species for which there were insufficient data for this full analysis. This includes the maximum recorded distance (shown in Figure 9.6), but no other distances.

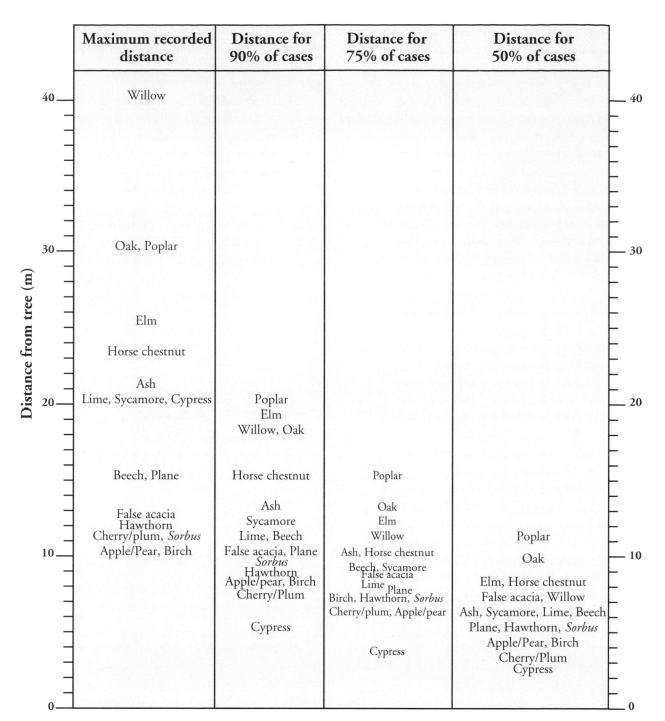

Maximum recorded distance	Distance for 90% of cases	Distance for 75% of cases	Distance for 50% of cases
Willow			
Oak, Poplar			
Elm			
Horse chestnut			
Ash			
Lime, Sycamore, Cypress	Poplar		
	Elm		
	Willow, Oak		
Beech, Plane	Horse chestnut	Poplar	
False acacia	Ash	Oak	
Hawthorn	Sycamore	Elm	
Cherry/plum, *Sorbus*	Lime, Beech	Willow	Poplar
Apple/Pear, Birch	False acacia, Plane	Ash, Horse chestnut	Oak
	Sorbus	Beech, Sycamore	
	Hawthorn	False acacia	Elm, Horse chestnut
	Apple/pear, Birch	Lime	False acacia, Willow
	Cherry/Plum	Plane	Ash, Sycamore, Lime, Beech
		Birch, Hawthorn, *Sorbus*	Plane, Hawthorn, *Sorbus*
		Cherry/plum, Apple/pear	Apple/Pear, Birch
	Cypress		Cherry/Plum
		Cypress	Cypress

Figure 9.5

Table showing rank order of radial influence of different species of tree based on records of the distance between the tree and damaged structure. The four columns are obtained from differing analysis of the same data, and in each case are spaced vertically to show the relevant distance from the tree.

(Derived from Cutler and Richardson, 1989)

Species	Distance (m)
Hornbeam	17
Locust	15
Elder, Walnut, Pine	
Laburnum	
Fig, Magnolia, Yew	5
Alder, Lilac	4
Hazel, Holly, Pagoda, Tree of Heaven, Monkey puzzle	3
Firs	2
Redwoods	1

Figure 9.6

Supplement to column 1 of Figure 9.5, showing maximum recorded distance for species for which there are insufficient data for full analysis.

Rank order based on propensity to cause damage

BRE Digest 298 provides a rank order of the risk of damage by different species. It is stated that this is derived from the Kew Root Survey, but the method of analysis is neither defined nor readily apparent. It is reproduced in column 1 of Figure 9.7.

The Kew Root Survey itself provides data on the number of records of each species causing damage, expressed as a percentage of the total number of records of damage. This rank order is shown in column 2 of Figure 9.7. This percentage frequency is likely to be influenced by the overall abundance of the species, with common species obviously more likely to be recorded. Allowance for this can be made by comparing the occurrence of trees which cause damage with their overall occurrence in the population. The Kew Root survey includes data on the occurrence of different species in the overall population, derived from the planting records of the London Boroughs. Using these data, column 3 of Figure 9.7 provides the rank order of the frequency of the species to cause damage as a ratio of its planting frequency. In this analysis, a ratio of 1 means that the percentage frequency for causing damage (as shown in column 2 of Figure 9.7), is the same as the percentage occurrence of that species in the overall tree population. Thus oak provides 11.5% of the cases of damage (column 2) but only comprises 2.1% of the overall population, giving it a ratio of 5.5 in column 3 (i.e. it is 5.5 times more likely to cause damage than the average).

As about 80% of all urban trees are likely to be found on land in private ownership (Land Use Consultants, 1993), local authority planting records may not be a suitable source for this information. An alternative source is provided by Trees in Towns (Land Use Consultants, 1993), which includes data on the overall proportion of the different species groups found in a sample selection of 66 towns and villages scattered throughout England. Column 4 of Figure 9.7 provides the rank order of the frequency of the species to cause damage as a ratio of frequency in this survey. This survey does not distinguish species which comprise less than 2% of the overall population, instead grouping these under the heading of 'Other'; to allow a calculation, each of these species have been assumed to comprise 1% of the overall population.

Oak stands out at the top of this table regardless of the method of analysis, and birch and *Sorbus* are consistently near the bottom, but other species occupy very different positions. Obviously the differences between columns 3 and 4 merely reflect the differences in the method of estimating the proportion of that species in the overall tree population.

1	2		3		4	
BRE Digest 298	Occurrence (% of total damage records)		Ratio relative to London Borough planting records		Ratio relative to 'Trees in Towns'	
Oak	Oak	11.5	Oak	5.5	Oak*	11.5
Poplar	Plane	11.0	Poplar	2.9	Plane*	11.0
Lime	Poplar	8.7	Ash	2.5	Poplar*	8.7
Ash	Sycamore	8.3	Acacia	1.7	Acacia*	3.0
Plane	Lime	8.2	Horse ch'nut	1.3	Horse ch'nut*	2.9
Willow	Ash	7.5	Hawthorn	1.3	Lime	2.7
Elm	Cherry	6.4	Lime	1.3	Elm*	2.0
Hawthorn	Willow	5.7	Willow	1.3	Willow	1.9
Sycamore	Apple	5.7	Beech	1.0	Ash	1.9
Cherry	Hawthorn	4.6	Plane	0.8	Apple	1.4
Beech	Acacia	3.0	Apple	0.8	Sycamore	1.0
Birch	Cypress	3.0	Sycamore	0.6	Beech*	1.0
Sorbus	Horse ch'nut	2.9	Cherry	0.4	Hawthorn	0.9
Cypress	*Sorbus*	2.3	Birch	0.3	Cherry	0.8
	Elm	2.0	Cypress	0.3	*Sorbus*	0.5
	Birch	1.5	*Sorbus*	0.2	Birch	0.3
	Beech	1.0			Cypress	0.1

Figure 9.7

Various derivations of rank order based on propensity to cause damage.
Column 1: BRE Digest 298, based on Kew Root Survey.
Columns 2-4 derived from Kew Root Survey (see text for details).
* No specific data; assumed that species comprises 1% of population.

An alternative approach for determining a rank order was adopted by Reynolds and Alder (1980). They conducted a 'Delphi' analysis in which a questionnaire was sent out to 50 professionals, from a variety of disciplines, all of whom were involved in assessment of cases of tree root damage. The respondents were asked to provide a subjective opinion by giving a numerical score of risk for a whole range of features, one of which was the likelihood of damage associated with 17 species of tree. There were 18 replies with varying degrees of completeness. Overall, tree species was considered to be the second most relevant feature for determining the risk (the geological formation was the most relevant).

If all of the responses are used, the species can be placed into the following rank order from the greatest mean risk of damage to the least: poplar, willow, elm†, oak†, plane†, sycamore†, ash†, lime†, horse chestnut, whitebeam†‡, Prunus‡, maple, birch, conifers/alders‡, holly‡. (Species marked with an ‡ were less often within the experience of individuals, and species which received a rather equivocal score are marked with a † (especially was this true of whitebeam and elm)).

Many of these replies omitted some or all of the species, but if a statistical F test is made on the 13 replies which listed 7 of the commoner species, the rank order shown in Figure 9.8 is achieved (Reynolds - personal communication). This figure shows the mean score and the least significant difference (i.e. the vertical bars indicate the species whose difference cannot be statistically distinguished).

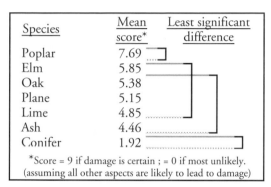

Species	Mean score*	Least significant difference
Poplar	7.69	
Elm	5.85	
Oak	5.38	
Plane	5.15	
Lime	4.85	
Ash	4.46	
Conifer	1.92	

*Score = 9 if damage is certain ; = 0 if most unlikely. (assuming all other aspects are likely to lead to damage)

Figure 9.8

Likelihood of seven common trees to be associated with damage to adjacent buildings, as determined by Delphi analysis. From Reynolds (Personal Communication)

A similar analysis on the 6 replies which included all 17 species provides the rank order shown in Figure 9.9. In these analyses the statistical effect of respondents and species was highly significant (the first merely illustrating the fact that different experts used consistently different scores). This demonstrates that these scores may be viable for determining a rank order, but should not be used as absolute values of risk.

In any analysis of this sort it is difficult to know whether the response by the experts reflects their own practical experience, or whether they are prejudiced by previously published data.

Rank order based on 'water demand'

When making recommendations to the National House-Building Council for the revision of what was then Practice Note 3, I advocated a classification of tree species based on their 'water demand' (Biddle 1981b). This term was subsequently embodied in NHBC Practice Note 3, (1985). For the purposes of the Practice Note it was a useful and simple phrase to present to builders (who are the prime target of the

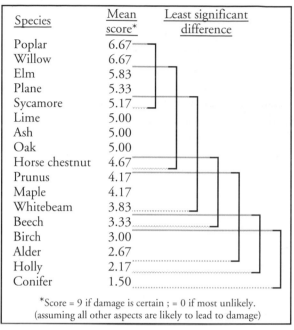

Species	Mean score*	Least significant difference
Poplar	6.67	
Willow	6.67	
Elm	5.83	
Plane	5.33	
Sycamore	5.17	
Lime	5.00	
Ash	5.00	
Oak	5.00	
Horse chestnut	4.67	
Prunus	4.17	
Maple	4.17	
Whitebeam	3.83	
Beech	3.33	
Birch	3.00	
Alder	2.67	
Holly	2.17	
Conifer	1.50	

*Score = 9 if damage is certain ; = 0 if most unlikely. (assuming all other aspects are likely to lead to damage)

Figure 9.9

Likelihood of 17 species to be associated with damage to adjacent buildings, as determined by Delphi analysis. From Reynolds (Personal Communication)

Practice Note) the concept that species differ in their ability to cause drying of a clay subsoil. It is a term which has subsequently been widely adopted and is commonly used to describe the different effects of tree species.

The meaning of water demand has not previously been defined. Although it might appear to describe a similar concept, it would be incorrect to equate it to the suction exerted by roots. In temperate climates, suction is fairly similar for all species, with a maximum of about 1500 kPa, and so does not provide a suitable basis for classification. Instead I suggest that, in the context in which the phrase is commonly used, **water demand should be defined as the ability of vegetation to cause drying of a clay subsoil.** This definition seeks to take account of all of the factors which influence soil drying, such as the suction applied by the roots and the ability of the roots to exploit the hostile environment of a clay soil. The definition specifies clay, as the ability to dry other soils may be very different and not necessarily relevant, and it also specifies subsoil, as behaviour in surface soils (above foundation level) is also of limited relevance to buildings.

The patterns of soil moisture deficit in proximity to trees, such as those shown in Figure 9.4 and also for each of the trees in Volume 2, show the ability of these individual trees to cause drying of the clay subsoil, i.e. their water demand. However, as noted in respect of Figure 9.4, the patterns of drying can be very different and so any classification of damage risk ideally should take account of the depth and the radial extent of soil drying, and the angular distortion induced as a result.

As the term 'water demand' was coined for NHBC Practice Note 3 (1985), it is to be expected that these guidelines (and their subsequent revision as NHBC Standards Chapter 4.2) will come nearest to providing a classification based on this criterion. These guidelines classify all broad-leafed trees into either high, moderate or low water demand, and conifers into either high or moderate water demand. The foundation depths which are advocated by the guidelines at varying distance from a tree are illustrated by Figure 9.10 (for a soil with a plasticity index greater than 40).

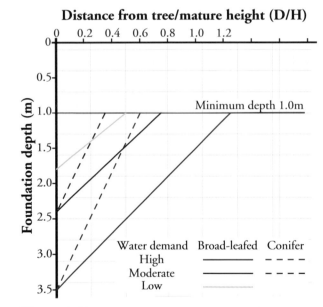

Figure 9.10

Foundation depths recommended in NHBC Standards Chapter 4.2 for trees of differing water demand growing on soils of high shrinkage potential.

For a high water demand tree the NHBC guidelines advocate a foundation depth of 3.5m in immediate proximity to a tree, with the depth gradually diminishing within a radial extent of 1.25 x mature tree height. For a moderate water demand tree the depth in proximity to a tree is 2.4m, diminishing within a radial extent of 0.75 x tree height, and for a low water demand tree the corresponding depth is 1.8m and radial extent is 0.5 x tree height. This classification therefore takes some account of both the depth and radial

extent of influence of the tree. Figure 9.10 also includes the recommended foundation depths for the two categories of conifer, and demonstrates how, by altering the slope of the line, the concept takes some account of the angular distortion as a result of root activity. Thus, for high water demand conifers and broad-leafed trees the maximum depth is the same (3.5m), but for conifers the radial extent is only 0.6 x tree height, compared with 1.25 x tree height for the broad-leafed genera.

The results from Volume 2 emphasise the variation between individual trees and certainly do not provide nearly enough examples to classify trees, even into a simple 3-stage classification of this sort. Instead the allocation of species to the three NHBC categories of water demand was essentially subjective, based in part on the research but more on past experience of NHBC and cases of damage investigated by various practitioners (Biddle 1981b). Appendix 4.2-B of NHBC Standards Chapter 4.2 (1992) provides the full details of the allocation, but Figure 9.11 provides a simplified version (note that it is to generic, rather than species, level).

High	*Moderate*	*Low*
Broad-leafed trees		
Elm	All	Beech
Eucalyptus	other	Birch
Oak	genera	Holly
Poplar		Magnolia
Willow		Mulberry
Conifers		
Cypresses	All others.	

Figure 9.11

NHBC classification of water demand of genera.

It is apparent that the majority of genera are lumped together within the moderate category. These genera have been distinguished from those which are most or least likely to cause damage, which are allocated into the high and low categories respectively. Ideally it might be desirable to differentiate between all species. (See also Chapter 18, page 306).

I have previously produced a list of the rank order of water demand of different species, based on my personal experience (Biddle, 1979). This included comparison with similar lists by Ward (1947) based on his experience, primarily in south east England and by Hammer and Thompson (1966), based on their north American experience. This comparison is reproduced in Figure 9.12. The low rank of oak and the high rank of alder in Ward's list are at particular variance with current opinion.

On the basis of my further experience, I would now modify my previous list. Figure 9.13 presents a six stage classification, based on my current tentative and subjective opinions. As with the NHBC classification, this distinguishes between broad-leafed trees and conifers, in recognition that these two groups generally have a different pattern of radial influence (i.e. a different slope to the line in Figure 9.10). It is probable that the ideal classification should also recognize a range of slopes applicable to each of these six categories (rather than just distinguishing between broad-leafed and coniferous trees), but any attempt at this would be beyond the current state of knowledge.

Those species of tree which grow to the largest size will tend to have the greatest radial spread of roots and might therefore be expected to have the highest water demand. McCombie (1993) recognised this, and used unpublished data on tree height from the Kew Root Survey to analyse the distance to damage : height (d/h) ratio. To make allowance for the height, he normalised the data by dividing the height of the individual tree (h) by the maximum height for the species (h_{max}). Figure 9.14 presents the results, combining observations from all of the tree species. In this Figure, data near the base of the graph (i.e. for trees which are very close to the building relative to the tree height) are of limited interest for determining the influence of a tree - it is the data from the outer limits of potential influence of

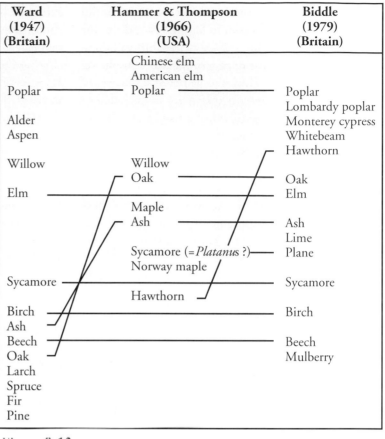

Figure 9.13

Comparison of lists by different authors showing rank order of water demand of different species of tree.

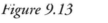

Highest water demand (deepest and furthest extent)					Lowest water demand (shallowest and least extent)
Broad-leafed genera					
Eucalyptus	*Crataegus*	*Aesculus*	*Acer*	*Ailanthus*	*Catalpa*
Populus	*Salix*	*Fraxinus*	*Castanea*	*Alnus*	*Corylus*
Quercus	*Sorbus* (simple-leafed)	*Platanus*	*Fagus*	*Betula*	*Ficus*
	Ulmus	*Tilia*	*Malus*	*Carpinus*	*Liquidambar*
			Prunus	*Gleditsia*	*Liriodendron*
			Pyrus	*Ilex*	*Magnolia*
			Robinia	*Juglans*	*Morus*
			Sorbus (compound-leafed)	*Laburnum*	*Sambucus*
Coniferous genera					
Cupressus	*Chamaecyparis* x *Cupressocyparis*	*Sequoiadendron*	*Cedrus* *Thuja*	*Juniperus* *Taxus* *Tsuga*	*Abies* *Araucaria* *Ginkgo* *Larix* *Picea* *Pinus*

Figure 9.13

A tentative classification of the 'water demand' of different genera, based on my current opinion. The distinction between Sorbus with simple or compound leaves may be because those with simple leaves (e.g. S. aria) are often grafted onto Crataegus rootstock; it is probably the rootstock rather than the leaf type which controls any difference.

the trees in the upper parts of the graph which are of greatest relevance. McCombie suggests that 5% of the data in the upper scatter should be rejected as potentially anomalous or extreme results, and that the remaining 95% of data (k_{95}) will lie below a line with a slope of -0.7. A line with this slope in included in Figure 9.14, but examination of this Figure suggests that a much steeper slope, of about -1.4, would provide a better fit to the data.

A negative slope, whether -0.7 or some other value, demonstrates that trees of smaller size will tend to have an influence at proportionally greater distance than larger specimens. McCombie suggests that this is due to a change in leaf distribution within the canopy as the tree matures, with small trees having leaves throughout their canopy, whilst large trees only have leaves on the outer surface. Alteration in the root:shoot ratio as the tree matures provides a simpler explanation.

McCombie further suggested that a slope of -0.7 is applicable to all species. The higher this line intercepts the X (left hand) axis, the greater the potential influence of the tree, and he proposed the value of this intercept as a more reliable measure of the relative water demand of different species. If this method was valid, it would produce a rank order of (with values of the k_{95} intercept in brackets): *Pyrus* (2.00), *Salix* (1.92), *Prunus* (1.85), *Malus* (1.85), *Crataegus* (1.65), *Quercus* (1.64), *Sorbus* (1.42), *Aesculus* (1.41), *Tilia* (1.41), *Ulmus* (1.41), *Acer* (1.40), *Fagus* (1.38), *Robinia* (1.28), *Fraxinus* (1.26), *Betula* (1.24), *Platanus* (1.17). However, it is pertinent to question the values of h_{max} which McCombie adopted, and also his assumption that the slope of the line for all species was the same (-0.7). Considerable differences from his proposed rank order can be obtained by using more appropriate values for h_{max} or the slope.

Although detailed analysis of this sort is not reliable, it is apparent from Figure 9.14 that it is the high water demand trees (as defined by NHBC) which tend to be distributed in the upper and right parts of the graph, with the low water demand in the bottom and left parts, thus confirming their status. The main exceptions are the various species of fruit tree (*Prunus,*

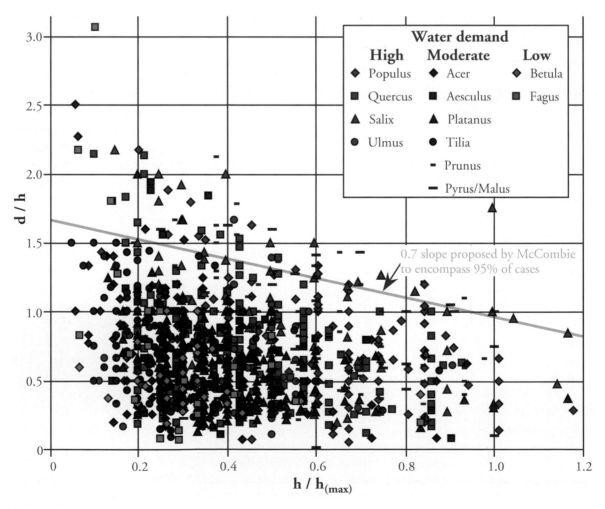

Figure 9.14

Graph, derived from unpublished data of the Kew Root Survey, plotting the ratio of distance to damage : height against the ratio height : maximum height, for various tree species.　　　*Derived from McCombie (1993).*

Malus and *Pyrus*), which are categorised as moderate water demand but have a similar distribution to the high water demand species.

Another method of classification is provided by Lawson (1995). He quite reasonably criticised the use of the term "water demand", but instead proposed a classification based on the capability of roots to exploit the potential rooting volume. For this purpose he proposed that trees are classified as obligate deep-rooting species, facultative deep-rooting species and shallow rooting species. It is questionable whether this distinction is valid, and it pays no regard to lateral root spread nor to the intensity of soil drying. Furthermore, as his allocation of species to these three categories appears virtually identical to the NHBC categories of high, moderate and low water demand, the classification serves no practical purpose. Whilst water demand is not an ideal term, this proposal advocating other equally inappropriate terms is merely confusing.

Stock / scion interaction

Many trees are grown by grafting onto a suitable rootstock. It is well known from work with fruit trees that the root stock can have a major influence on the growth of the crown, producing varying degrees of dwarfing or enhanced growth. It can be expected that this will produce very different patterns of soil drying.

Many ornamental trees are also grown by grafting. For instance, whitebeam (*Sorbus aria*) is often grafted onto hawthorn (*Crataegus*) rootstock as it tends to be unstable on its own roots. In my experience this stock/scion combination tends to produce very severe soil drying, comparable or worse than hawthorn when it is grown on its own roots. By contrast, other species of *Sorbus*, for instance the many varieties of mountain ash which are normally grown on *S. aucuparia* rootstock, are very rarely involved in damage. It would require specific investigations to confirm whether the severe soil drying induced by *S. aria* is due to the scion (irrespective of the rootstock), or to the influence of the *Crataegus* stock. Similar stock / scion interactions may exist with many other species which are grown in this way, but there is no information on the patterns of soil drying which may occur as a result.

The effects of rows and groups of trees

Ward (1953) investigated cases of damage to buildings by trees, and plotted the distance of the tree from the damage, against the tree height. On the basis of this he suggested that buildings with shallow foundations should be kept away from trees to a distance equal to the height of the mature tree (see also Chapter 18). On the basis of this analysis he further proposed that, in the case of dense rows of trees with paved areas adjoining the building, trees should be kept at a distance from buildings in excess of 1.5 x tree height. This concept of increased radial influence of rows and groups of trees was subsequently embodied in BRE Digest 63 (1965), and in the initial edition of NHBRC Practice Note 3 (1969) (although note that the reference to dense rows and to intervening paving was omitted in these publications). The subsequent revision of NHBC Practice Note 3 (1974) further modified this concept by requiring a 50% increase in depth of foundations where trees are in rows or groups.

However, the original proposal that there is an increased effect of rows or groups does not stand up to statistical analysis. Furthermore, subsequent investigations, for instance the Kew Root Survey, concluded that there were no differences between the root spread of trees in these various associations (Cutler and Richardson, 1981), and likewise my investigations show neither increased depth nor radial spread of trees in rows or groups.

On theoretical biological grounds there is no reason to suspect that such effect would exist. Where trees are growing in close proximity they will be in competition with each other; this will diminish the rate of growth and water requirements of the individual trees. The energy input (for photosynthesis), and thus the rate of transpiration and extent of root exploitation for water, will relate to the area occupied by the crown, and cannot be increased by competition.

Figure 9.15 provides a simple diagram to show this. Figure 9.15a depicts a tree which is forked near the base; it will have a single crown and act like a single tree. Likewise, two separate trees growing in close proximity to each other will also in effect have a single crown, with no significant difference from the forked tree (9.15b). If the trees are moved further apart, their influence will overlap and compete, but not in a cumulative fashion (9.15c). When they are entirely separate, they will still be acting as single trees (9.15d). This does not necessarily mean that a row of trees is no more likely to cause damage than a single tree. The influence of a single tree may be localised, with a building able to bridge over the soil which it is affecting. By contrast, a row of trees aligned parallel to the building will be likely to affect the whole of one side, and thereby make it more vulnerable to damage.

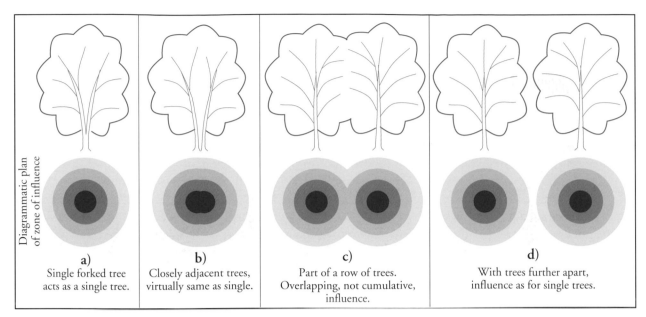

a) Single forked tree acts as a single tree.

b) Closely adjacent trees, virtually same as single.

c) Part of a row of trees. Overlapping, not cumulative, influence.

d) With trees further apart, influence as for single trees.

Diagrammatic plan of zone of influence

Figure 9.15

Diagram to show how influence of rows or groups of trees develops in overlapping, rather than cumulative, fashion.

In the light of this evidence, the 1985 revision of NHBC Practice Note 3 (and subsequent versions) intentionally dropped the reference to rows and groups. Despite this, the original concept has lingered, sometimes with elaborate extra calculations which bear no relationship to biological principles (e.g. SEMSELB, 1990).

Shrubs

Chapter 5 has emphasised that any vegetation will cause soil drying. For instance, grass can cause intense soil drying, usually creating far greater suction than trees, but only down to a depth of about 1.2m and only in its immediate proximity (Chapter 5, page 74). An important feature of woody vegetation is the development of secondary thickening which allows branches and roots to maintain growth and to radiate out. Trees have taken this process to its maximum extent; shrubs have an essentially similar structure but have not evolved to the same size. The distinction between trees and shrubs is entirely artificial (a tree is defined as a woody, perennial plant which can attain a stature of 6m or more on a single stem (Mitchell, 1974); a shrub is a woody, perennial plant without these attributes of size).

Shrubs have avoided the need to invest their energy in a massive trunk and branch structure but can still grow to considerable size. In terms of their leaf area, they may be as large, or even larger, than a small tree. This leaf area may be supported on a single stem, behaving just like a tree without a trunk, or the shrub may have increased its size by the development of multiple stems growing off a common root system. If there is a single stem, the pattern of soil drying will be similar to that depicted in Figure 9.15a; if there are multiple stems there will be an overlapping influence similar to Figure 9.15c. A shrub on a single stem can therefore cause localised soil drying, potentially associated with considerable angular distortion. Near the centre of a wall the foundations may be able to bridge such influence, but near a corner, particularly if there are window openings, localised movement and damage can occur. By contrast, mass planting or a shrub growing with multiple stems can influence the whole length of a wall. There is therefore considerable potential for shrubs to cause damage.

In some respects shrubs have a greater potential for causing damage. A tree on a tall trunk growing in close proximity to a building may block the light, be a cause of anxiety about its safety or cause inconvenience from leaves falling in gutters. These factors may result in the removal of the tree long before it reaches a size where it may cause damage. By contrast, a shrub of comparable leaf area growing close to the ground will not create the same problems and so is more likely to be retained. The growth of large shrubs close to a building is particularly common as a means of screening a windowless flank wall. Mass shrub planting, in this or similar locations, is becoming a popular landscape feature. Even if there are windows, a large shrub may be trimmed around them (Figure 9.16). Climbers, such as ivy, Virginia creeper or Wisteria, can often cover a very extensive area off a single stem with the potential to cause intense soil drying in that location.

Figure 9.16

Shrubs are sometimes grown to large size in close proximity to buildings, and have the ability to cause damage, particularly where they influence a whole section of wall. Pyracantha, seen here, is one of the shrub species most commonly associated with damage.

A few genera include both shrub and tree species. For instance Hilliers' Manual of Trees and Shrubs lists 47 shrub species of willow, some of which are dwarf alpine species only a few centimetres tall. It also lists 31 species of willow growing to the size of large shrubs/trees, and 18 species growing to full-size trees, with the largest (*Salix alba*) reaching 25m height. However, the majority of genera of shrubs do not include any tree species, and vice versa. Figure 14.4 (page 222) lists some of the commoner tree and shrub genera.

Although shrubs have the ability to cause damage, there is little information on the influence of different species, or their propensity to cause damage. Experience suggests that some of the shrubs in the *Rosaceae* family are the most likely to cause damage, particularly *Pyracantha* and *Cotoneaster*, possibly because these are frequently grown to large size in immediate proximity to buildings (Figure 9.16). Other genera in the *Rosaceae* (see Figure 14.1, page 219) are encountered more frequently as a cause of damage, compared with genera from other families.

Although some shrubs may cause soil drying to sufficient depth to cause some damage, it seems probable that these effects will always be comparatively shallow and entirely seasonal.

Summary

1.   Whilst it is reasonable to expect that the effects of different species can be placed into a rank order, it must be recognised that there is massive variation between individual trees of the same species, caused either by variation in site conditions or by genetic variation between individuals. To a large extent this variation between individuals masks any inter-specific variation; in other words, there will be **very considerable overlap between different species in their rank order**, however this is defined.

2.   The factors which control the influence of a tree are not necessarily linked to taxonomic features. For this reason, related species or genera will not necessarily have a similar influence, or similar position in a rank order.

3.   There are different methods by which a rank order of species might be determined, for instance:

- the radial extent of root influence;

- the depth of root influence;

- the intensity of soil drying;

- angular distortion of foundations induced by soil drying;

- propensity to cause damage.

The order will not necessarily be the same for each; indeed, different methods produce different results.

4.   "Water demand" is a commonly used term, but it is inappropriate to think in terms of differing demand for water. If the term is used, it should be defined as the ability of vegetation to cause drying of a clay subsoil. It seeks to combine consideration of the various factors identified in paragraph 3 above. The classification used by NHBC is based on this concept.

5.   Likewise, my own tentative more detailed classification (Figure 9.13) can only describe influence in terms of "water demand", and does not attempt to define separate factors such as the radial extent or depth of root influence, particularly as these factors are so heavily influenced by site conditions.

6.   There is no evidence, nor reason to expect, that rows or groups or trees will have an enhanced effect, compared to single trees. The influence of trees grown in proximity will overlap with each other, rather than be cumulative.

*Hedgerow, including vigorous oak tree, closely adjacent to flank wall –
Previous underpinning inadequate – Level monitoring demonstrates 11mm seasonal movement –
Selective felling and pruning reduce amplitude to less than 2mm – Further damage prevented.*

The subject property forms the right hand half of a semi-detached two storey house, built in 1962. A single storey extension with flat felt roof was added across the full width of the rear of both halves of the building in 1967. It is located in Essex, with the Geological Survey map indicating a Boulder Clay soil.

The trees

Adjacent to the right flank wall was an old hedgerow of mixed species; this had been allowed to grow with minimal management, so that it consisted of closely grown trees. Their location and species are identified in CS Figure 9.1.

The most significant of these trees was a vigorous young oak with a height of 12m and diameter 38cm, 3.6m from the front of the flank wall. A second oak, only 6.0m high, was only 3.4m from the front corner. There was a 10m high ash tree with a broad crown growing as coppice with multiple stems, 7.0m from the rear corner of the extension.

Other species in the hedge were hazel which was probably last coppiced in the 1960s, field maple up to 9m high, hawthorn and young hornbeam (CS Figure 9.2).

These trees were owned by the local authority, and provided an attractive screen adjacent to a busy cycle track.

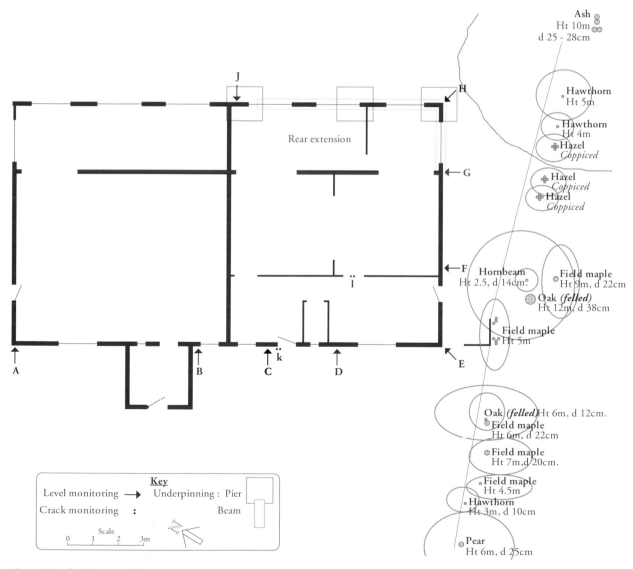

Case Study Figure 9.1

Site plan showing location and species of trees in adjacent hedgerow, and location of monitoring stations.

153

Case Study Figure 9.2

Remaining trees adjacent to flank wall in January 1987, 9 months after felling and pruning.

Previous history

The property was purchased by my clients in 1977. In the late summer of 1978 various cracks appeared, resulting in a claim for subsidence damage. Most of the damage was in the rear extension and around the flank wall, but some cracks were present throughout the property.

Trial holes were excavated and showed trench-fill foundations at the front corner to a depth of 1.3m, and the extension to be on strip foundations to a depth of 0.61m. The underlying soil was described as clay, but no tests were undertaken. Roots taken from the front corner were identified as *Acer* (field maple) and *Quercus* (oak), and from adjacent to the flank of the extension as *Fraxinus* (ash) and oak.

Negotiations with the local authority for removal of the trees were unsuccessful. During the winter the cracks closed but then reopened the following summer and, as the local authority still refused to act, underpinning was deemed essential. Two alternative schemes were proposed, both using a pier and beam system. One involved all external walls but was not implemented as the main damage was in the rear extension. The work finally implemented in late summer of 1980 involved 3 piers across the rear extension, each to a depth of 2.4m. These were linked by a beam cast within the original footings, with this cantilevered as a transition beam along the flank of the extension (CS Figure 9.1).

Further minor damage occurred in 1981 and 1982, with a significant deterioration in 1983. Cosmetic repairs were attempted in spring 1984.

I was instructed in November 1984 to advise on appropriate remedial action and on the liability of the local authority, and on possible liability of the underpinning contractor for defective work. At the time of my instructions the worst damage was a vertical crack above the front door. This followed the edge of a rendered panel to eaves level where it was 8mm wide. There was corresponding internal damage, and also internal cracks in the partition wall adjacent to the flank wall with a crack above a doorway. There was extensive differential movement at the junction of ceilings and partition walls, particularly at first floor level. The rear extension showed little damage, apart from a hairline diagonal crack below the window in the flank wall. Overall I assessed the damage as category 2-3.

Changes in level (mm) relative to datum at station A (flank of adjacent building), compared to readings on 12/2/85:													
Station	18/12/84	12/2/85	14/10/85	19/12/85	14/5/86	4/8/86	19/9/86	12/1/87	28/5/87	2/10/87	14/4/88	29/9/88	13/8/90
A	Datum	Datum	Datum	Datum	Datum	Datum	Datum	Datum	Datum	Datum	Datum	Datum	Datum
B	-0.2	0	-0.3	+0.2	+0.4	0	0	+0.1	+0.3	+0.4	+0.8	+0.8	+0.8
C	-0.3	0	-0.7	0	+0.2	0	-0.4	0	+0.3	+0.1	+0.3	+0.6	-
D	-1.0	0	-2.8	-1.3	-0.3	-0.2	-0.7	+0.3	-	+0.6	+2.0	+1.5	-
E	-2.9	0	-8.9	-4.2	+0.4	0	-0.1	+2.1	+3.8	+3.5	+5.8	+5.2	+4.7
F	-2.3	0	-6.9	-3.4	+0.6	-	+0.4	+1.9	+3.3	+3.0	+5.3	-	-
G	-1.4	0	-4.1	-2.6	+0.4	-	+0.1	+1.4	+2.3	+1.8	+3.6	-	-
H	-0.4	0	-1.4	-1.5	+0.1	-	-0.5	+0.1	+0.1	-0.1	+0.1	-0.4	-
J	-0.1	0	-0.4	-1	+0.4	-	+0.1	+0.3	+0	+0.5	+0.2	0	-
Changes in crack width (μm), compared to 12/2/85:													
$k_{(horiz)}$	1400	0	3100	-	-420	-400	-320	-640	-1320	-1300			
$k_{(vert)}$	101	0	300	-	-41	-68	-73	-114	-107	-115			
l	470	0	1396	-	-350	-330	-	-	-	-			

Case Study Figure 9.3

Results of level and crack monitoring.

Monitoring of building movements

In December 1984 I set up level monitoring at 9 locations around the building, including two stations on the other half of the semi-detached. Crack monitoring by demec gauge was also started on the vertical crack above the front door and on an internal crack above the doorway to the kitchen. Further readings were taken through 1985 to record the movements during the winter and summer. The crack monitoring ceased when the property was repaired and redecorated in 1987, but occasional readings on the level markers continued until August 1990. The results are shown in CS Figure 9.3, and are shown graphically for selected level stations in CS Figure 9.4 and for the cracks in CS Figure 9.5.

The level monitoring used station A on the other half of the semi-detached as an assumed stable datum. It will be noted that stations B and C on the front elevation, and J on the rear party wall, showed no significant movement relative to this datum (less than 1mm).

Cause of damage

The level monitoring at the front corner (station E) during the first winter showed upward recovery, followed during the summer of 1985 by 8.9mm of subsidence (actual movements would have been slightly greater, as these are compared with readings on 12/2/85; additional recovery would have occurred during the spring). Slight movement extended along the front elevation to station D, but with negligible movement at C adjacent to the front door. Movements diminished along the flank wall, but there was still 4.1mm at the junction with the extension, despite the cantilevered underpinning beam. These movements caused the crack above the front door to open by 3.1mm.

This pattern of movement was clearly related to the effects of vegetation, with the extent of movement correlated to the proximity of the hedgerow. There was no other vegetation which was likely to be involved.

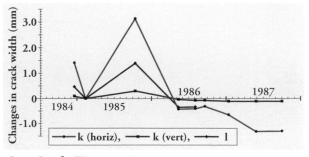

Case Study Figure 9.5
Results of crack monitoring.

The monitoring also demonstrated that the underpinning piers were performing satisfactorily (1.4mm of movement at station H on the rear corner).

Remedial action

I expressed the opinion that the movements could be reduced sufficiently by removal of the large oak tree, 50% reduction in the field maple adjacent to the front corner and by minor pruning of the remaining trees. Failing this, extensive underpinning would be required to stop the existing movements, and to allow for potential increase in effects of the oak as it continued to grow.

Negotiations for this started in February 1985, as soon as the first set of monitoring results were available. The local authority prevaricated, expressing concern about the risks of heave. Although no site investigations had been undertaken, I was satisfied that, although some long-term recovery might occur, the risk of significant heave on the Boulder Clay soil was very remote, particularly with a comparatively young oak. The local authority suggested that a root barrier might provide an alternative. Apart from the practical problems of installing a barrier in this location, the costs were likely to approach those of full underpinning, and, if there was a risk of heave as suggested by the authority, a barrier would sever the roots and allow such movements to occur.

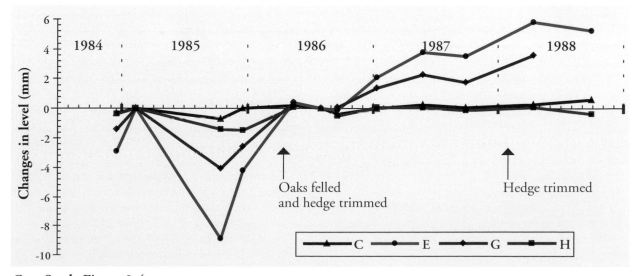

Case Study Figure 9.4
Results of level monitoring for selected stations, relative to station A.

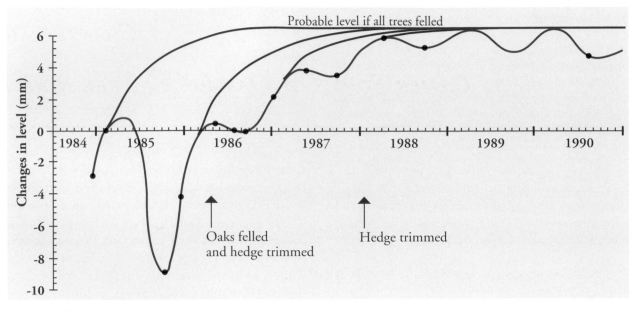

Case Study Figure 9.6.

Results for level monitoring of station E on front corner, interpreted to show probable pattern of movement throughout period.

Eventually the local authority agreed to take the required action, with these works eventually completed early in April 1986. The effect of treatment was immediately apparent during the subsequent summer, with the front corner only subsiding by 0.5mm between May and September and similar small movements at the other stations.

Comparison of the rate of recovery movement through the winter of 1985/86 showed that the rate only reduced slightly in the second half, implying that some further recovery was likely. During the following two winters this anticipated recovery occurred, with a further upward movement of 5.4mm at the front corner (comparing April '86 and April '88). During each of the intervening summers, the direction of movement reversed, with very slight seasonal subsidence. The eventual recovery was approximately half the seasonal movements which had been occurring prior to the tree felling and hedge trimming, and was obviously far preferable to those unacceptable seasonal movements.

During the winter 1986/87 it was agreed that the rate of movements had slowed sufficiently to allow full reinstatement, but this work was not completed until later that year.

A Court Order was agreed with the local authority, requiring that they continue to maintain the trees on a 3 yearly cycle to within the dimensions shown on the plan in CS Figure 9.1. As the trees were recovering rapidly after the initial pruning, it was agreed that the first such re-treatment should be after only 2 years. The hedge was therefore trimmed again early in 1988.

The level monitoring was continued with further readings at the end of the summer after this second treatment. Movements recorded at the front corner during that summer were only 0.6mm.

Although the job was completed and the file closed at that time, the markers were left in place. This allowed me to return in August 1990, near the end of a dry summer and the end of the 3 year period before the next pruning, to check on the situation. This indicated a seasonal movement of 1.1mm (compared to spring 1988). This was likely to increase slightly through September, but was unlikely to exceed 2mm. My clients reported no further damage.

CS Figure 9.6 shows the movements of the front corner, interpreting the probable movements occurring over the whole period. It also indicates the recovery which would probably have occurred if all of the hedgerow had been felled.

Lessons to be learnt

*   The partial underpinning was only effective in stabilising the extension. Although the foundations of the main building were deeper, unacceptable movements and damage continued to occur.

*   The level monitoring could demonstrate that these movements were entirely consistent with the probable influence of the hedge.

*   Prompt action by the owners of the hedge could have prevented a further year of seasonal movement.

*   On the Boulder Clay, significant heave was unlikely; it was considered that boreholes would be ineffective for accurate prediction of any risk which might exist.

*   The eventual felling of the oak and pruning of the hedge reduced the amplitude of movement drastically, from about 11mm per annum down to less than 2mm. This was superimposed on about 6mm of long-term recovery, which continued for a further 2 winters. This was effective in stopping further damage.

*   Level monitoring throughout this period was essential for checking the efficacy of the treatment.

Although by far the greatest proportion of damage by tree roots is from their indirect action in causing drying and shrinking of a clay soil, they do occasionally cause damage by other means. Two types of damage are of particular importance:-

i)   Direct physical damage from pressure exerted by the growing roots;

ii)   Damage to drains and underground services.

These types of damage can occur **on any soil**; damage is not just restricted to clay soils.

Direct physical damage

Mechanism of damage

Roots can exert pressure as a result of their growth, and in some circumstances this can cause damage to adjacent structures. It is necessary to understand how roots generate this pressure in order to understand how damage of this sort develops, and how it is best prevented or remedied.

A useful analogy for the mechanism of damage is provided by balloons, especially the long thin ones used for modelling animals. As these are inflated, they progressively elongate, just as a root will elongate as it grows through the soil. As noted in Chapter 3 (page 26), the elongation of the cells just behind the root tip is driven by their turgor which is maintained by the osmotic pressure of the cell contents; likewise the inflation of the balloon is provided by the pressure provided by one's lungs. A modelling balloon grows primarily in length, with radial growth restrained by the elasticity of the rubber; in the same way, biochemical relaxation of the cell wall allows the cell to elongate but restricts radial growth. One can envisage inflating one of these balloons into a container of small polystyrene balls with these balls being pushed aside in just the same way as soil particles will be pushed aside by a root. However, if the polystyrene balls are first compacted by a heavy weight on their surface, inflation would be difficult, just as a root cannot push through heavily compacted soil.

This analogy can be taken further to demonstrate how structures can be affected. If a single brick is placed on an inflated balloon, the balloon will distort but can still lift the brick (Figure 10.1a). Place a second brick on the first to double the load, and they will squash the balloon flat (Figure 10.1b). However, with an additional balloon inserted, the bricks can still be lifted (Figure 10.1c). In the same way a light structure can be lifted by the growth of roots, but a heavier structure cannot be lifted and will cause the root to distort, unless the combined pressure of sufficient roots working together can overcome the load.

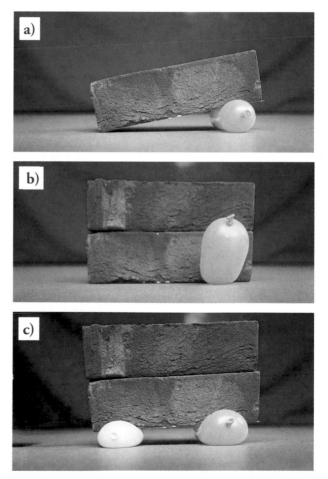

Figure 10.1

Balloons provide an analogy for the osmotic pressure of roots and their interaction with a building load. A light load can be lifted (a), but a heavier load forces the balloon to distort (b). Even this heavier load can be lifted by additional balloons (c).

157

Recent developments have made it possible to insert micro pressure-probes into individual cells to provide a direct measurement of the turgor pressure inside a cell (Pritchard, 1994) (the analogy breaks down - a balloon would burst, whereas the cell wall is able to seal onto a probe of only a few microns diameter). Using these probes it has been found that typical pressures are in the range from 350kPa to 800kPa. Most of these measurements have been in herbaceous crops but have included two tree species; the similarity in results suggests that this range is fairly universal for most plants. This turgor pressure is maintained even under conditions of low water potential or at low temperature, and with most species there is no increase in pressure as a result of mechanical impedance.

Misra *et al.* (1986) measured the axial and radial pressures exerted by the roots of pea seedlings, and also the axial pressure of sunflower and cotton seedlings; they also present the results obtained by other authors for various species. Figure 10.2 summarises all of these results. Most measurements have been of the axial pressure (which enables the root tip to push through the soil), with these generally higher than the radial pressure of the same species. This probably reflects the restraint imposed on axial and radial growth by the differential relaxation of the cell wall as the cells expand.

The mean axial pressure of all these results (weighted for the number of observations) is 1032kPa, and for radial pressure it is 866kPa. It is notable that these results show a considerable range of values, or in some cases standard error, suggesting a considerable variation between individual plants. It is also apparent that there is considerable variation in the results obtained for the same species by different authors, with this difference probably sufficient to mask any significant differences which might exist within or between species. The work by Misra et al. (1986) included measurements on 2 and 4 day old pea and sunflower seedlings, demonstrating significantly lower pressures for the 4 day seedlings, and also between different batches of pea seedlings, despite these being of the same variety. All of these results therefore suggest that there can be considerable variation in the radial pressures which are exerted, but an average value is about 860kPa.

It must be emphasised that all of these measurements are on the primary growth of young roots, and they are obtained from various crop plants, rather than tree species. The axial pressures are only being exerted over a very small area (the cross-section area of the growing root tip) and are usually only significant in respect of the ability of the root to push through the soil. It is only in exceptional circumstances that axial pressures cause damage, but it can occur (with any plant) with the vertical growth of a shoot pushing through hard surfaces (Figure 10.3). Likewise, the radial growth of fine roots, even in combination, is also insignificant as a cause of damage. Much of the radial growth of the fine roots will be accommodated within the inter-particle spaces in the soil, particularly as a root will tend to grow through soil which offers the least resistance, for instance utilising the natural fis-

Species	No. of obs.	Mean pressure (kPa)	Range of values (kPa)
Axial			
Bean	6	1082	704 - 1936
Cotton*	242	888	400 - 1300
	64	940	600 - 1600
	13	289	±40 (SE)
Groundnut	71	1150	500 - 2000
Maize*	10	1090	±187 (SE)
	4	1451	953 - 2494
Pea*	63	1300	600 - 2600
	290	1150	700 - 1600
	11	497	±26 (SE)
Sunflower	13	238	±20 (SE)
Vetch	2	1080	826 - 1333
Radial			
Bean	6	509	390 - 611
Maize	1	659	-
Pea	70	900	650 - 1250
(* the different results are those obtained by different authors. SE = standard error)			

Figure 10.2
Axial and radial root pressures exerted by radicles of seedlings of a variety of crop species.
Derived from Misra et al., 1986

Figure 10.3
Shoots of Horsetail (Equisetum), which is a very primitive plant form, pushing through the surface of a road. Even suckers developing off roots of trees are unlikely to emulate this behaviour and penetrate a road, although they may break paths and similar surfaces.

sures in a clay soil, or through old root channels or along soil biopores (created by worms or other animals). Soil immediately adjacent to the root may be compacted, but any radial pressure generated by the root will be limited to its immediate environs, dissipating with the square of the distance from the root (i.e. over a distance of only a few millimetres).

The potentially more significant pressures are those generated by the secondary growth of roots, when they continue their development to form conducting or structural roots (Chapter 3, page 29). The cell division in the cambium of these roots lays down fresh xylem and phloem, with all of this growth occurring radially. Although the axial and radial pressures generated by primary growth have been measured, there are no corresponding measurements of the pressure generated in secondary growth. However, the growth processes which are involved are essentially similar, which suggests that the pressures generated during secondary growth will also be about 860kPa.

The important difference with secondary growth, is that the roots are thicker and therefore exerting their force over a larger surface area; the total force which is generated is a function of both the pressure and the area over which it is exerted. In the case of structural roots near the base of the tree, individual roots may have a diameter of 20cm or more, making them far more significant than the smaller conducting roots. The base of the trunk where it enters the ground is the largest part, and over a period of time can obviously develop a very large contact area, and thus generate a massive force on any structure in its proximity (Figure 10.4).

Figure 10.4

Roots of olive trees causing distortion to an amphitheatre (Sehir Adalari, Turkey). Damage of this sort will have taken many years to develop (but not the full life of the amphitheatre!).
(Photo: M.C. Biddle).

Reaction of roots to mechanical impedance

In the few cases where turgor has been measured, there is generally no increase as a result of mechanical impedance, although it has been recorded with peas (Greacen and Oh, 1972). The overall morphology of the root system is however considerably affected, with a pronounced reduction in extension growth but increase in radial growth. For instance, seedlings from 21 different monocotyledon and dicotyledon species were grown in a special sand, compacted to give a penetrometer resistance of 4.2MPa (created by a vertical load on this soil of only 14.2kPa). This degree of compaction produced an average 94% reduction in the rate of root elongation, with little difference between the two different groups of plants. This dramatic reduction in potential length was accompanied by an increase in diameter of 41% for the monocotyledon species and 87% for the dicotyledons. (Materechera et al., 1991).

At the cellular level, this change is produced by altered shape of the individual cells, rather than a change in cell number or distribution. The increase in diameter has the practical benefit of increasing the deformation of the soil ahead of the root, making subsequent penetration easier.

Observations by Zwieniecki and Newton (1994) of root growth in rock fissures show that roots can penetrate through fissures as thin as 100μm. These roots retained a near cylindrical central stele (core) but with a flattened wing-like cortex filling the fissure. The species involved was *Arbutus* which can adapt to growing under these conditions; pine roots were limited to cracks >0.5mm. These observations may be of relevance in desiccated clay soils; the mechanical impedance of these soils is likely to be sufficient to restrict or prevent root growth through the soil peds, but roots can still penetrate if fine cracks develop.

Simple observation shows that roots subjected to mechanical impedance during secondary growth can deform considerably around any object which imposes sufficient force to restrict growth. This may involve simple flattening of the root, often over a large area if the root is of sufficient size, or the root may overgrow the edge of the object and start to envelop it; this is commonly seen where concrete slabs or kerbs are left adjacent to the base of trees (Figure 10.5). Likewise, if roots grow through a rigid hole they can expand on either side while remaining constricted through the hole. With aerial parts, constriction

Figure 10.5

Buttress roots moulding themselves around restraining kerb stones.

of this sort will soon lead to death of the distal portion, as the trunk or branch relies on the current season's xylem for water transport. However, with the less organized structure of roots, they can continue to conduct water, albeit presumably with reduced efficiency.

Just as there are no definitive data on the forces exerted by secondary growth, there is no information on any alteration in these forces induced by deformation. However, practical observations suggest that they are not increased. If anything, an area which has been constrained for some time appears to have a reduced ability to resume growth if the constraint is removed, suggesting that these areas would not be exerting the same force as the peripheral areas where contact is first being made.

Roots will frequently produce irregular growth or excrescences, often as a reaction to exposure to light, mechanical stimulus or minor injury. The callus growth produced in this way can often be far larger than the root it is growing on, so that, on the assumption that the cellular pressure it exerts is similar, the overall force produced by the callus may be far greater.

Wound reaction of this sort is often stimulated by hardcore laid beneath drive surfaces, particularly if the passage of vehicles intermittently pushes the hardcore into contact with the root. Any resulting callus growth on the root will increase the rate of diameter growth and the likelihood of subsequent damage of the drive surface. Some species of tree further aggravate the problem by producing sucker shoots off these surface roots (see Chapter 17, page 279).

Calculation of forces causing direct damage

Structures can be vulnerable to damage either from vertical distortion as a result of roots growing beneath them, or lateral distortion from adjacent roots (or a combination of the two). In either case the mechanism is the same; the total force exerted by the root (or roots) must be sufficient to overcome the resistance of the object if distortion is to occur.

MacLeod and Cram (1996) provide a number of examples to illustrate the calculations which can, in theory at least, be made to determine whether an object will be distorted and liable to damage. However, in practice there are many complications which make accurate calculations difficult, if not impossible, in the majority of situations.

For example, a large concrete paving slab measures 900mm x 600mm x 50mm and weighs about 69kg; under the influence of gravity this exerts a downward force of 69 x 9.8 = 676N. Imagine a fine primary root, with a diameter of 1mm, which has grown straight across beneath the centre of this slab. This root starts secondary growth, bringing it into contact with the underside of the slab over a width of 1mm. It will exert pressure over the area in contact, i.e. 600mm x 1mm = 0.0006m². Assuming that this root can generate a pressure of 860kPa, the total upward force will be 860 x 0.0006 = 0.516kN or 516N. This is less than the downward force exerted by the root and so the slab will not be lifted.

If this root continues to grow so that the width in contact is 1.3mm, the total area in contact will increase to 0.00078m², so that it exerts a force of 671N, i.e. almost exactly in balance with the force exerted by the slab. In theory any further increase in diameter could lift the slab. However, it does not follow that any further increase would necessarily lift it. The root has only been able to grow to 1.3mm because the adjacent soil could be deformed by the swelling pressure of the root. Likewise, if further deformation of the soil can occur more easily than lifting the slab, it will be the soil which will deform, rather than the slab be lifted. For the slab to be lifted by the root, the root must impose an equal and opposite downward pressure of 860kPa on the immediately adjacent soil. Information is therefore required on the consolidation characteristics of the soil. With loads of this magnitude, most soils will be subject to some settlement, with cohesive soils particularly prone to consolidation and settlement. For this reason, problems of direct damage tend to be worse on dense gravel or rock which have high values of allowable bearing pressure, whilst soft clays are least vulnerable.

With a thin 1.3mm diameter root, the strength of the root is negligible and can be ignored; it is only the soil parameters which would need to be determined to decide whether it would be the soil or slab which distorts. However, if one was to consider a thick but short root which comes into contact over the same contact area of $780mm^2$ (e.g. over an area of 28mm x 28mm), it could exert sufficient force to start to lift the slab. A thick root would have an inherent stiffness so that the opposing force which it exerts on the adjacent soil would be spread over a much wider area. In practice, any calculations therefore require information on both the soil and root characteristics to determine whether the slab will be lifted, or the root and soil deform.

This example of a single slab is very simple but the calculations are already potentially complicated If this slab was part of a paved area, there would be the added complication of friction between adjacent slabs, which would greatly increase the force required to lift an individual slab. If, rather than a paving slab, the surface was a continuous concrete slab (for instance a driveway cast as a single slab) the edges of which are held rigid, one would require to know the modulus of rupture of the slab. This information is available for engineered structures and would allow valid calculations for a properly constructed raft, but the types of domestic structure with which one is normally concerned may not have been constructed to appropriate specifications.

Similar calculations can be applied to a brick wall. A boundary wall of single skin brickwork 11cm thick, 2m long and 1m high would weigh about 450kg and therefore exert a downward force of 4410N. A root passing beneath this wall in contact over a width of 47mm would exert a force of 860 x (47/1000) x (110/1000) x 1000 = 4446N, i.e. just sufficient to start to lift the wall, assuming it could be lifted. However, if the ends of the wall are held rigid, it would require considerable additional force to rupture and crack the

wall. One therefore needs to know all of the parameters of how the wall is constructed, and any potential planes of weakness, before one can determine how it will react to pressure exerted by roots.

Growth, particularly at the base of the trunk, will also produce a lateral force. This will be resisted, not by the weight of the object, but by:

i)   friction of the object on surrounding objects;

ii) resistance imposed on the opposite side of the object;

iii) bending resistance of the object.

It is easy to appreciate that a single kerb stone could be pushed aside easily, but the friction imposed by an extensive concrete slab might be sufficient to resist any lateral force. It is always important to consider the restraint imposed on the opposite side of the object. For instance, lateral forces on the foundations of a wall will be resisted by the soil on the opposite side of the wall; the stiffness of the wall will ensure that any localised force exerted by a root is spread over a wide area and it would only require minimal restraint over this wide area to ensure that the wall does not fail.

Wall failure is most likely to occur in situations where this opposing lateral restraint does not exist. The commonest examples of this are retaining walls, where it is only the bending resistance of the wall that provides any restraint. It requires engineering calculations to calculate whether failure will occur under these circumstances; this will be very dependent on the exact construction of the wall, the location of any lateral pressure, the consolidation of the soil against the wall and the stiffness of the root.

In the various calculations above, it has been assumed that the pressure exerted by the root will be about 860kPa; however it must be remembered that this can vary considerably, immediately introducing potential errors in any calculation. These calculations consider only a single root. In practice there will usually be many roots, of varying diameter and at varying distance from the structure. For any accurate analysis, the cumulative force exerted by all of these would need to be determined.

It should be appreciated from these considerations that it is usually impractical to make precise calculations on whether roots from a tree have caused damage, or might be capable of causing damage. It is preferable to rely on general conclusions that:

Figure 10.6

Massive distortion to kerbs and surface of a poorly constructed carpark, caused by structural roots of a cherry.

i) roots will distort around any object which imposes sufficient restraint;

ii) paving slabs and flexible drive surfaces with minimal base will be very vulnerable to damage (Figure 10.6). Even a small root will be capable of causing displacement and damage;

iii) a more substantial surface such as a concrete drive will also be vulnerable to lifting and cracking, unless it has sufficient rigidity to resist this;

iv) low boundary walls are very vulnerable to damage, but the risks of such damage start to reduce with increasing height and weight;

v) a lightly loaded structure such as a garage will be vulnerable to damage, unless the foundation slab has sufficient rigidity;

vi) a more heavily loaded structure such as a house foundation is likely to withstand any lifting force exerted by roots;

vii) lateral forces are likely to be resisted if there is any effective restraint on the opposite side of the object;

viii) retaining walls, which have no such restraint, will be very vulnerable to lateral forces;

ix) in all of these situations the greatest risk of damage will be in close proximity to the base of the tree where there are the largest buttress and structural roots. The risks of damage will diminish rapidly with distance from the trunk, but this does not preclude the possibility that roots can cause damage at considerable distance, if the circumstances conspire.

Studies on damage to pavements and kerbs

It is obvious from the preceding comments that the most common, and worst, problems from direct physical damage are from street trees which are planted in pavements. It has been estimated that the average cost of repairs of pavements in Northern Californian cities is $27,000 per annum (Hamilton, 1984a). In addition, there can be potential legal implications if pedestrians trip on damaged pavements.

There have been several studies of this problem. Investigations in Manchester (Wong et al., 1988) showed that 30% of the street trees were causing some damage to pavements, and 12% of the trees were causing moderate or severe damage. This damage either consisted of lifting paving slabs, or producing cracks, usually radiating out from the tree, in tarmac surfaces. Kerb stones were also displaced, either horizontally or vertically. Damage to these was not as common as to pavings, probably as a result of their more substantial construction, but even so 13% of trees were causing some damage, and 5% were causing moderate or severe kerb damage.

The percentage of each species involved in the damage, combining the results for kerbs and pavements, was:

Ash	49%
Lime	42
Horse chestnut	37
Oaks	23
Sycamore / maple	23
Birch	22
Whitebeam / rowan	17
Cherry	16

There were insufficient numbers of other species for meaningful analysis. As some species may tend to be planted in positions of greater risk, this order may be biased, but it does not differ significantly from my own experience, except to note that poplar can often cause problems (there were insufficient of this species for analysis in the Manchester survey).

As might be anticipated, the risk of damage increases as the trees grow. Figure 10.7 summarises the results from these observations in Manchester. It is notable that the proportion of trees which cause damage does not continue in the larger size classes (>40cm d.b.h.), possibly because damage had occurred at an earlier stage when the trees were smaller, and had been repaired in the past.

These studies have also shown that the most serious damage to pavements occurs within 2m of the trunk. Where trees are growing in a planting strip

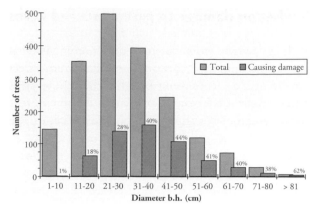

Figure 10.7

Frequency of damage to pavements by trees of differing size (combining all species).   From Wong et al. (1988).

with exposed soil, the risk of damage was reduced, and studies in America have shown that the wider the strip, the less the risk (Figure 10.8). These American studies show that damage to kerbs does not diminish with distance to the same degree as it does with sidewalks (pavements). No explanation for this is given, but my observations show that the lateral forces on kerbs are often transmitted through intervening pavement slabs. The base of the trunk pushes direct on a slab, and, if the slabs do not interlock with each other, this can move several adjacent slabs and the kerb.

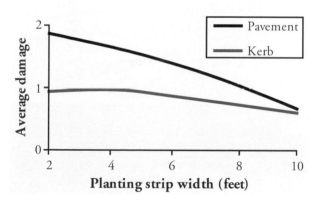

Figure 10.8

Effect of planting strip width on damage to pavements and kerbs. (Damage scale: 0 = no damage, to 3 = >2in (50mm) displacement.)

From Wagar and Barker (1983).

Nichol and Armstrong (1997) studied the root architecture of five 30-year-old flowering cherry, growing on wild cherry rootstock, and the patterns of surface crack damage to the pavement in which they were growing. This pavement consisted of tarmac generally 4-5cm thick, but sometimes as thin as 2cm, laid over a 7-8cm thick gravel and clinker bed. Lateral root spread was constricted by the kerb on one side and a boundary wall on the opposite side of the pave-

ment, and no roots had grown deeper than 0.57m. Roots less than 2cm diameter did not appear to have caused damage. The most severe damage was caused by larger roots growing in contact with the underside of the pavement, where cracks approximately followed the root direction. Roots in excess of 15cm diameter at greater depth (down to 0.4m) also caused damage, but the cracks followed the direction of the roots less precisely. Wild cherry tends to produce particularly large structural roots and be particularly prone to causing severe damage (Figure 10.6); *Malus sieboldii* planted in the same pavement had caused no damage.

Their studies also found that the effectiveness of chiselling down the upper surface of roots before relaying a pavement was short-lived, as roots soon callus around the chiselled area, with this callus providing an even larger contact area. Chiselling or severing roots was associated with rot extending back into the base of the trunk, with potential consequences for tree stability.

Direct root penetration of brick walls

Householders are sometimes alarmed at the sight of small roots appearing directly through moist, earth-retaining walls, for instance in cellars or inspection chambers of drains. They fear that the root will grow and damage the wall, or that the roots are damaging the mortar. There is no risk of such problems. Roots are not capable of picking the mortar out from between the bricks to create a gap and are quite incapable of damaging normal brickwork by their increase in diameter. They are merely exploiting existing gaps in the mortar, to obtain the water and nutrients contained in the brickwork. Once through the bricks, if the inner surface is dark and damp, feeder roots can continue to grow over the surface. Conditions usually soon change, and the roots die back naturally. Alternatively, they can be killed, for instance by applying a dilute solution of domestic bleach.

Diagnosis of physical damage

If direct root growth is the cause of damage, a large root is almost invariably present. A direct line of damage radiating out from the tree is often present, indicating the alignment of the root. A vertical crack in a wall is usually almost directly above a large root, and measurements can show that the wall is distorted upwards near the crack. In these situations, excavation will usually expose an obvious culprit. If walls or kerbs have been laterally distorted, the maximum distortion will be directly opposite the trunk.

However, it is wrong to conclude that, just because there is a tree in the vicinity of the crack, it must be the cause. Surfaces can crack for many reasons, in particular inadequate consolidation of the base will cause settlement. Settlement cracks can usually be distinguished from cracks caused by roots, particularly by their distribution and because settlement produces a downwards movement, whereas root growth lifts the structure. If necessary, the damaged surface can be excavated to check for the presence of a large root.

Direct root damage develops slowly, associated with the rate of growth of the root (Figure 10.4). The damage, and any evidence of previous repairs, should be consistent with this. An exception to this can occur if a structure has been lifted and supported by the root but then suddenly cracks; the support must have been present for a time but failure can occur suddenly.

Prevention and repair of direct damage

Damage can be prevented by avoiding growing large trees near potentially vulnerable structures. Guidance is provided by Table 2 of BS 5837:1991 "Trees in Relation to Construction". The guidance in that Standard is based on the mature height of the tree, but as it is increase in diameter which causes damage, and as height and diameter will not be related if trees are pollarded or reduced, it is preferable to use diameter as the basis for classification. Figure 10.9 is therefore adapted from Table 2 of BS 5837, but using diameter as the defining criterion.

	Diameter (b.h.) at maturity		
	<30cm	30 to 60cm	>60cm
Buildings and heavily loaded structures	-	0.5	1.2
Lightly loaded structures such as garages, porches etc.	-	0.7	1.5
Drains and underground services			
less than 1m deep	0.5	1.5	3.0
more than 1m deep	-	1.0	2.0
*Masonry boundary walls	-	0.5	1.0
	-	(1.0)	(2.0)
*In situ concrete paths and drives	-	0.5	1.5
	(0.5)	(1.0)	(2.5)
*Paths and drives with flexible surfaces or paving slabs.	-	0.5	1.0
	(0.7)	(1.5)	(3.0)

> * These distances assume that some movement and minor damage might occur. Guidance on distances which will generally avoid all damage are given in brackets.

Figure 10.9
Minimum distances (m) between centre of tree and structure, to allow for future tree growth.

This table can be used as guidance for tree planting in the vicinity of vulnerable structures, or for building in the proximity of existing trees. However, if building near existing trees, it must be emphasised that care will be needed to prevent excessive damage to trees which might render them unstable or kill them; sections 7 and 8 of BS 5837:1991 give guidance.

In situations where a tree and a potentially vulnerable structure are already present, it is usually possible to take precautions to prevent direct damage from developing. Paths or slabs close to the base of a tree can be removed to allow for further growth; in some situations the base of a wall can be cut away and a lintel inserted (Figure 10.10). Once space has been made, a loosely compacted soil (or ideally a very low density material such as vermiculite) can be used as a backfill to allow space for further growth. If a tree has already started to overgrow the edge of a slab (Figure 10.5), the slab can usually be removed, taking care to avoid damage to the bark and cambium.

Figure 10.10
a) Damage to a low boundary wall adjacent to base of large plane tree. b) Adjacent section of wall after repair, with concrete lintel inserted to span large structural roots of a similar tree.

If the structure cannot be cut away to provide space, another option is to cut away the offending root; this is considered in further detail in the next section.

Where it is necessary to build or repair a structure in proximity to a tree and there is concern about damage developing at any time in the future, appropriate precautions should be taken at the time of construction. There are three potential options:

i) allow sufficient space for future growth;

ii) ensure that the structure is sufficiently rigid so that the roots will distort around it;

iii) use a flexible structure which can distort without damage.

The particular method used in any situation will depend on the circumstances but these different approaches can be illustrated by considering the design of a garden (boundary) wall. Space can be allowed for growth by omitting foundations close to the tree, and bridging this length of wall with a reinforced concrete lintel or beam, at or just above ground level (Figure 10.11). Alternatively the wall can be made more flexible by building in short sections, incorporating a movement joint at intervals. This is usually the best method if there is also a risk of seasonal movement on a clay soil. Lateral distortion of the foundations can be prevented by inclusion of reinforcement, so that the pressure exerted by the tree is distributed over sufficient area for it to be resisted by soil pressure on the opposite side.

Figure 10.11

Repaired boundary wall, incorporating a movement joint and a concrete lintel over the structural roots of a mountain ash tree.

A more robust structure is required for a retaining wall in close proximity to a tree. Normal construction of such walls (in the absence of a tree) will usually include a toe projecting from the base of the wall. If space allows this toe to project away from the tree, construction should cause no problem; the size of the toe and amount of reinforcement must be sufficient to resist pressure from future growth. Figure 10.12 shows an alternative method which is particularly useful if a toe cannot be constructed on the downhill side of the retaining wall (for instance if the wall forms the boundary). The soil is retained by a reinforced wall with appropriate facing bricks or stone, with this tied back by stainless steel bars to an anchor wall located on the opposite side of the tree. This must be at suffi-

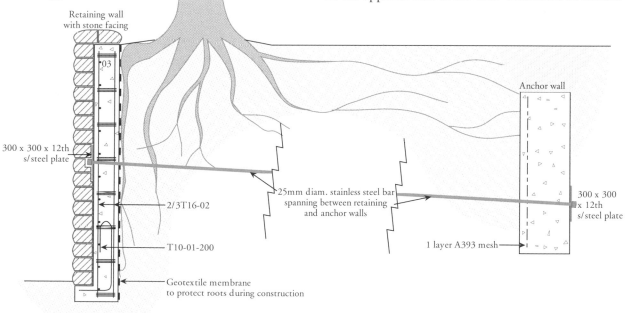

Figure 10.12

Section through retaining wall constructed to resist lateral pressure exerted by growth of base of trunk and roots. Section shows cage reinforcement in proximity to the stainless steel retaining bar; elsewhere reinforcement could be reduced (e.g. 1 layer A252 mesh). Derived from drawing by Simpson Associates, Consulting Engineers.

165

cient distance from the tree to ensure that excavation for this wall does not cause damage to the roots and destabilize the tree. This method is well suited to repair of a wall which has been distorted by root growth, but great care must be taken to avoid cutting or damaging roots which are exposed when the old wall is removed.

Similar principles can be applied to other structures. For instance, garages are best constructed using a raft which is stiff enough to prevent distortion if it is lifted. However, as paths are so vulnerable, it is preferable for them to be as flexible as possible, for instance, using brick setts laid on a sand and weak mortar base.

In some situations it may be possible to delay the onset of damage by redirecting root growth away from a vulnerable structure by some form of root barrier; various commercial products are available for this purpose. However, the efficacy of these in the long term is dubious, as roots will always tend to grow in the most suitable locations and in response to external stresses. Furthermore, products which restrict the proper development of the root system may adversely affect the future stability and safety of the tree.

Remedial action to trees to prevent damage

Damage from direct physical growth of roots develops slowly as the roots grow. There is therefore a long warning period, usually not heeded, between minor damage starting and it reaching the stage where rebuilding is required. If the damage is likely to progress further, there is often opportunity to prevent this from occurring during the warning period.

If the damage is being caused by the growth of the base of the trunk, there is probably no alternative to felling the tree (assuming that the structure cannot be repaired, as described in the previous section). The stump can be left to decay. However, if the damage is being caused by a root, or roots, running close to the surface, it may be possible to sever these to prevent further growth. To prevent the tree from becoming unstable, the roots should be cut as far as possible from the trunk; i.e. immediately adjacent to the damaged structure. As the roots are usually directly beneath, or close to, the cracks in the structure, it is easy to locate them. They can be cut through with an axe or sharp mattock. Roots which are cut in this way will regenerate from around the edges, but the mass of smaller roots are less likely to cause further problems, at least for a considerable time, after which the treatment can be repeated.

Ideally roots should not be cut close to the trunk, as this may give rise to problems of instability. As an approximate rule-of-thumb, a tree will not be made unstable provided any roots are severed at a distance from the centre of the tree greater than the circumference of the trunk. Greater distances may be required for an asymmetric root system. Although a tree may remain stable, major root severance may kill or damage the tree, and severed or damaged roots may provide entry for decay fungi. If in doubt, seek professional advice from an arboriculturist.

If the area of contact between an object and the tree is reasonably small, it is sometimes possible just to eliminate the area of contact, for instance by cutting a notch into a buttress root which is in contact with a wall. As radial growth only occurs from the cambium, a notch which removes the cambium will prevent further growth from this area. However, the cambium will continue to grow from around the edges of the cut, producing a ridge of callus; further trimming of this may be required if it again comes into contact with the object. Case Study 10 provides an example of this sort, in that case requiring removal of a large contact area with associated extensive injury, and then further trimming of the callus growth after 5 years.

Damage to drains and underground services

Root invasion of drains

The disturbed backfill soil around drains provides an ideal rooting environment which encourages root growth. To these roots, a properly constructed watertight drain or water main is little different from a stone or any other obstruction; a root has no means of sensing the water within and actively seeking it. However, if there is a leak into the soil and a root chances to encounter the moist conditions, it will exploit the water and grow along the moisture gradient towards the source. As long as the leak continues, the roots will proliferate and persist. This often produces a mass of roots adjacent to a leak, which may lead to the mistaken belief that it is this root growth which has damaged the drain in the first place.

Leaks from foul or surface water drains are usually intermittent and at low pressure, and so, if the crack is large enough for a fine root to grow through, the drain can be entered. Very fine roots can enter in this way. Once inside the drain, the root can proliferate to produce a mass of fine roots to utilise the water. These

Figure 10.13

20m long mass of fibrous root removed from a drain - presumably blocked for some time! (Photo: *Reading Evening Post*).

can quickly build up until they are sufficient, either on their own or in combination with any solids in the drain, to cause a blockage (Figure 10.13). Although there may be a mass of root within the drain, at the position where it passes through the crack, it usually narrows to a thin, flattened section. If the edges of the crack are sufficiently weak, the growth of the root may enlarge the original defect.

The ability of species to penetrate cracks in drains and cause problems of this sort appears to differ significantly. Willow has a well deserved reputation of being the most invasive, and from my experience sycamore is also very liable to cause problems (it was the species involved in Figure 10.13). Some comparative data is available from the Kew Root Survey; Figure 10.14 records the frequency of different species being involved, expressed as a percentage of the total number of recorded cases of root invasion.

Species	%
Poplar	24.0
Willow	18.5
Horse chestnut	11.0
Acer (includes sycamore)	9.6
Plane	7.5
Birch	5.5
Prunus	4.5
Ash	4.5
Oak	3.5
Apple / Pear	2.0
Hawthorn	1.6
Lime	1.0
Beech	< 1
Elm	< 1
False acacia	< 1
Sorbus	< 1

Figure 10.14

Identification of root samples from drains, expressed as a percentage of all recorded cases of root invasion of drains. Derived from Cutler and Richardson (1989)

Role of roots in initiating damage

Inspection of drains by CCTV shows that many old clay drains have a variety of defects such as displaced joints, circumferential and longitudinal cracking, uneven falls leading to ponding, obstruction with grease, etc. **These defects can be present on any soil, and regardless of the proximity of trees.** Their existence does not indicate that a tree has caused the defect, even if a root has grown through a crack.

The forces generated by the direct growth of a root will not be capable of fracturing an intact clay pipe; the circular cross section provides enormous strength and resistance. However, under some rare circumstances roots can cause movement of a drain which can initiate the damage. Mattheck and Breloer (1994) have analysed the way that roots can interact with drains. Problems will be restricted to the immediate area of the root plate where the tree is transferring the stress from the trunk into the surrounding soil. Within this area on the windward side of the trunk the roots will be under tension, and on the leeward side under shear and compression. If a root has happened to grow partially round a drain, it can gain some support from it and transfer some of the load to the drain; if a root is gaining support in this way it is advantageous for the tree to maximise that support by enhanced growth of the root. This can result in the development of "tension slings" in a root under tension under a drain , or a thickened "knee" on a root under compression. A root under tension from movement of the crown and which is gripping a pipe with a tension sling, can transfer considerable load, possibly leading to movement and cracking of the drain. By contrast, compression loads are not transmitted so effectively, and so there is less risk of damage on the leeward side of a tree. If a drain passes directly beneath a tree at right angles to the direction of prevailing wind, it will be near the neutral pivot point and so will be less liable to damage in this way.

Where the soil is clay, it is possible that soil movements associated with seasonal or persistent moisture deficits can cause flexing of the drain, and that this can cause the initial crack which the root then exploits. The risk of damage of this sort will be increased by shallow drains, and also if a drain which is subject to soil movement enters a rigid structure such as a deep inspection chamber or a building with deep foundations. Differential movement is liable to shear the drain and allow root penetration.

Undoubtedly drains can be damaged by these means; tension slings are probably very rare and as a result, even when a tree is uprooted, it is unusual for it to disturb adjacent drains. Damage from clay shrinkage is probably more common. However, examination of drains indicates that these mechanisms probably only cause a small percentage of the cracks which are present. Virtually any defect in the urban situation, regardless of its original cause, will be within range of root activity of trees or shrubs and thus potentially vulnerable to invasion. It is only if this invasion causes a blockage that the drain is inspected and the damage noted. The original damage may then be attributed, quite incorrectly, to the tree.

It is usually impractical to get direct evidence on whether the defect was caused by the tree, and so circumstantial evidence is needed. This should involve inspection of all of the drains, both close to and away from the tree, to assess their overall condition and to determine whether there is a statistical increase in frequency or severity of damage associated with the tree. It is only if there is such evidence that the tree should possibly be implicated, although even so it may be coincidence.

Prevention and repair of damage to drains

The growth of roots into drains with subsequent blockage can be avoided by careful construction, ensuring that all connections are watertight.

Initiation of direct damage will only occur in the close proximity to the trunk where the stresses of crown movement are being transmitted to the surrounding soil. BS 5837:1991 advocates the spatial separation shown in Figure 10.15 to prevent damage of this sort. However, even for trees in considerably closer proximity, the risks of damage are so remote and unpredict-

able that it does not provide justifiable cause for concern or action against trees which are closer than these distances.

	Mature height of tree		
	< 8m	8m to 15m	> 15m
Drain less than 1m deep	0.5	1.5	3.0
Drain more than 1m deep	-	1.0	2.0

Figure 10.15

Minimum distances (m) advocated by BS 5837 for avoiding direct damage to drains.

Damage due to flexing of drains in clay soils can be prevented by using a flexible system, such as the modern plastic pipes with rubber gasket seals. With these materials damage is very unusual. For existing clay pipes which do not have this inherent flexibility, there is no published data on the frequency of damage, or on the species of tree and proximity. It is therefore impractical to provide reliable guidance for preventing damage of this sort. This is supported by the National Joint Utilities Group publication No. 10, "Guidelines for the Planning, Installation and Maintenance of Utility Services in Proximity to Trees" (1995) which states in paragraph 5.1:

> "The inherently variable nature of root systems, and also the generally low incidence of damage to services, makes it neither practical not justifiable to impose strict limits on the proximity of trees to services".

Where a drain is damaged and leaking, it is usually necessary to correct the defect. This should apply whether or not root penetration has occurred. Repair may involve excavation and relaying, in which case replacement with modern materials should avoid recurrence of similar problems. Alternatively there are techniques which allow the existing drain to be repaired with a resin-soaked liner which will provide a full and watertight seal. It appears that these liners are effective in preventing re-invasion. If these repairs ensure that similar problems will not re-occur, there is no justification in requiring the removal of trees whose roots have been identified in drains.

In those situations where the leak is unimportant, for instance in surface water drains, repair may be unnecessary but action is needed to prevent further blockage. Rodding to remove the obstructing mass of roots will provide temporary relief, but will leave the broken ends of the root in the crack. These are likely to regenerate and in due course recreate the problem.

A preferable alternative is to use a herbicide which will kill off not only the invading root but also an adjacent section outside the drain, but without affecting the whole tree. The dead section of root within the crack will reduce the risk of re-invasion, at least until it decays when repeat treatment may be required. Success has been reported using a foaming agent with a solution of metham sodium and dichlobenil as the herbicide (Leonard and Townley, 1971), with this method gaining widespread use in the U.S.A. However, metham sodium is no longer generally available and is detrimental in sewage treatment plants. Recent work (Groninger *et al.*, 1997) has tested alternative materials, with glufosinate providing the most effective root mortality, but also causing some damage to the test plants. Further work is required to determine the most effective materials and method of treatment. If the use of any such materials is contemplated, liaison with the local water company would be essential.

Whatever the method of controlling root invasion, the cost or effort of routine maintenance of this sort is not excessive, especially in comparison with the value of most trees.

Where damage to drains is occurring, there is no action which can be taken with the tree, such as pruning, which will prevent recurrence, short of complete removal of the tree. As noted above, either repairs to the drain or routine maintenance should be sufficient to prevent problems from developing, and so encroachment into drains should not usually provide justification for removing a tree.

Damage to other underground services

The role of tree roots as a cause of damage to other underground services such as gas, electricity or water mains has been poorly documented. Where damage occurs, the presence of a root is often claimed to be the cause, based solely on the circumstantial evidence of its presence. As the backfill around services provides the disturbed soil which is conducive to root growth, it is not surprising that roots are often found in the proximity of the service; it does not establish that they are the cause of any damage which may have occurred.

Representatives of the Public Utilities (water authorities, electricity boards, Telecom and British Gas) discussed this problem at the 1981 National Arboricultural Conference, and generally concluded that the problem was insignificant (Chapman, 1982); a view which was supported by National Joint Utilities Group (1995).

Although direct root damage to underground services is insignificant, the indirect effects of clay shrinkage can increase the risk of fracture. In dry summers, the incidence of fractures in gas mains increases in late autumn when the soil reaches its driest conditions. A similar, or greater, risk of failure occurs in mid winter, associated with thermal shrinkage of the pipe (Owen 1984).

Some comparison can be made of the potential effects of clay movement and thermal shrinkage. Movement of the soil at pipe depth in the vicinity of a tree does not usually exceed 50mm, even in the close proximity of a large tree on a highly shrinkable clay. This movement is distributed over a wide area, usually at least 20m. Provided soil conditions are uniform and the pipe is not anchored, the angular distortion induced is therefore very small (0° 9') and the increase in length of the pipe to accommodate this bend is only 0.125mm. By contrast, the seasonal variation in soil temperature at pipe depth is likely to be at least 10°C. With a steel pipe with a coefficient of linear expansion of 1.2×10^{-5}, a 20m length would be subject to 2.4mm contraction, i.e. approximately 20 times greater than the seasonal movement near trees caused by clay shrinkage. The National Joint Utilities Group (1995) recognize that the stresses caused to services by clay shrinkage can stretch the service, but the movement should be within its range of tolerance.

Summary

1.   The majority of damage caused by trees is from their **indirect** effects in causing drying and shrinkage of a clay subsoil. However, in some circumstances they can also cause **direct** damage as a result of pressure generated by the growth of the roots.

2.   These pressures relate to the osmotic potential within the cell. Research on pressures generated by the primary (fine) roots of various crops suggest that radial pressures are about 860kPa. There are no reliable measurements of pressures generated by secondary growth of the large structural roots, but they are probably of similar magnitude. There is no information on variation between species, but the considerable variation between individuals may mask any such effect.

3.   If one knows the area of contact of a root on a structure, by applying this value of radial pressure one can calculate the total force being generated. In theory, by comparing this with the restraint imposed by the structure, either as a result of its load or its construc-

tion, one can determine whether the structure will be liable to distortion. However, any such calculations must also take account of the ability of the soil to support the root under this load, which in turn requires knowledge of the stiffness of the root. With engineered structures this information may be available and calculations possible, but they would rarely be reliable in the type of situations where damage usually occurs.

4.   It is preferable to work on the general guidance that:

i)   the greatest risk of direct damage is with the large structural roots close to the trunk;

ii)   light structures, or those with negligible lateral restraint, will be most vulnerable to displacement and damage;

iii)   a heavier or rigid structure, or one with lateral restraint, is likely to resist the force which can be generated;

iv)   roots will distort around any object which imposes sufficient restraint.

5.   Even a vulnerable structure in close proximity to a root will not necessarily suffer damage. If damage does occur, it will develop slowly, related to the growth of the root. As minor damage to this sort of structure can usually be repaired fairly easily, there is usually no justification in taking preventative action.

6.   If damage does occur, it is usually possible to identify the offending root, and to cut or trim this to prevent further development of damage.

7.   Damage can be prevented:

i)   by avoiding planting new trees too close to vulnerable structures;

ii)   if constructing near existing trees, by ensuring that the structure is either sufficiently rigid to withstand the forces which might be imposed, or else sufficiently flexible to tolerate the displacement.

8.   Drains very frequently have inherent cracks and leaks. Roots will favour growing in the backfill soil around drains. A root which encounters moisture leaking from a drain will be encouraged to proliferate, and may enter the drain and cause a blockage. In the vast majority of situations the root has not caused the initial damage.

9.   Only rarely do roots initiate damage to drains. The greatest risk is to shallow drains on clay soil which are subject to seasonal flexing. There are no data on the vulnerability of drains to such damage. This damage can be prevented by use of modern materials and careful design and construction.

10.   Drains which have defects will usually need to be repaired. These repairs (which may involve relaying or lining) can usually allow the tree to be retained. If the drain is not repaired, there will probably be a need for periodic maintenance. Damage to drains should not be justification for tree removal.

11.   Other underground services can usually tolerate any direct or indirect stresses imposed by tree roots. Special precautions are not usually justified.

Additional reading

MacLeod, R.D. and W.J. Cram. (1996) Forces exerted by tree roots. Arbor. Research and Information Note **134**, AAIS. 8pp.

Bulbous base of tree trunk in contact with wall causing direct damage –
No distortion where adequate lateral restraint from floor joists and foundations –
Removal of encroaching tissue allowed wall to be rebuilt and retention of tree.

The site is in an affluent residential area of south west London, with the Geological Survey map indicating that the subsoil should be London Clay. The subject property is a substantial two-storey property built in about 1908. The original construction included a single storey projection on the right flank, the outer wall of which extended to the property boundary. This extension had a flat roof with low parapet walls to form a balcony. It was originally part of the main oak panelled living room, but in 1966 the property was converted into two flats, with this projecting section partitioned off from the remainder of the living room for use as a kitchen.

The property, including the extension, provide an early example of cavity wall construction. Investigations revealed a suspended floor beneath the lounge and extension with a 1.27m deep underfloor area above the oversight concrete. The suspended floor was supported at regular intervals by substantial brick piers, with three of these piers integral with the flank wall. These piers supported a wall plate, with a 110mm x 50mm soft wood joists running at right angles to the flank wall (CS Figure 10.1).

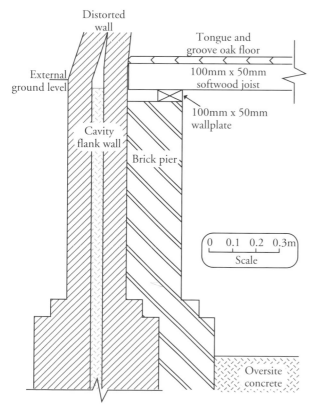

Case Study Figure 10.1

Section through flank wall showing lateral restraint from joists.

Case Study Figure 10.2

California laurel growing immediately adjacent to flank wall.

The tree

In the front garden of the adjacent property, immediately beside the flank wall of the kitchen extension, there was a Californian laurel tree (*Umbellularia californica*). It was believed that this tree had been planted shortly prior to construction of the subject property, and was now protected by a Tree Preservation Order. The height of this tree was approximately 10m, with a broad spreading crown with the branches overhanging the balcony above the kitchen projection (CS Figure 10.2). At a height of 1.5m the trunk had a diameter of 63cm, but below this level the trunk flared out to produce a swollen bulbous base thickly covered with epicormic shoots. At ground level the swollen base of the trunk had a diameter of approximately 1.6m (measured parallel to the flank wall), and projected 1.25m from the flank. The base of the trunk was in direct contact with the flank wall to a height of 0.85m above ground, and for a length of 1.4m at ground level. Above this bulbous area of contact the main trunk leant away from the flank wall.

Damage to property

The flank wall of the kitchen projection was distorted inwards. I measured the extent of this distortion with the aid of a plumb bob and line. This could be suspended from the projecting stone capping to the wall, the edge of which was straight. Measurements were taken at 0.5m intervals along the length of the wall just below the capping, and on a 0.5m square grid over the whole area of the wall, and also immediately above external ground level. The extent of lateral distortion is shown in CS Figure 10.3, which also shows the area where the tree was in direct contact.

Internally the flank wall showed a corresponding concave curve, but the cupboards and kitchen appliances prevented precise measurements. This distortion had caused cracking and damage to the plasterwork and prevented installation of kitchen units and appliances. From careful examination of the plasterwork, it could be established that there must have been significant distortion and damage at the time the room was converted to use as a kitchen. Cracks which had developed since this conversion, for instance behind the cupboards (CS Figure 10.4) were about 5mm wide, whereas on the immediately adjacent sections above and below the cupboard they were approximately 1.5mm wide. Clearly the cracks had been repaired on various occasions, and even the most recent cracks had paint within them showing that it had been present at the time of last redecoration, approximately three years previously.

Cause of damage

It was clear that the flank wall was distorted, with the pattern of distortion indicating that this was caused by lateral pressure exerted by growth of the base of the tree. The maximum distortion was about 0.6m above ground level. As this area was hidden by the trunk of the tree, the exact amount could not be measured but was likely to be at least 100mm.

It was notable that the measurements showed that there was little, or no, distortion at ground level, but distortion increased very rapidly above this level. At ground level the inside of the wall had lateral restraint provided by the substantial timber joists (CS Figure 10.1), which transmitted any lateral pressure to the opposite side of the building. Potentially the 1.2m high walls of the subfloor area had no restraint and might be vulnerable to pressure from the underground parts of the root system. However, the buttressing by the sleeper piers and the lateral restraint provided by the bottom of the foundations and oversight concrete appears to have been sufficient to withstand any lateral pressure exerted by the underground parts of the root system.

The distortion and damage of the above ground parts of the wall was being caused by the growth of the bulbous base of the tree. This unusual growth pattern caused pressure to be exerted on the above ground sections of the wall, where the cavity construction provided very limited lateral restraint. The cavity had collapsed and the growth had also distorted the inner leaf of brickwork.

From the shape of the base of the tree it was probable that the centre of the trunk was about 0.4m from the base of the wall. The base of the trunk had grown by 0.8m to the front and sides, but on the wall side, after it had grown by 0.4m, it came into contact. Thereafter, growth has produced a flattening on this side of the trunk, except in the area above ground level where the restraint had been inadequate and the 100mm of distortion had developed. This is, strictly speaking, damage by the trunk rather than roots, but the principles remain the same.

There was no evidence of cracks or distortion of the type which might be caused by foundation movement associated with shrinking or swelling of a clay subsoil, and it was agreed with the surveyor acting for the property owner that there was no evidence of subsidence. Likewise, there was no evidence that any roots passing beneath the foundations had caused any lifting of the building.

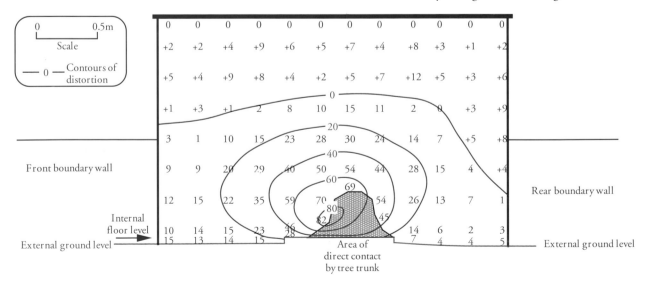

Case Study Figure 10.3.

Elevation diagram of flank wall of kitchen extension, showing extent of lateral distortion (in millimetres) as measured by plumb bob from straight edge of parapet.

Case Study Figure 10.4

Internal cracks and collapsing plaster (behind cooker). Careful examination shows long history of development of cracks and distortion with recurrent repairs.

Remedial action

It was clear that, whilst complete rebuilding of the kitchen was unnecessary, the flank wall needed to be demolished and rebuilt so as to straighten the wall and eliminate the concavity. Such rebuilding could not be accomplished while the tree encroached into the original location of the wall.

The tree was a rare and unusual species, located in a very conspicuous position, and quite correctly the subject of a Tree Preservation Order. Although the branches overhung the extension, they did not block light to the building, as there was only a nominal window opening on the adjacent wall. Retention of the tree was therefore highly desirable, provided it did not cause further damage.

Legal aspects

Prior to my involvement the owner of the property had started legal proceedings in 1989. The Statement of Claim alleged that "roots from the tree extended and still extent under the plaintiff's property and since about 1987 have undermined the foundations to the plaintiff's house and/or withdrawn moisture from the soil under the said foundations". It was subsequently agreed with the plaintiff's surveyor that no such damage was occurring. The Statement of Claim further alleged that "The tree trunk and/or roots of the tree where they reach the surface of the ground have grown to an extent whereby the plaintiff's kitchen wall is compressed and continues to be under pressure and has cracked". This part of the allegation was clearly correct.

It was claimed that the whole of the plaintiff's kitchen required to be demolished and rebuilt at an estimated cost in excess of £16,000 plus various additional fees. An Injunction was also sought "to restrain the defendant from allowing the roots of a tree and the tree trunk to encroach onto the plaintiff's property to cause a nuisance".

I was instructed on behalf of the defendant. It could be clearly established that substantial distortion was already present in 1966 when the room was converted to a kitchen, and also that only very slight additional movement had occurred during the previous six years. The scope of remedial works had not altered significantly during the previous six years limitation period, and on this basis the defendant denied liability. The claim was subsequently discontinued.

However, it was apparent that the base of the trunk was encroaching onto the plaintiff's property, and the plaintiff was entitled to the Injunction to restrain this encroachment.

To achieve this, I proposed that a slice of wood should be removed from the rear of the tree, so as to leave a gap of about 50mm between the face of the wall (when rebuilt) and the trimmed surface of the trunk. There would be no further growth on the main area of exposed wood, but there would be continued callus growth from the cambium around the edges. The 50mm clearance provided some scope for this, and it was anticipated that this callus growth would need to be trimmed off at intervals in future.

Although the plaintiff's surveyor had been claiming that there was a risk of heave if the tree was felled, these claims were dropped in the absence of any evidence of subsidence damage. He further agreed that, as there was no evidence of distortion of the foundations or underground parts of the wall, rebuilding was only required on the distorted area above ground level, and there was no necessity to underpin or install new foundations.

The distorted area of wall was therefore demolished. This exposed the flattened area of trunk where the tree had previously been in contact. The exposed face of the trunk was far more irregular in shape than I had anticipated, with a mixture of adventitious roots and invaginations in the bark. These had combined to trap a considerable amount of soil, all of which had to be cleaned off before the tree could be sawn (CS Figure 10.5). Even with this care, the chainsaw required sharpening three times during the operation as a result of encountering stones which had been trapped within the bark and then grown into the tree. However, the cut was successfully completed down to ground level (CS Figure 10.6) to provide the required 50mm clearance between the back of the tree and the face of the wall. The wall was subsequently rebuilt (CS Figure 10.7), with these works completed in May 1990.

Case Study Figure 10.5

Flank wall partially demolished, and vertical slice being taken with chainsaw from rear of base of trunk.

As anticipated, after six seasons the callus growth around the edges of the cut were sufficient to bring it again into contact with the brickwork. It was a simple task to trim this callus growth off all around the edge down to ground level, to recreate the gap.

Although treatment of this sort will be detrimental to the tree, it continues to flourish.

Lessons to be learnt

- Despite the massive growth and extreme proximity of this tree to the wall, the internal lateral restraint below ground level was sufficient to prevent any distortion by the root system.

- Distortion above ground level, where there was negligible restraint, had developed slowly and progressively, probably over at least 50 years. The deterioration during the previous six years was negligible, and there was no liability for the damage.

- Despite the probable presence of a clay soil, there was no evidence of indirect damage from clay shrinkage.

- Removal of the slice of wood allowed the wall to be rebuilt, and the tree to be successfully retained with periodic subsequent maintenance.

Case Study Figure 10.6

Base of trunk after removal of slice to provide 50mm clearance.

Case Study Figure 10.7

Base of trunk and adjacent wall after rebuilding (photograph taken 6 years after remedial work, with callus regrowth beginning to come into contact again.)

Causes of Damage

There are many potential causes of damage to buildings; consideration of these goes far beyond the scope of this book. The book "Defects in Buildings" produced by the Property Services Agency of the Department of Environment (HMSO, 1989) provides a detailed description of 181 defects. For each of these it gives brief details of the symptoms, the investigations which are needed, and of the diagnosis and cure. There are also excellent introductory chapters on the causes of deterioration, the principles of diagnosis and investigation techniques. However, a limitation of the book is that it is based on the symptoms rather than the causes; thus subsidence damage appears in various sections related to the different types of symptoms which can occur. BRE Digest 361 "Why do buildings crack?" provides an abbreviated version of the book.

Many defects are caused by defective materials or construction practices and affect only the superstructure; Bonshor and Bonshor (1996) provides a useful description of the various mechanisms. Others are caused by foundation movements, with these movements causing damage to the superstructure. These foundation movements may be caused by:

i) settlement:
   a) initial , within design parameters;
   b) excessive movements, caused by excessive load or defective material beneath the foundations.

ii) subsidence:
   a) as a result of shrinkage of a clay subsoil from root activity;
   b) collapse of mine workings, tunnelling or related works;
   c) slope instability;
   d) leaking drains causing washout of fines;
   e) fluctuation in ground water level.

iii) heave:
   a) from rehydration and swelling of previously desiccated soil;
   b) removal of load;
   c) frost action.

All of these different mechanisms, whether caused by defects in the superstructure or by one of the various mechanisms of foundation movement, produce different patterns of damage. One aim of investigations is to establish which of these causes is operating.

There is no doubt that, where foundation movements are involved, tree root activity is the commonest cause of these movements. Thus, the Institution of Structural Engineers (1994) estimate that over 80% of subsidence claims on shrinkable clay soils are attributable to trees and shrubs close to the property; I suspect this may be an underestimate. However, trees are by no means the only cause, and frequently there are multiple causes operating simultaneously. For this reason, it is essential that all cases of damage are properly investigated, without any preconceived notions. It can be tempting to see a tree in close proximity to a building and to leap to the immediate conclusion that it must be involved. Such an approach ignores the fact that the majority of buildings are close to trees, and so, whatever the cause of damage, there is likely to be a tree in the vicinity.

Where tree root activity is involved, Chapters 5, 6 and 7 have identified the different types of movement which might be occurring:

i) Seasonal movement caused by seasonal changes in moisture content produced by the tree;

ii) subsidence associated with development of a persistent deficit;

iii) heave associated with recovery from a persistent deficit;

iv) dynamic settlement;

v) a combination of the above. Such combination may be acting at the same time (for instance, seasonal movement which is also causing dynamic settlement), or at different times (for instance, subsidence while a tree was present, followed by heave or recovery after its removal).

Objectives of investigation

The objectives when investigating damage are two-fold:

i)   To identify the cause, or causes;

ii) To determine the appropriate remedy.

These two objectives may require different methods or emphasis in the investigation. Remedial measures are considered in Chapter 17; two basic options are identified:

i)   stabilise foundations by vegetation management, usually by tree felling or pruning.

or **ii)   stabilise the foundations by underpinning.**

Too often investigations which are undertaken may establish the cause, but are of little assistance for determining the remedy. Indeed, in most situations, investigations need to concentrate on deciding about the appropriate remedial action, as the cause will become obvious as a by-product of this work.

Scope of investigations

The previous Chapters have considered the separate components; i.e. the tree and its root system (Chapters 2 and 3), the soil (Chapter 4), the way in which these interact to produce either seasonal (Chapter 5) or persistent soil drying (Chapter 6), and the interaction of all of these factors with the building (Chapter 7) and the weather (Chapter 8). They have also emphasised the inherent variability of these components. Buildings will vary in their susceptibility to distortion and to dynamic settlement. Soil can vary enormously (both vertically and horizontally) even on the same site, with this affecting the permeability and shrinkage characteristics. Even with detailed investigations, accurate diagnosis of soil behaviour is usually impractical. The tree introduces even more variation. Species differ in their ability to exploit and desiccate different types of soils, but these differences are masked by the variation imposed by the site conditions, by genetic differences between individuals, and by variation through the life of the tree (Chapter 7). **As a result of all of this variation, it must be recognized that the whole interacting system of trees, soils and buildings is inherently variable and unpredictable. The only predictable aspects of the behaviour of trees on clay soils, and their effect on buildings, is their unpredictability.**

This should not be taken to imply that investigation of damage is difficult or impractical. It merely means:

i)   each site must be treated on its own merits, without preconceptions;

ii) keep an open mind when deciding on the most appropriate method of investigation;

iii) do not seek to rely on standard guidelines.

The different causes of damage all have different characteristics, and diagnostic features. Investigations must aim at identifying sufficient of these features to prove the cause and determine the remedy. This may involve consideration of:

i)   The building (Chapter 12):
   a)   the history of the site, and of the building and construction methods;
   b)   analysis of the damage, and the history of this damage;
   d)   determination of foundation depth and construction;
   c)   measurement of the existing distortion;
   d)   monitoring any ongoing distortion (Chapter 15).

ii) The soil (Chapter 13):
   a)   geology;
   b)   one or more profiles from boreholes;
   c)   assessment of desiccation from:
         moisture content;
         soil suctions;
         shear strength;
   d)   soil classification.

iii) The tree (Chapter 14):
   a)   identification and dimensions;
   b)   assessment of past and future growth;
   c)   root identification;
   d)   assessment of fine root activity in boreholes.

Further details of these investigations are presented in the following four Chapters (12-15). No set formula should be followed, but rather the investigations should be undertaken appropriate to the particular situation, so as to build up a coherent overall picture. Throughout, it is important to keep in mind the basic objectives, as identified in the previous section; i.e. determination of the cause and the most appropriate remedial action. For this purpose, it can help to pose questions aimed at deciding on the type of investigations which are most appropriate for the particular circumstances. As all cases should be judged on their own merits, the exact scope of the questions will vary, but typically they might be:

i) how serious is the damage?

ii) is the damage likely to recur and if so, under what conditions?

iii) is the soil desiccated?

iv) how deep is any desiccation of the soil?

v) how long will it take for the soil to recover to its normal moisture content?

vi) how much movement might occur during this recovery, and what will be the effect of this movement?

vii) how extensive beneath the building are:-
   a) existing soil movements?
   b) potential future soil movements?

viii) if underpinning is to be used, which parts of the building require such treatment?

ix) to what depth should such underpinning be taken to counteract:
   a) existing soil movements?
   b) potential future soil movements?

x) should the underpinning include anti-heave precautions?

Additional information or particular emphasis may be required in any case where any type of legal action may become involved (Chapter 19), for instance:

i) a claim for nuisance against an adjacent tree owner;

ii) a negligence claim against a designer, builder, surveyor, engineer or other party;

iii) application for an injunction for tree removal;

iv) applications for work to trees covered by a Tree Preservation Order or other protection.

Too often an expert is called in at a late stage, by which time it is no longer practical to obtain the relevant evidence, or parts of the investigation must be repeated in order to obtain essential details.

The role of monitoring

Most of the basic information which is required can be collected by a single individual in a single day on site, plus the laboratory work on soil and root analysis. Investigations of this sort during a single visit might be likened to a single photograph of the problem. Some deductions might be drawn from this photograph about the past history or possible future behaviour but such deductions are of limited value. Tree root damage involves foundation movement, and Chapters 5 and 6 have described the highly dynamic interaction between the tree and soil, with constant change in moisture content and associated soil movement. Far more information can be obtained by studying this movement. For instance, as described in Chapter 5, a characteristic feature where living tree root activity is involved is a pattern of subsidence during the summer followed by recovery in the winter. Alternatively, if a tree has been felled or water uptake curtailed for any reason, progressive upward heave or recovery movements may occur. These movements, i.e. seasonal or progressive upward, are highly diagnostic and will invariably be present if trees either are, or have been, involved. Demonstrating that there are seasonal or heave movements is the most accurate and reliable method for distinguishing vegetation-induced damage from other causes, such as settlement or slope instability (which cause progressive downward movement) or from damage caused by movement of the superstructure (where there would be no foundation movement).

These movements can be demonstrated and accurately quantified by monitoring over a period of time. Rather than a single photograph, this can provide a movie-image. Any monitoring can be useful, but as the underlying cause of any damage are the *changes in foundation level* which are occurring, **level monitoring is by far the most valuable technique, and should be an essential part of almost all investigations.** Techniques for monitoring levels and other forms of monitoring are described in Chapter 15.

Valuable information can be obtained from monitoring over a brief period, in many cases a matter of a few weeks will suffice, but there is usually opportunity to extend the observations over a longer period. Not only does level monitoring provide by far the most accurate means of diagnosis, but it is also invaluable for predicting future movements. This information is essential for decisions on the appropriate remedial work. Level monitoring is also required for demonstrating the efficacy (or otherwise) of any remedial measures which have been taken, particularly if these involve any form of vegetation management. It usually helps if any continuing movements can be compared with movements occurring prior to the remedy.

For this reason, **level monitoring should be installed and initial readings taken at the earliest opportunity, preferably during the first site visit.** Subsequent readings can then be used to confirm any initial diagnosis, as an aid to decisions on remedial measures, and to confirm the efficacy of these measures.

Cost effectiveness of investigation

Whilst detailed investigations are highly desirable, the realities of cost will often limit the scope. Available resources should therefore be used as effectively as possible. If the investigations are to be limited, particular care is required to decide which are the most relevant, but in general terms I would recommend that the order of priority should be:

i)   the information which is readily available at minimal cost or effort, e.g.:
   a) geology;
   b) history of building;
   c) history of development of damage;
   d) identification of any relevant trees.

ii) monitoring building level;

iii) level distortion survey;

iv) assessment of past and future tree growth;

v)   determination of foundation depth;

vi) borehole with moisture content determination;

vii) soil classification tests;

viii) crack monitoring and analysis of crack patterns;

ix) assessment of fine root activity in borehole;

x)   root identification;

xi) soil suction tests (useful, but expensive).

These priorities are very different to the scope of investigations which are normally undertaken by others. However, they have developed in the light of my experience, as being as the most appropriate and relevant approach to the particular problems posed by tree root damage to buildings. Their practical application is seen in the Case Studies.

Reviewing the results of investigations

It has been emphasised that investigations should start without any preconceived notions about the cause. As the information becomes available, all of the possible causes should be tested, and the scope of the investigations modified as appropriate so as to ensure that a correct diagnosis is made. If any part of the overall picture is incompatible with the diagnosis, one's suspicions should be aroused and further checks made to explain such incompatibility. If several parts are incompatible, more detailed investigations are essential.

If several individuals are required to deal with the different disciplines involved, it may be sensible for one to coordinate the team and to allocate tasks and priorities. However, it is desirable that all members are kept advised of all aspects of the results. It is only by doing so that they may spot factors which are incompatible with their own evidence.

Summary

1.   There are two main options for remedial action (see also Chapter 17):

   i)   stabilise foundations by tree management;

or ii)   stabilise the foundations by underpinning.

2.   The scope of investigations should depend on the circumstances of each case, but should be directed towards:

   i)   identifying the cause, or causes;

   ii) if tree roots are involved, determining which remedy is appropriate.

3.   Far too often the site investigations which are carried out are stereotyped and inappropriate, and do not provide the required information.

4.   Tree root damage involves movement of the foundations. The direction and timing of these movements are highly diagnostic, and can be determined very easily by level monitoring. Level monitoring also provides essential information for deciding on remedial action, and confirming the efficacy of any remedial work. **Level monitoring is the most useful, and cost-effective, part of any investigation and it should be a routine part of all investigations** (see Chapter 15, page 239 for further details).

CASE STUDY 11

*Long history of minor damage – Site conditions make underpinning impractical –
Felling Monterey cypress stabilises front corner –
Continuing movements of rear corner stabilised after pear tree is felled.*

The site is located in north west London, with the Geological Survey map indicating that the subsoil should be London Clay. The subject property is the right half of a two-storey semi-detached house built in the early 1930s. Both halves have a front bay and a projecting section on the rear elevation, with a single storey addition in the area enclosed by these projections. On the front elevation there is a recessed porch with brick arch over it. Elevations are pebble-dash rendered except for the frontage.

A 2.4m wide drive passes beside the right flank wall to a rear garage. This drive is surfaced with irregular paving. Immediately beyond the drive is the boundary to three gardens which back onto the subject property.

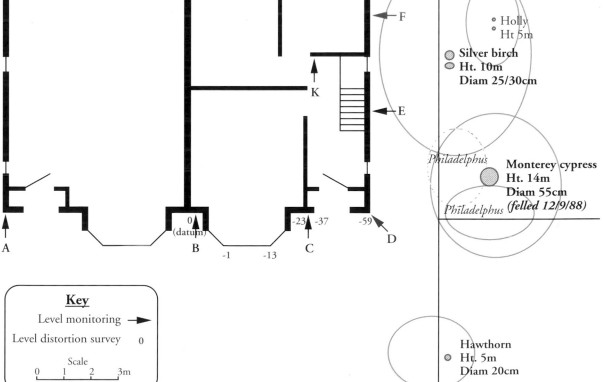

Case Study Figure 11.1

Site plan showing location of adjacent trees, results of level distortion survey and location of level monitoring stations.

179

The trees

In these adjacent rear gardens were a variety of trees, the locations of which are shown on the site plan in CS Figure 11.1.

The largest of these was a Monterey cypress (*Cupressus macrocarpa*). This tree had a height of 14m and trunk diameter of 55cm, and was beginning to develop the broader crown shape of a mature specimen. It was located 4.1m from the front of the flank wall of the subject property.

Opposite the middle of the flank wall there was a double stemmed silver birch (*Betula pendula*), with a height of 10m and diameters of 25cm and 30cm. This was a mature specimen, showing slow growth. It was located close to the boundary, 2.8m from the flank wall.

Just beyond the rear corner of the flank wall there was a mature pear tree (*Pyrus*), with a height of 9m and diameter of 40cm. This tree was 3.5m from the rear corner, and there was a further similar pear tree 7.5m from the rear.

In addition to these main trees, there were various large *Philadelphus* shrubs and holly opposite the flank wall, and a hawthorn and further pear trees to the front. There were no significant trees on the subject property, nor in the other half of the semi-detached.

Previous history

Fine structural cracks were first noted following the drought summer of 1976, but were not considered to be serious. During 1986, damage had escalated and the insured alerted his insurance company. A structural engineer was appointed, and a trial pit established that the flank wall was on foundations 730mm deep. At that stage external damage was restricted to the arch over the front porch adjacent to the flank wall, with corresponding internal cracking and also cracks in the ceilings of most rooms. Underpinning to a depth of 2.5m was recommended for the flank elevation with short returns on the front and rear walls.

Before implementing these works, hand boreholes were drilled at two locations adjacent to the flank wall and also in the rear garden. The deepest of these boreholes (opposite the front corner) demonstrated a sandy clay with occasional gravel to a depth of 2.45m, with similar conditions in the other shallower holes. The soil below about 1m had a plasticity index in excess of 50. The clay was very hard and alleged to be desiccated, but interpretation of moisture contents was complicated by the presence of gravel; for instance, a moisture content of 9.0% almost certainly reflected sand or gravel within the sample.

Underpinning contractors attempted to install a pier and beam underpinning scheme to the designed depth of 2.4m below ground level. When this depth was achieved for the initial pier, the Building Inspector requested that the piers should extend to a greater depth because of the presence of tree roots. This scheme was abandoned with a recommendation that piles should be used.

A piling rig then drilled a test bore. This encountered clay with occasional gravel to 5m depth; this clay was described as being increasingly desiccated to 2.5m, sufficient to make for very slow drilling from 2.5 to 4.25m. Below 5m there was wet brown silty sand to a depth of 11.5m. It was concluded that drilled piles would be unsuitable for these ground conditions, and that driven piles would involve excessive disruption of the property. It was suggested that the original pier and beam scheme should be reconsidered, but with doubts expressed about the suitability of the sand as a bearing strata.

Insurers were becoming increasingly concerned about the magnitude of the proposed works and instructed an engineer to review the situation. He suggested that consideration should be given to tree removal, and as a result I was appointed in April 1988.

Damage to property

At the time of my appointment, the main external damage was restricted to the front elevation adjacent to the flank wall, with cracks above the door arch, and diagonal cracking extending through the first floor window. There was very minor damage on the front bay. The right hand flank elevation had no obvious damage in the render, but there was slight cracking on the rear elevation above and below the first floor bedroom window over the single storey addition. Internally there was extensive but minor damage in the recent decorations. A notable feature of this were the cracks in the ceilings, all of which were aligned diagonally across the house, consistent with subsidence of the front right corner.

Level distortion survey

The render only allowed measurements to be taken across the front elevation; the results are shown on the site plan in CS Figure 11.1. They indicate a downward distortion of the front corner by 59mm relative to the party wall, which is consistent with the damage in this locality.

Level monitoring

I recommended the immediate start of level monitoring. Markers were attached at 8 locations around the periphery of the property. An additional marker was located well away from any vegetation on the front corner of the other half of the semi-detached to provide a suitable datum. In autumn 1989 an additional marker was placed on an internal wall. The location of the stations is shown on CS Figure 11.1, and the results of all readings are shown in CS Figure 11.2. For convenience of presentation, these results are shown relative to the readings taken at the end of the winter 1988/89 when seasonal recovery had occurred.

	5/5/88	11/7/88	1/9/88	29/3/89	16/11/89	4/1/90	23/4/90	2/5/91	30/10/91	17/6/92	4/9/92	14/4/93	2/11/93
A	Datum	Datum	Datum	Datum	Datum	Datum	Datum	Datum	Datum	Datum	Datum	Datum	Datum
B	-0.1	-0.1	-0.3	0	+1.2	+1.3	+1.4	+1.4	+1.6	+1.3	+1.5	+1.6	+1.7
C	-2.8	-4.1	-6.2	0	+4.7	+4.9	+5.3	+5.7	+6.1	+6.1	+6.3	+6.1	+6.3
D	-2.6	-4.6	-9.1	0	+4.1	+4.7	+5.1	+5.9	+6.5	+6.1	+6.5	+6.3	+6.3
E	-2.5	-3.9	-7.6	0	+1.5	+2.7	+4.0	+4.6	+3.0	+3.9	+2.1	+4.5	+4.9
F	-0.6	-1.0	-4.4	0	-1.9	+0.3	+3.3	+4.2	-1.6	+1.4	-2.0	+3.1	+3.8
G	-1.0	-0.8	-3.4	0	-5.5	-2.5	+1.9	+2.7	-6.9	-1.2	-6.7	+1.8	+3.1
H	-1.2	-0.3	-1.5	0	-2.1	-2.0	+1.6	+2.3	-3.5	-0.2	-3.5	+1.7	+2.5
J	-0.4	-0.1	-0.7	0	Marker damaged	-	-	-	-	-	-	-	-
K (compared with 16.11.89)						+0.4	+1.9	+1.9	-1.3	+0.1	-1.1	+1.2	+1.5

Case Study Figure 11.2

Results of level monitoring (mm), presented relative to Station A as a datum, and to readings on 29/3/89.

The results for three of the stations are also shown graphically in CS Figure 11.3.

Remedial action

I recommended the immediate removal of the Monterey cypress, based on my experience of the extreme influence which this species can have on clay soils. I recognised that some recovery movement was likely. However, I was optimistic that the presence of the gravel within the clay would improve the permeability, and that the underlying water-laden sand would allow rehydration to occur from below, as well as from above from rainfall.

I could see no advantage in further soil investigations, but suggested that the level monitoring would provide the best method for determining the extent and duration of any recovery movements. In the event of unacceptable recovery movements continuing, underpinning would remain an option. This would need to incorporate anti-heave precautions, but such precautions would have been required regardless of whether the tree had been retained, as this species is very susceptible to the lethal fungal disease *Seiridium cardinale* and so liable to die at any time.

Initially I considered that there was inadequate evidence to implicate the pear tree or any other trees as the cause of the damage, but recommended that their involvement should be re-assessed in the light of the results of the level monitoring.

Although my recommendation for felling the cypress was submitted in May, the owner prevaricated, and it was not felled until September. By that time, the front corner had subsided by 6.5mm. The extent of movement progressively diminished along the flank elevation, with only 2.4mm at the rear corner. Significant movement was also occurring on the front elevation (station C), but negligible movement either at the front or rear of the party wall. Recovery during the subsequent winter (to 29/3/89) was slightly greater than the downward movements recorded during the previous summer, suggesting that some seasonal movement had already occurred by the time the monitoring was started in May. This was to be expected with an evergreen which can start growth and transpiration early in the summer.

Subsequent events

The level monitoring during the subsequent summer (1989) showed the front corner recovering by a further 4.1mm by November. This rate of movement slowed dra-

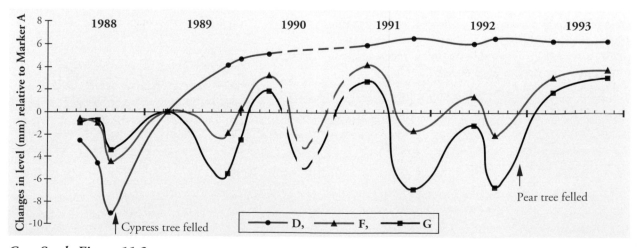

Case Study Figure 11.3

Results of level monitoring for selected stations.

matically during the winter, with only a further 1mm of movement. Clearly the rate of recovery had not been diminished by the very dry weather during the summer of 1989. Virtually identical recovery movements were recorded at station C on the front elevation, and the front of the party wall remained static.

During the summer of 1989 the rear corner of the flank wall (station G) subsided by 5.5mm. Clearly, seasonal movements were continuing as a result of the remaining vegetation adjacent to the rear of the flank wall. However, these movements did not appear to be causing any damage, and it was therefore considered reasonable not to take any further action.

Although it was known that active movements were continuing, temporary cosmetic decorations were undertaken in autumn 1988. Not surprisingly, further cracking was recorded in these decorations, apparently associated with the recovery movements.

It was hoped that my involvement was completed by spring 1990. However, the following year the owner's engineer reported further damage. Unfortunately this was not reported until the spring of 1991, and so no measurements were taken of the extent of recovery from the seasonal movement during 1990. Further monitoring during the dry summer of 1991 recorded 9.6mm of subsidence at station G at the rear of the flank wall. By contrast, the front corner of the building showed a further 0.6mm of recovery during this period. Whereas previously the whole of the flank wall had been behaving fairly uniformly, there was now differential movement plus additional stress created by the slight recovery. This was sufficient to cause the minor fresh damage, the pattern of which was consistent with this movement.

Further remedial action was required with the adjacent vegetation to prevent this continuing movement. As the centre of the flank wall (opposite the birch trees) was showing less movement, I recommended that the nearest pear tree should be felled (or alternatively severely reduced although it would be of little value after such treatment). No action was taken on this recommendation, and a further cycle of seasonal movement was allowed to occur during 1992. However, during the following winter the nearest pear tree was felled, and in addition (but not requested) the further pear tree was heavily reduced.

Subsequent level monitoring during the following summer (1993) demonstrated that this treatment had been effective in stabilising the rear corner. Furthermore, stations E and F opposite the silver birch showed no further seasonal movement, thus confirming that this tree was not involved, despite its close proximity. This further monitoring also demonstrated no continuing movement at the front corner.

Lessons to be learnt

• The initial efforts to underpin were aborted. The more elaborate scheme which was being contemplated would have involved exorbitant costs.

• The site investigations provided scant information on the depth of desiccation or permeability of the clay to allow a judgement on the extent of duration of recovery. However, the level monitoring was able to show a rapid reduction in the rate of movement.

• Removal of the Monterey cypress allowed rapid restabilisation at the front corner of the building. At this location the majority of the overall recovery (85%) was complete within 12 months of the tree being felled, and 96% complete after a further winter.

• My initial opinion that the movement at the rear was not significant was proved incorrect. The continuing differential movement of the flank caused further minor damage, particularly during the extreme drought of 1991.

• Subsequent felling of the pear tree to the rear allowed rapid restability of the rear of the flank wall.

• The foundations were effectively stabilised without the need for underpinning.

• Level monitoring was essential throughout the period.

Objectives

The main objective when studying the building is to develop an overall picture of the structure and any damage. This can then be related to soil conditions and potential effects of adjacent trees, to provide a coherent picture. For this one needs to:

i)   build-up an overall picture of the building:
a)   history of site;
b)   method of construction;
c)   subsequent alterations.

ii) assess the distortion and damage which has occurred both recently and historically:
a)   analysis of crack patterns and distortion (recent and historic);
b)   level and verticality distortion surveys.

iii) assess vulnerability to damage from seasonal movement or heave:
a)   determination of foundation depth;
b)   assessment of foundation load;
c)   analysis of weak spots;
d)   analysis of angular distortion.

iv) determine the condition of ancillary structures:
a)   drains;
b)   boundary and retaining walls.

The methods for achieving this will usually include the investigations which are described in the following sections. As emphasised in Chapter 11, the scope of investigations will vary depending on the circumstances; only those investigations which are directly relevant to the problem should be undertaken.

History of site

The use of a site prior to construction of a building can be relevant to subsequent foundation movements. In particular, any trees which have been removed may have left a moisture deficit which can cause heave. Alternatively, previous use may influence the load bearing capacity, for instance if there are areas of fill material or if there was a previous building on the site. In-formation on previous use of the site can often be obtained from maps or plans which pre-date the construction, or from aerial photographs.

The age of a building can usually be obtained from the owner, or from the deeds of the property. In many cases architectural styles or materials will indicate the era. Where precise dates are required, for instance of the time of year when the foundation trenches were excavated, the Local Authority Building Inspector's records can assist.

Knowledge of the age is required to determine whether a building is older than adjacent trees, and whether there can be a continuing risk from heave as a result of removal of trees previously growing on the site. It can provide guidance on the type of construction likely to have been in vogue at that time, and on what Codes of Practice were in force.

Special care is required in identifying any later extensions, as they can be particularly vulnerable to damage. Settlement of extensions often produces differential movement at the junction with the original structure; this can cause damage or abnormal distortion patterns. Extensions may have different foundation depths. Similarly, alterations to a building, particularly if involving structural walls, can alter the foundation loading and give rise to damage.

Analysis of damage to the building

Damage occurs to a building when the stresses imposed by distortion exceed the ability of the building to withstand this distortion. It is important to emphasise that many buildings have the ability to tolerate considerable distortion without manifesting any apparent damage, but that when damage does occur the pattern and extent of this will depend on many inter-acting factors, and can be very variable.

The most obvious manifestation of damage is the development of cracks. The pattern of this cracking can provide information on the direction of differential movement.

At its simplest, subsidence normally creates a rotational movement of a panel of brickwork, with maximum movement at one end of the panel. This causes a bend in the foundations, and a tapering crack opens in response (Figure 12.1). If the bend is downwards, the crack will be widest at the top; if it is upwards, it will be widest at the base. The direction of differential movement is at right angles to the direction of cracking (as shown by the red arrow).

Figure 12.1

Typical subsidence-type rotational crack in a panel of brickwork. The red arrow indicates the direction of rotation (N.B. the extent of movement is exaggerated, with an angular distortion of 1:25)

The wide end of the crack must be on an edge which can move. In the very simple situation shown in Figure 12.1 this free edge is the top of the wall. In a building it is often a corner of the building which rotates outwards, with cracks tapering away on both adjacent walls, or it can be at the junction with the roof with movements occurring within the roof timbers, or at the damp-proof course (d.p.c.) with lateral movements along this plane of weakness. Most cracks will taper gradually along their length, until they eventually disappear. Cracks may develop singly, or more commonly there will be an array of cracks. Where there is an array, the width of each crack must be considered, to deduce the overall movement of brickwork.

Cracks will try to follow planes of weakness within the building. The most obvious weakness is in door and window openings, and so cracks will usually extend through these openings. They may originate as a fine crack on one side of the opening, distort the opening, and then continue as a wider crack on the opposite side towards a free edge such as a corner. The distortion of door frames will often make the door difficult to open or prevent catches from working; similarly windows can become jammed.

Whereas windows and doors are points of weakness, internal partition walls can provide support for an external wall and help to prevent cracking. Similarly, the restraint provided by floor or roof joists can restrict the movement of brickwork, but only on the walls which support these timbers; walls without timbers can be more susceptible to movement.

Brickwork has only limited tensile strength, and so will tend to crack fairly easily if stretched. Conversely it is very strong in compression, and so will transmit compressive forces widely. As subsidence normally involves a downwards and outwards rotation which stretches the building, the damage can remain fairly localised to the area of subsidence. However, if movements affect structural elements such as lintels or timber joists, the movement and damage can be transmitted to the far end of the element, with further damage manifest at that position.

Cracks should normally be present on both faces of a wall although they may be partially hidden by decorative finishes. With solid brickwork the cracks on the two faces will be close to each other, but with cavity brickwork the cracks in the two panels can be well apart with shear movements through the intervening cavity.

Different types of cracking may be distinguished. Tensile cracks involve simple opening of the crack. Compressive movements of cracks can also occur, particularly if a tensile crack is filled with a rigid material and then subsequently tries to close (as can occur with seasonal soil movements). This can squeeze the material out and crush of the edges of the crack.

Shear cracks are another common type of failure, involving differential movement on either side of the crack. Examination of these can provide information on the direction of differential movements which have occurred. In brick or plaster work this can be deduced by careful study and matching of the two sides of the crack (Figure 12.2a). Wallpaper may hide shear cracks at the junction between two walls or between walls

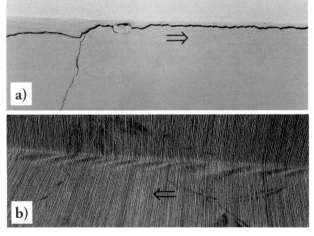

Figure 12.2

a) Shear movement in plaster shows as lateral movements of the edges of the crack, with development of secondary crack. b) Compression causes cracks to close and forces plaster outwards. Arrows show direction of movement.

and ceilings, but shear movements can stretch the paper and cause it to pucker (Figure 12.2b). The alignment of the puckering indicates the direction of movement of the adjacent parts of the building, which can then be related to the overall movements.

When clay swelling and heave damage occur, not only is there vertical movement of the foundations and associated damage, but there is often horizontal swelling and damage. These horizontal movements often show as vertical cracks below d.p.c. level, accompanied by shear movements along the d.p.c. and outward distortion of the brickwork at the corner of the building (Figure 12.3). Deep trench foundations can be particularly vulnerable to lateral movements of this sort.

Figure 12.3

Lateral movement of brickwork below d.p.c. caused by lateral swelling of clay during heave. (Photo P. Kelsey)

Figure 12.4

Diagram of crack damage. Care must be taken if using such information to interpret the direction of movement.

By studying all of the damage throughout a building it is often possible to deduce the pattern of movement which has occurred. For instance, Figure 12.4 provides a simple diagram looking only at the external brickwork on a single elevation. The dominant feature in this is the pattern of diagonal cracking in the left hand side, particularly around the bay, all of which indicates subsidence of the left hand side.

Many engineers rely on these patterns of crack damage as the sole means of diagnosing the building movements which have occurred. Although in some cases this may be sufficient, in many situations it is inadequate or even misleading. Of the 20 Case Studies described in this book, in 8 of them an incorrect diagnosis had been made on the basis of the crack pattern (Case Studies 1*, 4*, 7, 8, 12, 14*, 18*, 19); in the four marked with an asterisk this had led to serious errors in remedial work. The proportion of such examples of incorrect diagnosis in these Case Studies is higher than the norm, but, in my experience, where movements are diagnosed by crack patterns, errors are being made in about 10% of cases. For this reason, crack patterns should be studied and analysed, but reliance should not be placed on them as the sole method of diagnosis. Additional information (such as a distortion survey, page 188) should always be sought.

As an example of the way crack patterns can be misleading, Figure 12.4 may appear to show subsidence of the left side. However, this includes the area of the bay which will be particularly vulnerable to damage. There is other cracking shown throughout the building, some of which is contradictory. The diagram also includes a crack below d.p.c. level on the right hand side, and (perhaps barely discernible, but it is not always obvious) a lateral movement of brickwork below the d.p.c.. These other cracks may indicate upward heave of the right hand side of the building. On the basis of crack pattern either, or both, may be correct. The building may have subsided at the left hand end:

or alternatively it may have been subject to heave at the right hand end, with this heave not extending across the full width of the building:

185

History of damage

The development of damage can provide important clues on the cause. Subsidence associated with clay shrinkage will normally develop during the late summer when the ground is at its driest. If possible, the occupier should be questioned on this, and also whether there is evidence of cracks closing during the winter (detailed monitoring of movements is considered in greater detail in Chapter 15). If doors jam during the summer and become free in the winter, it can also indicate seasonal soil movement.

When questioning occupiers, it is important to realise that many people fail to see cracks until something draws them to their attention. They may then be convinced that the crack has only just occurred, although it might have been present for a long time. Inspection of a crack can give some indication of its age. Fresh cracks have sharp edges and a clean surface. With time the edges will erode, particularly if the crack is opening and closing, and dust and dirt will enter. If there has been any decoration, there will be paint inside the edges (but the crack may have increased in width since it was painted).

When studying the damage in a building it is also important to look for previous evidence of movement and past repairs. This can show in many ways. Repairs to brickwork can usually be detected by difference in mortar, and old repairs in render are usually obvious. Internal cracks often show evidence of previous repairs and the layers of differ-

Figure 12.5

Newspaper taken from a crack in 1976; clearly similar damage had been present in 1959.

HC	Hairline crack
VC	Vertical crack
CMG	Old crack made good
CMGR	Old crack made good reopened
6	6mm crack width
≈6	Approximately 6mm crack width
$\frac{0.6}{}$]2.1	Components of movement in a crack
✕	Direction of movement across crack
╱ 7	Fall in floor 7mm per metre (if not 1 metre, then e.g. 7/0.9)
╱ $^7/_D$	Fall across door head
CT	Ceiling tiles
COD	Crack over door
<2 or } (length on plan)	Crack in partition not shown on an elevation
///////	Parallel shear cracks
///////	Parallel shear creases
⊢7	Lean out or in at top of 1.0 metre
6 ⊢	Lean at top, with bottom part of metre height vertical
4 ⊣ 4	Bulge within 1.0 metre
↔	Vertical within 1.0m height
▌8	Crack width decreasing in direction of arrow; maximum width in millimetres
⊕ ⊙ } 6 (in) (out)	Out of plane movement in wall face - view facing
6→⌐	Out of plane movement in wall face - viewed in line
CR	Crack
OC	Old crack
COW	Crack over window
CUW	Crack under window
CC	Ceiling crack
e	Estimated
d/f	Door frame
w/f	Window frame
sl	Slight
o/p	Out of plane
⑦	Location of photographs

Figure 12.6

Symbols for crack diagrams   *(from Kelsey, 1979).*

ent fillers can be identified. I have encountered "new" cracks which have "only just appeared", but which are stuffed with newspapers reporting engagements during the Boer War! Figure 12.5 is a piece of newspaper taken from a crack which reopened in the drought of 1976; clearly there had been similar movement in 1959. Cracks in plaster often only become evident when wallpaper is removed, or multiple layers of old wallpaper may show the gradual development of cracking. Parts of a building which are not normally decorated, such as insides of cupboards or the roof space, can indicate the total movements of cracks and be contrasted with crack widths on adjacent decorated surfaces. Doors or windows may have distorted in the past and wedge shape fillets been inserted. The number of coats of paint over the fillet may indicate the age. Similarly, the striking plates on door catches or old bolts may have been realigned frequently.

If damage is appearing for the first time, it indicates that any trees in the vicinity have not been having any influence in the past. Conversely, long-standing similar damage indicates a history of similar movement. In either case this can be considered in the context of the history of vegetation on the site (see Chapter 14), to help indicate whether the existing vegetation, or some other factor, is likely to be involved.

If similar damage has been present in the past and has been repaired, it implies that similar repairs should suffice, provided the foundations have now been stabilised so as to prevent the problems recurring. More extensive repairs might provide significant betterment.

Recording of cracks

All of the information on the pattern of damage should be recorded. This is most easily done in diagrammatic form. Different methods of description are used by different authors, but one of the most comprehensive, but at the same time simple and understandable, is that used by Peter Kelsey & Partners, and reproduced with their permission in Figure 12.6. Where damage is extensive, it may be necessary to record damage for individual rooms. Exploded diagrams (Figure 12.7) can assist in this.

Severity of damage

If a report provides full detailed descriptions for all of the damage to a property, it is possible for a reader to appreciate the severity and significance of the damage. However, many reports provide only a brief summary of the damage, from which it is difficult to gain an overall picture of the problems. Such summaries frequently use subjective descriptions for the extent of damage, such as 'slight' or 'severe', but the basis of these descriptions clearly differ greatly with different authors. It is therefore preferable to have one uniform system for describing and categorising the severity of damage.

Such a system is proposed in BRE Digest 251 "Assessment of damage in low rise buildings", and is reproduced in Figure 12.8. This defines six categories of damage, based on the visible damage at the time of inspection, and also taking account of the ease of repair. It includes descriptions of crack width and frequency, but it is emphasised that this should not be the sole basis of classification, as the ease of repair is the key factor in determining the overall category of damage.

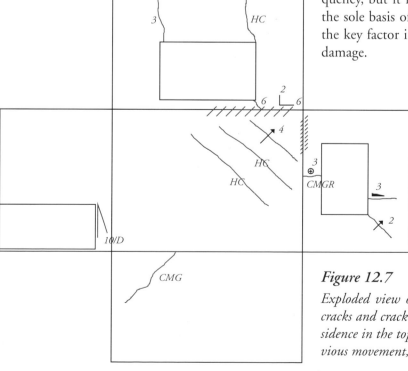

Figure 12.7

Exploded view of ceilings and walls of room, showing cracks and crack description. The diagram implies subsidence in the top right corner, but with evidence of previous movement, not necessarily from the same cause.

Category of damage	Degree[1] of damage	Description of typical damage *Ease of repair in italic type*	Approximate crack width (mm)
0	Negligible	Hairline cracks of less than about O.1mm width are classed as negligible.	Up to 0.1[2]
1	Very slight	*Fine cracks which can easily be treated during normal decoration.* Perhaps isolated slight fracturing in building. Cracks rarely visible in external brickwork.	Up to 1[2]
2	Slight	*Cracks easily filled. Redecoration probably required. Recurrent cracks can be masked by suitable linings.* Cracks not necessarily visible externally; *some external repointing may be required to ensure weathertightness.* Doors and windows may stick slightly.	Up to 5[2]
3	Moderate	*The cracks require some opening up and can be patched by a mason. Repointing of external brickwork and possibly a small amount of brickwork to be replaced.* Doors and windows sticking. Service pipes may fracture. Weathertightness often impaired.	5 - 15[2] (or a number of cracks up to 3.
4	Severe	*Extensive repair work involving breaking out and replacing sections of walls, especially over doors and windows.* Window and door frames distorted, floors sloping noticeably[3]. Walls leaning[3] or bulging noticeably, some loss of bearing in beams. Service pipes disrupted.	15 - 25[2] but also depends on number of cracks.
5	Very severe	*This requires a major repair job involving partial or complete rebuilding.* Beams lose bearing, walls lean badly and require shoring. Windows broken with distortion. Danger of instability.	Usually greater than 25[2] but depends on number of cracks.

Notes:
1. It must be emphasised that in assessing the degree of damage account must be taken of the location in the building or structure where it occurs, and also of the function of the building or structure.
2. Crack width is one factor in assessing category of damage and should not be used on its own as direct measure of it.
3. Local deviations of slope, from the horizontal or vertical, of more than 1/100 will normally be clearly visible. Overall deviations in excess of 1/150 are undesirable.

Figure 12.8

Classification of visible damage to walls with particular reference to ease of repair of plaster and brickwork or masonry.

from BRE Digest 251 'Assessment of damage in low-rise buildings.'

In this classification, categories 0, 1 and 2 represent aesthetic damage. Categories 3 and 4 include effects on the serviceability of the property, and category 5 indicates effects on the stability.

BRE Digest 251 also provides a classification system for ground floor slab settlements.

Measurement of the distortion of the building

Buildings are normally constructed to fairly close tolerances of level. If measurements show any significant departure from level, it can therefore indicate the extent of differential movements which have occurred at some time during the life of the building. Measurements of level are comparatively simple to take, and should form an essential part of any site investigation. Similarly, measurements of verticality or the lateral bowing of walls can provide valuable evidence on the cause of damage to a building.

Some investigators dismiss level surveys on the grounds that it is not known whether the building was originally constructed level. Such individuals have perhaps never bothered to take levels; those who do so on a routine basis find they are an invaluable aid to diagnosis. Like any evidence, they should not be followed slavishly, but used in conjunction with all of the other sources of information such as analysis of crack patterns, and consideration of soil movements likely to be caused by tree roots. It is alarming how frequently cases of subsidence are diagnosed, when the damaged part of the building shows a distinct upward trend (e.g. Case Studies 1 and 14). In such cases, subsequent investigations usually shows that heave rather than subsidence has been involved.

Builders normally take some care to ensure that brick courses, particularly in the lower parts of the building, are horizontal. For this reason, measurements are usually best made on a brickcourse at or near the level of the d.p.c.. However in practice it is often easier to use a course a few above or below the d.p.c., and excess mortar in the d.p.c. often makes it difficult to use this course. Before starting, check to ensure that the course is exposed around the whole building, and not obscured by changes in ground level, concrete plinths or steps in the d.p.c. Extra care will be needed when there are wide spans without exposed brickwork, particularly if the adjacent soil level is uneven.

Inevitably some variations in level occur, but these are normally haphazard and random, and usually not in excess of ±15mm around the periphery of a typical detached house. By contrast, buildings which are showing damage as a result of differential foundation movement usually show a distinct trend in level, frequently in excess of 40mm. Such trends provide strong evidence that differential movements have occurred some time during the life of the building.

If brickwork is covered by rendering, any other convenient feature can be utilised, provided there are reasonable grounds to believe that it will have been constructed level originally. Air bricks can be used, provided it can be shown they were placed in the same brickcourse. Windowsills can also be used, either just across the width of a single sill, or comparing different sills if they rest on the same course. Plinths on the rendering are often not reliable.

Level measurements can also be taken of internal floors. They can be particularly valuable in providing corroboration of external levels. The most useful information is obtained with solid "in situ" floors. With suspended floors, measurements are best taken around the edge, although measurements in the centre of the room can indicate how sleeper walls are performing. Floor measurements are particularly useful in cases where settlement of the floor slab is suspected.

Methods of measuring levels:

i) Water level

Measurements should be taken around as much as possible of the building. A spirit level or similar is therefore inadequate, except for checking the horizontal or vertical alignment of doors or windows.

The cheapest equipment for measuring levels is a water level. It works on the principle that the level of water at the two ends of a partially water-filled tube will be the same. Commercially made models are available, or alternatively they can be made very cheaply from readily available materials.

I used a home-made water level for many years and found this quite sufficient for most purposes. It consisted of approximately 15 metres of 8mm i.d. polythene tube, with the two ends connected to snap couplings which can seal the tube during transport and be opened when readings are taken. To enable the readings to be taken single-handed, one end of the tube is attached to a convenient support such as a gutter downpipe, ensuring that the top is at least 1m above the brick course which is being measured, and that the bottom support is below this course. The other free end of the tube has a friction sliding scale made from reinforced polythene tube riveted to a 300mm scale with a central zero marker (Figure 12.9).

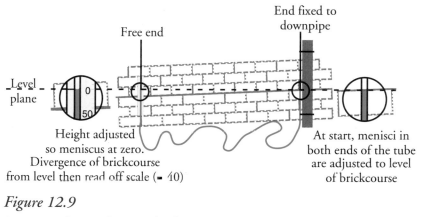

Free end   End fixed to downpipe

Level plane

Height adjusted so meniscus at zero. Divergence of brickcourse from level then read off scale (= 40)

At start, menisci in both ends of the tube are adjusted to level of brickcourse

Figure 12.9
Diagram of a simple water level in use.

Before use, all bubbles must be carefully removed. The free end of the tube is placed beside the end attached to the downpipe and is raised or lowered so that the level in the two ends of the tube is the same as the brick course for measurement. The sliding scale is then adjusted to this position, zeroed on the brick course and the water level. Measurements are then taken by moving the free end progressively around the building, usually at about 1 metre intervals. At each location the water level is raised or lowered so that it corresponds to the zero on the scale; the displacement of the brick course is then measured off from the attached rule. Ideally there should be a second observer to check the water level in the other end of the tube, but provided care is taken to avoid any change in volume of the tube or the water, this precaution can be omitted. Particular care is required to prevent kinks in the tube, and if the tube is left in the sun, volume changes can occur. Problems can also occur with measurements over very uneven ground, as increased hydrostatic pressure can affect the volume of the tube.

A 15m length of tube is not usually sufficient to reach right round a typical building, but can be reset to another convenient position, making appropriate adjustments to the zero setting.

With reasonable care, a closing error of less than 5mm can be achieved with a water level, with all measurements within this tolerance. This is less than the normal variation within the building and far less than the distortion that is normally present when subsidence has occurred. It is therefore quite sufficient for most purposes of routine measurement.

ii) Optic level

Although the water level is cheap, greater speed and precision can be obtained with a surveyor's optic level. Improved efficiency will quickly recoup the initial cost of the equipment, and an accurate instrument becomes essential if it is also used for monitoring.

Virtually all optic levels manufactured these days are automatic or self-aligning, incorporating a 'stabiliser' prism within the telescope tube. The instrument is set up on its tripod and approximately levelled by adjusting screws in the base so that the bubble on the instrument is centred. This is sufficient to allow the stabiliser to correct any slight inaccuracy, so that the line of sight through the centre of the level, or collimation, is horizontal. The level can be rotated through 360° to define a horizontal plane, with measurements taken off this to the brickcourse or other surface which is being used.

The telescopes in modern levels are compact and powerful, usually with x 20 or x 25 magnification, although they have a very narrow field of view (1° 30'). They can be focused to 0.5m or less which is very advantageous, particularly when taking readings in restricted space inside buildings. A good quality precision instrument and substantial tripod are well worth the investment.

Care must be taken to ensure that the line of sight is horizontal before the instrument is used. There is a standard surveying technique for this (the "two peg" method), and this check should be made periodically. Despite this, no adjustment is perfect, and there are additional rules of observation to help minimise error. In particular, any error in collimation will cancel if the length of the foresight and backsight are made equal. This is a counsel of perfection which is usually difficult to achieve. Sights are often necessarily unequal, but one should aim to equalise the sum of backsights and the sum of foresights in the traverse around the building. Care must also be taken to ensure that the levelling staff is held vertically, that the staff does not move or sink when it is turned to face a new instrument station, and also that the tripod is stable and not liable to settlement or other movement. Wherever possible a complete levelling circuit around the building should be made to check for any closing error; with reasonable care this should not exceed 1mm.

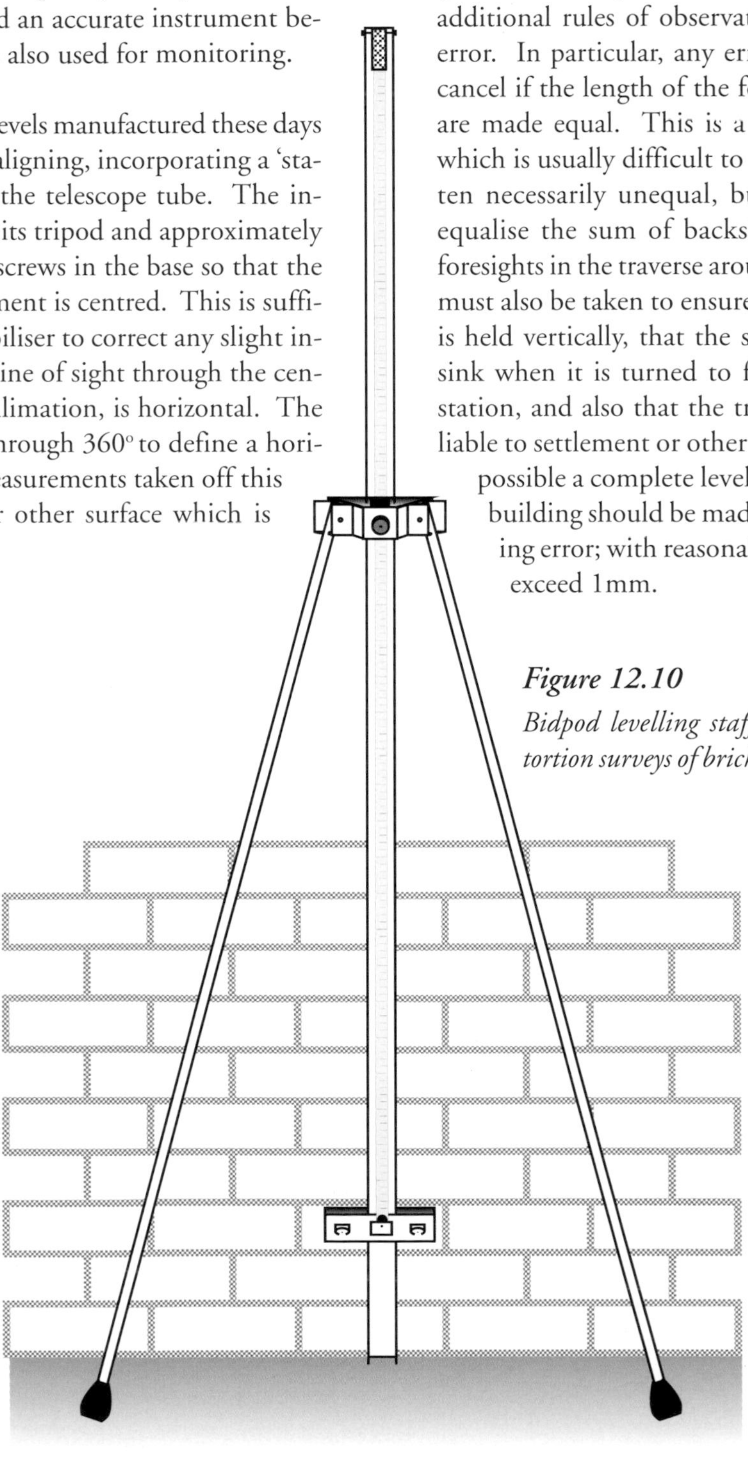

Figure 12.10

Bidpod levelling staff for single-handed distortion surveys of brickcourses or other features.

Levelling Staff

Some surveyors use a traditional surveying staff. These staffs are intended for resting on the ground, which makes them ill-suited for taking measurements against the side of a wall. This problem can be overcome by driving a masonry nail into the brickcourse and supporting the staff on this, but the method is cumbersome and liable to error if the nail is not inserted level and at the same position in the course each time. Furthermore, surveying staffs are intended for observing over long distances; for level measurements around a building, a finer scale with smaller numbering is preferable. A metric scale, with clear millimetre divisions and centimetre markings, is ideal.

If an assistant is available to hold the staff, a long steel metric rule, at least 1.8m long is suitable. The base of this can be held against the relevant brickcourse, taking care that it does not slip. Alternatively, it can be stood on the floor or whatever other object is being measured.

The staff which I have developed and prefer is intended primarily for singled-handed operation. This staff is available commercially, exclusively from P.G.

Biddle, under the name of the Bidpod (Figure 12.10). It utilises a 3.0m long flexible steel Stanley tape measure with a "Power lock". This is supported on the top of an aluminium "U" section staff, 1.95m long. A sliding bracket carries the end of the tape. When measurements are taken, the top edge of this slider is placed against the top of the brick, with the powerlock on the tape providing a convenient friction device to allow the slider to be moved. For single-handed operation, the staff is supported by two aluminium legs on an adjustable bracket, which are locked onto the staff with a wheel-nut. This allows the staff to be set up either against the building or facing along the building (Figure 12.11). After setting up the staff, the observer returns to the level to take the reading off the tape to the nearest millimetre. This operation is then repeated for each reading. The sliding bracket and the support for the legs each project by 60mm at right angles to the staff on either side. This allows the staff to be held clear of the wall to make it easier to view around downpipes or other obstructions.

When measurements are required off the floor or other horizontal surface, the slider is removed and the end of the tape hooked into the base of the staff. If the powerlock is released, the tape is held taut under the slight tension of the return spring. The staff is also used in this mode at transfer stations when moving the level to a new observation position around the building. The staff can also be used for measurements off monitoring markers (further details in Chapter 15, page 241).

In poor light conditions it is easy to illuminate the staff using a small torch mounted on a spring clip; the small adjustable "Durabeam" torch riveted onto a bulldog stationery clip is convenient for this (Figure 12.12). This also allows measurements to be taken in the dark, and makes it easier to see the tape if viewing through a window with a lot of surface reflections.

Figure 12.11
Bidpod levelling staff in use on level distortion survey.

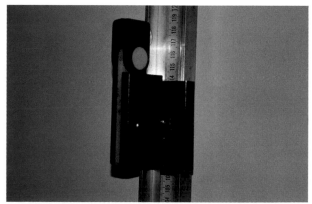

Figure 12.12
Convenient illumination for the Bidpod.

Presentation of level results

The number and location of readings taken in a level survey must depend on the circumstances of each case, but preferably they should be at about 1m intervals. Where there are window or door openings, readings should be taken on either side. Measurements just at the corner of a building are inadequate for useful interpretation (and can be misleading). For internal floor levels, a 1m square grid can be laid out, and measurements taken at each intersection.

Results can be shown on a simple plan view, with the values at the appropriate position adjacent to the wall or object being measured (Figure 12.13). If required, contours can also be included. However, it is often easier to visualise and interpret the results if they are shown on a three-dimensional isometric plan (Figure 12.14), particularly if the building is a fairly simple rectangular outline shape. Computer-aided drawing programs make it easy to draw isometric plans. Wall outlines can be shown on the diagonal (30º) lines using a 1:100 scale, and the vertical distortion on the vertical lines at a 1:1 scale. If a complete internal grid is available, it can also be shown, joining the top of the vertical bars to show the distortion as a "relief map".

As the object of the distortion survey is to measure the differences in level around the building, it is easiest to present the results as differences in level relative to an appropriate zero datum, rather than as absolute values. The choice of this zero datum can be selected

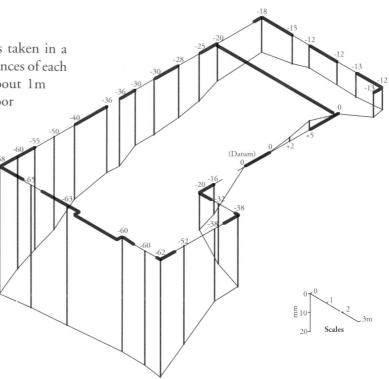

Figure 12.14

Level distortion survey presented on an isometric plan, using the same values and datum point as in Figure 12.11.

to make interpretation as easy as possible. Thus, if it appears that part of a building is stable but other parts have subsided, the datum can be selected at the highest part of the brickcourse (or other feature) with all of the values shown negative (to indicate the possible extent of subsidence). Figure 12.14 is presented in this way and appears to show subsidence at the left hand end. Conversely, if heave is suspected, the lowest part can be used as the datum, with values shown as positive to indicate the possible extent of relative upward movement. Figure 12.15 presents the same results as in Figure 12.14 but with the lowest point as datum, and now appears to show heave of the right end. Selecting the datum in this way may give rise to allegations of trying to bias the interpretation. For this reason it may be preferable to use a standard and entirely arbitrary datum (e.g. beside the front door), showing relatively higher levels as positive values and vice versa (as in Figure 12.13 and 12.14), but this can have the disadvantage of making it harder to interpret the results.

If results include measurement on more than one feature, for instance both external walls and internal floors, they obviously will not have a common datum. Interpretation of such results is often made easier if one set of values is adjusted by a constant amount to try to achieve generally similar values on adjacent features.

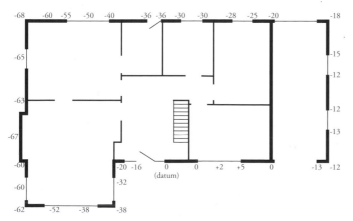

Figure 12.13

Typical results for a level distortion survey, with levels presented in millimetres relative to an arbitrary zero datum adjacent to the front door.

Interpretation of level surveys

The information from a level survey is frequently the most valuable information which can be obtained during a single site visit, but it should be considered with discrimination and only in conjunction with all of the other evidence to determine the most logical explanation. The results show differences in level which might demonstrate the extent of differential movements which have occurred sometime during the life of the building, from whatever cause. They do not indicate the mechanism of movement nor the direction, but deductions on this can usually be made.

The basic assumption that the building was originally constructed level is sometimes challenged. Observation on new buildings, and on old buildings constructed on stable subsoils, show that this assumption is reasonable in most situations. Obviously there are some variations in level, but these tend to be random with no clear trend or pattern, and usually with less than 30mm difference between the maximum and minimum levels. These reflect the normal building tolerances.

On one occasion, while puzzling over some unusual results during an investigation of damage which was occurring to houses while they were still being built, I was approached by the foreman who was clearly feeling most sheepish. It transpired that he had dropped his dumpy level before setting out the buildings and he had not appreciated until later that it was badly out of collimation. My unusual results were explained, but might otherwise have remained a considerable mystery. Despite such exceptions, it is my experience that it is usually reasonable to rely on the assumption that houses approximate to level when built.

Where significant differential foundation movements have occurred, there is usually a clear trend with a pronounced tilt either of the whole building, or a localised upward or downward tilt of one part. Where these movements are sufficient to cause structural cracking, the differences in the trend of levels is usually at least 40mm. It might be the result of one part of the building going up, or the other down, but the direction of the tilt should be consistent with the suspected cause and the pattern of any cracking. Thus, if subsidence or dynamic settlement caused by tree root activity is suspected, it should be anticipated that the building will tilt down towards the tree. If more than one tree might be involved in different positions around the building, the greatest tilt will probably be towards the tree which has had the greatest influence. Conversely if heave is suspected, it should be anticipated that the building will tilt up towards the position from where the tree has been removed.

As an example, it has been noted that Figure 12.14 appears to show subsidence of the left hand end of the building. This would be a logical result if there was suspected tree root activity at the left hand end. In fact there were trees growing close to the front right corner, and reason to believe that there had been heave at this right end of the building, despite the fact that trees were present. Further details and the explanation of this unusual situation are given in Case Study 1.

This Case Study illustrates a common situation for mis-diagnosis which can occur when there is a tree adjacent to a recently constructed building which suffers damage (see also Case Study 19). If the damage is close to the trees, there is a tendency to leap to the conclusion that this must be subsidence on the assumption that the tree must be causing shrinkage of

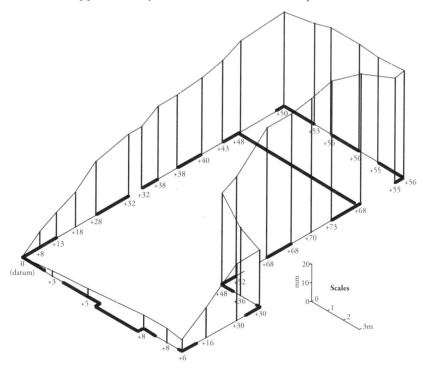

Figure 12.15

The same level distortion as shown in Figure 12.12, but presented relative to the lowest point on the brickcourse as the zero datum. Presented in this way it is easier to appreciate the probable explanation that the distortion is caused by heave of the front right hand corner.

the subsoil. However, measurements of level frequently show a pronounced upwards tilt towards the tree. This suggests either that the building was originally constructed with an even greater tilt and has subsided to its current position (which is extremely unlikely) or that the part closest to the tree has suffered heave. The usual reason for this is that the construction works caused extensive root severance or damage, which effectively killed the roots beneath the building, thereby allowing heave to occur. A level survey will help to ensure a correct diagnosis.

When interpreting the results it is important to consider the time of year and the type of movements which may have been occurring. In the autumn the survey will record seasonal distortion, as well as the effects of any dynamic settlement and / or subsidence caused by development of a persistent deficit. By contrast, in the spring seasonal recovery will have occurred and so any distortion will be either the effects of dynamic settlement or from a persistent deficit - distinguishing between these is considered in Chapter 16.

The construction of the building must also be considered. Deep foundations such as cellars will usually be less vulnerable to seasonal movement and thus to dynamic settlement and so will tend to provide a high area on the distortion survey. On soft soils, the effects of dynamic settlement often show very clearly. With these soils, foundations with light loads, such as single storey bay windows or extensions, will show a pronounced upward tilt, as a result of suffering from less settlement that the main building. This should be contrasted with the situation on stiff clay soils where bay windows projecting towards a tree suffer greater subsidence as a result of the greater soil shrinkage nearer the tree. Distortion and crack patterns will be very different in the two situations.

The trends revealed by a distortion survey may not show any clear pattern. There are many possible reasons, such as variations in soil shrinkage, presence of fill, slope instability, settlement, previous foundations etc. It must be remembered that a level survey records distortion which has occurred throughout the life of the building. In an old building, distortion may have been caused by heave soon after construction, or by dynamic settlement by a tree which has since been removed and all evidence of its existence lost. Evidence of old repairs may still be present. Any anomalous results should be investigated with extra care. It also follows that, just because the levels suggest the involvement of a tree as a cause of subsidence, there might also be any of these other causes also involved, and the presence of the tree might be mere coincidence.

Verticality survey

Measurement of level is very quick and easy, and should form part of any investigation. In addition, useful information can be obtained from a verticality survey. These measurements are not as easy to take, but can provide valuable confirmation (or otherwise) of the level survey. Measurements are usually only taken on the outside of external walls, as differences in plaster thickness on internal walls cause excessive random variation. The interpretation of results is based on the assumption that walls are constructed vertically, although it should be noted that there is a tendency for most builders to tilt walls outwards slightly near the top.

Measurements can be taken by plumb-line, but there are practical difficulties about taking readings at different heights and the line is difficult to steady in windy conditions. It is therefore preferable to use a theodolite. Just as the optic level defines a horizontal plane, the theodolite can define a vertical (or also horizontal) plane.

It is necessary to hold a scale against the wall for taking the readings. Figure 12.16 shows the device which I have copied from Peter Kelsey and Partners and which is easy to use. The scale is held at right angles to the wall by vertical and horizontal vanes, and it is supported at the required height by standard chimney sweep rods, one reading being taken at each increment in staff length. By starting from the top of the wall and progressively removing rods, a complete wall can be measured in a few minutes.

Figure 12.16

Simple support for measuring offsets from a wall in a verticality survey (home-made, based on description by Peter Kelsey & Partners)

The face of the wall adjacent to the d.p.c. should be used as the zero datum for each set of vertical readings. Results are usually shown on a scale diagram, preferably showing all the results on a single isometric plan.

Where subsidence from clay shrinkage is involved, the wall which has subsided most is likely to be tilted outwards markedly, although often turning inwards near the top as a result of restraint from the roof. Tension transmitted through the roof is liable to pull the wall on the opposite side.

Conversely, if heave is the cause of the problem, the wall closest to the heave is likely to show the most movement. If the worst heave is occurring outside the building, the wall will tilt away, but may show little tilt on the opposite side of the building. Heave beneath the building, or subsidence of both sides, will produce outward bowing of both walls.

It should be noted that foundation movements caused by swelling or shrinking of the soil usually produce considerable horizontal rotation, detectable by a verticality survey. By contrast, movements caused by settling of foundations on soft or made ground cause little rotation, the walls generally remaining more vertical even though the whole building may be considerably tilted.

Verticality surveys can also be useful for diagnosing damage caused by roof spread or thermal movements. With these causes the greatest curvature typically occurs at high level on opposite sides of the building.

Horizontal bulges of walls can be detected either by measurements with theodolite, or from a tensioned string held clear of the wall (Case Study 10). In both cases, a simple millimetre scale can be held against the d.p.c. at intervals along the wall. Outward bulging of a wall below d.p.c. can be caused by horizontal soil swelling during heave; this may also cause an outward bulge of other walls around the perimeter. These measurements are also useful for detecting cases of lateral slip due to slope instability. In these cases, both external walls at right angles to the slope have similar convex curves pointing down the direction of slope.

Foundation depth and construction

Knowledge of foundation depth and construction is essential for assessing the potential effects of clay shrinkage; the deeper the foundations, the less the effect of seasonal soil movements. It is also relevant for assessing the ability of the foundations to transmit the building load to the underlying soil, and the vulnerability of the foundations to dynamic settlement.

The only reliable method for assessing depth is by excavation of trial pits. Even with modern buildings where records exist of foundation construction, it is unwise to rely on these unless they are recorded by an independent observer. Excavation need not be the massive trial pit sometimes employed. A narrow trench 0.5m wide and projecting far enough from the wall to provide working space for a spade is quite sufficient to expose most foundations. The depth of the base of the foundations should be recorded, and also any projection which extends their width, either by corbelling of the brickcourses, or in the footings.

The location for trial pits should be determined after consideration of the results of the level distortion survey. This will have helped to identify those parts of the building which have been subject to greatest movement and thus where information on the foundations may be most relevant. Trial pits may be required in other positions to try to explain any other features of the level survey or crack pattern.

It must be remembered that foundations are not necessarily of uniform depth. The National House-Building Council guidelines advocate variation of foundation depth in the proximity of existing trees (which may have subsequently have been felled), and the depth may be varied for many other reasons. Properties built on sloping ground will often have stepped foundations. The level of the underside of these should be related to the existing soil level and also to the original soil levels (Case Study 18).

The construction of the footings should also be noted. With houses constructed in the 19th century or earlier, it is not unusual to find the brickwork extending to the base, supported directly on the underlying subsoil. Other foundations used varying mixes of concrete, often with considerable clinker or other compacted material. There is nothing inherently inadequate about such foundations, providing they fulfil their purpose of transferring the load of the building to the subsoil. Indeed, there can be advantages in such foundations for the rapid movement of water beneath a building (Case Study 6). Foundations of this sort also illustrate that structural integrity of the footings is not necessarily essential, although in modern buildings with trench foundations any cracks may diminish the stiffness and ability to withstand slight soil movements.

The soil conditions exposed on the side of the trial pit facing the foundations should be noted. Soil movements (and root activity) in this layer is not of direct relevance, but can provide information on the original soil levels and on the suitability of the soil for root growth and its moisture retention characteristics, but these are matters considered in further detail in the next chapter.

Foundation load

The weight of the building and the load imposed on the foundations will need to be estimated. This load will need to be checked against the ability of the soil to withstand the load, and the settlement movements which will occur as a result of the load. These are engineering matters beyond the scope of this book.

Drain and services survey

The location and depth of all underground services should be determined, as these can influence the pattern of root activity and the drainage and permeability of the soil. Excavations within a 45° angle of the underside of the foundations can also influence the ability of the foundations to support the load.

The condition of foul and surface water drains may need to be checked. Their ability to hold water can be checked by blocking the lower end of the drain with a purpose-made inflatable balloon, and then filling the drain with water and seeing whether the level drops with time. A test of this sort will not locate the defect or its nature. This is best determined by a CCTV scan; many specialist companies offer this service. The location of defects should be related to the above ground features, particularly the external walls of the building, to see if failure is associated with external load (See also Chapter 10, page 168).

Summary

1.   Inspection of the building should aim to build up an overall picture of the building, particularly in relation to its vulnerability to movement and damage, and to identify any movements and damage which have occurred.

2.   It is relevant to look at any recent movement, and also at historical movement, and to try to ascertain whether these are related to the same cause.

3.   A level distortion survey provides a very effective method of determining the extent of differential movement which has occurred some time in the life of the building. It should be an essential preliminary part of any investigation.

4.   Examination of crack patterns, both recent and historic, is also valuable. However, they are sometimes misleading on the direction of differential movement and so should be compared with other sources of information, such as the level survey.

5.   The depth and condition of foundations should be determined by trial pits. The location and number of these should be determined on the basis of the level distortion and crack surveys.

6.   **The overall behaviour of the building should be considered in the light of information on sub-soil conditions (Chapter 13), and the history of trees and other vegetation in the locality (Chapter 14).**

Property suffered damage in 1975 and 1976 – Underpinned in 1978 but further damage –
Level distortion survey sufficient to indicate wrong part of building underpinned –
Subsequent investigation confirmed extensive poor quality fill – Tree incorrectly implicated.

The subject property is a two-storey detached house with gable front and rear elevations, and with a single storey projection on the left flank linking to a garage (CS Figure 12.1). It was built in 1969 and is located on a Boulder Clay soil in Hertfordshire.

In 1978 I was instructed by the insurers of the adjacent property in which a horse chestnut tree was growing.

Previous history

The subject property had been occupied by the current owners since 1974. In 1975 they noticed a vertical crack running through the large window above the stairwell in the right hand flank wall. This was merely filled and redecorated, but it subsequently re-opened during 1976 when other cracking also developed. The other main fracture was midway along the left flank wall, with a number of other minor internal and external cracks.

Structural engineers were appointed and they diagnosed subsidence of the front right hand and rear left hand corners of the building which they attributed to leaking drains. They devised a scheme of underpinning involving continuous strip underpinning along the front half of the right hand flank wall, and piers beneath the front left and rear left corners, all as shown in CS Figure 12.2.

During the course of this underpinning the contractors encountered soft backfill soil, particularly beneath the rear left hand corner, which necessitated the base of the underpinning being extended to a depth of 3.75m.

Roots, identified as horse chestnut, were encountered below foundation level during excavation for the pier beneath the front left corner. On the basis of the presence of these roots, the loss adjuster acting for the property insurers submitted the claim against the adjacent tree owner. The soil in this location was described as a sandy gravel with a high clay content, and with glass and other fill material above the level of the footings.

The underpinning work was completed in July 1978. By the time of my involvement in October 1978 the original crack in the right hand flank wall was again apparent.

Case Study Figure 12.1

Front of subject property (partially obscured by hawthorn) and adjacent horse chestnut.

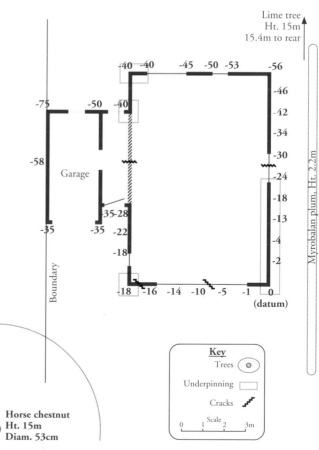

Case Study Figure 12.2

Site plan, including results of level distortion survey (mm) in October 1978, relative to arbitrary zero datum at highest point on brickcourse.

197

The tree

The tree which was alleged to be involved was a horse chestnut (*Aesculus hippocastanum*). It had a height of 10m, a trunk diameter of 53cm, and a radial spread of 5m (CS Figure 12.1). It stood 9.3m from the front left corner of the subject property. The tree was highly visible close to the front boundary and road, and was justifiably the subject of a Tree Preservation Order.

In addition to this tree, at 2.2m from the right flank wall, there was a 2.2m high hedge of Myrobolan plum (*Prunus cerasifera*). In the rear garden of the subject property, 15.4m from the rear corner, there was a 15m high lime tree (*Tilia* x *europaea*) with a diameter of 53cm and radial spread of 6m.

Level distortion survey

During my initial visit I used a water level to record the relative level of a peripheral brickcourse around the house and garage. The results are included in CS Figure 12.2.

DISCUSSION

The level distortion survey contradicts the conclusion drawn by the structural engineer that one of the main areas of subsidence was the front right hand corner. To the contrary, this corner of the building is the highest point, but despite this, was the main area which was underpinned. The lowest part of the main building was the rear right corner which had been omitted from the underpinning.

As the underpinning had revealed the presence of a soft fill soil beneath the rear left hand corner, it seemed probable that similar, or perhaps worse, conditions extended beneath the rear right corner in the area of maximum subsidence. This opinion was subsequently confirmed when the whole of the rear of the building was eventually underpinned. Extensive fill, including gas masks and other debris, was uncovered.

The claim against my principals was obviously dropped in the light of this information. The corner of the building closest to the trees was marginally lower (-18mm), but included some fill material which could account for this variation. Furthermore, the sandy gravel soil, despite having a clay content, was described by the engineers as non-cohesive.

Lessons to be learnt

• A simple level distortion survey showed that the original diagnosis was faulty and would have shown that the scheme of remedial work was inappropriate and likely to fail.

• It might be easy to assume that an inexperienced engineer was involved and therefore to dismiss this case. However, not only was it a well known engineering practice, but also one which at that time was receiving considerable publicity because of their involvement acting for many householders on a housing estate which had suffered from extensive settlement problems of a similar nature.

• This case emphasises that, even where trees are in close proximity, careful and full diagnosis is essential.

• The allegation that the tree was involved originated from the loss adjusters. (In partial exoneration of the engineers, it should be noted that they had not implicated the trees; instead they blamed leaking drains). The loss adjusters should have appreciated that the mere presence of tree roots was inadequate to establish the involvement of the adjacent horse chestnut tree.

Introduction

Chapter 4 has described the soil, and emphasised the difficulties in determining the amount of soil shrinkage which can occur as a result of soil drying. A qualitative assessment can be made which can indicate the general behaviour of the soil, but any quantitative assessment of soil shrinkage is subject to so many ill-defined variables that only a rough approximation can be made. For this reason there is limited value in detailed investigation of soil conditions, but some information is essential.

In particular it is necessary to determine:

i) whether a shrinkable soil exists;

ii) the overall permeability of the soil, and its ability to recover from soil drying.

In addition, in some circumstances it is desirable to determine:

iii) the existence of root activity;

iv) whether the soil is desiccated;

v) the potential shrinkage characteristics of the soil;

vi) the approximate amount of shrinkage associated with desiccation;

vii) the ability of the soil to support the foundation load.

This information is derived from a combination of various investigations, which are considered in this Chapter. Some general information about probable soil conditions can be obtained from Geological Survey maps, but in most situations site-specific information is essential. This must involve drilling boreholes and interpretation of the soil conditions, sometimes supplemented by laboratory analysis.

Geological Survey maps

Valuable preliminary information on the possible subsoil conditions can be obtained from Geological Survey maps. Wherever possible, reference should be made to these.

The majority of the country is covered at a scale of either 1:63360 (1 inch to a mile) or 1:50000 (approximately 1.25 inches to a mile); Figure 13.1 shows the current availability of these maps for England and Wales; similar maps for Scotland are also available. Most of these are available as either 'Drift' or 'Solid with Drift' editions; the latter are to be preferred as they show the recent superficial deposits as well as the original geological strata. They usually provide an accurate indication on the probable surface geology, and are of sufficient scale to pinpoint most locations. Obviously some discretion is needed, particularly near the boundaries of deposits, and even more so when the boundary is shown by a dotted line. The maps at 1:63360 scale are usually based on old maps, and so the features such as roads and housing are now considerably out of date. Care is needed in identifying locations on these maps, but cross referencing to an Ordnance Survey map by grid reference can assist. 1:63360 maps are gradually being reprinted at 1:50000 scale, and the opportunity taken to print onto an up-to-date Ordnance Survey base.

More detailed maps at 1:10560 (six inches to mile) or 1:10000 scale are also available for much of the country. They provide some additional information, particularly in strata encountered by boreholes and wells etc., and the larger scale makes it easier to locate a precise point. However, this precision in location is not accompanied by increased accuracy in defining the boundaries of strata, and so there is little benefit in these larger scale maps. These maps are generally only available from the British Geological Survey, who can provide an index on availability. In many cases, they are out of print, but can be reproduced as dyelines or photographic copies.

By locating the relevant area on the map and by comparison of the colour shading and the letter or symbol with the legend, it is possible to determine the prob-

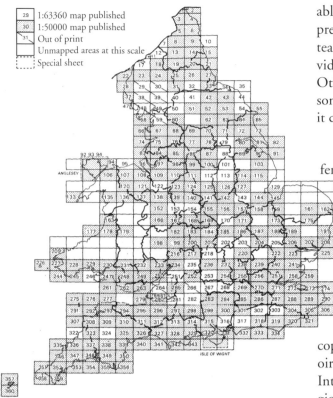

Figure 13.1

Availability of 1:50,000 or 1;63,360 scale geological survey maps for England and Wales. New maps are often being produced, and so a current catalogue should be consulted.

Figure 13.2

Areas covered by the British Regional Geology Handbooks.

able underlying deposit. It is then a matter of interpretation. Many deposits, e.g. London Clay or Plateau Gravel, are explanatory by their name and provide an indication of their likely chief constituent. Other names, e.g. Gault, are less descriptive, while some, e.g. Tunbridge Wells Sand can be misleading as it can contain considerable clay.

General descriptions of the properties of the different strata can be obtained from the relevant British Regional Geology booklet, published by HMSO. There are 13 of these booklets covering England and Wales, and six for Scotland; Figure 13.2 reproduces the index map for these. Reference to these will usually provide some guidance on the main constituents of the strata in the general locality. More detailed information is available in Memoirs, but these are mostly out of print and only available at specialist libraries or as photocopies from the British Geological Survey. These memoirs and other descriptive articles are reviewed in the Introduction and bibliographies to the relevant Regional Geology booklet.

It must be emphasised that, even over a limited area, a stratum can vary considerably. For this reason it is preferable for interpretation to be based on local knowledge of the conditions. Knowledge about a stratum derived from one area should not necessarily be relied on elsewhere.

Soil Survey maps are also produced by The Soil Survey of England and Wales but in general these are less useful than the Geological Survey maps. They are intended primarily for agricultural and related land use, providing detailed information on the surface soil layers. The classification bears a relation to the underlying geology, but includes additional subdivisions of the strata, dependent mainly on the drainage characteristics of the soil. The maps are far more complicated to interpret, and do not enjoy the widespread use and recognition accorded to the Geological Survey. Although primarily intended for agricultural areas, they are extended into urban areas based on knowledge of the underlying geology, lithology and interpretation of the drainage patterns.

Boreholes

Although Geological Survey maps can provide a general indication of the soil conditions in an area, the only way to get site-specific information is by boreholes.

When drilling boreholes it is important to be clear what information is required. Typically this will be:-

i) to reveal the soil conditions:
   a) to confirm that a clay exists at relevant depths;
   b) to allow judgement of soil permeability;
   c) to determine depth of fine root activity;
   d) to check that the soil is suitable to support the foundations;

ii) to allow classification tests as a basis for estimating shrinkage potential;

iii) to determine whether the soil is desiccated:
   a) by moisture content determination;
   b) by soil suction tests;
   c) by penetrometer tests;

iv) to allow estimation of potential for swelling of a desiccated soil.

The number, location, depth and diameter of the boreholes which are drilled should reflect the type of information which is required and the anticipated soil conditions. For instance, a small diameter borehole (50mm diameter) is quite sufficient for taking disturbed soil samples down to depths of 5-6m in a clay soil for determination of moisture content and for soil classification, and is also adequate for observing fine root activity. However, a larger diameter (100mm) will be required for undisturbed samples for triaxial soil tests or for more detailed observation of soil structure and root activity, and a 150mm diameter should be preferred, but is not essential, for soil suction tests.

The time of year will also influence the type of information which can be obtained. Thus, a hole drilled in the spring can only be expected to show a persistent deficit; information must be obtained in the autumn to show whether there is any seasonal drying. Despite this one often sees elaborate boreholes and detailed tests to try to demonstrate soil conditions which common sense will say have disappeared long before. To allow interpretation of any borehole, it is of course essential that the date of drilling is recorded.

For 50mm diameter boreholes into clay, I find that the Edelman or Dutch auger (Figure 13.3 centre) is the easiest to use. The tip cuts down into the soil, and the vertical side plates then sever the sample and retain it while it is lifted from the soil. This type of auger is easier to use than a spiral auger, which will cut down into clay very easily, but it can then be difficult

Figure 13.3

The Edelman or Dutch auger (centre) is ideal for small diameter holes in clay soil with the intermediate type (top) for larger holes. A gravel auger (bottom) may be required for stoney soils.

to withdraw. Various patterns of Edelman auger are available for different soils. For sandy soils, one with wider vertical flanges can be used. An intermediate combination auger may be required for larger diameter holes (Figure 13.3 top). If gravel soils are encountered, it is usually necessary to use a larger (150mm diameter) gravel auger (Figure 13.3 bottom). This has clap plates designed to let the gravel pass but then flap shut when lifting the material. It is convenient for penetrating surface layers of gravel, but is difficult to use at depths in excess of 1m.

A set of extension rods is necessary to allow holes to be taken to sufficient depth. Purpose-made auger rods with bayonet or screw connections are available, but I find that three-quarter inch galvanised iron pipe is cheaper and more practical; such pipe with a BSP thread is suitable for the augers in Figure 13.3. Rods of 1, 2 and 3 metre length can be used to 3m depth, and these can be combined by straight couplings to give a total 6m length, although (mercifully) this is

Figure 13.4

Hand augering with a 50mm Edelman auger is the easiest way to obtain disturbed samples to at least 5m depth.

not commonly required. A simple 'T' piece at the top of the auger with arms about 24cm long (from the centre-line) will provide a handle which allows sufficient torque without being inconvenient to use.

Figure 13.5

A lightweight mechanical auger may be required for larger boreholes or for undisturbed core samples.

(Photo: R.M. Brown Foundation Investigation Ltd.)

Simple equipment of this sort is quite sufficient for manual augering 50mm diameter holes to depths of 5 or 6m, but below this lifting and handling the rods becomes impractical. In a reasonable clay soil, I find I can drill and sample to a depth of 3m in about half an hour (Figure 13.4); deeper holes take proportionately far more time. Rates of drilling will be slower in very desiccated soil.

For larger diameter (100mm or greater) boreholes, it becomes far less practical to drill to any depth by hand. For many years I drilled 100mm diameter holes with the aid of a hand-held two-stroke power auger (Stihl 040), but I now find the 50mm diameter manual auger to be quite sufficient for most purposes. Where larger or deeper holes are required, a specialist soil investigation firm with mechanical equipment such as a Minuteman (Figure 13.5) may be needed.

Assessment of soil conditions

One of the objects of a borehole is to allow a general assessment of the soil conditions on which to base a judgement of the overall permeability of the soil. Such judgement is inevitably subjective and must be based on past experience. For this reason it is very advantageous to drill small diameter manual boreholes oneself, rather than relying on sub-contractors. It enables one to inspect the arisings as they are removed, and quite literally get a feel for the conditions. Not only does this provide a better appreciation of the soil, but also allows one to adjust the depth of drilling to suit the conditions which are encountered.

A lot of information on the soil conditions can be determined from its appearance and feel. Sand and gravel soils are obvious, with the individual particles down to the size of fine sand being distinguishable to the naked eye (see particle size definitions in Chapter 4, page 41). As the clay and silt content progressively increases, the soil will change from a non-cohesive sand, through the various classes of sandy clay etc. to a pure silt or clay or silty clay. With practice, the proportion of sand can be assessed by visual examination and by rubbing the fingers to feel the particles. Greater sensitivity is provided by the teeth; a pure clay will have the smoothness of butter whereas sand particles grate (but the taste leaves a lot to be desired!).

Even apparently uniform clay soils rarely maintain this uniformity throughout the profile. Examination of the profiles in Volume 2, particularly those which show the spring moisture content profiles for the five boreholes near each of the trees, shows the considerable natural variation in moisture content which can occur irrespective of any root activity. In some but not all cases this variation can be related to bands of sand or other material which were recorded when the holes were being drilled for the access tubes. These bands of sand are a common occurrence, and can have a major influence on the soil conditions (see Case Studies 2, 3, 6 and 13). Of course, if one encounters a layer of sand when drilling a borehole, one does not know whether it is a localised pocket which will make little difference to the overall soil, or whether it is a widespread band or lens which could have a major influence on water movement.

Of even greater importance than these macro-features is the distribution of permeable pathways within the finer soil structure. In the surface few metres where the soil has a structure, the distribution of particles is usually not uniform through the soil, but instead the coarser materials tend to be concentrated along the fracture planes between the soil peds. When the soil dries and cracks it will do so along these fracture planes, but even when the soil is fully rehydrated and the cracks are closed, the coarser materials provide a pathway which can enhance water movement. Moisture then only has to penetrate a short distance to the interior of the soil ped. For this reason the soil must be carefully examined for the composition of the peds and particles along the cracks. Although the soil samples which are obtained with an Edelman auger have been disturbed, it is usually possible to distinguish the original cracks, although it may be difficult to distinguish whether any fine laminations of sand were originally in a horizontal or vertical plane. Splitting larger undisturbed soil samples apart along their natural fracture plane will allow a better appreciation of soil structure and allow more detailed examination of the distribution of soil particles within the cracks.

An assessment of the soil should consider all of these features, with the observations recorded as the samples are taken. The record should include the depth of any change in lithology as well as changes in colour or texture. BS 5930:1981 provides descriptions of the different soil types, and Table 11 of that Standard shows the recommended symbols for describing soils in diagrams of borehole logs.

A note should be made of any free water entering the borehole from the sides as this can indicate the availability of moisture for rehydration of a desiccated soil. When drilling a borehole, problems are sometimes encountered from surplus water running in from the top of the hole, particularly if there is a permeable soil overlying clay. This can usually be prevented by driving a short length of 100mm plastic gutter downpipe into the clay, and augering down using the pipe as a casing. Provided surplus water is not entering the hole in this way, it is advantageous to leave the hole for at least 24 hours, recording the depth of the water level at the end of that period, although this does not necessarily correspond to the depth of the water table.

Inspection for fine root activity

It is the fine roots, typically less than 1mm diameter, which are active in water absorption (see Chapter 3, page 27), and the relative abundance of these can be assessed by careful examination of samples taken during drilling.

The best way of doing this is with undisturbed core samples of about 75mm diameter. These can be split in half along the structural cracks between the soil peds. As the fine roots tend to grow along these cracks, this will expose these roots on the surface (Figure 13.6).

Chapter 3 has emphasised that fine root activity is ephemeral. The majority of these roots die after a short time, and only a few go on to suberise and to develop secondary thickening. These dead roots can persist in the soil for a considerable time, depending on the amount of microbial activity. The rate of break down will be faster near the surface, but below 2m, traces of even fine roots can persist for several years in a heavy clay. For this reason many of the roots which can be seen may have been dead and inactive for several years.

Figure 13.6

Fine root activity is most easily seen by splitting a core sample in half along its natural fissures.

As the white roots only live for a short time, if these are present and can be distinguished by hand lens, they will probably be alive. However, it is very difficult to determine whether brown suberised roots are alive or dead. Relict imprints of fine roots as well as decayed remnants of larger roots (2mm or larger) can persist in the soil for many years or even decades.

Although fine roots are most easily seen in undisturbed samples, they can also be found in disturbed samples. A disturbed sample will still split along its original fissure planes to expose the fine roots, although they may be harder to find. In order to avoid unnecessary exposure of samples which are needed for laboratory analysis, it is preferable to inspect the arisings taken from between sampling positions, as these can be picked through carefully and then discarded.

When observing fine root activity, I assess and record the relative abundance on a scale of 1 - 5 (5 = very abundant, 1 very occasional, and 0 = absent). Provided the root system is still alive and seasonal re-hydration has not occurred, this scale may be a correlated with evidence of desiccation, as determined by other methods (see Case Study 16). However, as noted in Chapter 14, (page 221), the presence of fine roots is not necessarily indicative of soil drying.

Particle size analysis

If necessary, the descriptive assessment of the soil can be supported by particle size analysis. This involves wet sieve analysis (BS1377:1990, section 9.2) to determine the proportions of gravel, coarse, medium and fine sand, down to a particle size of 63μm. If the soil contains 65% or more particles greater than 63μm, it should be classified as non-cohesive and non-shrinkable (BS 5930:1981). Particle size analysis of fine grained materials (silt and clay) is more complicated, involving pipette or hydrometer tests (BS1377:1990, sections 9.4 and 9.5) and is not usually necessary.

Classification of soil shrinkage

Chapter 4 has described the difficulties in trying to determine the behaviour of a soil as it dries and shrinks. The only way to get detailed information is by elaborate laboratory techniques to determine the suction curves (such as Figure 4.12) and then relate these changes in moisture content to changes in volume (such as Figure 4.18). These tests are far too elaborate and time-consuming to have any practical value for site investigations.

As noted in Chapter 4, in the absence of methods of direct measurement, it is necessary to rely on empirical methods. Of these, the plasticity index, derived from the classification tests for plastic and liquid limit, provides the best indication of shrinkage potential. However, it must be remembered that these tests are only showing the range of moisture content over which a soil sample which is being artificially moulded will remain in a plastic state. In the field, soils will not be drying over the same wide range, nor are they being moulded so that all of their structure is destroyed. In particular, classification tests can take no account of the effect of air entering the soil as it dries, nor the influence of the development of cracks within a natural structured soil. The tests provide a means for objectively classifying a soil, rather than giving a quantitative value of shrinkage potential; as emphasised in Chapter 4, the correlation between either plasticity index or liquid limit, and soil shrinkage over the available water range is not statistically significant.

The classification which has gained general acceptance is that used in N.H.B.C. Standards Chapter 4.2, which divides the soils into three categories of high, medium and low shrinkage potential. However, as the high category includes all soils with a plasticity index greater than 40, it is preferable to use the classification in BRE Digest 240 (1993), which takes account of the exceptional soils with a plasticity index in excess of 60. The recommended classification is therefore:

Shrinkage potential	Plasticity index
Low	10 - 20
Medium	20 - 40
High	40 - 60
Very high	> 60

The methods for determining liquid and plastic limits are defined in sections 4 and 5 respectively of BS 1377:1990.

Before undertaking these tests it is a requirement that all particles greater than 425μm should be removed by sieving an air dried sample. This is difficult and laborious, but can be omitted with most of the highly shrinkable clay soils (London Clay, Gault Clay, Oxford Clay, etc.). With these soils any coarse particles can be picked out by hand during preparation for the tests. However, sieving may be needed with Boulder Clay and other more heterogeneous soils; the percentage of material which does not pass the 425μm sieve should be recorded.

There are two alternative methods for determining the **liquid limit**. The cone penetrometer (BS 1377 section 4.3) is meant to give the more reproducible results, but BRE Digest 412 has noted that the results of even this test are subject to considerable variation. Although possibly slightly less accurate, the one-point method using the Casagrande apparatus (BS 1377 section 4.6) has the advantage of being far quicker and thus cheaper. If funds are limited it is better to use this test on many samples, rather than having a more precise value on a smaller number of samples.

The Casagrande apparatus is simple to use; it is illustrated in Figure 13.7a. The test requires that the sample is prepared by mixing thoroughly with water until it becomes a homogeneous paste at the approximate liquid limit. It is stored in this condition for 24 hours before testing. A portion of the soil-paste is placed in the cup while it is resting at an angle on the base, and the surface of the soil is then levelled off. A groove is then cut though this paste with a special tool; this divides the soil into two parts of defined shape, separated by a 2mm gap (Figure 13.7 b). By winding the handle of the apparatus, the cup is raised by 10mm and then suddenly dropped onto the rubber base plate. If the paste is exactly at the liquid limit, after 25 blows of this sort the two parts of the soil will have closed the groove and come into contact along a distance of 13mm (Figure 13.7c) The cup is refilled and the test repeated to confirm the number of blows, and then the contents of the cup are taken for determination of moisture content. If exactly 25 blows are required, the moisture content will be equal to the liquid limit; a correction factor can be applied if more or less blows are required. Full details, and also the correction factors, are specified in section 4.6 of BS 1377:1990.

Any surplus soil which has been prepared to its liquid limit can be used for determination of the **linear shrinkage**. For this a paste of the soil at its liquid limit is placed in a 14cm long semi-circular special brass mould, gently jarred to remove air pockets and then the surface trimmed off across the top of the mould. It is then slowly dried in the air until the edges separate from the mould before being oven dried (Figure 13.8). The length of the dried sample is measured, and the shrinkage calculated as a percentage of the length of the mould. As this test measures shrinkage over the maximum range from the liquid limit to oven dried, it is not surprising that it has a close correlation with the plasticity index. This is illustrated in Figure 13.9 which uses

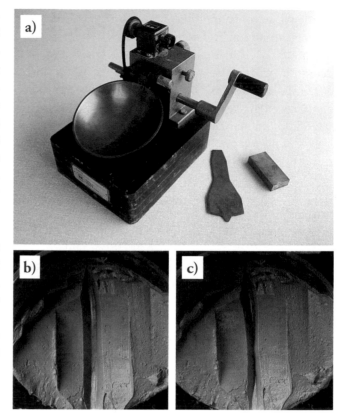

Figure 13.7

a) Casagrande apparatus used for determination of liquid limit. b) Soil sample in cup with groove prepared, and ready for testing. c) The edges of the groove closed along a length of 13mm on completion of test.

the data in Volume 2 from all of the samples for which these values are recorded. However, this test has the same limitations as plasticity index, in not indicating the shrinkage potential over the available water range.

Plastic limit is determined by mixing a sample of about 20g of soil thoroughly with water to a stiff homogeneous paste which can be shaped into a ball. The ball is moulded between the fingers and in the palm of the hand until the

Figure 13.8

Shrinkage mould and soil sample before and after drying for determination of percentage linear shrinkage.

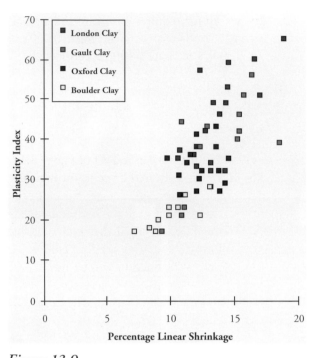

Figure 13.9

Correlation between percentage linear shrinkage and plasticity index for soil samples described in Volume 2.

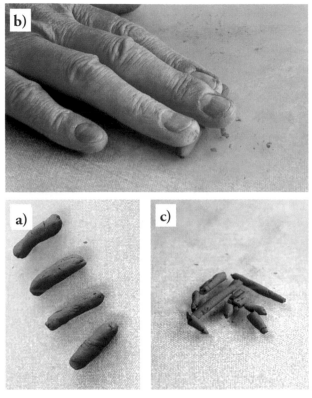

Figure 13.10

Determination of plastic limit. a) Short 6mm diameter samples prior to rolling. b) Rolling the sample on a glass plate. c) At the plastic limit, the soil shears longitudinally and transversely.

heat of the hand has dried it sufficiently for fine cracks to appear in the surface. It is then subdivided into two, with separate determinations made on each half. For this, each of the sub-samples is further divided into four parts. Each of these parts is formed into a short thread about 6mm diameter (Figure 13.10 a), and this is then rolled between the finger tips and a glass plate (Figure 13.10 b), using sufficient pressure to reduce the diameter of the thread to about 3mm within 5 - 10 forward and back movements of the hand. If an intact thread can be formed, it is remoulded to dry further, and the process then repeated until the thread shears both longitudinally and transversely when it is rolled to 3mm. At this point the soil is at its plastic limit (Figure 13.10 c).   The pieces are immediately transferred to an air-tight container, and the process repeated on the other 3 parts, with all the pieces grouped together. The other half of the sub-sample is then tested in the same way, with the pieces placed into a separate container. The moisture content of the two sub-samples are then determined and, provided they are within 0.5% of each other, the average is taken as the plastic limit (expressed to the nearest whole number). The test may appear simple and crude, but produces very reproducible results. Full details are specified in section 5.3 of BS 1377:1990.

Moisture content determination

Soil samples for moisture content determination should be taken at appropriate depth intervals. Examination of the moisture content profiles in Volume 2 shows that the influence of root activity can diminish very abruptly at any depth below about 1.0m. For this reason samples taken at 1.0 or even 0.5m intervals are too far apart and are likely to miss relevant changes in the profile. The profiles in Volume 2 are all defined at 0.1m intervals; this provides great accuracy and is practical with the neutron probe but becomes impractical for routine sampling and laboratory analysis. However, samples should not be further apart than 0.25m; this interval provides a reasonable compromise between convenience and accuracy. Likewise, the depth of sampling should be appropriate for the likely effects of the tree. In most situations 10 samples taken at 0.25m intervals from 0.75 to 3m depth will be far more useful (and cheaper) than the same number of samples at 0.5m intervals from 1.0 to 5.5m. Volume 2 shows that it is rare for significant changes in moisture content to extend below 3.0m, except with species such as poplar and oak or with more permeable soils which encourage deeper rooting.

Samples for moisture content determinations should be placed into a sealed container as soon as they are removed from the ground; heavy duty polythene bags supplied in rolls for use in freezers are ideal. These have a prepared surface for recording details of borehole number and depth. Surplus air should be sucked out, and the bag sealed with an overhand knot. Bags should be kept out of the sun, and taken to the laboratory as soon as possible for analysis. Analysis should not be delayed as there is a gradual loss of moisture, even from intact freezer bags. I have found that the moisture content of a soil sample at field capacity, taken as described above and kept at a temperature of about 18^0, falls by about 1.0% every 3 weeks.

Moisture content should be determined in accordance with BS 1377:1990, section 3.2, except that it is preferable to record the results to the nearest 0.1%.

Interpretation of the results is easiest if they are presented graphically as moisture content profiles, as seen in many of the Case Studies. The horizontal axis (of moisture content) should be adjusted to show only the relevant range of values; inclusion of the zero point only makes it more difficult to appreciate any variation.

Soil suction

In recent years, research by Chandler and Gutierrez (1986) with refinements by Chandler *et al.* (1992) has led to the practical development of a direct measurement of soil suction using filter papers. The technique is further described in BRE Information Paper IP 4/93 (Crilly and Chandler, 1993), and so will only be summarised here.

The test requires that a core of soil is cut into a series of discs. A piece of Whatman's No. 42 filter paper is placed between each of the discs, which are then reassembled, so that the filter papers are sandwiched in close contact with the soil between the discs. The whole mass of soil and paper is then sealed to prevent evaporation and kept at constant temperature for five days. During this period the moisture in the soil equilibrates between the soil and the filter paper. The soil and filter papers are then unsealed and dismantled, and the moisture content of the filter papers determined as rapidly and accurately as possible. The matric suction of the soil is determined from this moisture content using published calibration curves.

As described on page 210, the determination of soil suction in this way has some advantages for assessing whether a soil is desiccated. However, the limitations of the technique must be recognised. Some of these are barely mentioned in BRE IP 4/93; in particular:

i) the technique requires great care and a precision analytical balance (measuring to 0.0001g). This makes accurate testing expensive;

ii) the accuracy diminishes if the soil is less than 90% saturated. Most soils do not maintain this level of saturation;

iii) as noted on page 47 in respect of Figure 4.12, if a clay soil is sheared at constant moisture content, its suction will change. Sampling the soil will cause such change. This becomes particularly significant in small diameter cores, but even 100mm diameter cores will be influenced. On soft clays the suction will be under estimated; on stiff clays it is over estimated. With U100 samples in London Clay, the correction factor is about -50 kPa;

iv) Unless measurements are made in comparable soil away from the influence of root activity to determine the natural profile of suction in the soil, there can be difficulty in interpreting the results (an assumed profile will depend on the coefficient of earth pressure at rest (K_o) which with a stiff over-consolidated clay can vary between values of about 1.0 and 2.5).

In order to minimise these problems it is recommended that:

i) care is taken to ensure that the laboratory which undertakes the analysis has the necessary expertise and equipment;

ii) particular care is taken in interpretation of results from soils with significant quantities of sand, or with unusual drainage characteristics;

iii) the core samples used should be as large as possible, preferably at least 100mm diameter;

iv) results for the individual filter papers should be provided, to allow calculation of the standard error;

v) adequate samples are taken to ensure accurate definition of the profile;

vi) if possible suction profiles should also be taken for a site well away from tree root activity as a comparison.

Field determination of shear strength

The shear strength of a soil is a function of the inter-particle friction. As a clay soil dries, the particles are drawn closer together. This increases the friction, and thus the shear strength. In this way, shear strength can provide an indication of desiccation.

The simplest way of estimating shear strength is to mould the clay in the hand, in accordance with the criteria in Figure 13.11. The descriptive terms and values are those used in BS 5930:1981.

Shear strength (kPa)	Descriptive term	Characteristic
< 20	Very soft	Exudes between fingers when squeezed
20 - 40	Soft	Moulded by light finger pressure
40 - 75	Firm	Moulded by strong finger pressure
75 - 150	Stiff	Can be indented by thumb
150 - 300	Very stiff	Can be indented by thumb nail
> 300	Hard	

Figure 13.11

Manual estimation of shear strength of clays.

A shear vane provides one method for the quantitative assessment in the field of the undrained shear strength; measurements can be taken with this at appropriate intervals whilst drilling a borehole. However, the maximum reading which can be taken with a shear vane is about 140 kPa. In practice this places a serious limitation on the application of the technique for determining desiccation, as many stiff over-consolidated clays are at or near this value at their natural moisture content. Even with a soft or firm clay, any drying takes the shear strength rapidly beyond the range of the instrument.

An alternative method is to use a dial penetrometer, as described by Pugh, Parnell and Parkes (1995). This small hand-held tool provides a measure of the presumed bearing value of the soil, which is related to the undrained shear strength. It allows direct measurements to be made into the base or side of trial pits or underpinning excavations, and is particularly useful if boreholes are being drilled with a driven-tube window sampler. These samplers provide undisturbed cores, with the window in the side of the sampling tube allowing penetrometer readings of the core at regular intervals down the profile.

If there is any doubt about the ability of the soil to support the foundation load without suffering shear failure, undisturbed soil samples may be required for triaxial testing. These tests and their interpretation are beyond the scope of this book.

Assessment of desiccation

The tests described in the previous sections (soil classification, moisture content determination, soil suction, and shear strength) all provide data which can be interpreted to provide an assessment of desiccation. BRE Digest 412 provides a detailed description of criteria which should be applied to the various tests; reference should be made to that Digest, and the methods and criteria will not be repeated here. The Digest also describes methods for quantifying the extent of desiccation; these methods and their limitations are considered in Chapter 16 (page 264), in the assessment of the extent of heave or recovery movement.

Although details will not be considered here, it is important to emphasize the caveat in BRE Digest 412 that the detection of desiccation in clay soils can be more difficult than is often assumed. A severely desiccated soil can usually be distinguished quite reliably, but this is of limited practicality as even slight desiccation can cause significant soil movement, particularly if it extends through a considerable depth. For this reason one needs an accurate and reliable method which defines the onset of significant desiccation as precisely as possible. The most reliable methods generally involve comparison of profiles, particularly of moisture content, soil suction or shear strength. However, even these methods have problems. Other methods, such as comparison of moisture content with soil classification tests, are even less reliable. As all methods have their disadvantages, BRE Digest 412 quite rightly advocates that **reliance should not be placed on any single method, but rather on an overall assessment of all available information.** Despite this, one frequently sees reports claiming the presence of significant desiccation based on the flimsiest of evidence.

A common-sense approach is often more valid than theoretical consideration of profiles or classification tests. In particular, when drilling boreholes a careful note should be made of soil conditions, and particularly of the presence of free water. If bands of water-laden sand are present, these will be supplying adjacent areas of clay which are unlikely to be desiccated. Likewise, water permeating from a sandy clay indicates that the soil is saturated. Even with these obvious indicators of saturated conditions, it is surprising how often it is alleged that the soil is desiccated.

Some of the problems which can be encountered in the interpretation of soil tests are considered in the next two sections.

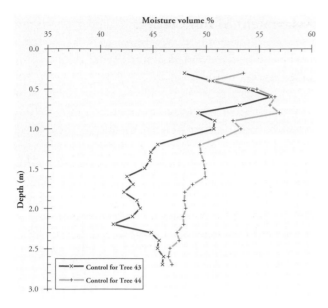

Figure 13.12

Dissimilar moisture content profiles for two control access tubes in similar conditions in London Clay, 34m apart and well away from any potential influence of trees.

Limitations in assessment of desiccation: i) by comparison of profiles

If the soil across a site is uniform, it should be possible to compare soil conditions close to a tree where desiccation may be present with the conditions beyond the range of potential influence of the tree. This method is widely applied in site investigations and is the basis of the "assumed persistent deficits" which are considered in Chapter 6 (page 88). However, Figures 6.6 and 6.7 in that Chapter illustrate the variation in profiles which can occur, particularly with the less homogeneous Boulder Clay. Figure 13.12 shows a further example of two moisture content profiles. The profile in red is drier than the one in green from 0.6

down to 2.6m, and appears to indicate significant desiccation. However, both of these profiles are for the control access tubes in similar conditions in a park, 24m from a pair of 12m high Leyland cypress, and well away from any potential influence of other trees. These two access tubes are only 34m apart, but despite the apparently similar conditions, produce very different profiles.

Figure 13.13 shows further examples of very dissimilar profiles for control access tubes located in close proximity to each other. Figure 3.13 a) is for trees 28 and 29 which are on Gault clay and about 45m apart; b) is for trees 13 and 14, which are on Oxford Clay and about 40m apart; c) shows the three profiles for the control access tubes 30m from the plane trees on London Clay used in the pruning experiment. These three tubes are in a line, about 25m apart, and in each case 30m from the nearest tree.

All of these examples show significant differences in the profiles, despite being well away from any trees, in apparently similar conditions in parks where the soil is unlikely to have been disturbed, and with clay soils which are normally considered to be very uniform.

In the research project there were 7 sites where there were closely adjacent control access tubes of this sort in conditions which might be expected to be uniform (in other cases there was only one tree per site). Figures 6.7, 6.8, 13.12 and 13.13 have illustrated the variation between the profiles in six of these examples. Figure 13.14 shows profiles for the only pair of access tubes which were essentially similar; these are 36m apart on Gault Clay.

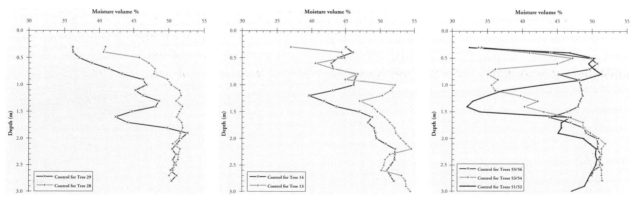

Figure 13.13

Dissimilar moisture content profiles for control access tubes in similar conditions and well away from any potential influence of trees.

a) 45m apart in Gault Clay   b) 40m apart in Oxford Clay   c) 25m apart in London Clay

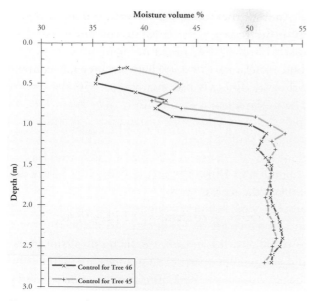

Figure 13.14

Very similar moisture content profiles 36m apart in Gault Clay. This was the only site (out of 7) to give similar profiles for a pair of control access tubes which were away from any potential influence of trees.

These examples show that, even on sites which have been comparatively undisturbed and with soils which are noted for their uniformity, moisture content profiles are likely to be very different even without any influence of root activity. For this reason trying to assess desiccation by comparing moisture content profiles on any site is liable to give misleading results. With the more heterogeneous soils, for instance Boulder Clay, profiles are likely to be even more variable and unreliable. Likewise, sites which have been disturbed by development are likely to be more variable.

In theory the soil suction test should overcome the need for a control profile, as the suction in the absence of drying by root activity should be related solely to the overburden stress, which should be reasonably constant across a site. It should therefore be possible to assess desiccation without relying on a control borehole which is beyond the influence of root activity. However, as noted on page 207, the accuracy of soil suction tests diminishes if a soil is less than 90% saturated. An example, quoted by Chandler *et al.* (1992), where a clay soil overlay a layer of drained sand (Case D in that paper), illustrates the anomalous results which can occur. In addition, any assumption about the equilibrium profile in the absence of desiccation is dependent on the value of the coefficient of earth pressure at rest (K_o) which is adopted. Typically for London Clay this value will lie between 2 and 2.5, but with other clays it may vary between 0.5 and 3.0. Although the assumed value of K_o can introduce some uncertainty, the suction created by desiccation is usually far greater

than the variation attributable to K_o, and so this is not a serious limitation. If necessary, a control suction profile can be determined so as to avoid the need for these assumptions.

In some situations measurement of undrained shear strength using a dial penetrometer can provide a method for assessing desiccation in the absence of a control profile. Based on many hundreds of investigations, Pugh, Parnell and Parkes (1995) suggest that, with London Clay under equilibrium conditions (i.e. with no desiccation), there is a single typical profile, and that the inherent compositional variation over the lateral extent of the outcrop of London Clay produces only a limited range of variation about this mean. A significant increase in the dial penetrometer readings above this range of values should provide an indication of desiccation. Their paper provides examples.

Figure 13.15 shows results of dial penetrometer readings for 6 boreholes at a site on London Clay in Hampshire, and includes the typical equilibrium profile and range of values suggested by Pugh, Parnell and Parkes. The profiles appear to indicate desiccation between about 1.5 to 4.5m depth in all 6 boreholes, and were used by an engineer to substantiate claims for an extensive persistent deficit (the holes were drilled in late February when seasonal recovery would be nearly complete). However, the boreholes are at varying distance from a row of oak trees, and there is no correla-

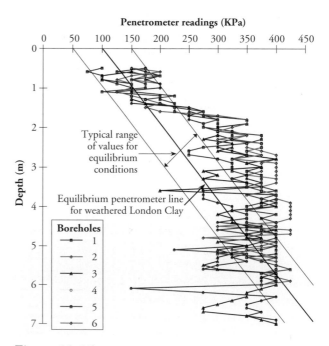

Figure 13.15

Profiles of penetrometer readings in London Clay, together with profile proposed by Pugh et al. (1995) as typical for London Clay. In this case the elevated values probably do not indicate desiccation.

tion between their proximity and the degree of desiccation. Furthermore, level monitoring on an adjacent building after removal of four of the closest trees demonstrated that no recovery movements occurred (but showed that seasonal movement had been stopped). This suggests that no significant deficit was present, and that the typical equilibrium profile may not be reliable, at least in this example. Until there is greater experience in the application of this technique, it would advisable to use a control profile away from the tree as a comparison, and a control is certainly required for soils other than London Clay. Even where a control profile is used, the possibility of inherent variation, similar to that observed with moisture content profiles, should be considered.

Limitations in assessment of desiccation: ii) from soil classification tests

If comparison of profiles can be unreliable, the alternative is to depend on a direct assessment of the soil. Figure 4.15 in Chapter 4 (page 48) has noted the correlation between moisture content and liquid limit for soils at a suction of 10 kPa (pF = 2) and 100 kPa (pF = 3). This has led Driscoll (1983) to propose that the onset of desiccation occurs if the moisture content falls below a value of 0.5 x liquid limit (LL), with significant desiccation below 0.4 x liquid limit. In this way, comparison of the moisture content with the liquid limit provides a direct assessment of desiccation.

This relationship is now often used, but one sees it applied to all sorts of clays without appreciation of its limitations. As noted in Chapter 4, it is generally valid and provides a useful approximation for overconsolidated clays with high values of liquid limit. However, the statistical relationship breaks down at lower values of liquid limit, and so should be treated with caution if the liquid limit is less than 80. It is probably unreliable if the liquid limit is less than 60, and is certainly not applicable to an unconsolidated clay.

It must also be noted that this relationship is only applicable to soils at comparatively shallow depths (down to about 3.0m). With increasing depth the equilibrium moisture content of the soil diminishes, and so it will naturally fall below a value of 0.4 x LL. A suction of 100 kPa was used by Driscoll as this equates approximately to the pressure exerted by a two-storey building. For taller buildings, with higher foundation pressures, the liquid limit should be multiplied by a factor less than 0.4.

Another method which is often quoted is that a soil is desiccated if the moisture content is less than plastic limit + 2. As noted in Figure 4.14, there is a good correlation (r = 0.95) between moisture content and plastic limit (PL) at a suction of 250 kPa; at this suction the linear regression is;

moisture content = 1.22 PL - 3.3.

If one uses the data and moisture release curves for the range of soils shown in Figure 4.13, at a suction of 100 kPa the regression is:

moisture content = 1.82 PL - 15.4.

It is clear that this equation bears no similarity to the suggestion that moisture content = PL + 2. If the plastic limit happens to be 21.2, either equation will indicate an equilibrium moisture content of 23.2 i.e.:

$$1.82 \times 21.2 - 15.4 = 23.2,$$
$$\text{or} \quad 21.2 + 2 = 23.2$$

The plastic limit of clay is often about 21, and so PL +2 may appear to give the correct result. However, it will not be accurate at other values. Whilst the regression formula should be accurate at other values, it has a lower correlation coefficient (r - 0.89) than 0.4 x LL, and may not be applicable to all types of clay.

For these reasons relationships based on the plastic limit should be considered a less reliable method for assessing desiccation.

Summary

1. A general indication of probable soil conditions in a locality can be obtained from the Geological Survey maps. As a stratum can vary considerably in different parts of the country, interpretation of a map should be linked to experience of that stratum in the locality.

2. Site specific information must depend on site investigations, usually involving boreholes.

3. The depth and diameter of the borehole, and the method of augering, should depend on the type of information which is required.

4. For most purposes a 50mm diameter borehole providing disturbed samples is quite adequate. This can be used for the assessment of soil conditions, inspection for fine root activity, determination of moisture content and soil classification tests. A 3m deep

borehole is usually sufficient, but 5 or 6m holes may occasionally be required. Holes of this sort can be drilled by hand.

5.	Personal experience of the soil conditions, which can only be obtained from drilling holes, provides the best method for judging the overall permeability of the soil.

6.	The plasticity index of a soil is the range of moisture content over which it will remain plastic. Over this range, a change in moisture content will be accompanied by volumetric change. The plasticity index therefore provides a useful indication of the potential of the soil for volumetric change.

7.	However, under field conditions soils are not being subject to the same wide range of change, nor are they being artificially moulded. Interpretation of the plasticity index should therefore be tempered by experience of the behaviour of the soil in the field, particularly with regard to its structural development as it dries.

8.	Severely desiccated soils are generally easily recognised, but assessing the onset of desiccation is difficult. For this reason the total extent of desiccation is usually difficult to define.

9.	If moisture content profiles are being determined, samples should be taken at close intervals (not greater than every 0.25m). However, comparison of moisture content profiles, even with an apparently uniform clay, does not provide a reliable method of assessing desiccation. Even under ideal conditions, profiles which differ by 10% (v/v) may be the result of inherent variation in the soil, rather than an indication of desiccation.

10.	Likewise, profiles of undrained shear strength and soil suction can be subject to significant inherent variation.

11.	Soil suction tests provide a more direct measure of soil conditions, but even these must be interpreted with care.

12.	There are limitations to the assessment of desiccation based on comparison of moisture content with the liquid limit or the plastic limit. In particular, these methods should only be applied to heavy clays.

13.	Overall assessment of soil conditions should consider **all of the available information, both from the laboratory tests and from field examination. As soil conditions are variable and difficult to predict, it must be appreciated that even detailed tests will not necessarily provide precise answers.**

14.	Soil moisture content will vary through the year. In the spring, only a persistent deficit will be demonstrable. Investigations in the autumn will identify both seasonal and persistent effects. The type of information which is required should therefore govern the time of year for the site work.

Additional reading

BRE Digest 412 (1996) Desiccation in clay soils.

BRE Information Paper IP 4/93 (1993) A method of determining the state of desiccation in clay soils.

Sources of Equipment

Geological survey maps:

British Geological Survey
Keyworth
Nottingham NG12 5GG

National Map Centre
22 Caxton Street
London SW1H 0QU

Soil investigation and analytical equipment

Engineering Laboratory Equipment Ltd.
Eastman Way
Hemel Hempstead
Herts, HP2 7HB

Van Walt Ltd (agents for Eijkelkamp)
Prestwick Lane
Grayswood
Haslemere Surrey, GU27 2DU

Bungalow built close to overmature oak tree – Dieback of tree allows soil to rehydrate and heave –
Subsequent recovery of tree starts seasonal movements and damage –
Tree eventually felled – Monitoring shows restability achieved with minimal further heave.

The subject property is an 'L' shaped detached bungalow with integral garage (CS Figure 13.1), located in Gloucestershire on Lower Lias Clay. It is one of several similar bungalows which were built in 1975/76. An extension was added to the rear soon after construction. The bungalow stands on a site which slopes gently down to the front and left, but with the angle of this slope significantly increasing to the front of the property. To accommodate these changes in level, the ground adjacent to the front left corner had been raised by approximately 0.5m.

Towards the end of the summer of 1976, soon after it was constructed, a vertical crack developed below the lounge window on the front elevation. This was repaired, and no further problems were encountered until 1984 when further cracking started to occur.

I was instructed in January 1986 by which time there was severe diagonal and horizontal cracking in the front left corner of the lounge, with this extending as a vertical crack below the right side of the lounge window. There was some horizontal outward displacement of the brickwork below d.p.c. on the front and flank elevations. Lesser amounts of cracking were also present on the left flank wall around the kitchen door and kitchen window. Internally there was corresponding damage and other areas of minor movement throughout the front of the property, with the amount of damage diminishing towards the rear. The owner advised that these cracks had been far wider during the previous summer.

The tree

In the garden of the adjacent bungalow 8.3m from the front left corner there was an oak tree (*Quercus robur*) with a height of 20m and trunk diameter of 95cm. The branch structure of this tree extended over the front corner of the subject property. Examination of the crown structure showed that the tree had suffered from extensive dieback of twigs and foliage in recent years leading to large amounts of dead wood throughout the crown. Despite this extensive dead wood, the surviving parts of the lower crown had made vigorous shoot extension growth during the previous summer. The tree had been made the subject of a Tree Preservation Order at the time of development.

There was also a hedgerow, including large mature oak trees, approximately 25m to the rear of the bungalow.

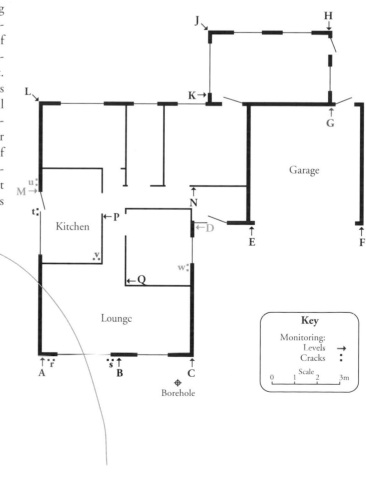

Case Study Figure 13.1

Site plan, showing location of tree and of level and crack monitoring stations.

Previous investigations

Engineers had previously excavated a trial hole on the front elevation near the left corner. This had exposed strip foundations passing through 0.5m of fill, and resting on brown/grey mottled clay at 1.2m below external ground level. Part way along the front wall there was a step up in the foundations with no overlap of the concrete footings at this position. The crack below the lounge window extended through this step.

The trial hole demonstrated extensive root activity, undoubtedly originating from the oak tree. The engineers diagnosed subsidence, with a recommendation for underpinning. I was instructed by the loss adjusters to advise on possible alternative remedies and on liability.

Level distortion survey

Preliminary observations during my initial visit suggested that the front corner closest to the oak tree was tilted up. This was confirmed in my subsequent visit by a complete survey around the original building; the results are shown in CS Figure 13.2, presented relative to an arbitrary zero datum adjacent to the front door. The front elevation has a difference in level of 18mm and the flank elevation has a difference in level of 24mm, with the highest point closest to the tree.

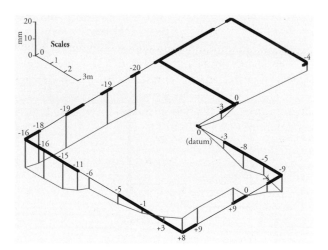

Case Study Figure 13.2

Results of level distortion survey in April 1986, relative to arbitrary datum at front door.

Level and crack monitoring

At the time of my initial visit I set up level monitoring markers on 12 locations on external walls plus three markers on internal partition walls. The location of these stations is shown in CS Figure 13.1, and the movements recorded during subsequent visits are shown in CS Figure 13.3. These results are shown graphically for a selection of these stations in CS Figure 13.5.

Crack monitoring was started on my second visit. The location of the stations is shown in CS Figure 13.1 and the results in CS Figure 13.3 and 13.6.

Changes in level (mm) compared to 21/1/86:						
	18/4/86	31/3/87	10/8/87	20/10/87	12/2/88	19/9/88	2/3/89
A	4.3	2	5.1	5.2	3.3	6.5	7.4
B	2.4	2.4	4.8	4.4	2.4	4.9	5.4
C	-0.3	-0.5	1.7	1.6	-0.5	1.6	2.1
D	-0.1	-0.1	1.5	0.6	0.1	1.5	1.7
E	-0.1	-0.2	1.1	0.2	-0.2	1	1.6
F	-0.4	-0.4	0.5	-0.6	-0.5	0	1.3
G	-0.2	0.1	0	-	0.1	-0.2	-0.2
H	0	0	-0.4	-	-0.1	-0.9	-0.2
J	Datum	Datum	Datum	Datum	Datum	Datum	Datum
K	0	0.1	0.4	0.6	0	0.3	0.3
L	0.4	0.1	0.9	0.8	-0.1	1.6	2.2
M	3.9	2.4	3.9	4.6	4	5.5	6
N	0	0.1	1.1	-	0.1	1.2	1
P	-0.7	0	0.9	-	0.6	0.6	1
Q	0.6	-0.2	0.9	-	0.8	0.8	1.8
Crack movements (µm) compared to 18/4/86:						
r	0	1051	356	147	102	54	-73
s	0	813	495	496	439	371	355
t	0	186	-157	71	181	63	183
u	0	122	-404	-394	-355	-559	-553
v	0	56	56	-	40	54	54
w	0	40	41	-	33	8	82

Case Study Figure 13.3

Results of level and crack monitoring

Subsoil conditions

In April 1986 I drilled a borehole 1.3m from the front left corner. This encountered fill soil below the surface to 0.4m, below which was a stiff yellow brown clay. This clay became increasingly dark and silty, and at 1.25m it was the typical silty laminated clay encountered in the Lower Lias. Essentially similar conditions continued to the base of the borehole, with a gradual increase in the shaliness of the soil.

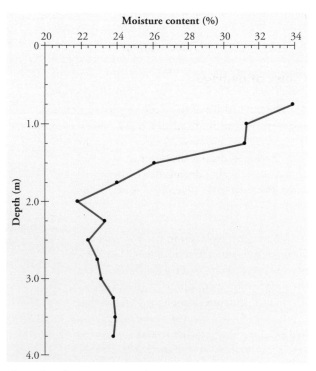

Case Study Figure 13.4

Soil moisture content profile in April 1986.

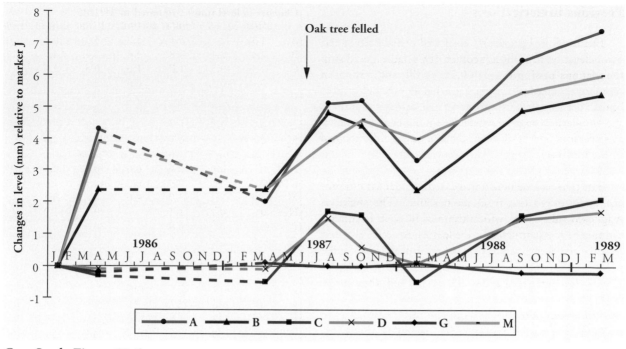

Case Study Figure 13.5

Results of level monitoring for selected stations, relative to station J as datum.

At 3.9m the borehole encountered impenetrable shale, and at the same time water started to seep rapidly into the hole, soon rising to 2.8m below the surface. The moisture content profile from this borehole is shown in CS Figure 13.4.

I attempted to drill a control borehole in the front garden of the adjacent property beyond the garage. Immediately below the soil surface I encountered the typical laminated clay found below 2.0m in the other hole. It was apparent that ground levels had been significantly lowered and that the soil in the two boreholes would not be comparable. This control hole was therefore discontinued.

DISCUSSION

Cause of damage

The upward tilt of the building close to the oak tree is not consistent with subsidence, but suggests that heave had been occurring. However, the description that recent cracks had developed during the summer but had closed considerably during the winter indicated that seasonal movements were occurring.

The logical explanation for this anomaly was apparent from the condition of the crown of the tree. Very extensive dieback was present; from the condition of the twig and fine branch structure, it could be deduced that this had developed soon after the bungalows had been built. A mature oak of this sort is very susceptible to disturbance and damage of the root system, and from the changes of level in the garden it was apparent that considerable disturbance must have occurred at

that time. This would have led to death of much of the fine root system, thereby preventing water uptake, with this leading to death of the foliage and dieback of the peripheral parts of the crown. This reduction in water uptake would allow the soil to rehydrate and swell and thus produce the upward tilt of the building close to the tree.

The initial damage in 1976 was probably caused by subsidence. At that stage the roots would still have had energy reserves laid down prior to development; these would have allowed the roots to continue to function during the drought conditions of that year.

Although the tree had suffered massive damage, by the mid-1980's it was beginning to recover, as demonstrated by the vigorous shoot extension growth on the remaining foliage in the lower crown. This was sufficient to reverse the heave and allow the seasonal movements to start to develop.

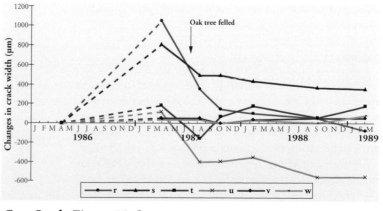

Case Study Figure 13.6

Results of crack monitoring

215

Remedial action.

The level monitoring in April 1986 showed that the front corner (station A) had recovered by 4.3mm since January, i.e. a rate of 0.35mm per week. This rate of movement in the latter part of the winter suggested that seasonal movements of at least 10mm were occurring, but this rapid rate of recovery also suggested that there must be potential for some further heave. In contradiction to this, the modest amount of heave which had occurred as a result of the dieback suggested that the total heave potential should be limited. The lack of any control borehole made it difficult to assess the extent of any soil desiccation, but the evidence of free moisture in the soil at 3.9m and its rapid rise under hydrostatic pressure, suggested that any desiccation could be corrected both by upward movement of the water table as well as downward penetration of rainfall. In these circumstances I considered that the extent and duration of further heave should be tolerable.

As an alternative, the leaf area created by the recent regrowth could have been removed sufficient to prevent seasonal movements (together with the dead wood so as to eliminate the hazard which it posed), but this amount of surgery would have reduced the tree to a stump of negligible amenity value. In these circumstances I therefore recommended that the tree should be felled.

I drew attention to the presence of the Tree Preservation Order but advised that the tree could be felled under the exemptions which allow work which is necessary for "prevention or abatement of a nuisance".

Although these recommendations were made in May 1986, no action was taken during that summer. Damage again developed but regrettably, despite emphasising the need for further monitoring, no instructions were given to continue the readings during that summer.

It was not until the following April (1987) that I received further instructions. The monitoring readings taken then were almost exactly 12 months after the previous set and therefore do not record any intervening seasonal movement, as indicated by a dotted line in CS Figure 13.5. The crack monitoring showed that they were wider than the previous spring and, from the owners observations, it was apparent that they had opened far more during the previous summer but had then closed during the winter.

Negotiations by the loss adjuster for the removal of the tree had still not been successful. The owner of the tree was apparently keen to remove it but the local authority were resisting such action. I reiterated that their consent was not required in these circumstances and that, if there was any further delay, the only alternative option would be extensive underpinning, for which the tree owner would undoubtedly be liable. Eventually, in mid-June 1987, most of the tree was felled (effectively removing all foliage) with the work completed by August.

After the tree was felled the monitoring was continued. A surprising set of results was recorded the following February. The readings on that date show the front elevation moving downwards by an almost uniform 2mm, with lesser movements recorded at the middle of the building (for instance stations D and M) and virtual stability at the rear (e.g. station G on CS Figure 13.3). The closing error on the circuit was only 0.1mm, and I have no reason to doubt their accuracy. Two explanations are possible:-

i) very slight movement of the steeply sloping site;

ii) slight seasonal movements affecting the datum; upward seasonal recovery of this would make other stations appear to subside. Such movements could possibly have been caused by the distant oak trees to the rear of the bungalow.

The next set of readings (in September 1988) showed the recovery to be continuing but at a far slower rate than the previous summer, with this rate continuing to decline the following March (1989). These readings showed no evidence of the reversal in direction which had been recorded during the previous winter period. This suggested that slope instability might have been involved.

Throughout this period of monitoring subsequent to tree felling, the cracks gradually closed and stabilised.

Some simple cosmetic redecoration was undertaken in August 1987 to mask the worst of the cracks. Final superstructure repairs and decoration were then put in hand in 1989. This included inserting a reinforced beam above the level of the existing footings at the position of the defective and cracked step in the front foundations.

Lessons to be learnt

- The level distortion survey shows that heave occurred after construction, as a result of damage to the root system allowing rehydration of the clay.

- In this situation, with the tree owned by a third party, the existence of a Tree Preservation Order should not cause any delay. The Town & Country Planning Act provides exemptions for work in this situation. The failure of the tree owner to remove the tree delayed the recovery process by 12 months.

- It would have been very desirable for the seasonal movements to have been recorded during that year (but no instructions were given for this work). This would have established the full extent of seasonal movement. It might have been essential if further problems had been encountered with the tree owner.

- Interpretation of the level monitoring results in February 1988 would have been aided by a deep datum.

- Both the level and crack monitoring show the efficacy of tree removal and that heave was of short duration.

CHAPTER 14

SITE INVESTIGATIONS   III) THE TREE

Objectives

Investigation of the tree will normally involve:

i)   identification;

ii)   consideration of roots, including identification and condition;

iii) assessing the size, growth rate, and water requirements of the tree;

iv)   assessing previous growth and water requirement;

v)   estimating probable future water requirements;

vi)   safety, condition and future management.

Introduction

If one is to utilise any existing knowledge on the comparative effects of different species (see Chapter 9), and also advance our future knowledge, correct identification of any trees which are involved in damage to buildings is essential.

Approximately 1700 different species of tree may be encountered in Britain. Only a very few specialists can identify all of these reliably. However, the majority of these species are usually only found in arboreta (specialist tree collections) so that identification of these species is more a matter of intellectual interest than practical value. Although many of these species are rare, about half this number, from 50 different families, can be found in Britain's streets, parks and gardens.

Most arboriculturists should have been trained to identify most, if not all, of these commoner species, or at least to use the specialist reference books to aid identification. For others with an interest in identification, there are many books which can assist.

Botanical nomenclature

Our understanding of trees is greatly aided if one has some knowledge of taxonomy and systematic botany. For most purposes the common (English) name may be sufficient to denote the tree which is being referred to. However, the common name has many disadvantages. Common names are not universal and this can give rise to confusion. For instance, the sycamore in Britain is *Acer pseudoplatanus* but to an American the name "sycamore" would denote a very different tree (*Platanus occidentalis*). Superficially they both have some similarities, with palmate 5-pointed leaves and flaking bark on the trunk of mature trees, but these similarities are of no relevance to their botanical or evolutionary relationship.

The common name used for many of our commonest species tell one nothing about their relationship to other trees. Thus, from their names one would not know that rowan, whitebeam and the service tree are all closely related (respectively *Sorbus aucuparia, S. aria,* and *S. torminalis*). Some trees also have a number of different regional names which have now become more widespread; rowan or mountain ash are examples. In some cases the common names can imply a relationship that does not exist; for instance mountain ash (*Sorbus aucuparia*) is quite unrelated to the common ash (*Fraxinus excelsior*), the only similarity being pinnate leaves (each leaf composed of multiple leaflets along a central stalk).

To avoid these problems it is advantageous to use, or at least know, the botanical names which are employed in the Linnaean system of classification. This is a hierarchical system which shows the relationship between all plants (and animals), with this reflecting their evolutionary development. In this system the major subdivisions into Classes and Orders need be of no concern except to note that Orders which include trees are the *Coniferales* (most of the conifers), *Taxales* (yew etc.), *Ginkgoales* (Maidenhair tree), *Monocotyledoneae* (palms) and the *Dicotyledoneae* (all other trees).

The relevant subdivisions are into families, in some cases sub-families, genera and species. The family is indicated by the name ending in - *aceae* (as in *Rosaceae*) (with *Leguminoseae* as an exception). Some families are divided into sub-families which are indicated by the name ending in - *oideae* (as in *Prunoideae*). Below this are the genus and the species, with these used to define the name. The genus always uses a capital initial letter and usually ends in - *us* (as in *Prunus*). Where it is obvious which family is being referred to, this may be abbreviated to the initial letter only. The species name is more variable; it may indicate some identifying overall characteristic (e.g. *pendula*, indicating a pendulous shape), or a leaf shape (e.g. *platyphyllos*, indicating broad-leaved), or perhaps indicate a similarity in leaf shape to some other genus (e.g. *prunifolia* where the leaves are like *Prunus*). Many other features of the plant may be reflected in the specific name, for instance *sylvatica* if it usually grows in woods, or *avium* because the fruit is eaten by birds. As the language used for these names is Latin, a classical education may assist. In some cases the plant will bear the name of its discoverer or whoever first described it; thus *forrestii* indicates that it was first described by the early 20th century plant collector George Forrest, rather than that the plant usually grows in a forest. Hillier's Manual of Trees and Shrubs provides a useful list of commonly used specific names and their meanings.

Within the geographic range of a species there may be distinct populations, these are referred to as varieties and denoted as var. (e.g. *Prunus communis* var. *insititia*). During cultivation genetic mutations may arise which differ from the parent in some characteristic. Mutants of this sort will not breed true to their form, but instead must be vegetatively propagated as identical clonal material. These are known as cultivars, or "cv.", and are denoted by the name in ordinary case and single quotes (e.g. *Prunus serrulata* 'Kanzan'). These cultivars have been heavily exploited by arboriculturists and help to give variety of shape and colour to the amenity tree population. For instance, *P. serrulata* 'Kanzan' is only one of about 40 cultivars of Japanese cherry, and Hillier's Manual of Trees and Shrubs lists 82 cultivars of Lawson cypress (*Chamaecyparis lawsoniana*). These have varying foliar shades of silver, gold and blue, difference of crown shape and foliar texture, and come in all sizes from large trees to dwarf rock plants. Each of these will have its cultivar name, e.g. *C. lawsoniana* 'erecta'.

Figure 14.1 uses the *Rosaceae* or rose family to illustrate this hierarchical subdivision, including only species in this very large family which develop into trees and shrubs. As well as these trees and woody shrubs, there are also many perennial and annual plants all within this family. The feature which all of these have in common is the configuration of their flowers. As the flowers are the basis of sexual reproduction, this similarity in their flowers reflects a common genetic origin. It also shows how evolutionary development has produced genetic diversity, with the different sub-families being characterised by how their similar flowers develop into different arrangements of the seed-bearing fruit.

Within a genus, all of the species will have a number of common attributes. The structure of the flowers will be similar, although colour and size may vary between species, and features such as the attachment of leaves and leaf shape may be similar. At the microscopic level, wood structures of different genera within a family are usually, but not always, sufficient to distinguish the genera, and there are usually minor differences between species within a genus which enable wood to be identified to the species level.

These differences between genera are almost invariably sufficient to prevent cross-breeding between genera. A few exceptions exist, most notably Leyland cypress which is an inter generic hybrid between Nootka cypress (*Chamaecyparis nootkatensis*) and Monterey cypress (*Cupressus macrocarpa*). The botanical name for Leyland cypress shows the hybrid origin by an x before the name (X *Cupressocyparis leylandii*). As it is an inter-generic hybrid, the x is a capital and placed before the genus name. These species have been cross-bred more than once, with the most suitable off-spring selected for propagation. Each of these forms a clone or cultivar, with a cultivar name.

Species are defined as being naturally occurring populations in which all of the individuals should be capable of cross-fertilisation. They are usually distinct from other adjacent populations, but many examples exist of different species, which in nature may be geographically isolated, being capable of cross fertilisation if brought together artificially, although the progeny are usually sterile. A species such as the London plane (*Platanus* x *acerifolia*) is an example, this being a cross between the Oriental plane (*P. orientalis*) and the North American plane (*P. occidentalis*). Again the x, in this case before the specific name, indicates its inter-specific hybrid origin.

Although individuals within a species should be capable of cross fertilisation this does not prevent the occurrence of significant genetically inherited differences. In particular, species which have a wide geographic range can differ markedly in size or shape.

Family:	Rosaceae				
Sub-family:	*Prunoideae*		*Pomoideae*		*Rosoideae*
Trees					
Prunus		*Crataegus*			
P. avium	Wild cherry, gean	C. crus-galli	Cockspur thorn		
P. cerasifera	Myrobalan plum	C. monogyna	Hawthorn		
'Pissardii'	Purple-leaved plum	*Cydonia*			
P. domestica	Plum	C. oblonga	Quince		
P. dulcis	Almond	*Malus*			
P. padus	Bird cherry	M. domestica	Apple		
P. persica	Peach	M. floribunda	Japanese crab		
P. sargentii	Sargent's cherry	M. sieboldii	Japanese crab		
P. serrula	Tibetan cherry	M. sylvestris	Crab apple		
P. serrulata	Japanese cherry	M. tschonoskii	Pillar apple		
P. spinosa	Blackthorn	*Mespilus*			
P. subhirtella	Spring cherry	M. germanica	Medlar		
P. x yedoensis	Yoshino cherry	*Pyrus*			
		P. communis	Pear		
		P. salicifolia	Willow-leaf pear		
		Sorbus			
		S. aucuparia	Mountain ash, rowan		
		S. aria	Whitebeam		
		S. commixta	Japanese rowan		
		S. domestica	Service tree		
		S. intermedia	Swedish whitebeam		
		S. sargentiana	Sargent's rowan		
		S. torminalis	Wild service tree		
		S. vilmorinii	Vilmorin's rowan		
Shrubs					
P. laurocerasus	Cherry laurel	*Amelanchier*		*Kerria japonica*	
P. lusitanica	Portugal laurel	A. lamarkii	Snowy Mespilus	*Potentilla fruticosa*	
		Chaenomeles		*Rosa* sp.	Roses
		C. speciosa	Japonica	*Rubus fruticosus*	Blackberry
		Cotoneaster		*Spiraea* sp.	Spiraea
		C. frigidus	Tree cotoneaster		
		C. salicifolius	Cotoneaster		
		Pyracantha			
		P. coccinea	Firethorn		

Figure 14.1

Subdivisions of the family Rosaceae into sub-families, genus and species. Only the commoner tree and shrub species are included. Many of the species have a large number of varieties or cultivars. Root identification can only distinguish between the sub-families.

These attributes are often exploited by foresters who will select seed from a particular location, known as a provenance, in order to obtain particular favourable genetically inherited characteristics. Arboriculturists have been slow to investigate and exploit similar differences which must exist within the amenity tree population. Chapter 9 has emphasised that there is considerable intra-specific variation in the spatial patterns of water uptake, and if these are genetically inherited, it should be possible to identify and breed from individuals with particular characteristics. However, nothing is known about any variation in the patterns of soil drying of different cultivars.

Identification

Although the flower provides the definitive basis for taxonomy, they are usually only present for a short period so they are of limited value for identification purposes. Instead one must rely on features such as leaf shape, size and colour, the attachment of the leaves to the twigs, bud shape and colour, and characteristics of the bark, as well as the general shape and appearance of the crown.

If carefully used, features of this sort are sufficient to identify all species of tree, but one must be certain that a tree matches its description in all characteristics. For instance the pinnate compound leaf (Figure 14.2) may be very distinctive but is found in many totally unrelated species covering a wide number of genera and families. It is a feature of all of the *Juglandaceae* (such as walnut (*Juglans*) and *Carya*) and many but not all of the *Leguminoseae* (*Robinia, Gleditsia, Sophora, Cladrastis*, but not *Cercis* or *Laburnum*). They also feature in all of the species of some genera, such as ash (*Fraxinus*) (apart from some rare cultivars) and Trees of Heaven (*Ailanthus*), whereas other genera such as *Sorbus* have species with both pinnate leaves (*S. aucuparia*) and simple leaves (*S. aria*). Most maples (*Acer*) have simple lobed leaves, but the box elder (*A. negundo*) alone in this genus has a pinnate leaf.

Figure 14.2
The pinnate leaf is an example of a feature which does not provide a reliable basis for identification.

A number of books provide useful guidance on identification, including simple keys which can aid a systematic approach. The most suitable book for any individual is often a matter of personal choice, but the Collins Guide to the Trees of Britain and N. Europe by Alan Mitchell (1974) is justifiably one of the most popular, and will identify all trees except those from the most esoteric collections. The keys are detailed and easy to use, and the use of italicised words in the descriptions draw attention to the crucial features. The pocket manual Tree Recognition by Ian Richardson and Rowena Gale (1994) provides simple keys for iden-

tifying many common trees, either from their leaves or twigs. It includes simple line drawings and the text draws attention to the important features and to the similar species with which the tree may be confused.

Relevance of root identification

Far too often the identification of roots taken from trial pits is considered to be an essential part of any investigation. Even worse, a positive identification of such roots is often thought to be relevant and conclusive proof of the involvement of a particular tree as the cause of damage. An identified root provides no such proof, and indeed can often be misleading.

Roots which are taken for identification are typically 5 to 10mm diameter. A skilled specialist may be able to identify finer roots down to 2 or even 0.5mm diameter, but all such roots will be suberised and with secondary thickening - they are conducting roots which are not themselves involved in water uptake. As the diameter of a root provides no indication about its potential length, one cannot tell whether the root is conducting water from the immediate locality of the trial hole or from a more distant source where the soil conditions may be very different. Furthermore, one does not even know if the root is active in conducting water, as roots can remain alive in the soil for a period of time, even when they are inactive.

If more than one tree is present, the identification of a single root will never give opportunity to determine the presence of more than one root system. Despite this, a single root is often considered relevant. Even if multiple roots are taken and identified and are all from the same species, it does not eliminate the possible involvement of another species. The roots of one may be large and readily apparent, whilst another species, which is having an equal influence on the soil moisture, may have much finer roots which are easily missed. Alternatively, root samples taken from a shallow depth may not include the roots of another species which can exploit the soil at greater depth and which may be of far greater relevance as a cause of soil drying.

Caveats of this sort should be considered whenever root samples are taken for identification. **A positive identification indicates a possible involvement of that species but does not prove it nor eliminate the possible involvement of others.** A legal case may require the positive identification of roots from a particular tree but this must be linked to other relevant expert testimony.

Chapter 3 has emphasised that root systems are opportunistic, proliferating wherever conditions are most favourable. Their spatial patterns can be very variable and unpredictable. For this reason one should never be surprised to encounter roots beyond where one might expect them, nor conversely be surprised at their absence in a place where they might be expected - conditions elsewhere may be even more favourable. In particular it is not surprising that roots are commonly found beneath foundations. Foundation trenches aid the movement of water and air into the soil, particularly if there is any fill soil adjacent to the foundation, and thus provide conditions which are ideal for root growth. For this reason few foundations will be devoid of any roots.

It must be emphasised that even the presence of live fine roots within a clay soil does not prove that they are causing drying and shrinkage of the clay. Roots will take moisture preferentially from the most readily available source where least suction is required. As noted in Chapter 4, page 49, initial soil drying occurs in the structural shrinkage stage, with water being taken from the structural voids, without any volumetric change. The cracks between the soil peds, which are often lined with sand, form typical structural voids, and as noted in Chapter 13 and Figure 13.6 (page 203), fine roots are typically found within these cracks. It is only when all of the structural voids are emptied of water that the soil moves into the normal shrinkage stage, and root activity starts to cause significant volumetric change; this stage may not necessarily occur. Fine root activity within bands of sand is of even less relevance as an indication of soil drying.

Damage will only occur where all of the predisposing factors co-exist, including roots capable of growing into the soil below foundation level, a shrinkable soil with water abstraction occurring within the normal, rather than structural, shrinkage stage, and a building unable to tolerate differential movement. The discovery of roots below foundations only establishes the first of these criteria.

Methods for root identification

With a few exceptions, noted at the end of this section, the identification of roots relies on examination of thin sections under a microscope. This is specialist work, with a service of identification offered by some firms. Much of the early work was undertaken by the Royal Botanic Gardens at Kew, which built up a large reference collection of root samples and slides. One of the persons most involved, Dr. Ian Richardson, subsequently left to set up his own firm of Richardson's Botanical Identifications, and continues to offer a very reliable service.

The book 'Root Identification Manual of Trees and Shrubs' by Cutler et al. (1987) includes photomicrographs of sections of many species, together with technical descriptions of root structure. Whilst this is a valuable aid, the authors emphasise that root structure is very variable, depending on the conditions of growth and for this reason it is desirable to have a large reference collection of known roots against which a sample can be compared. Figure 14.3 compares the cross section of three roots of sycamore to illustrate this varia-

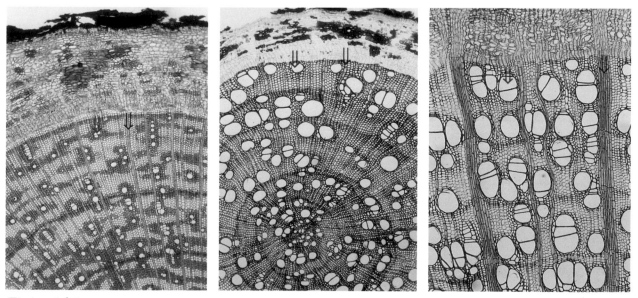

Figure 14.3

Transverse section of three roots of sycamore, to show potential for variation in root structure (each magnified x 42).
Note particularly the size and grouping of vessels (⇓), and width of rays (⇓). (Photos: P. Gasson, Royal Botanic Gardens, Kew).

tion. For this reason, identifications are usually couched in terms such as "the sample most closely resembles ... "

Roots can usually be identified reliably to the genus; only in rare cases can the species be identified. In some cases, closely related genera cannot be distinguished; for instance poplar (*Populus*) and willow (*Salix*) tend to have a slight difference in the shape of some cells in the rays, but there is so much overlap as to prevent reliable distinction between these. In many cases the root can only be identified to the family, and unfortunately all of the genera in *Rosaceae*, which is one of the largest families, share many characteristics, only enabling identification to the sub-family. Figure 14.1 has shown the constituent genera of the sub-families of *Rosaceae* whose roots cannot be distinguished. Figure 14.4 lists the common genera, or families, which can normally be distinguished by their root structure.

The most convenient size of root for identification purposes has a diameter of between 5 to 10mm. 2mm diameter roots can normally be identified, and in some cases even roots down to 0.5mm, but for these small roots it is preferable to provide a reliable short-list of candidates, which should include all trees and shrubs in the locality, as well as adjacent herbaceous plants. Root samples about 5cm long, sufficient for easy handling, are quite adequate. The bark on roots has valuable diagnostic features, and so it is important that it is included and intact.

Trees		Shrubs	
Abies (Fir)	*Liquidambar* (Liquidambar)	*Araliaceae*, which includes:	*Hypericum*
Acer (Sycamore, Maple)	*Liriodendron* (Tulip Tree)	*Aralia, Fatsia, Hedera*	*Lavandula*
Aesculus (Horse Chestnut, Buckeye)	*Magnolia*	*Aucuba*	*Leguminosae*, which includes:
Ailanthus (Tree-of-Heaven)	*Morus* (Mulberry)	*Bignonia*	*Colutea, Genista,*
Alnus (Alder)	*Nothofagus* (Southern Beech)	*Berberidaceae*, which includes:	*Spartium, Wisteria*
Araucaria (Monkey-puzzle)	*Paulownia* (Foxglove Tree)	*Berberis, Mahonia*	*Mahonia*
Arbutus (Strawberry tree)	*Parrotia* (Iron bark)	*Buddleja*	*Malvaceae*, which includes:
Betula (Birch)	*Picea* (Spruce)	*Buxus*	*Abutilon, Hibiscus,*
Carpinus (Hornbeam)	*Pinus* (Pine)	*Caprifoliaceae*, which includes:	*Lavatera*
Castanea (Sweet Chestnut)	Platanus (Plane)	*Abelia, Diervilla, Dipelta,*	*Oleaceae*, which includes:
Catalpa (Indian Bean Tree)	*Prunus* (See Figure 14.1)	*Leycesteria, Kolkwitzia,*	*Forestiera, Forsythia,*
Cedrus (Cedar)	*Pseudotsuga* (Douglas fir)	*Lonicera, Weigela,*	*Jasminum, Ligustrum,*
Corylus (Hazel)	*Quercus* (Oak)	*Symphoricarpos, Viburnum,*	*Osmanthus, Phillyria,*
Cupressaceae, which includes:	*Rosaceae-Pomoideae* group:	*Camellia*	*Olearia*
Chamaecyparis, Cupressus,	(See Figure 14.1)	*Ceonothus*	*Passiflora*
X *Cupressocyparis* (Cypress),	*Salicaceae*, which includes:	*Celastrus*	*Philadelphaceae*, which includes:
Juniperus (Juniper),	*Populus* (Poplar),	*Clematis*	*Carpenteria, Philadelphus*
Thuja (Red Cedar)	*Salix* (Willow)	*Cornaceae*, which includes:	*Pittosporum*
Diospyros (Persimmon)	*Styracaceae*, which includes:	*Cornus, Griselinia,*	*Polygonum*
Eucalyptus (Gum)	*Halesia, Styrax* (Storax)	*Cotinus*	*Prunus* (Cherry laurel,
Fagus (Beech)	*Tamarix* (Tamarisk)	*Cytisus*	Portugal laurel)
Ficus (Fig)	*Taxus* (Yew)	*Daphne*	*Rhamnus*
Fraxinus (Ash)	*Taxodiaceae* group	*Deutzia*	*Rhododendron*
Ginkgo (Maidenhair Tree)	*Cryptomeria* (Japanese cedar),	*Eleagnus*, which includes:	*Rhus*
Ilex (Holly)	*Sequoia* (Coast redwood),	*Eleagnus, Hippophae*	*Ribes*
Juglandaceae, which includes:	*Sequoiadendron* (Giant redwood)	*Embothrium*	*Rosaceae-Pomoideae* group:
Carya (Hickory),	*Tilia* (Lime)	*Ericaceae*, which includes:	(see Figure 14.1)
Juglans (Walnut),	*Tsuga* (Hemlock)	*Azalia, Calluna, Kalmia,*	*Rosaceae-Rosoideae* group:
Pterocarya (Wingnut)	*Ulmus* (Elm)	*Daboecia, Enkianthus,*	(see Figure 14.1)
Larix (Larch)	*Zelkova/Celtis* (Hackberry)	*Pieris, Pernettya,*	*Rosmarinus*
Laurus (Bay)		*Oxydendrum, Skimmia*	*Sambucus*
Leguminosae, which includes:		*Escallonia*	*Sarcococca*
Acacia (Mimosa),		*Euonymus*	*Senecio*
Cercis (Judas Tree),		*Fuchsia*	*Staphylea*
Gleditsia (Honey-locust),		*Garrya*	*Styrax*
Gymnocladus (Coffee Tree),		*Hamamelidaceae*, which includes:	*Syringa*
Laburnum (Laburnum)		*Fothergilla, Hamamelis*	*Vitaceae*, which includes:
Robinia (False Acacia),		*Hebe*	*Ampelopsis, Parthenocissus,*
Sophora (Pagoda Tree)		*Hydrangea*	*Vitis*

Figure 14.4

Common genera or plant groups which can be distinguished by root structure
Derived from Cutler et al. (1987), with comments by R. Gale and I.B.K. Richardson

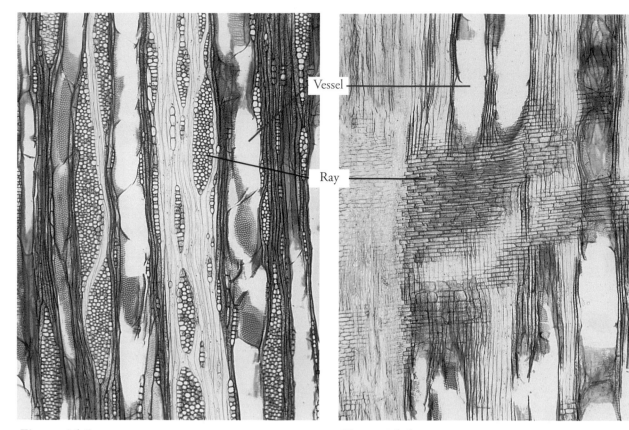

Vessel

Ray

Figure 14.5

Longitudinal tangential section of sycamore root (mag. x 75)
(Photo: P. Gasson, Royal Botanic Gardens, Kew).

Figure 14.6

Longitudinal radial section of sycamore root (mag. x 75)
(Photo: P. Gasson, Royal Botanic Gardens, Kew).

Roots which are sent for identification should be allowed to dry and are then best placed into a paper envelope, labelled as appropriate. If several roots are placed together, each should be labelled in case they break in transit and thus appear to multiply in number. Roots should not be sent in polythene bags or wrapped in damp material, as this encourages rapid breakdown of the tissue. If a mass of roots has been taken from a drain, they should be sorted to find the thickest piece and just this piece sent, preferably after washing!

Examination involves boiling the roots in water to soften them, and then cutting sections, less than about 10μm thick, ideally with a microtome, although careful hand sectioning can suffice. Three different types of section are required to show different aspects of the structure; these are a transverse cross section (Figure 14.3) and two longitudinal sections, one tangential so that it cuts across the rays and the other radial along the same plane as the rays (Figures 14.5 and 14.6).

The thin sections are floated onto microscope slides. Temporary mounts, which are sufficient for identification and for storage for a period of weeks, can be made just using diluted glycerin, or with 1% aqueous safranin for added contrast. The sections are then ready for microscopic examination, requiring facilities for

magnification of up to x 400. For details of the features which are used for identification, reference should be made to Cutler *et al.* (1987).

Although definitive identification must involve microscopic examination, some roots have particular characteristics which enable them to be distinguished in the field. For instance, elm (*Ulmus*) is heavily mucilaginous, and the roots of *Leguminosae* often have a slight but distinct smell of peas. The colour and fleshiness of roots is too generalised for diagnosis, but, with experience, can be sufficient to at least distinguish between species which differ in these features.

Age and condition of roots

Unlike the aerial parts of a tree, roots do not produce regular annual growth rings. A transverse section may show a series of concentric rings, but these rings are not annual and may be separated by intervals of at least 10 years (Fayle, 1978). They show periods of differing growth rate, which may be caused by variation in water availability, periods of drought stress or any other factor causing intermittent use of the root. For these reasons, determination of the age of a root should not be considered reliable.

The root system is used as a store for starch reserves for the tree. The starch, which is made by the polymerisation of sugar produced during photosynthesis, can be reconverted to sugar and utilised in times of stress or high energy use such as the initial flush of growth each spring. If a root dies, this starch will be broken down by bacteria. Over a much longer period, the cellulose and lignin of the cell walls will also be broken down by fungal and bacterial action. Provided a living root sample is dried after it is taken, and stored in dry conditions, bacterial action is prevented and the starch will remain in the root over a long period.

The presence of starch within a root can be determined very easily by staining a transverse section with a solution of potassium iodide - the starch grains are turned a dark purplish black and can be easily distinguished with a microscope.

This test for the presence of starch is often used to indicate that a root was alive when sampled. Care must be taken of the interpretation of "alive". If a tree is felled, or a root is severed so as to break continuity with the crown, the starch will still be present and the bark and living cambium still alive. While these remain alive, they will protect the root from bacterial or fungal attack. Under aerobic conditions near the soil surface, the bark may not survive for long, and so bacterial attack of the starch will be complete within weeks or a few months, with the root appearing to be "dead" thereafter. However, at depth in a clay soil, under anaerobic conditions, starch can remain in severed roots for a long period. Precise data is not available, but observations suggest that roots can continue to give a positive starch test for years or even decades after a tree has been felled (Richardson, 1995).

Conversely, a living root of a tree under stress may have been depleted of most of its starch, and thus give a negative test.

For these reasons it is preferable to inspect and determine the condition of the root at the time of sampling. A living root will invariably have a living cambium, which can usually be distinguished by its fresh white appearance when alive, contrasting with brown discolouration when dead. However, just as starch can remain in severed roots for many years, the cambium can remain alive for long periods after a tree is felled. The process of drying a root will kill the cambium, and so the condition of the cambium must be determined when the sample is first taken (but remember to leave the bark and cambium intact on samples sent for identification).

Measurement of size of tree

The parameters of tree size which are usually measured are the trunk diameter, overall height and radial branch spread. These provide an indication of the size of the crown, and by implication from the root:shoot ratio, an indication of the size of the root system. However, it must be emphasised that these parameters do not indicate the extent or location of the root system.

Diameter is traditionally measured at breast height, which is now defined as 1.5m above ground level. On a sloping site, average ground level is used. Although the trunk may not be exactly circular, it is usually considered to be so and the diameter is calculated by measuring the circumference (girth) and dividing by π (3.14). If a tree forks at low level, measurement should be made at the level of minimum diameter, with this height defined. For trees forking at ground level, measurements can be taken on the individual stems.

The exact measurement of height is not usually critical - particularly as it does not bear any relationship to root spread. It is usually determined by simple triangulation. Instruments, known as hypsometers, exist for this purpose. These either have a fixed angle, of 30° or 45°, or can measure the angle; this, combined with the distance of the observer from the tree, allows calculation of the height. However, simpler methods will normally suffice. I favour defining a point on the trunk at 2.5m (which I can just reach with an extended arm), and then stand well back to get a clear view of the crown and top of the tree, and determine how many multiples of 2.5m, or parts therefore, are required for the full height. Estimating the points for 5m, 10m and if necessary 20m can assist the process.

Another frequently used method relies on defining equilateral triangles. One measures the distance along a straight stick from the eye to the palm of the hand when the arm is outstretched in front of you (Figure 14.7a); the stick is trimmed to this length. If the stick is then held vertically in the palm of the outstretched arm (Figure 14.7b), its distance from the eye is equal to its length. Equilateral triangles define that, if one now observes a tree and adjusts ones position so that the top of the stick aligns with the top of the tree and the bottom with the base of the trunk, the height of the tree will be equal to its distance from the observer (Figure 14.7c). This distance can then be measured.

Whatever method is used, care must be taken to ensure that the top of the tree is being sighted. If a tree has a rounded crown, it can be difficult to see the

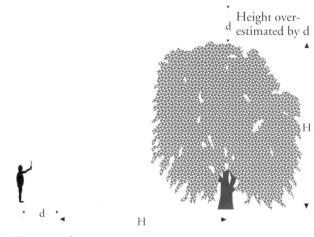

Height over-
estimated by d

Figure 14.8

If a tree has a rounded crown or wide-spreading branches, care must be taken to observe the true top, or the height will be overestimated.

top unless one can get well away, which is often impractical. From close distance, observation of the edge of the crown can give a false impression of tree height (Figure 14.8), and so it is important to locate and view the true top of the tree.

The horizontal spread of the branches (radial crown spread) can be observed directly from ground level. If shown on a plan, it is preferable to depict the actual shape, rather than a circle. If a circle is used, it should show the full extent, rather than a symbolic small size.

As the amount of water which is transpired is related to leaf area, it would be desirable to estimate this leaf area. Such estimates are impractical except under research conditions, and even if such information is obtained there is currently no method of interpreting this in terms of water uptake. A simpler method is to look at the overall crown volume or crown area, which can be estimated from the crown dimensions. Again at present there is no means of interpreting such data (except in the method of risk analysis described in Chapter 18, page 312), but it may be more relevant to consider parameters such as these, rather than the traditional emphasis on tree height.

Determination of age and growth rate

As described in Chapter 2, growth under temperate conditions follows an annual cycle. Each year there is further shoot extension growth and a further concentric ring of tissue is laid down on all aerial woody parts. These annual cycles of growth provide a complete history of the tree, recording both the age and growth rate throughout, and can thus be used to determine the date of past events.

a)

b)

c)

H

H

Figure 14.7

A simple method for estimating tree height. Cut a stick to a length equal to the distance from eye to the base of the fingers (a), hold this stick vertical at arm's length, and adjust ones position so that the stick aligns to the top and bottom of the tree (b). Height is then equal to one's distance from the tree (c).

The annual growth rings of ring-porous species (see Chapter 2, page 12) can usually be seen with the naked eye, but a hand lens is needed for distinguishing any very narrow rings. Care must be taken with some species such as elm which have concentric bands of parenchymatous tissue which can be mistaken for a growth ring. The annual rings of diffuse porous species may be discernible with the naked eye, but a minimum of a hand lens is advisable. With many species, a binocular microscope is essential.

Study of the growth rings does not require the tree to be felled, as an increment borer (Figure 14.9) can be used to take a core sample (Figure 14.10) from the trunk or branches. The borer consists of a long hollow drill with a sharp cutting edge and threaded section near the tip. This is screwed into the tree, cutting a core of wood as it goes. After cutting to the desired depth, an extractor is pushed up into the borer to hold the sample while it is broken at the base by a half turn outwards. The core can then be withdrawn for examination. The cores are usually 5mm diameter, with the borers coming in lengths of up to 50cm. This is sufficient to penetrate the full length of the radius of most trees. The majority of species can be sampled in this way, but some hard timbers, particularly beech, can be

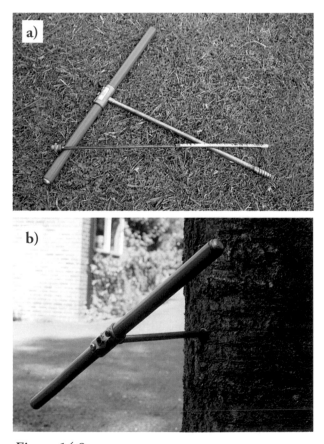

Figure 14.9

a) Increment borer with core extractor. b) Borer partially inserted for taking a short core.

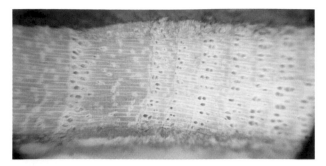

Figure 14.10

Increment core of a ring-porous tree (ash) showing a sudden change in ring width (caused by damage to the root system).

difficult. Wood which is decayed will collapse without providing a core and hollow trees can make withdrawal of the borer difficult.

The hole created by the borer will soon be covered by fresh rings of growth, and the small diameter of the injury greatly restricts the risk of a pathogen entering and causing decay or other problems. However, it can aggravate the spread of existing decay, and any injury to a tree is best avoided. For this reason core samples should only be taken when specific information is required, and they should only be taken to sufficient depth to obtain that information, i.e. if one is only interested in growth rate during the past decade, there is no need to drill to the centre. After drilling, there is no advantage in sealing the hole. Some species are prone to bleed; for this reason it is preferable to avoid drilling in the spring.

For convenience, samples are normally taken at about waist height. Below this level, rates of growth are liable to be influenced by varying growth rate of the buttresses. If necessary, cores can be taken from any position in the tree, for instance for determining the age of a branch which has developed after a tree has been pollarded, in order to determine the date of pollarding. Avoid sampling from tissue which is likely to be disturbed for any reason, e.g. mechanical stress or callus tissue developing over an old injury.

If it is necessary to determine the precise age and therefore it is essential to penetrate the centre, the approximate centre can usually be guessed. Drill just past this point, insert the core extractor facing upwards, and then withdraw the borer a full turn. With the core still in the extractor, clear the exposed surface to reveal the growth rings and radiating rays. Use these to estimate the depth to the centre and by how much (and on which side), the core missed the centre (Figure 14.11 a). Remove the core from the extractor which is then re-inserted into the bore hole to show its align-

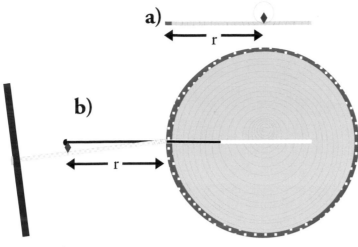

Figure 14.11

Location of tree centre with increment borer. If initial core misses the centre, examine growth rings to estimate location of centre point (a) and its distance from the core (♦). Use these dimensions to offset borer and drill second hole (b) above or below the initial hole

ment, with the end projecting to a distance equal to the depth to the centre. Drill a second hole starting directly below the first, but with the borer at an angle to the first hole such that the distance between the end of the extractor and the borer is equal to the distance by which the centre was missed. In this way the centre of the tree should be located (Figure 14.11b).

Alternatively it is usually sufficient to pass close to the centre, and then examine the core to estimate the number of rings which have been missed. For this the core is first mounted and trimmed, as described below. A few of the growth rings on the core nearest to the centre on the tree are marked with a sharp pencil, and these are matched to a circle of corresponding diameter; the centre of the circle should indicate the location of the centre of the tree (Figure 14.12). In addition, some of the radial growth rays near the centre can be marked and their alignment extended as pointers to the centre of the tree. Once the location of the centre has been determined, an estimate can be made

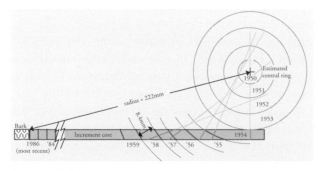

Figure 14.12

Estimation of location of centre of tree from increment core, using concentric growth rings and radial rays.

of the number of missing rings, using the width of the available growth rings as a basis for the growth rate in the missing years.

Cores are fragile. Before examination they are best stuck down to a thin narrow wooden batten (Figure 14.13b). Water-based PVA type glues are ideal for this purpose. Care must be taken to align the core with the fibres at right angles to the mount; a mark on both ends of the core on the alignment of the fibres can assist (note that some cores develop a slight spiral twist while being taken and so it may not be possible to align the full length). The wood is liable to distort until the glue is dry, and so the core should be held in place, sandwiched with another strip of wood, and held by one or more spring clips (Figure 14.13a).

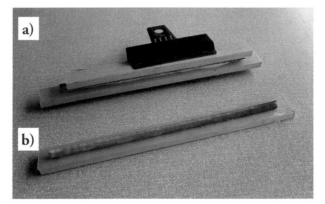

Figure 14.13

a) A core glued to a wooden batten, and held in place with a second batten and spring clip while the glue dries. b) The core mounted and trimmed for examination under a binocular microscope.

Once the glue is dry, the exposed surface should be trimmed with a very sharp knife. A disposable No. 24 scalpel blade is ideal for this purpose. Cuts should be as long, rapid, and as even as possible so as to expose a clear surface devoid of marks from the blade.

Cores are best examined under a binocular microscope, at a magnification of x 20. With most species the annual growth rings are readily discernible and can be counted and measured. If a microscope is being used, the width can be measured accurately to a fraction of a millimetre using a micrometer graticule in the eyepiece.

Measurements of the width of the growth rings are best presented in the form of a histogram, such as Figure 14.14 (overleaf). Diagrams of this sort are easily computer generated, and provide an immediate visual picture of the history of radial growth.

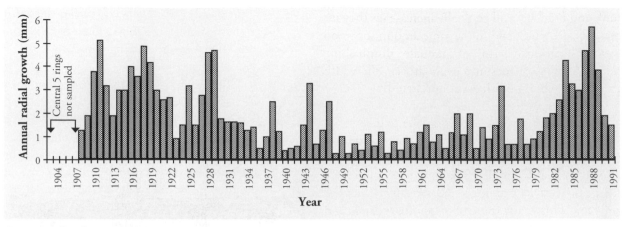

Figure 14.14

Histogram showing annual radial growth (measurements on increment core taken from the plane tree illustrated in Figure 14.15)

Interpretation of patterns of radial growth

Counting the number of annual growth rings will determine the age. The core in Figure 14.14 was taken in February 1992, and therefore the most recent growth ring was laid down in 1991. The core includes 84 annual growth rings, which takes the date back to 1908. The core missed the centre by about 6mm, probably representing about 5 years (at a rate of 1.2mm per annum as in 1908; it would be a shorter period if there had been more vigorous growth in the nursery). The tree was probably planted in 1908, or later if it was larger nursery stock.

Determination of age in this way can be subject to error. In particular in some circumstances trees can produce a "false ring", consisting of a ring of large vessels or parenchymatous tissue, similar to typical spring wood production, as a result of abnormal weather conditions or from injury to the cambium. On the surface of a cut stump these false rings will normally only extend around a limited arc, but this cannot be determined on a small core. Any injury to the cambium which prevents growth will produce missing rings, but these are normally obvious as it will produce a break in the core and the subsequent growth rings will be abnormal with callus tissue. Where ring widths are very narrow (less than 0.5mm) it can be difficult to distinguish individual rings, particularly with ring porous species where the large vessels of successive years tend to overlap with each other.

A core of wood also provides a record of the growth rate throughout the life of the tree. Anything which encourages or inhibits growth will influence the rate of wood production and thus the width of the growth ring which is being laid down. However, growth is rarely uniform, as it is influenced by a multitude of environmental factors, and so ring width can fluctuate through the life of the tree. Growth rates (or ring widths) can also vary in different sectors of the trunk (so that the rings do not form a series of perfectly concentric circles), and the relative growth rates in the sectors can vary through the life of the tree. For these reasons, it is the patterns of change in width, rather than the absolute growth rate, which are most relevant.

Climate is the most obvious environmental factor to influence the width of the growth rings. In this country, rainfall is usually limiting to tree growth each summer, and so there is usually a close correlation between the width of the growth rings and the summer rainfall (Figure 2.5, page 17). For this reason, years of extreme drought such as 1976 will often show as a distinct narrow growth ring. However, if water is readily available from sources other than rainfall, this correlation may not exist, or growth may even be enhanced by the higher temperatures which usually accompany a drought (Case Study 3).

Climate is only one of many factors which can influence growth. Competition with other trees, nutritional status, defoliating insects or pathological problems are all examples of factors occurring naturally which can produce long or short-term variations. These variations will be superimposed on the long term variations which occur during the life of the tree. Chapter 2 has noted how the growth rings in the early life of a tree, after initial establishment, tend to be fairly uniform in width, with this being maintained through the period of rapid height growth and development of a full canopy. Once the full canopy is achieved, the tree can maintain a long period of fairly uniform growth. During this period the surface area of the trunk and branches will gradually increase (as they increase in diameter), and so the same amount of wood tissue will produce a ring of gradually diminishing width. As the tree goes into overmaturity, the width of the rings will diminish even more rapidly.

The activities of man can produce major divergence from the long-term trend, with these being far greater than the natural variations in growth rate. Minor pruning of a tree may be similar to natural defoliation from insects, but heavier pruning will drastically reduce the leaf area. This limits the rate of photosynthesis and the production of sugar which is essential to growth. As a result, heavy pruning will produce a far narrower growth ring. If the tree is allowed to recover and redevelop its crown area, the growth rate will gradually increase until it returns to its previous level. As a tree is not entirely dependent on sugar production during the current growing season for wood production in the current growth ring, but also utilises reserves laid down as starch in previous years in the roots, the width of the growth ring may not drop instantly. If the reserves have been depleted prior to the pruning, the effects of reduced leaf area will usually show immediately.

Figure 14.15

Plane tree from which core of wood in Figure 14.14 was taken.

Damage to the root system which reduces water uptake will prevent a tree from maintaining turgor in the leaves so that the leaf stomata close. This will restrict photosynthesis, and thus the width of the growth ring. The narrow rings will continue to be laid down until the root system is able to recover and maintain adequate water uptake. Disturbance of the soil and root system during building works will often damage the root system, and cause an obvious reduction in ring width. Some pathogens such as honey fungus (*Armillaria mellea*) can cause gradual death and decay of a root system, producing a characteristic gradual reduction in annual ring width.

As there are so many factors which can influence ring width, whenever possible interpretation of the pattern should not be in isolation, but should consider other sources of information. For instance, the histogram in Figure 14.14 shows the normal pattern of rapid early growth, which was maintained until 1923. The sudden drop in growth in that year and again in 1926, in each case followed by a progressive rise, suggests initial pollarding followed by rapid recovery. Thereafter, from the 1930's to the late 1970's, growth continues at a very slow rate with occasional periods of progressive improvement (such as from 1940 - 1944). This suggests that, throughout this period, the tree was being kept pollarded on a regular annual or biannual basis, never allowing the development of a

larger crown (apart from in the war years when the pruning was temporarily suspended). This interpretation can be confirmed by examination of the crown structure of this tree (Figure 14.15) which shows the characteristic enlarged knuckles on the branches at about 5.5m height (in line with the roof ridge on the photograph) which develop when a tree is being regularly pollarded in this way. The multiple stems developing from about 3.8m height (in line with gutters) will be the regrowth from one of the earlier prunings. After 1978 the growth rate of this tree rises progressively until 1984 when there is a slight reduction, followed by a further increase to 1988. This progressive increase suggests recovery of the crown, with this confirmed by the crown shape which shows multiple stems developing from previous pollard level (above the ridge line). In 1990 and 1991 there is a further drop in growth, associated with the reduction in the length of these branches, with new twig growth developing from these cuts. If necessary, cores could be taken from the branches developing above the pollard points to determine their age.

By these means, combining interpretation of the crown shape with information on the growth rate and age of the tree and branches, one can build up a picture of the probable size of the tree at any time in its life.

Water requirements derived from increment cores

As production of wood tissue is related to the photosynthetic production of sugar, and as photosynthetic production is closely linked to transpiration loss of water from the leaves, determination of the total tissue formed during the year should provide an indication of the amount of water utilised by the tree during the season. Any analysis of this sort should take some account of the balance of the energy reserves laid down in the roots as starch, and also the efficiency of water use during photosynthesis, but within these constraints it should provide a reliable estimate of water use.

Unfortunately determination of total wood production is impractical, as it is being laid down to varying thickness over the whole envelope of the trunk, branches and twigs, as well as in the deciduous leaves. Sampling all of these parts of the tree to determine their surface area and the amount of wood tissue laid down during the year would be a massive and impractical operation. Instead, sampling needs to be restricted to readily available increment core samples. However, simple analysis of ring width is clearly inadequate, as a ring near the centre of a tree will involve far less wood tissue than a ring of similar width further out. Allowance can be made for this by using the measurements of radial growth to calculate the basal area increment each year. This can be determined from:

$$\text{Basal area increment} = \pi \, (R^2 - r^2)$$

where r is the initial radius and R is the radius after a further year of growth.

Figure 14.16 shows the data from Figure 14.14 transformed in this way. This immediately emphasises the far greater significance of the increase in ring width during the 1980's; wood production during this period was far greater than early in the life of the tree, although ring width during both periods was similar.

Although basal area increment will provide a better indication of wood production than ring width, ideally it requires a model which takes account of the height of the trunk and also the number of branches and twigs. This could provide a value by which to multiply the basal area, in order to convert the area to a total volume. However, although this would improve the estimate, the surface area of the trunk and branches only alters slowly, and the taper of the trunk means that the greatest thickness of wood tissue is being laid down near the base where the sample is being taken. Derivation of basal area increment from a core sample will therefore provide an adequate estimate and can be obtained very easily. It will show changes of wood production over short periods, and, with consideration of total crown size, provide an indication of the changing pattern over the full life of the tree.

Although it is valid to estimate changing patterns in growth rate and water use of an individual tree in this way, it will be less reliable for comparing two individuals of the same species, particularly as their crown size and efficiency of water use may differ. The method should certainly not be used for comparing trees of different species, as this would introduce far too many unknown variables.

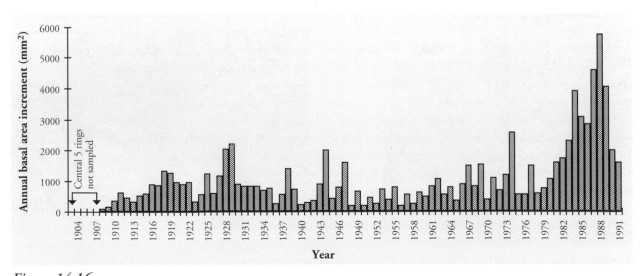

Figure 14.16

Histogram derived from the same data as Figure 14.14, to show the annual basal area increment.

Other indications of growth rate

The length of shoot extension growth each year can be seen on most species of tree, either on the leading shoot at the top of the trunk, or on lateral branches. The base of the extension growth is usually marked by the scars made by bud scales, and these remain visible for several years so that growth rate in recent years can be assessed very readily.

On some species the terminal bud which forms each winter is surrounded by lateral buds, and all of these develop in the spring. This produces a whorl of lateral branches surrounding the terminal shoot. In the autumn each of these lateral branches, as well as the terminal shoot, will produce a terminal bud surrounded lateral buds, with this process repeating in successive years to produce first, second, third, etc., order lateral branching. Regular development of this sort is most marked in some species of conifer, particularly pine. Pine do not usually produce any other lateral branches, and so the simple annual pattern of branching remains very obvious, and the number of whorls of branches on the main trunk can often be counted to determine the age and growth rate (Figure 14.17). Other genera in the *Pinaceae* tend to produce additional lateral branches between the whorls which tends to obscure the regular pattern, and in other conifers, for instance *Cupressaceae*, shoot development is indeterminate. Some deciduous trees, particularly poplars, have sufficiently well developed annual growth whorls to allow an estimate of age and growth rate, at least during early years when growth is very rapid.

The pattern of growth of many species of tree tends to vary with age and maturity. When young, most trees have well developed apical dominance, so that the most rapid growth occurs in the main leading shoot, with decreasing rates of growth in the first, second, etc., order laterals. This produces a regular conical shape, with a narrow angle at the top of the tree indicative of particularly rapid growth. Apical dominance is often maintained throughout the period of rapid height growth, but as the tree reaches maturity, it is gradually lost and the crown loses its conical shape. For instance, with pine trees, the angle of the top gradually widens as the lateral branches grow more rapidly, and eventually height growth will virtually cease so that it produces the flat-topped crown, typical of mature pine (Figure 14.18). The same effect is seen in many other species, with the crown shape becoming wider and more rounded with maturity.

Number of whorls since current year

⇐ 1

⇐ 2

⇐ 3

⇐ 4

⇐ 5

⇐ 6

⇐ 7

⇐ 8

⇐ 9

⇐ 10

<Indistinct>

Figure 14.17
Regular branching pattern and annual growth whorls produced by a pine.

Figure 14.18
Typical flat-topped shape of a mature pine, indicating negligible further height growth. The Wellingtonia in the background is also developing a rounded top, indicating little further height growth.

Figure 14.19

Crown shape is not necessarily a reliable indicator of growth rate. The Catalpa (left foreground) has a rounded crown but is growing very rapidly (age 22 years). By contrast, the Liquidambar (central, with red autumnal colour) has a narrow crown which is often indicative of fast growth, but this tree has barely increased in height for 25 years, whereas the similar shaped Metasequoia (deciduous conifer in right foreground) has grown from a cutting in 25 years. (Photo from author's garden).

Although crown shape can be a useful indication of growth rate of a tree, it must always be tempered with knowledge of the growth habit of that species. Some species, for instance Lombardy poplar, naturally produce a narrow crown even when mature, whereas other, for instance *Catalpa*, tend to produce a well rounded crown even when growing rapidly. The crown shapes of the different species in Figure 14.19 will provide little information on their growth rate without knowledge of this sort.

When a tree is fully mature, not only is the rate of extension growth reduced, but the development is concentrated in lateral shoots. This maintains the density of the existing crown, but with negligible increase in overall crown size.

As a tree passes into overmaturity, the physiological processes of aging develop. The most obvious symptoms of this is crown dieback. However, as noted in Chapter 6 (page 94), water uptake and the extent of soil drying may have started to diminish long before obvious symptoms of this sort become apparent. The

first symptoms of dieback are usually seen in the upper crown, with a reduction in size and density of the foliage, followed by defoliation of the terminal twigs. As more twigs die, the whole upper crown can become very sparse, and eventually large dead branches will be projecting, giving rise to the expression that the crown is stag-headed. This dieback is often accompanied by increased epicormic growth (shoots developing from buds beneath the bark on the trunk or branches); in some cases this renewed growth can recreate a new crown within the former crown volume, particularly if the tree is able to recover from a stress which initiated the original dieback (Figure 14.20).

Safety and condition of the tree

The general health and condition of the tree should be assessed to determine whether it is suitable for retention. There is little advantage in great efforts to retain a tree which is causing damage, for instance by underpinning an adjacent building, if it has a limited life expectancy. If it creates a significant hazard to per-

Figure 14.20

Stag-headed ash with large dead branches in upper crown, but tree rejuvenating and forming a new lower crown.

sons or property, it should be removed immediately or made safe by appropriate surgery (Case Study 3). Even if a tree is healthy at present, it is desirable to consider its life expectancy, including its susceptibility to potentially fatal diseases (Case Study 16). The health and safety of a tree, and its susceptibility to disease, should be assessed by an arboriculturist, but the methods for this fall outside the scope of this book.

A tree which is healthy and vigorous and with a life expectancy which may be measured in decades, if not centuries, may be of great value to the amenity of a locality and to the setting of a building. With a tree of this sort it may be worth going to considerable effort and expense to retain it. A method exists for assessing the amenity value of a tree, commonly known as the Helliwell method, after the original author (Helliwell, 1967). The method is described in the Arboricultural Association booklet "Amenity Valuation of Trees and Woodlands" (1990); further details should be obtained from that booklet.

Summary

1.   Trees should be correctly identified to their genus and species.

2.   Root samples, even if taken from below foundation level and correctly identified, are of limited diagnostic value. They may indicate involvement of that species in any damage which may have occurred, but do not prove it nor eliminate the possible involvement of other species, nor do they indicate that damage will occur in future.

3.   Roots can appear to be "alive" (with a positive starch test) long after a tree has been felled.

4.   **It is more relevant to consider the species of tree, its vigour and condition, its previous and potential future growth and water requirements, and then relate this to the pattern and history of damage (Chapter 12), and the soil conditions (Chapter 13).**

5.   The condition and safety of trees, and also their amenity value, should be assessed, so that these aspects can be given proper consideration when deciding on remedial measures.

Additional reading

For tree identification:

A field guide to the trees of Britain and Northern Europe. Alan Mitchell (1974). Collins. 415pp.

Tree recognition. A pocket manual. Ian Richardson and Rowena Gale (1994). Richardson's Botanical Identifications. 140pp.

Previous incorrect diagnosis of subsidence rather than heave – Unsuitable underpinning design –
Continuing damage – Level monitoring demonstrates seasonal and ongoing heave movements –
Interpretation complicated by lack of deep datum.

The subject property is a two-storey detached house, built in 1970. Ground levels generally slope steeply down to the rear (north east), with this slope terraced to accommodate a small development of four houses. The site is located in Surrey, with the Geological Survey map indicating the underlying soil to be Gault Clay. The ground floor layout is shown in CS Figure 14.1.

The trees

The only significant trees are shown in CS Figure 14.1. The largest was an oak (*Quercus robur*) with a height of 14m, located 8.7m from the right flank wall, on the line of the rear elevation. This was still a comparatively young tree, with potential to grow considerably larger. 4m from the front right corner of the building there was a 7m high vigorous yew tree (*Taxus baccata*) in early maturity.

Opposite the left flank wall were a variety of trees forming a rough hedge. The most significant of these were a 7m high English elm (*Ulmus procera*), 5m from the front corner, a 9m sycamore (*Acer pseudoplatanus*) 6.2m from the middle of the flank, and a 7m apple (*Malus*) 4.7m from the rear of the flank. The elm and sycamore were vigorous young trees, with the apple over-mature and dying back.

In addition to the elm there were a number of other small elm trees growing on the bank at least 4m to the rear of the property. There was other general scrub growth of elder and bramble on this bank.

Previous history

The property suffered damage during the drought conditions of 1976. There were no records of site investigations from that time, but the underpinning contractors concluded that the damage was caused by "moisture variations in the clay subsoil as a result of atmospheric conditions and the extraction of moisture by tree roots from the nearby trees or shrubs". As a result of this damage the left end of the building was underpinned. This underpinning used a pier and beam system, with the beams cast within the original footings. There were three piers beneath the left flank wall, and a further three piers beneath the partition wall between lounge and dining room/hall. All of these piers were to a specified depth of 3m, apart from the one near the centre of the front elevation which was 2.7m. A cantilevered transition beam extended along the front and rear elevations for 6.5 and 7.5m from the flank respectively. The locations of these piers and beams are shown in CS Figures 14.1 and 14.2.

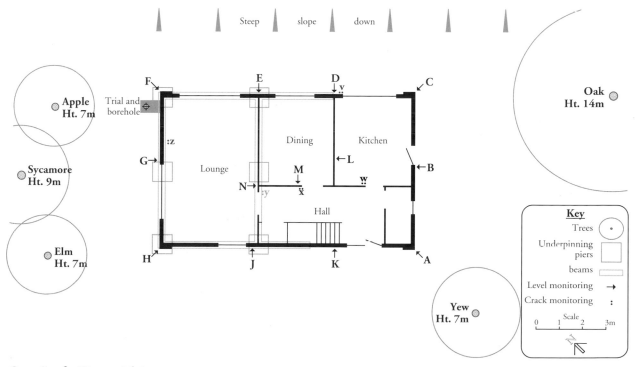

Case Study Figure 14.1
Site plan showing location of trees, underpinning, and of level and crack monitoring stations.

By early 1984 the owner reported further damage, and the underpinning contractor again inspected. They reported:-

> "I noticed the trees still remain within your garden but are within their own full grown natural height of your building and because shrinkable clay subsoil was encountered during underpinning, these trees should be cut down and their roots grubbed out or poisoned without delay. Removal of the trees should have been attended to following the underpinning as recommended."

The owner appointed a surveyor, and the loss adjusters acting for the insurers appointed a structural engineer. This engineer recommended my involvement "with a view to severely restricting the activity of the trees". I was instructed by the loss adjusters in May 1985 to consider the involvement of the trees, and whether removal of the trees might cause problems of slope instability.

Damage to property

Three main aspects of damage could be distinguished:-

i) Minor structural cracking of the external walls. This was most apparent in a panel of Bradstone brickwork on the front elevation, but there were also minor cracks on the rear elevation. Cracks were also present on the internal skin of the brickwork, particularly around the window in the left flank wall of the lounge and around the front door entrance.

ii) Cracks in the internal partition walls. There was extensive minor cracking in these walls, particularly around the door openings. This included various cracks in the partition wall of the lounge which had previously been underpinned.

iii) Settlement of the floor slab of the kitchen and the suspended floors of the other rooms relative to the peripheral walls. This differential movement was greatest towards the rear of the property.

Although there was this extensive damage to the property, the majority of it was comparatively minor in nature, and would be described as Category 2 "Slight". White emulsion paint on all internal walls made all of this minor cracking very obvious.

Soil and foundations

A trial hole was excavated adjacent to the rear of the left flank and extended by borehole. This revealed:-

0. - 0.95m	topsoil and fill
0.95 - 1.2m	soft-firm brown clay
1.2 - 1.45m	stones and gravel with occasional clay
1.45 - 1.67m	clay with occasional gravel
1.67 - 3.0m	typical grey Gault Clay

A representative sample of this clay from 2m had the following index properties:-

Plastic limit	30
Liquid limit	71
Plasticity index	41
% linear shrinkage	11.8

Root activity

In the surface topsoil of the trial hole adjacent to the left flank wall were a number of roots of *Rosaceae* sub-family *Pomoideae*, consistent with the adjacent apple tree. In addition, there were many old large decayed roots. Near the surface these were too decayed for identification, but a sample from 2.3m could be identified as *Quercus* (oak). Decaying oak roots were also identified from a trial hole beneath the floor of the dining room.

Level distortion survey

During my initial visit I carried out a level distortion survey. The results are shown as an isometric diagram in CS Figure 14.2.

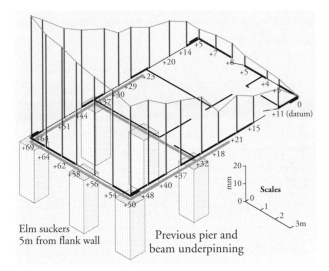

Elm suckers 5m from flank wall

Previous pier and beam underpinning

Case Study Figure 14.2

Results of level distortion survey presented relative to lowest point on brickcourse (south east corner) (17/5/85).

Level and crack monitoring

At the time of my initial visit I also set up level monitoring with markers at the four corners, at two positions midway along the front and rear elevation and at one position along each flank wall. In addition, I attached three markers on internal partition walls. The positions of all of these are shown in CS Figure 14.1.

Three subsequent sets of readings were taken over the next eight month period; the results are shown in CS Figure 14.3.

Changes in level (mm) compared to 17/5/85:-			
Station	2/7/85	2/10/85	7/1/86
A	Datum	Datum	Datum
B	-0.4	-1.4	+0.4
C	-0.3	-2.2	+1.1
D	-0.2	-1.1	+0.4
E	+0.1	+0.7	+0.6
F	+0.4	+4.0	+2.2
G	+0.4	+5.1	+2.9
H	+0.4	+6.9	+4.2
J	+0.2	+4.7	+2.7
K	+0.2	+2.2	+0.9
L	-0.2	-2.5	+1.4
M	+0.1	-0.6	+0.3
N	-0.9	+0.1	+0.6

Case Study Figure 14.3

Results of level monitoring.

For the presentation of these results I have assumed that station A is a stable datum and they are presented relative to this datum. The distortion recorded on two of the dates is shown as an isometric plan in CS Figure 14.4. The validity of station A as a datum is further discussed below.

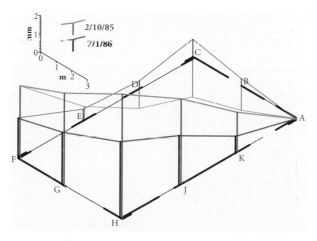

Case Study Figure 14.4

Isometric diagram showing distortion on two dates compared to initial readings on 17/5/85, presented relative to station A as arbitrary datum (see also CS Figure 14.6 for alternative presentation of these results).

I also attached demec strain gauge markers across a number of the cracks. The location of these is shown in CS Figure 14.1, with the subsequent movements tabulated in CS Figure 14.5 and shown graphically in CS Figure 14.7.

Changes in crack width (μm) compared to 17/5/85:-				
Station	2/7/85	2/10/85	13/12/85	7/1/86
v	-215	-566	-388	+54
w	-61	-610	-475	-45
x	-92	-274	-191	+332
y	+45	+563	+412	+144
z	-124	+304	+191	+21

Case Study Figure 14.5

Results of crack monitoring.

DISCUSSION

Cause of 1976 damage

The level distortion survey shows a clear trend upwards to the left flank wall (or down of the right). This must cast massive doubt on the original diagnosis that the left end of the building had subsided during the drought of 1976. A much more logical conclusion was that the left end was subject to heave following its construction six years earlier. This heave may have been caused by the former oak tree whose roots were found in the trial hole. Alternatively, the elm suckers adjacent to the left flank wall and on the bank to the rear of the house suggested that one or more elm trees had previously grown in this location. This species suckers vigorously from the root system after it is felled, and the age of these suckers was consistent with a tree being felled shortly prior to construction. Unfortunately, attempts to locate aerial photographs of the site to show any former trees were unsuccessful.

Although heave was probably the underlying cause of the stress and damage, it is possible that the foundations were also subject to seasonal movement during the drought of 1976. Additional stress from this cause might have accounted for the development of damage in the autumn.

With the clear indication that heave was involved at the left end of the building, one must question the design of the underpinning beneath this end of the building, as it did not include any anti-heave precautions.

Cause of further damage

The level monitoring during the summer of 1985 (17th May to 2nd October) showed the development of significant differential movement, with a maximum of 9.1mm between stations C and H (and even greater movement at the internal station L). This direction could be consistent either with continuing heave of the left end or subsidence of the right end.

Further monitoring during the winter period (from 2nd October to 7th January 1986) showed the amount of differential movement diminishing (to 3.2mm between stations C and H). This recovery indicated that seasonal movements of the right end of the building, particularly the rear corner closest to the young oak tree, were a major component of the movement.

If movements were affecting the right end of the building, it implied that station A would be providing an unreliable stable datum. CS Figure 14.4 plots the distortion which had developed between 17/5/85 and 2/10/85 (as red lines) and also 7/1/86 (blue lines), using station A as the assumed datum. On this basis, the left end of the building would have heaved during the summer, but then subsided during the winter; this is obviously unlikely. Likewise, it is unlikely that station C would have recovered to above its initial level by January.

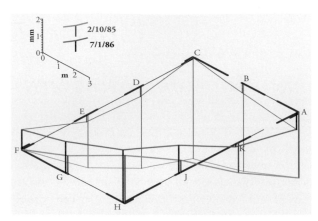

Case Study Figure 14.6

Isometric diagram showing distortion on two dates compared to initial readings on 17/5/85, presented to show rational patterns of movement (i.e. seasonal movement of right end of building, with continuing heave of left end) (see also Figure 14.4).

A more probable explanation for the movements is provided by CS Figure 14.6. For this, I have assumed that station F remained static during the summer, with station C subsiding by 6.2mm (red lines). On this basis, station H would have continued to show heave movements (of 2.9mm) during the summer. To plot the results for the winter (blue lines), I have assumed that station C had recovered fully by January 1986. This would then imply further heave movement must have been affecting the left end of the building.

Whilst an interpretation of this sort provides a logical explanation of the movement, ideally in this situation level monitoring should have been related to a deep stable datum. However, even without a datum this logical explanation indicates that there must have been a significant element of seasonal movement of the right end of the building, and also some continuing heave of the left end.

The crack monitoring confirmed that stresses associated with the seasonal movements were affecting the whole building, with all of the cracks showing a seasonal change in direction. However, the cracks at the right end (stations v,w,x) closed during the summer and opened during the winter, whereas those at the left end showed the opposite pattern. These results contradict those one might expect, i.e. one would expect cracks in the area of seasonal stress to open rather than close in the summer, and where heave predominates one might expect the cracks to close during the summer (as the heave is reversed) and open during the winter.

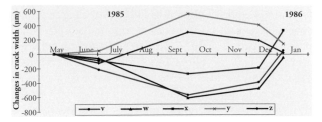

Case Study Figure 14.7

Results of crack monitoring

Settlement of floor slab

The surveyor and engineer had investigated the floor slab of the kitchen and the suspended floors throughout the rest of the building. The kitchen slab had a poorly compacted fill with this resting on a highly organic topsoil. The suspended floors were all supported on sleeper walls which were independent of the external walls and partition walls. These sleeper walls were taken off the oversite concrete, which was also resting on the organic loam topsoil. Investigations indicated that this topsoil was about a metre thick, increasing in thickness to the rear of the building. Settlement of the floors was clearly related to the inadequacy of this material.

Subsequent events

At this stage in the investigations the owner settled his insurance claim on a diminution in value basis and the property was sold. As a result, further investigations ceased.

The case had a further twist in 1991, when I was again approached by the same loss adjusters. They had been instructed by a different firm of insurers, with a further claim for subsidence damage from new owners of the same property. Subsidence cover had apparently been reinstated with no declaration of the previous problems.

Lessons to be learnt

- The failure to carry out a level distortion survey in 1976 resulted in a faulty diagnosis (of subsidence rather than heave), and the installation of unsuitable underpinning with no anti-heave precautions.

- In 1985 the level distortion survey could demonstrate these previous mistakes.

- The level monitoring demonstrated that the underpinning was still subject to differential movement, and that seasonal movements were also affecting the other end of the building.

- As different mechanisms of movement were affecting different parts of the building, a deep stable datum would have been highly desirable, and would have allowed more accurate interpretation of the results.

- Even without this datum a rational pattern of movement can be deduced on the basis of movements which are consistent with potential mechanisms (of seasonal movement, heave, or slope instability). Actual movements might have differed slightly from this, but any significant departure from this proposal would involve highly improbable patterns of movement.

- The demands for tree felling were ill-advised. Although felling the oak should have been effective in stopping the seasonal movements, it would not have stopped the heave component.

Introduction

The strategy for site investigations described in Chapter 11 emphasises the value of monitoring. It is usually the most cost-effective part of any site investigation, and should be a routine part of most investigations. If damage is occurring, it is a result of movement, and it is logical to study this movement.

Many people associate monitoring solely with crack movement, but this is only one, and perhaps the least important, feature for measurement. If vertical foundation movements are occurring, it is far more relevant to measure these changes in level, rather than the indirect effects which may, or may not, become manifest as cracks in the superstructure. Frequently the behaviour of the superstructure is complicated as a result of different parts of the foundations moving at different rates, by different amounts, or at different times. This can produce apparently anomalous crack movements which are difficult to interpret or may even be misleading (e.g. Case Study 4). Furthermore, if a crack opens progressively, it is not necessarily obvious whether this is caused by settlement or heave, and even apparent seasonal movement of cracks may be caused by moisture content or temperature changes of the superstructure, rather than by foundation movement. Monitoring changes in foundation level will usually resolve these problems.

Obviously, measurements of cracks is useful, and becomes essential if the level monitoring shows that the foundations are stable (i.e. if the problem is being caused by thermal movements, or spread of a roof etc.). Very occasionally monitoring changes in moisture content of the soil may be justified. These moisture content changes can then be compared with the movements of the building, as determined by level monitoring.

When to monitor

There is sometimes reluctance to start monitoring because of concern that the client will not wait long enough for results. Such objections misunderstand the objective of monitoring. Initial site investigations can still be used for giving an initial opinion, and appropriate interim action taken on that basis. As the results of monitoring become available, they can be used to confirm and refine that opinion, with this information often essential before a final decision is taken on the type and scope of remedial action. Conversely it may show that the initial diagnosis was wrong. If vegetation control is used to stabilise the foundations, the monitoring will need to be continued to show whether the action has been sufficient. In the majority of the cases in which I am involved, the problem (or damage) first arose at least 12 months previously. If the building had been monitored during that period, almost all of the questions could have been answered. Frequently a brief period of a few weeks is sufficient to elucidate a complicated case.

Monitoring should be used as a means of gaining essential information, and not merely as a means of confirming whether a building is still moving.

Level monitoring is particularly valuable and should form part of any investigation:-

i)   as a diagnostic aid wherever there is any abnormal feature which indicates any doubt about the cause of damage, e.g.:
     (a) any building or extension less than 10 years old;
     (b) unusual history of damage development;
     (c) any abnormalities in the distortion survey;
     (d) any building with previous, or partial, underpinning;
     (e) any building on a significant slope or with earth retaining walls;
     (f) any evidence of tree removal.

ii) as an aid for deciding whether a persistent deficit is present (Figure 16.5, page 259);

iii) if tree felling or pruning is adopted as the remedy, for checking whether such action has been effective;

iv) before underpinning is adopted, for determining the full extent of existing building movement.

As most site investigations will fall into at least one of these four categories, level monitoring should be included in most investigations.

When to start monitoring

The value of monitoring increases the longer it has been underway and so the sooner it is started the better. For this reason it is usually sensible to start monitoring at the first site visit.

This need not necessarily imply that useful results will only be obtained over a long period. For instance, most cases of damage caused by trees develop in the late summer when peak moisture deficits occur. If monitoring starts immediately in the autumn, the first set of readings (after the initial set-up) is often sufficient to demonstrate whether the pattern of foundation movement is consistent with the probable effect of trees in the proximity. These first readings may therefore provide an essential diagnostic aid. With further sets of readings, the pattern of recovery movement through the winter can be studied. If this slows significantly or ceases during the winter, it indicates that there is little or no persistent deficit. If all of this information is available, it will be far easier to make reliable decisions in the spring about the cause of damage and the appropriate remedial action. If there is strong evidence of this sort, it will be far easier to ensure that essential remedial action is implemented immediately. The monitoring can then be continued through the summer to check whether movements have ceased. With a scenario of this sort, although the readings have been taken over an extended 12 month period, useful results have been obtained over a far shorter period, with the readings serving different purposes at different times. Thus, the initial readings are used as a diagnostic aid (by demonstrating recovery at positions consistent with the influence of adjacent trees), subsequent readings in the late winter are used to check for a persistent deficit, and readings in the summer to confirm the efficacy of remedial action.

Even if the monitoring has not been started in the autumn immediately after damage has occurred, it will still be advantageous to commence at the earliest opportunity. Depending on the time of year and circumstances of the case, useful results can usually be obtained over a short period.

The advice which one frequently sees in reports is that certain action should be taken (for instance a tree felled or pruned) and the building then monitored for 12 months to determine whether movements have ceased. If the monitoring is not started until the remedial action is taken, one has no means of telling how effective it has been. For instance, if it continues to detect subsidence, say by 5mm, during the summer, it is helpful to know how this compares with the previous movements which caused the damage. If the amount of recovery had been monitored after the damage and prior to remedial action, one has an immediate basis for comparison. Furthermore, a fixed 12 month period may also be quite inappropriate. A far shorter period, for instance covering the late summer and early winter, may be quite sufficient to demonstrate neither subsidence nor recovery, whereas a far longer period may be needed if there is a persistent deficit and long-term recovery.

Methods of level monitoring

BRE Digest 386 "Monitoring building and ground movement by precise levelling" describes techniques and equipment for level monitoring which achieves an accuracy consistently better than ±0.5mm. It advocates a precise level plus a parallel plate micrometer used with an invar precise staff. These latter pieces of equipment add nearly £2000 to the capital cost. For accurate use, the invar staff requires BRE levelling stations at nearly £10 each, or a typical cost of about £100 to instrument a building. Such costs may act as a deterrent, but more significant is that the methods are slow and laborious, albeit very accurate.

However, one must question whether such precision is essential. The great majority of level monitoring of buildings is for seasonal movements. The magnitude of these is often not appreciated. Seasonal movements with an amplitude of 10mm are commonplace, often causing no detectable problems, and seasonal movements in excess of 30mm can occur without necessarily causing damage (Case Study 15). An amplitude of only 12mm will involve 12mm subsidence in the summer and 12mm recovery in the winter, or an average rate of movement of 2mm per month; if readings are taken at 2 monthly intervals, differences of 4mm will be present, or even greater during periods of rapid movement. Movement of this magnitude can be detected without the need for extreme precision.

However, greater accuracy is important if the measurements are being used to predict how long heave or recovery movements are likely to continue. This requires definition of the shape of the recovery curve to see if the rate of movement is diminishing; inaccurate measurements which deviate around the true reading will make accurate prediction impossible.

Accuracy is also important for monitoring heave movements. The rate of these may be less than 5mm per annum, but as they are progressive, over a period of years this can induce sufficient distortion and stress to cause damage. Monitoring heave is usually most crucial in the early stages when the most rapid movements are occurring, but it may be desirable to detect changes in the rate of this movement. As the rate diminishes, readings are usually taken at longer intervals. It is often considered that continuing heave movements of 2mm per annum are tolerable, and so one should aim to detect movements of this magnitude, using readings taken at 6 monthly intervals.

For these reasons, monitoring should aim to achieve an accuracy of better than ± 1mm in a traverse around a typical house.

The methods described below are those which I have developed and used over the years. I find they usually provide a closing error of less than 0.5mm on a typical traverse around a building and are comparable to those presented in Figure 9 of BRE Digest 386 (which include a closing error of 1.52mm). The level monitoring described in the Case Studies have all used these techniques. The readings are quick and easy to take, and the whole operation can be done single-handed, thereby reducing labour and overall costs. The monitoring markers are also very unobtrusive and so can be left in situ without blighting a building.

The techniques advocated by BRE are justifiable where extreme precision is required, for instance with some of their long-term monitoring for research purposes. What are not acceptable are the techniques which one sees all too often, such as sets of measurements taken off a brickcourse, or a heavy levelling staff resting on a projecting nail which is bending under the weight and with no provision for precise interpolation between staff readings. Poor technique will only provide unreliable results.

Equipment for level monitoring

The level which I use is the same precise optic level as used for level distortion surveys (a Zeiss NI 020 A level with a specified mean square error accuracy of ± 2mm for a 1 km double run; this could be reduced to ± 0.7mm if a parallel plate micrometer is used). It is accurately collimated; although periodically checked, the settings have never needed adjustment. The same instrument is always used, and it is always set up in the same position. Simple precautions of this sort will help to eliminate any errors in collimation which might exist, as they will always be self-cancelling.

Likewise I use the same "Bidpod" described in Chapter 12 (on page 191), holding a standard Stanley tape measure with a "Power Lock". A tape of this sort is not made of Invar metal and so will, of course, be subject to some thermal movement - a 1.5m length will be subject to about 0.35mm change over a 20°C temperature range (which is unlikely to be exceeded even between summer and winter). However, provided all of the station markers are at a similar level, thermal movement is only relevant over the difference in their level. Thus, if the difference in level of the markers is only 0.2m, thermal movements would be less than 0.05mm over a 20°C temperature range, which is quite acceptable.

The markers which I use are round-head screws, driven in flush to the wall with the slot aligned horizontally (Figure 15.1a). A No. 10, 1¼ inch (30mm) round-head brass screw is ideal. Brass should be used to avoid rusting; once the head has tarnished they are very inconspicuous. The screw is inserted into an appropriate plastic wall plug which is drilled into a mortar bed as near ground level as possible and below any cracking. Care must be taken to avoid damage to the edges of the slot, and to ensure that it is horizontal; a small spirit level on the flat blade of a screw driver of the correct size will assist. With the screw flush to the wall there is negligible risk of accidental damage, and vandalism is unlikely on an inconspicuous screw worth only a few pence, but, if there is any risk of the screws being disturbed, both the screw and plug can be coated in Araldite epoxy resin before insertion.

Figure 15.1

a) a flush-mounted brass screw provides an inconspicuous marker. b) The tape can be hooked into the horizontal slot of the screw.

When the 'Bidpod' is used for monitoring, the adjustable slider is removed, and the staff is supported by its legs leaning against the wall with the base of the staff well above the screw. The staff must be kept vertical; use a spirit level or mark the wall with a short pencil line beside the top of the staff to ensure that it is set up in the same position each time. The friction lock on the tape is released to keep the tape under tension, the tape is extended below the base of the staff and the flange on the end of the tape is hooked into the slot of the screw (Figure 15.1b). As this flange can move slightly on the end of the tape it is important to ensure the tape is kept under tension with the internal spring..

Provided the length of sight is kept short (less than 10m), there is no difficulty in interpolating to the nearest 0.1mm between the millimetre divisions on the tape (Figure 15.2). Even if much longer sight lines are essential, reasonable interpolation to the nearest 0.1mm can be achieved. As previously noted, particular care must be taken with the collimation of the level and it should always be set up in the same place so as to cancel errors which might exist.

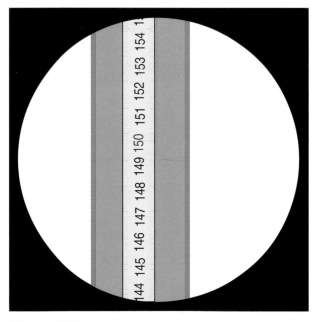

Figure 15.2

Field of view of tape at 5m range. Readings on the crosshair can be interpolated to the nearest 0.1mm, in this case 1492.6 (computer generated drawing).

The Bidpod has the advantage of single-handed operation. However, as it must be placed with its back flat against the wall when used for monitoring, it can be awkward when viewing obliquely along a wall as the tape can be hidden by the edges of the staff. If an assistant is available, a flexible steel measure can be used as an alternative. Markers used in this way should

have the head of the screw projecting just far enough for the measure to sit on the shaft of the screw; a semicircular groove of slightly larger diameter than the screw can be put in the end of the measure, with this used to locate the screw when the measure is held in place.

For single-handed readings in awkward situations where oblique views are essential, a steel measure of this sort can be used, with the top of the measure held loosely in place by round head screws (Figure 15.3).

Figure 15.3

A steel measure loosely restrained between screws at the top (a), and resting on a projecting screw as the marker (b).

As an alternative for oblique views, a projecting BRE levelling station can be used, with the Bidpod supported vertically by the levelling plug (Figure 15.4). BRE Digest 386 provides details of these levelling stations, but I find them far slower and more involved to insert than a simple screw, they are more disruptive and obvious, and are not as quick and easy to use for subsequent measurements.

Figure 15.4

A BRE levelling station in use with the Bidpod.

Location of monitoring stations

Monitoring screws should be placed at appropriate intervals around the building depending on the circumstances. Typically on a modern rectangular detached house this might involve the four corners, plus two stations at equidistant intervals along each long elevation and one on each short elevation (Case Study 14). However, before deciding on the exact locations, it is desirable to have carried out a level distortion survey to see if there are any areas of particular interest where additional stations may be required. Buildings of irregular shape or with extensions need sufficient stations to record movement of the different parts of the building, and large buildings may require a large number of stations (Case Study 5).

At the corners, a screw should be put in a short distance (half a brick) from the edge. A second screw is placed in a comparable position on the adjacent face, i.e. they will be about a brick apart. The error caused by differential movement between these adjacent screws will be negligible.

In many cases it is advantageous to include markers on internal partition walls, viewing these either through an open door or window. Markers can also be set on other features, such as floors. For this, the tape is hooked over the base of the staff and rested directly on the screw, or on a mark on the floor, ensuring that the staff is vertical.

Although the monitoring stations are normally placed around the outside of the building, consideration should always be given to carrying out the whole exercise internally. Case Study 5 is an example where an open-plan school building made it far easier to set the level up internally, particularly as information on the movement of internal walls was important. In other cases dense vegetation around the building has made it easier to work internally. In these situations, marker screws should be set just above any skirting board.

The use of a datum

Damage is caused by differential movement of the foundations. The object of monitoring is to detect which parts of the building are showing differential movement and the extent of these movements. Just as with the presentation of the results of a level survey, the movements must be related to a datum. Ideally this datum should be independent and entirely stable. One frequently finds adjacent features such as manholes, gateposts etc., being used for this purpose, but only very rarely will such features be sufficiently stable. The use of an unstable feature of this sort will only cause additional complications in interpretation.

In most circumstances, the monitoring will show negligible differential movements in most of the building which suggests that these areas are stable; this can be used to show the direction of movement of those parts of the building where movement is active. If seasonal movements are occurring, select the station which shows minimal movement, and which produces logical results for the other stations. Thus, if a station has been selected as a datum and the results for most of the others show the typical pattern of seasonal subsidence and recovery, except for one station which shows apparently anomalous results with the opposite pattern (apparent upward in summer, and down in winter), it indicates that the incorrect datum has been selected. Recalculating the results with the apparently anomalous station as datum will correct this, and produce logical results (of slightly greater amplitude) for all of the stations. If the movements are affecting the whole of the building, the direction of movement is usually self-evident if there is progressive subsidence or heave (Case Study 4).

In exceptional circumstances, for instance if a building might be heaving at one end while subsiding at the other or if the whole building might be moving, an independent stable deep datum should be considered (Case Studies 14 and 18). BRE Digest 386 provides details for installing such a datum, but again their methods are elaborate and would be expensive to install. This may be justified where very long-term monitoring is required or where exceptional depth is essential, but I find a much simpler datum is usually quite adequate. It requires a borehole to at least 5m depth, with this located in an area known to be clear of tree root activity e.g. the control borehole if soil samples are being taken. A 50mm diameter hole, dug by hand auger, is quite sufficient. The sides of the hole must be sleeved to prevent collapse; a 50mm diameter plastic drainage pipe is suitable for this purpose. A convenient datum rod is provided by a 6m length of 10 or 12mm diameter reinforcing rod. This rod is held centrally in the lining pipe by spacers such as polystyrene plugs pushed down to appropriate depths. The bottom of the rod is held firmly in the soil by driving it down beyond the base of the hole for about a metre, leaving the top just below the top of the liner, which is closed with a rubber bung. The whole assembly is then covered with an appropriate cover or camouflage. With soft clay, or if extra support is required, a short depth of concrete can be tamped into the bottom of the hole (spacers should be inserted afterwards, and the concrete must not be in contact with the liner). The top of the rod must be rounded off to provide a precise point for the staff to rest - if the staff will not fit into the liner, a short extender can be slipped over the end of the rod when readings are taken.

Even with these precautions it must be remembered that a deep datum may introduce a slight error due to thermal movement between summer and winter.

Timing and frequency of readings

The time and frequency of readings should be adjusted to suit the particular circumstances.

Where seasonal movements are occurring, the soil is usually driest with maximum subsidence in early autumn, typically in mid-September. The exact date will depend on the onset of wet weather, and on the time of formation of the abscission layer which precedes leaf fall. Wettest soil conditions usually occur in late April/early May, but this is also dependent on the date of leaf flushing. The soil near the surface will usually be wetter earlier in the year, and may already be drying under the influence of grass and other surface vegetation by the time the trees come into leaf. However, recovery of any deeper moisture deficits will continue at least until the trees flush, and often for several weeks thereafter, and so readings are best delayed in order to detect the maximum recovery (see the many diagrams showing the progressive development of soil moisture deficits in Volume 2).

Wherever seasonal movement is suspected, readings should be taken at these optimal times of year, as a minimum for detecting the full extent of seasonal subsidence and recovery. Even if movement is progressive, readings should be taken each autumn and spring so as to detect any seasonal effects which are superimposed.

If trees have been felled or pruned, but there is uncertainty about the efficacy of the treatment, regular readings through the summer are a sensible precaution. Significant downward movements do not usually start until mid-July, but readings then and in mid-August should detect early signs of unacceptable movement and allow time for additional remedial action.

	A	B	C	D	B'	C'	D'
1	Date	21.9.88	22.11.88	19.1.89	21.9.88	22.11.88	19.1.89
2	P	1590.4	1461.1	1671.6	Field reading	Field reading	Field reading
3			129.3	-81.2		B2-C2	B2-D2
4			**+2.0**	**+3.5**		C3-C6	D3-D6
5	Q	1548.4	1421.1	1633.1	Field reading	Field reading	Field reading
6			127.3	-84.7		B5-C5	B5-D5
7			**Datum**	**Datum**		Datum	Datum
8	R1	1516.8	1389.2	1601.1	Field reading	Field reading	Field reading
9			127.6	-84.3		B8-C8	B8-D8
10			**+0.3**	**+0.4**		C9-C6	D9-D6
11	R2	1624.9	1588.2	1602.8	Field reading	Field reading	Field reading
12			36.7	22.1		B11-C11	B11-D11
13			**0=36.4**	**0=21.7**		C12-C10	D12-D10
14	S	1689.7	1650.6	1665.1	Field reading	Field reading	Field reading
15			39.1	24.6		B14-C14	B14-D14
16			**+2.7**	**+2.9**		C15-C13	D15-D13

Figure 15.5

Example of method for recording and calculating results of level monitoring. Columns B, C and D show typical recorded results and calculations for three dates; columns B', C' and D' show how these results are calculated by reference to the column and row numbers. Column A identifies the station (P, Q, R and S), with Q assumed to be the datum. Stations P, Q and R1 are recorded from the initial set up of the level, with R2 and S as a subsequent set up.

As noted in Chapter 16, level monitoring can be used to detect the rate of recovery movement through the winter, which can help to decide whether there is a persistent deficit or whether movement is seasonal. For this it helps to have a reading in late autumn (late October/early November), as soon as leaves have fallen, to eliminate any uncertainty on the transition from seasonal subsidence to recovery. Thereafter, readings are best taken at about 6 weekly intervals (mid December, late January, mid March). This will provide 3 sets of data on the rate of movement, well before any potential risk of influence from the next cycle of drying. A further reliable set can usually be obtained from readings in late April, but very shallow foundations may be influenced by grass or other vegetation.

If all of these readings are taken to define the full cycle of subsidence and recovery, it would involve 9 sets of readings in the year. In practice, fewer will usually suffice. Sensible selection of dates to show relevant information can help to maximise the benefit whilst minimising the work and cost.

After remedial action has been taken, readings will usually be required for one or two years to confirm the efficacy of any treatment. Readings at the optimal times in spring and autumn are usually sufficient for this. If they are being taken at less frequent intervals, for instance for the long-term monitoring of heave, they should always be at the same time of year, so as to eliminate any seasonal effects which might also exist.

Once monitoring is complete, the inconspicuous marker screws can be left in situ just in case of any future problems, when monitoring can recommence with knowledge of the previous level and history of movement (Case Study 3).

Calculation and presentation of results

Results need to be presented as differences in level relative to the datum, compared with the initial readings. The custom sometimes seen of presenting the actual level of the marker is inconvenient, as this must be recalculated to show the movement. Indeed, the actual level of the marker is immaterial and need not be calculated. Figure 15.5 shows the field data as collected, and a simple method for calculating the differences compared with the initial set of readings.

The readings, which should always be taken to the nearest 0.1mm (or 0.01 if using a parallel plate micrometer), should be calculated and presented to the nearest 0.1mm. Readings which are only presented to the nearest 1.0mm may eliminate valuable information quite unnecessarily.

Wherever possible the monitoring should involve a circular traverse so that any closing error can be detected and calculated. Where this is done, the closing error should be calculated and shown in the results. BRE Digest 386 advocates that any closing error is not distributed, but this can give rise to difficulties in interpretation between the first and last stations of a traverse. If there is a closing error, its existence must be considered whenever the data is being interpreted; it is therefore easier and more helpful to record the closing error but then distribute this as appropriate between the stations.

Interpretation of the results is usually easiest if they are presented graphically, plotted against time (see most of the Case Studies). In most circumstances it is preferable to use a straight line to join consecutive readings. However, if readings of seasonal movements have

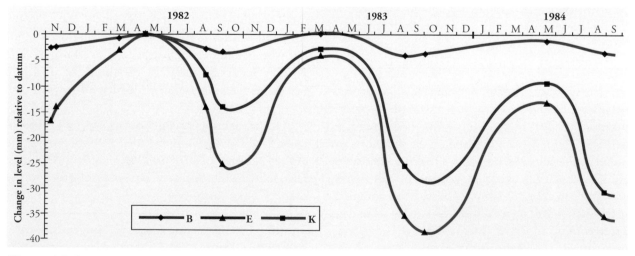

Figure 15.6
Typical level monitoring results, plotting changes in level against time.
(See Case Study at end of this Chapter for further details)

245

not been taken at the ideal time, it may be necessary to interpolate the lines with suitable curves to show the actual movements which probably occurred (Figure 15.6).

Where seasonal movements are occurring, interpretation is sometimes aided by isometric plans which compare the levels between spring and autumn (Figure 15.7) (or the recovery between autumn and spring).

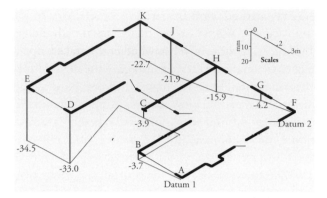

Figure 15.7

Level monitoring results presented as isometric plan. (Seasonal movements during 1983 - see Case Study 15 at end of this Chapter for further details)

Significance of extent of changes in level

To those who are more familiar with crack monitoring, it often comes as a surprise to discover the extent of foundation movements which are occurring. Case Study 15 involved maximum seasonal movements of 35mm, even in 1983 which was not an exceptionally dry year. As explained in that Case Study, this was sufficient to cause moderate damage, but only because of the ill-conceived partial underpinning scheme. It is almost certain that similar movements had been affecting the property prior to underpinning, without causing damage or being a cause for concern.

The significance of all movements will depend on the associated angular distortion and on the design and materials used in the building. For these reasons no definitive guidance can be given on the significance of different amounts of movement. However, where damage has occurred, seasonal movements usually have an amplitude in excess of 10mm. Conversely, movements of less than 5mm can usually be tolerated without damage becoming apparent, but may need to be less if it is necessary to stabilize existing cracks. Where movements are progressive so as to produce a cumulative angular distortion and stress, the rate of movement, rather than its amplitude, becomes significant. It is

generally considered that where heave movements (which are being superimposed on previous similar movement and stress) are less than 2mm per annum, they can be tolerated without significant damage.

Crack monitoring

As noted in the introduction to this Chapter, the prime purpose of crack monitoring should be for checking whether remedial works have been effective in stabilising the cracks, prior to reinstatement.

For this reason it is not essential for crack monitoring to start immediately. However, as it can be advantageous to compare crack behaviour before and after remedial works, an immediate start to crack monitoring is justifiable. If crack monitoring is being used, it can also be used as a aid to diagnosis of the cause of damage, but its use in this way should be subservient to level monitoring. The reaction of cracks to foundation movement can be erratic, and excessive reliance on crack monitoring is often misleading.

BRE Digest 343 "Simple measuring and monitoring of movement in low-rise buildings, Part 1: Cracks" provides many practical details and methods - reference should be made to that Digest for details. However, some parts of the Digest I find very impractical, and comments are made below on these aspects.

I endorse their caution about the use of plastic tell-tales across the cracks. Experience shows they are often inadequately attached or have been vandalised. Furthermore, observers often appear to have difficulty reading them, producing results which cannot be correct, for instance recording the positions of the cross-hairs so that they do not form a right angle. If they are used, one must record which side of the crack has the scale and which the cross-hairs, otherwise one cannot tell whether the crack is opening or closing. The 1.0mm accuracy is barely adequate for deciding whether a crack has stabilised sufficiently.

The use of callipers which are capable of reading to two decimal places is commended and will provide the desired accuracy of ± 0.1mm. Digital electronic callipers will provide this accuracy, and are easier to use than a vernier gauge.

Although callipers are adequate, I prefer the Demec strain gauge (Figure 15.8b). Provided large crack movements are not anticipated, it is faster and easier to use and in some cases the very precise accuracy is necessary; in one instance it demonstrated that a crack was

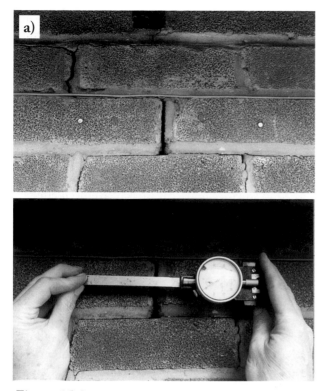

Figure 15.8

a)   *Demec strain gauge studs.*

b)   *Demec strain gauge in use.*

closing 5 days after tree removal, in contradiction to the claims of an engineer that it was still opening and that underpinning was therefore the only solution. The strain gauge discs (Figure 15.8a) are easy to attach and are unobtrusive, particularly if a small blob of Araldite is used, rather than the great globs of grey plastic padding which are often seen.

For these reasons the Demec discs are ideal, not only with the Demec gauge but also with callipers. The pointed ends of the callipers in their 'inside measurement mode' will locate precisely in the studs, and provide consistently reproducible results. Disturbance of the studs in this way may make a tiny difference to the precise Demec readings, but it does allow the callipers to replace the Demec gauge if the movements become too large and go off scale (provided the calliper readings start before the Demec is already off the scale).

The BRE Digest advocates the use of the 'permanent' rather than the 'rapid' type of Araldite. Unless a further visit to the site the next day is essential for other reasons, it seems difficult to justify the time and expense of a special visit when the rapid drying epoxy gives almost as good results. The rapid drying also has the advantage of allowing an early check that demec studs are attached satisfactorily and have not moved or come loose while the epoxy sets.

If screws, rather than studs, are used with a calliper, it is essential to ensure that they are rigidly fixed and that measurements are always taken on exactly the same part of the screw, for instance by using round head screws with the side of the callipers in contact with the back of the head. If measurements are taken anywhere along the length of the screw, readings will vary unless the screws are exactly parallel.

The BRE Digest recommends the use of the 'three screws' method for monitoring, in preference to the 'two screw'. Whilst I agree that there are advantages in measuring shear as well as whether the crack is opening or closing, I see little advantage in the method they describe. As I very rarely see it in use by others, I suspect this opinion is widespread. The major disadvantage is that the results cannot be instantly visualised as the readings are taken - the directions of movement are not apparent until they have been plotted. Furthermore, the plots cannot be related to a time scale and so one cannot see how the rate of movement will vary. Although the plots shown in figure 16 of BRE Digest appear linear, this is only because they are recording a progressive movement. If the movements are seasonal, the lines will double back and soon become indecipherable.

These problems can be overcome if the markers are set to directly record crack shear and opening. This requires the shear markers to be set closely adjacent to the two edges of the crack; one of these can also be used with an additional marker to record crack opening or closing (Figure 15.9). If screws are used as the markers, attachment close to the edges of the crack is liable to make the edges break away, but this is not a problem if Demec studs are glued on.

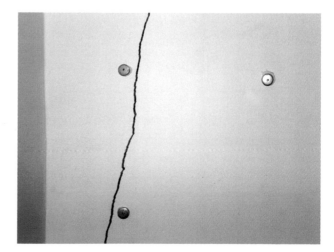

Figure 15.9

Monitoring of soil moisture content

Volume 2 describes the research applications of the neutron probe for monitoring changes in soil moisture content. In some circumstances it can also be a valuable aid for investigating problems, particularly when predictions on the rate of change of moisture content is needed. Obviously setting up such monitoring is more elaborate as it will involve installing one or more neutron probe access tubes, but this can be partially offset against the effort which would be needed anyway for drilling ordinary boreholes, for moisture content or for soil classification tests. Once installed, the neutron probe can record exactly what changes are occurring in the moisture content profile and this can be correlated with soil shrinkage or swelling recorded by level monitoring on an adjacent building. With detailed information of this sort, it becomes much easier to predict the duration of long-term heave movements. Case Study 15, at the end of this Chapter, provides an example of monitoring of this sort.

Summary

1.   Monitoring should form an essential part of virtually all investigations.

2.   **Monitoring changes in building level provides far more useful information than monitoring crack movements. It is the movement of the foundations which causes damage, and it is more logical to study these movements, rather than the indirect symptoms which they produce.**

3.   Level monitoring should aim to achieve a closing error of less than ± 1.0mm in a traverse around a typical detached house. Provided care is taken, this need not involve the elaborate equipment advocated in BRE Digest 386, but rigid markers, such as brass screws flush to the wall, and a good quality level and staff are essential. Readings should be recorded and presented to the nearest 0.1mm.

4.   Level monitoring should be started at the first opportunity, and continued for as long as required to provide the necessary information. Initial results will usually assist in diagnosis and for deciding on the scope of remedial work; further readings may be required to confirm the adequacy of any remedial action.

5.   Monitoring should not be embarked on for a predetermined period (for instance 12 months) or as a self-contained exercise. The information can be used to refine opinions as each set of readings becomes available, and decisions taken in the light of this information on the scope and frequency of further readings.

6.   Monitoring the recovery through the winter period can be just as useful, or often more useful, than the subsidence through the summer.

7.   If readings are being taken infrequently, they should as a minimum include readings at the optimal time for determining the maximum recovery (i.e. late April / early May) and maximum subsidence (mid-September). This will show the full extent of seasonal movement. Readings at annual intervals will only detect progressive movement.

8.   In most situations it is sufficient to select one of the level stations on the building as a suitable datum with results presented relative to this, but if movements are affecting the whole building, or if more than one cause is operative, an independent stable datum is desirable.

9.   It is important to appreciate the magnitude of movement which can occur, often without any damage being manifest. Interpretation of results should consider the distribution of movement, and the angular distortion. Seasonal movements in excess of 5mm can often be tolerated without damage. Where damage has occurred, the seasonal movements are usually more than 10mm, and may be in excess of 30mm.

9.   Crack monitoring can be a useful adjunct to level monitoring, particularly for showing whether remedial action has been sufficient to prevent crack movement. It is not a very reliable aid to diagnosis. For this reason crack monitoring need not start until remedial works have been undertaken.

10.   Crack monitoring should use callipers capable of achieving an error of less than ±0.1mm (i.e. reading to nearest 0.02mm), or a Demec strain gauge. The metal studs used for the Demec strain gauge, attached with epoxy resin, are preferable to screws or other types of markers. Readings taken parallel, and also at right angles, to a crack can be easier to interpret than the "three screw method".

Additional reading

BRE Digest 343. Simple measuring and monitoring of movement in low-rise buildings. Part 1 : Cracks.

BRE Digest 386. Monitoring building and ground movement by precise levelling.

Partial underpinning of semi-detached building – Ineffective root severance –
Continuing seasonal movement of rest of building of up to 38mm amplitude –
Angular distortion and damage made worse by underpinning –
Close correlation between moisture deficit and building movement.

The subject properties form two halves of a semi-detached house built in 1933. Each half has a forward projecting wing; the ground floor layout is shown on the site plan in CS Figure 15.1. Construction is of standard 23cm thick solid brick walls, under a double hip-ended tiled roof, with gable ends on the two front projections. The site is located in the north western outskirts of London, with the Geological Survey map indicating London Clay.

The tree

The most significant tree was a large mature oak growing in the grass verge adjacent to the pavement in front of the property. This tree had a height of about 20m and trunk diameter of 83cm, and was standing 11.7m from the line of the projecting sections of the building. The large crown had a radial spread of 8m, with some of the lower branches pruned (CS Figure 15.2).

Other oak trees grew along the pavement in front of adjacent properties. There was also a small pear tree 4m to the rear of the left-hand property and an apple tree 4m to the rear of the right half near the common boundary.

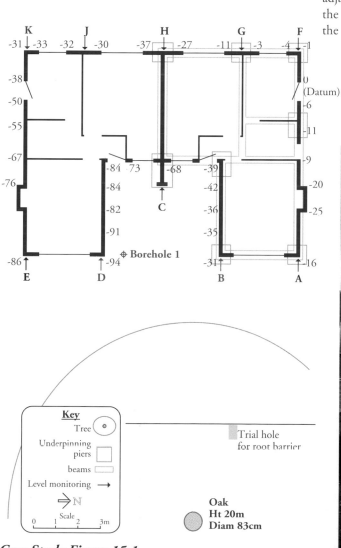

Case Study Figure 15.1

Site plan including location of level monitoring stations, and results of level distortion survey (mm) on 13/8/80 relative to datum at highest point on brickcourse.

Case Study Figure 15.2

Oak tree opposite front of projecting wings.

Previous history

It was believed that in the late 1950's there had been some damage and partial underpinning of the front walls of both of the projecting sections. It was subsequently confirmed that such underpinning had occurred, increasing the depth of the original foundations from about 0.45m to 0.95m.

During the drought of 1976 both halves of the building suffered extensive, but comparatively minor, damage. Records from that time indicate a maximum crack width of about 3mm. Both properties claimed on their insurance. The left half of the building was found to be inadequately insured and so only cosmetic repairs were undertaken. However, the right hand half, which was fully insured, was underpinned using a pier and beam system as indicated in CS Figure 15.1, with the piers taken to a depth of 2.4m.

I was instructed by the loss adjusters acting for both halves of the building in respect of recovering their principals' losses from the local authority, as owners of the tree.

Investigation of root barrier

The local authority denied the involvement of the tree, claiming that in 1970 they had put in a p.v.c. root barrier to protect the properties. The occupants could recall excavations to a depth of about 1.2m for this purpose and that gravel was delivered to site, preparatory to backfilling the trench with concrete. Apparently Water Board officials had objected to the use of such barrier and so the gravel was removed and the trench backfilled, but the occupants could not recall any polythene being inserted instead of the concrete.

I excavated and could identify the location of previous excavations. A root of 70mm diameter had been severed, and had subsequently regenerated with a number of roots up to 20mm diameter developing from the cut end. Many other roots up to 20mm diameter grew through the backfill soil. There was no evidence of any polythene or other material to restrict this root growth.

Level of building

In August 1980 I undertook a level distortion survey. The results are shown on CS Figure 15.1, and are presented relative to an arbitrary datum on the highest point on the brickcourse. It will be noted that both halves of the building show a downward tilt to the front, particularly in the front projecting wings, but the maximum distortion was far worse in the left half of the building.

This suggested that the 1976 underpinning might have been more appropriate beneath the left half of the building (if insurance funds had permitted). More importantly, if the left half of the building had been subject to movements of this magnitude in the past, and with a root barrier of dubious efficacy, I expressed grave concern that the underpinning would have created differential foundation depths and would have left the building even more vulnerable to future damage.

Level monitoring

In order to determine whether movements were continuing to affect the building, I attached level monitoring markers on 13th August 1980. Five stations were located across the front elevation, with markers attached at an additional five stations across the rear elevation in May 1982. Restricted access made it difficult to relate these measurements to each other, but it was hoped that the stations on the underpinned parts of the building would provide satisfactory stable datums. For this reason, stations A and F, on the front and rear of the right hand flank wall, both of which are above underpinning piers, were assumed to provide stable datum points.

After the markers were attached I received no instructions to take further readings for 15 months. Thereafter the proper monitoring commenced, with readings taken at intervals over an extended period, eventually amounting to a further three years. The results are presented in CS Figure 15.3, and are shown diagrammatically for selected stations in CS Figure 15.4 (with the change during the initial 15 month period shown as dotted lines).

	13/8/80	13/11/81	23/11/81	18/3/82	5/5/82	24/8/82	24/9/82	25/3/83	30/8/83	5/10/83	16/5/84	30/8/84
A	0	0	0	0	0	0	0	0	0	0	0	0
B	-2.1	-2.7	-2.5	-0.8	0	-2.9	-3.4	0	-4.0	-3.7	-1.3	-3.6
C	-1.0	-2.7	-1.4	+0.2	0	-1.6	-3.4	+0.3	-2.7	-3.6	-1.5	-3.3
D	-11.3	-15.2	-13.3	-2.4	0	-13.5	-24.9	-2.4	-32.4	-35.4	-10.4	-32.4
E	-13.6	-16.7	-14.0	-3.0	0	-14.0	-25.2	-4.0	-35.3	-38.5	-13.2	-35.5
F					0	0	0	0	0	-	0	0
G					0	0	-0.4	0	-2.1	-	0.5	-2.3
H					0	-3.4	-4.7	-1.6	-8.0	-	-2.9	-8.4
J					0	-6.6	-11.6	-1.6	-21.4	-	-6.2	-25.5
K					0	-7.9	-14	-2.8	-25.5	-	-9.4	-30.7

Case Study Figure 15.3

Results of level monitoring (mm) compared with readings on 5/5/82. Markers B to E (front elevation) related to station A (on underpinning pier at front of flank wall), and Markers G to K related to station F (on underpinning pier at rear of flank wall).

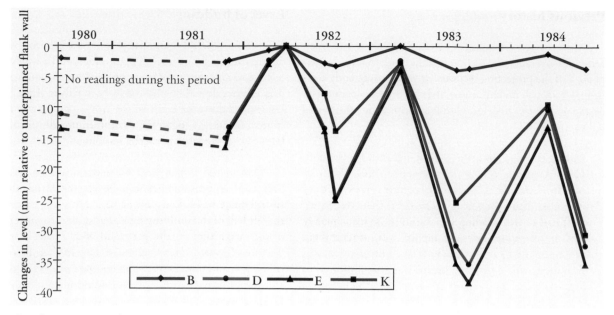

Case Study Figure 15.4

Results of level monitoring for selected stations. Results for stations B, D and E are presented relative to station A: station K presented relative to station F.

Subsoil conditions

On 23rd November 1981 I drilled boreholes for the insertion of two neutron probe access tubes at the locations shown in CS Figure 15.1. Both boreholes encountered similar soil conditions of typical uniform London Clay below the surface 0.5m of topsoil. While drilling these boreholes I took soil samples for gravimetric determination of moisture content; the results are shown in the profile in CS Figure 15.5.

Measurements of volumetric moisture content using the neutron probe were not started until the following March; a selection of the results are shown in CS Figures 15.9 and 15.10.

Root activity

There was dispute whether root samples which were taken during the underpinning in 1978 and identified as oak had been alive. It was claimed (by those acting for the local authority) that most of the roots had been dead.

During my investigation I encountered live oak roots up to 8mm in diameter to a depth of 0.6m adjacent to the front section of the left hand property. In addition, living fine root activity was recorded to a depth of 1.75m in borehole 1 adjacent to the front corner.

DISCUSSION

Cause of 1976 damage

The investigations demonstrated that no root barrier had been inserted, and that any root severance which occurred during the excavations had been negated by subsequent root growth. It would have been quite possible for the severed roots to grow back the 8m from the excavations to the house during the six year period after they were severed, and the 1.2m depth would not have severed all of the roots. Any remaining roots could have developed into the soil which had previously been exploited by the severed roots.

The level distortion survey was entirely consistent with the potential involvement of the tree, and the development of the damage was consistent.

The local authority subsequently accepted liability.

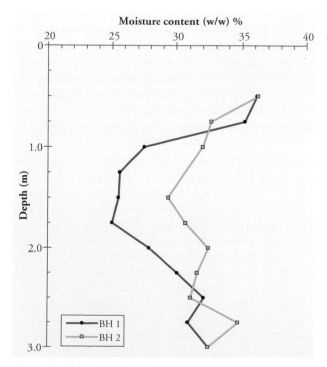

Case Study Figure 15.5

Moisture content profiles from soil samples (23/11/81).

Effect of partial underpinning

Although the original claim was settled, I was concerned about the potential for further damage, and that this might be exacerbated by the underpinning of only one half of the building. It was for this reason that I set up the level monitoring, and it was to investigate this aspect that my original instructions were extended.

Monitoring the recovery movements through the winter 1981/82 demonstrated:

i) slight movements (2.7mm) of stations B and C, despite these being on underpinning piers. The implication must remain that station A was not providing a stable datum, but, as the other stations appear to subside in summer and recover in winter, any movement at A must have been less than at B or C.

ii) considerably greater movement at stations D and E (15.2 and 16.7mm respectively).

Despite the extent of movement, there was no evidence of damage at that stage, but the potential for damage obviously existed with differential movements of this magnitude. In spring 1982 the level monitoring was extended to the rear elevation.

Case Study Figure 15.6

Crack in front elevation adjacent to party wall.

By 24th August 1982, the front had subsided almost back to the levels recorded the previous autumn, but still without the development of any damage. However, by 24th September further cracking had appeared. The worst damage was at ground floor level on the front elevation, adjacent to the party wall, where there was a 3mm crack on the front elevation (CS Figure 15.6), with associated movement in the front living room adjacent to the party wall. There were also 2.5mm wide cracks around the window in the bedroom in the projecting wing, and other minor damage throughout the property. This damage was described as being far worse than the original damage in 1976. The other half of the building which had been underpinned was unaffected.

This damage occurred when the subsidence of the front of the wing increased to 25mm. Station D was 6.8m from C, and allowing for the 3.4mm of subsidence at C, this indicates an angular distortion of 1:315 between stations C and D. In practice much of this distortion was probably concentrated on the recessed front elevation near the party wall.

These considerable movements were affecting not only the projecting front wing of the building which was within 12.3m from the oak tree, but also the stations J and K on the rear elevation which were 21m from the tree and showing movements of 11.6 and 14.0mm respectively. The angular distortion between stations H and J on the rear elevation adjacent to the party wall was 1:580.

During the winter 1982/83 the monitoring demonstrated virtual full recovery, but by the end of August 1983 the subsidence of the front wing at stations D and E had increased to more than 30mm, and by 5/10/83 to 35.4 and 38.5mm respectively; this is the largest seasonal movement which I have recorded. This movement indicates an angular distortion between stations C and D of 1:195, and was accompanied by increased width of all of the cracks which had developed the previous year, plus some additional cracking. During the following winter there was partial, but not complete, recovery with renewed subsidence during the summer of 1984. The levels recorded on 30/8/84 were almost identical to those recorded on the same date in 1983.

Correlation between soil moisture deficit and building movement

The neutron probe access tubes which were inserted when the boreholes were drilled allowed measurement of the changes in soil moisture deficit. Borehole 1 at the front of the building was closely adjacent to station D, and as the neutron probe readings were generally taken at the same time as the level monitoring, it allows comparison of the amount of movement with the soil moisture deficit. CS Figure 15.7 shows the values recorded on the various dates, calculating the soil moisture deficits by comparison with the profile on 5/5/82, and below a depth of 0.9m which corresponds to the underside of foundations. The levels are also compared against the same date.

	SMD Borehole 1	Level Marker D
18/3/82	0.5	-2.4
5/5/82	0	0
24/8/82	45.3	-13.5
24/9/82	67.8	-24.9
25/3/83	5.2	-2.4
30/8/83	95.9	-32.4
16/5/84	23.8	-10.4
30/8/84	97.3	-32.4
Persistent deficit	*60*	*20*

Case Study Figure 15.7

Correlation between soil moisture deficit at borehole 1 and movement of adjacent level station D

CS Figure 15.8 plots all of these values, and shows the very close correlation which exists. The slope of this correlation will be the water shrinkage factor. It has a value of exactly 3, implying perfect isotropic soil shrinkage.

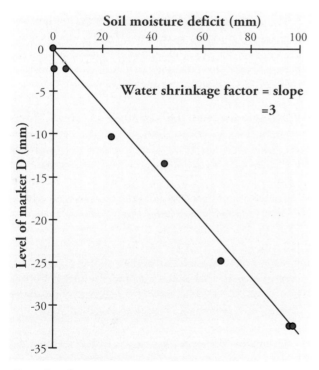

Case Study Figure 15.8

Correlation between soil moisture deficit at borehole 1 and movement of adjacent level monitoring station D.

The profiles obtained with the neutron probe (CS Figure 15.9) also show that the incomplete recovery movements recorded on 24/5/84 at the end of the winter was because of incomplete rehydration of the soil and the development of a slight semi-persistent deficit, rather than the effects of dynamic settlement.

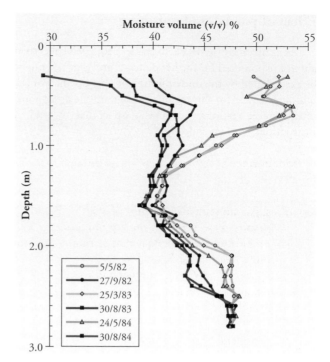

Case Study Figure 15.9

Moisture content profiles (by neutron probe) for borehole 1.

Implications for remedial action

Although there were seasonal movements affecting the underpinning to the rear of the building (stations G and H), which shows that root activity must have extended to at least 2.4m depth, at borehole 2, 3.3m further from the tree, it is apparent from CS Figure 15.10 that the changes in moisture content were restricted to the surface 1.0m. If this borehole was beyond the influence of the oak, it should provide an indication of the equilibrium moisture profile, assuming that the conditions were uniform across the site.

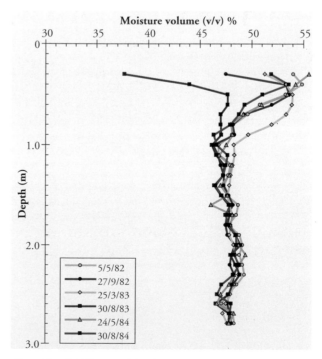

Case Study Figure 15.10

Moisture content profiles (by neutron probe) for borehole 2.

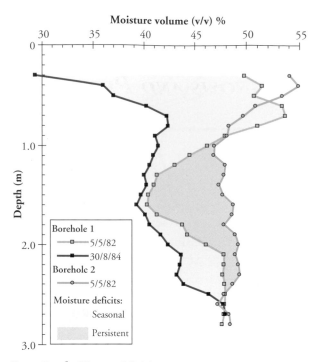

Case Study Figure 15.11

Extent of seasonal and persistent soil moisture deficit at borehole 1.

CS Figure 15.11 plots the spring and autumn profiles for borehole 1, and also the spring profile for borehole 2. It indicates the extent of the seasonal deficit and also the persistent deficit if this assumption of uniform conditions is correct. Calculation of this persistent moisture deficit gives a value of 60mm. If one assumes a water shrinkage factor of 3 (as derived from CS Figure 15.8), the soil shrinkage associated with this persistent deficit would have been about 20mm. This was considerably less than the seasonal movements which were occurring, and would therefore have been unlikely to cause significant damage if allowed to occur.

The moisture content profiles show that rehydration was occurring each winter to the full depth of desiccation, particularly down to about 1.3m, but also in the lower zones of desiccation from 2.0 to 2.7m depth. It was only between 1.3 to 2.0m depth that rehydration was limited, and a significant persistent deficit existed. This suggested that the soil was reasonably permeable and that any such persistent deficit would be short-lived.

It was therefore reasonable to conclude that, if the influence of the tree was removed, recovery of the persistent deficit would be fairly rapid and only involve about 20mm of recovery. However, if the tree was retained, large seasonal movements would continue, particularly in any dry year, with the associated angular distortion and damage exacerbated by the variation in foundation depth between the two halves of the building. With the existence of a persistent deficit, pruning was not a viable option.

The option of tree removal was put to the local authority as owners of the oak tree in May 1983. Their expert agreed that felling should avoid the need for further underpinning, and that underpinning would be essential if it was

retained. The contractor who had underpinned the right half of the building in 1977 now raised the spectre of heave, despite his original requirement that the tree should be removed. However, it was considered that any recovery would lift the right half off its piers and so should affect both halves of the building to a similar extent.

Although tree removal was a viable option, the local authority quite understandably considered that this fine oak tree should not be destroyed and refused to take such action. After further negotiation and delay, the left half of the building was eventually underpinned to match the right half, with the local authority having to accept liability for the costs of this work.

This underpinning started in September 1984, and I was alarmed to note that the contractors, who were aware of the monitoring and investigations, were not including any anti-heave precautions. The potential for movement was at least 35mm (from the seasonal deficit at that time of year) plus 20mm for the persistent deficit. Work had to be suspended while they incorporated appropriate precautions.

Lessons to be learnt.

- The level monitoring demonstrated that seasonal movements of up to 38mm were occurring in the dry summer of 1984. With this mature tree, it is reasonable to assume that the amplitude of movement would have been similar prior to the underpinning in 1977.

- During most years this amplitude of movement was not causing significant damage; however, in the exceptional conditions of 1976, movements were probably slightly greater and sufficient to initiate some damage.

- The attempt to prevent damage by root severance provided only temporary relief.

- The level distortion survey shows that the worse distortion was to the left half of the building. However, it was the right half which was underpinned (with this decision based solely on the availability of insurance funds, rather than any technical reason).

- This partial underpinning created differential foundation depths, with the left half of the building continuing seasonal movements of up to 38mm amplitude. Movement of up to 30mm affected the rear of the building 21m from the oak, and the 2.4m deep underpinning was also subject to seasonal movement of up to 8mm. The resulting angular distortion caused worse damage than prior to the underpinning.

- The detailed monitoring of levels and soil moisture content allowed prediction of the heave potential.

- Although tree removal would have been effective, the local authority (as owners of the tree) preferred to retain it and therefore had no option but to accept liability for underpinning the remainder of the building.

CHAPTER 16

HEAVE AND RECOVERY - DIAGNOSIS AND PREDICTION

Introduction

When a desiccated clay soil is allowed to rehydrate it will swell, generating forces which may be in excess of 300 kN/m² and quite capable of lifting a multi-storey building. This upward movement of the building is known as heave or recovery; the correct term depending on when the soil was desiccated:-

i)   if the soil has been desiccated prior to the laying of the foundations and is then allowed to rehydrate and swell, the subsequent uplift will take the building to above its originally constructed level - this is "**heave**".

ii)   if the foundations are laid and a tree then grows so that the soil becomes desiccated, it will cause soil shrinkage and subsidence. If the soil is then allowed to rehydrate, the uplift will take the building back towards its original level - this movement should be distinguished from heave, and be referred to as "**recovery**".

Although "seasonal recovery" occurring during a single winter associated with seasonal soil drying (Chapter 5) is a form of recovery, it is preferable for the terms heave or recovery to be restricted to movements occurring over a time scale in excess of a single winter. **They are therefore movements associated with rehydration of a persistent moisture deficit (Chapter 6).**

Where damage is occurring, a correct diagnosis is essential to determine whether heave is involved. Case Studies 1, 4, 13 and 14 provide examples of incorrect diagnosis leading to inappropriate remedial action. In addition, before deciding on the method of remedial work, it is crucial to know whether damage has been caused solely by seasonal movements, or whether there is a significant persistent deficit and attendant risk of unacceptable heave or recovery. If movements are predominantly seasonal, curtailing the water uptake of the trees can be a viable method of restabilizing the foundations. However, if there is a significant persistent deficit, any reduction in water uptake as a result of tree management will allow the soil to rehydrate with associated heave or recovery, and thereby prevent sta-

bility. If the time scale to achieve stability is excessive, underpinning becomes the only viable option (unless the movements can be tolerated).

Chapter 17 considers the options for remedial action, and emphasizes that it is essential to identify where there is a risk of heave or recovery, and be able to make a reasonable prediction on the probable duration and extent of movement.

In most situations it is sufficient to make a qualitative assessment. Is there is risk of heave? If there is, how long will it continue and will it cause unacceptable movement and damage during this period? Qualitative predictions of this sort are considered from page 261. In some circumstances it is necessary to make a quantitative prediction on the extent of heave. The methods and limitations of this are considered from page 264.

A persistent moisture deficit - the essential pre-requisite for heave

Chapter 6 has considered the factors which influence a persistent deficit, how the deficit develops, and the long-term changes which can occur through the life of a tree. Reference should be made to that chapter for these details.

In summary, there must be a soil of low permeability and a tree which is capable of causing desiccation of that soil to sufficient depth so that rehydration cannot occur within a single winter.

As noted in Chapter 4, the assessment of permeability is not easy. In general the higher the clay content and the higher the plasticity index of the soil, the lower the permeability. However, the soil structure is also of crucial importance. For instance, the development of cracks will provide a rapid flow path for water, and any large scale features such as bands of sand or gravel can also have a major influence. Soil cracks are often lined with coarser particles of sand as a result of erosion of the finer materials from the edges of the crack; even when cracks close these coarser particles can aid the movement of water between the soil peds.

Chapter 9 has considered the ability of different tree species to cause soil drying. Soil conditions will have a major influence on the ability of any species to root to depth, as clay soils of low permeability will have low oxygen status which can be incapable of supporting growth. In addition, mechanical impedance from the high density of clay soils can limit growth. Species which are best able to cope with these conditions, such as poplar, elm, willow and oak, are the most likely to produce a persistent deficit. With these species the influence can be very deep-seated and can extend a considerable distance radially (frequently in excess of a distance equal to tree height). Some species of cypress can produce an extreme deficit in the close proximity of the tree. All these species frequently cause severe problems of heave.

However, the deficit produced by most other species is predominantly seasonal; a persistent deficit might occur in the close proximity to the trunk, but is usually insignificant beyond a distance of about 0.2 x tree height. These species are capable of causing heave if foundations are laid directly over the previous position of the tree, particularly if they are laid in the autumn when a seasonal deficit is also present, but are far less likely to cause problems if the tree is more than 0.2 x tree height from the building.

Factors influencing amount, rate and duration of heave or recovery

The **amount** of heave or recovery is dependent on the total soil moisture deficit and the swelling potential of the clay. Swelling will start as soon as water input exceeds loss, and will continue until the swelling forces are counterbalanced by the load on the soil. Provided water remains freely available at all times, the rate of movement will be rapid initially, gradually reducing as the deficit diminishes, and finally stopping when the soil is fully rehydrated back to equilibrium with the load. This produces the characteristic shaped heave or recovery curve (Figure 16.1).

The **rate** of rehydration and thus the slope of the recovery curve depends on the permeability of the clay. The higher the permeability, the faster the rate of recovery and the steeper the curve. Figure 16.1 shows curves for a clay of high permeability where recovery is rapid and quickly reaches equilibrium, and also a clay of low permeability in which the rate of movement only decreases very slowly until it eventually reaches equilibrium.

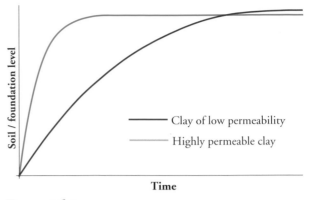

Figure 16.1
Rate of heave is dependent on permeability of the clay

For two samples of comparable permeability, the **duration** of the heave or recovery movements is dependent on the depth of desiccation and the total soil moisture deficit. The rate of rehydration may be similar initially, but a small and shallow deficit can rehydrate in a short period whereas an intense and deep-seated deficit in the same clay will only rehydrate over a prolonged period - in either case the initial shape of the recovery curve will be similar, but the time scale, and the total upward movement, will differ (Figure 16.2).

Curve 'a' in Figure 16.2 shows a deficit which is predominantly seasonal, with almost full rehydration occurring within the first winter. As noted in the introduction to this chapter, movement of this sort is better described as "seasonal recovery", with the terms "heave" or "recovery" restricted to upward movement occurring over a prolonged period. With curve 'b', the movements start at a similar rate but do not diminish significantly until the fourth year. In extreme cases, where there is a very extensive and deep-seated moisture deficit and a clay of low permeability, the movements can continue in excess of 20 years. The classic study by Samuels and Cheney (1974) on a row of cottages at Windsor built on London clay which had been desiccated by mature elm trees showed significant movement continuing for more than 15 years after the trees were felled, and some movement for more than 25 years (as shown in Figure 6.13, page 92).

It must be emphasised that the duration of swelling movements can be anywhere between these extremes of 2-3 decades, or 2-3 months (or even weeks or days), depending on the extent of the deficit and the permeability of the clay. As the term "heave" should be restricted to cases where rehydration takes more than a single winter, the movement must by definition continue for at least that long, but it does not necessarily mean that it will continue for many years.

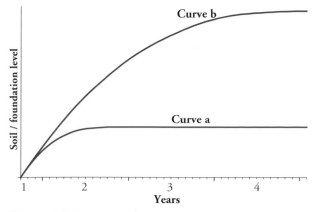

Figure 16.2

For soils of similar permeability, the duration and extent of heave is dependent on the depth of desiccation and total soil moisture deficit.

As can be seen from the shape of the curve, although initial stages are rapid, the final stages can be prolonged. As an approximate guide, it is often considered that if heave movements are less than 2mm per annum, there is unlikely to be any significant further damage (although this obviously depends on the amount of stress which has previously developed in the building and on the angular distortion). When deciding whether or not heave movements are tolerable, an assessment needs to be made of how much movement will occur and how long this will continue, and a decision made as to whether this is acceptable.

The initiation of heave

Heave most commonly occurs after a tree which has produced a persistent deficit is felled. Transpiration by the foliage ceases and so there will be no further water uptake by the roots and no further soil shrinkage (unless other vegetation is present).

Rehydration and swelling of the soil will start as soon as water is able to reach the zone of desiccation. In theory, if foundations are deep there may be a brief period while all movements, either subsidence or heave, will cease until water is able to penetrate to below foundation level, but in practice water can usually penetrate very rapidly down the side of foundation trenches to reach the underlying soil. As a result, the response to tree felling can be near instantaneous (Case Study 17).

Chapter 6 has noted that, once a persistent deficit becomes established, it remains fairly constant with only minor fluctuations after a particularly dry winter (restricting rehydration and causing a semi-persistent deficit). Above the zone of persistent desiccation, the surface layers of soil will be subject to considerable sea-

sonal drying and movement, but in the zone of the persistent deficit, there is an approximate equilibrium between the seasonal input and output of water. However, if there is any reduction in the water requirements of the tree, or of its ability to abstract water from the soil, it will upset the equilibrium and will allow the soil to rehydrate and swell. This can occur even though the tree is still present.

For instance, when trees are retained on building sites, the root systems are often severed by the foundation excavations or service trenches, allowing the soil beyond the trench to rehydrate. Even if the roots are not directly severed, root systems are very vulnerable to compaction or changes in soil level. This can inhibit fine root activity and prevent water uptake. This sort of damage to the root system occurs very commonly during building work if insufficient care is taken to protect the area surrounding the tree. It may eventually lead to dieback in the foliage, but in the meantime heave will develop if a persistent deficit was present (Case Study 13). Similarly, a trench excavated to form a root barrier must sever all roots if it is to be effective; if a persistent deficit is present, this will allow heave to occur beyond the barrier (Case Study 1). Despite this, it is surprising how often reports suggest that a tree should not be felled because of the risk of heave/recovery, but then go on to advocate installing a root barrier as an alternative remedy.

Likewise, natural decline in the condition of a tree or disease of the root system can reduce the water uptake and allow rehydration and heave, even though the tree is still present and apparently growing healthily. As noted in Chapter 6 (page 94), symptoms of dieback of the crown may not become apparent until after the persistent deficit has virtually disappeared and all heave has ceased. Pruning a tree which has produced a persistent deficit will reduce the amplitude of seasonal drying, and will therefore allow heave to develop. Case Study 9 provides an example, although in that case the extent of heave was tolerable. For this reason pruning does not provide an effective remedy if there is a persistent deficit (see also Chapter 17, page 281).

In any of these situations where some influence of the tree remains, or where there is some other vegetation sufficient to cause seasonal drying, the seasonal movement will be superimposed on the recovery curve, so that the rate of heave will slow and usually reverse during the summer, and then accelerate again in winter (Figure 16.3). The recovery curve becomes a combination of the progressive heave curve (as shown in Figure 16.1) and a sinusoidal curve of seasonal movement with a reduced amplitude.

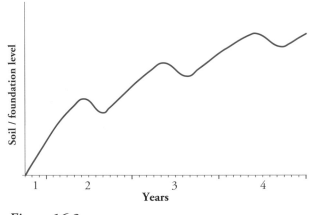

Figure 16.3

Heave with seasonal movements superimposed

It is often suggested that a reversal or reduction in the rate of heave is inevitable in the summer, but level monitoring demonstrates that such claims are incorrect (Case Studies 2, 4, 6, 17, 20; contrast these with Case Studies 5, 9, and 14, where vegetation was retained and partial reversal of movement occurs Case Studies 7 and 11 show both effects in different parts of the building). If rehydration is occurring within the zone where seasonal drying can develop, heave will slow or reverse. However, if the rehydration is occurring at deeper layers, it will remain at a steady rate, controlled by the permeability of the soil. It will only cease if all available moisture has been eliminated.

The diagnosis of heave

It is very important to recognise when heave damage is occurring and to distinguish it from seasonal movement, subsidence, or other causes of foundation movement. Incorrect diagnosis frequently leads to inappropriate remedial works which are ineffective against heave, so that further damage occurs. It must be remembered that heave may not be occurring in isolation, but may be an underlying trend with seasonal movements superimposed.

The systematic approach to investigations recommended in Chapters 11-14 will soon establish whether heave is involved, but the following aspects are particularly relevant:-

Age of building. Heave should always be suspected on any building less than 10 years old which shows damage. It will usually show up within 2 or 3 years of completion of a building, when the owner realises that what he thought was the initial settlement of the foundations is excessive, but it may be more than 3 years before the existence of a problem is recognised.

Conversely it is unusual to encounter heave (as opposed to recovery) on an older building, even if a tree has been felled. This is because, if there is a persistent deficit, there will invariably be considerable seasonal movement extending as deep as rehydration can occur each winter. The sides of foundations provide a ready path for water to penetrate to the underside, thereby increasing the depth of rehydration and ensuring that normal strip or trench foundations will be subject to considerable seasonal movement. If there is a risk of heave, these seasonal movements, plus distortion from dynamic settlement, are usually sufficient to cause damage within a few years. This will not apply to piled foundations; these may be adequate against subsidence but, if they do not incorporate anti-heave measures, may be vulnerable to heave after trees are felled (Case Study 16).

Removal of trees or root damage. As it is an essential prerequisite for heave that there must be a desiccated soil which is allowed to rehydrate, it follows that there must have been a tree in the vicinity. The stump of a tree, or regrowth from root suckers, may provide clear evidence of its previous existence. Plans of the site prior to construction may give details (but trees may have been omitted, or plans drawn up after trees are felled). A more reliable record of previous tree cover can be obtained from aerial photographs, if available.

It is important to remember that trees need not be felled to release problems of heave. Any action which curtails the water uptake by the tree can allow the soil to rehydrate. This might occur as a result of excavation of foundations or service trenches, or heavy pruning of the tree. Alternatively, heave may be initiated merely by the decline in water requirements as a tree becomes overmature, although in this situation there is usually a history of damage from previous seasonal movement.

Soil conditions. As heave can only occur if there is a persistent moisture deficit, soil investigations to establish the existence of such deficit are appropriate. The methods of assessing desiccation, and the limitations of these methods, are described in Chapter 13 (page 208). When undertaking such investigations, note must be taken of the time of year. In the autumn any desiccation may be associated with seasonal drying (rather than a persistent deficit), whereas desiccation in the spring must indicate a persistent deficit. If heave damage has been occurring, it is possible that rehydration is nearly complete; under these circumstances a persistent deficit may no longer be detectable.

Time of development of damage. Damage caused by seasonal movement typically develops in the early autumn. Damage developing at other times of year should be investigated with particular care, as heave may be involved. This does not imply that heave cannot be involved in damage which appears in late summer; it is probable that damage appearing at that time of year will have a component of seasonal movement, but the underlying stress within the building may be caused by progressive heave (Case Studies 1 and 13).

Distortion survey. A level distortion survey is the most valuable diagnostic aid for recognising heave. The greatest uplift is almost always closest to the felled (or root-damaged) tree, so that the building will be tilted-up towards it (Figure 16.4 and Case Study 1). A level survey provides a rapid and simple method of providing a correct preliminary diagnosis, and avoiding erroneous allegations based merely on the presence of a tree in proximity to a building.

If there is doubt whether one side of a building has suffered heave or the opposite side has subsided, confirmatory evidence may be obtained from a verticality survey. If heave is involved, the wall with maximum vertical distortion will probably be in the vicinity of the high point of the horizontal survey, whereas with subsidence the worst distorted wall will be near the low point.

Monitoring. Monitoring, particularly of changes in level, provides definitive confirmation on the direction of differential movement. It is strongly recommended that level monitoring is started immediately in any case where heave is suspected, especially as this information is also needed for predicting the duration of continuing movement. During the winter any movement associated with tree root activity will involve upward recovery (all three lines in Figure 16.5). However if the movements are entirely seasonal, the rate of movement will diminish through the winter as the soil returns to equilibrium moisture (green line in Figure 16.5), whereas if there is a persistent deficit the heave will continue at a uniform rate (red and blue lines). These differences will become even more obvious in the summer when upward heave movements

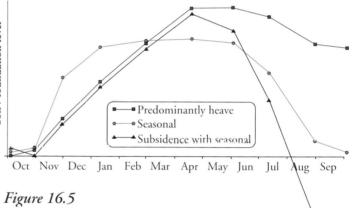

Figure 16.5

Monitoring can distinguish between different types of movement caused by heave, seasonal movement or subsidence

(red line) will continue (possibly at a diminished rate or with slight downward movement), whereas they will reverse if movements are caused by subsidence or seasonal movement (blue line). Over an annual cycle, the building will finish at a higher level if there is a component of heave (red line); if it finishes at the same level the movements must be seasonal (green line) whereas if it is at a lower level, either subsidence (from an increase in the persistent deficit) or dynamic settlement must be involved (blue line).

Cracks associated with heave may open progressively, but monitoring these, as with any crack monitoring, provides a less reliable indication. Cracks caused by seasonal movement may fail to close because of the direction of movement or because of debris, and different parts of the building heaving at different rates can also produce anomalous crack movements.

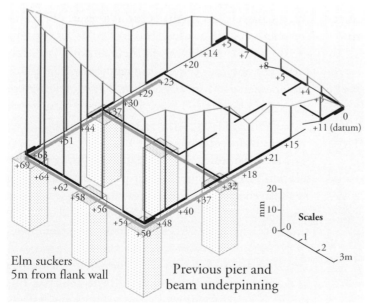

Figure 16.4

Level distortion survey in 1985 of property previously underpinned against subsidence in 1977. Original diagnosis was clearly in error, and so further damage had occurred (see Case Study 14 for further details).

Crack pattern. Diagnosis of heave based solely on the pattern of cracking of the superstructure is very unreliable, particularly as differential rates of heave can produce apparently anomalous results (Case Study 4). The broad principles of crack interpretation should be applied with considerable discretion for determining the direction of movement (see Chapter 12, page 183).

However, there is a characteristic pattern of cracking which is commonly, although not invariably, associated with heave. When clay swells, movements occur horizontally, as well as vertically. These horizontal movements can produce lateral distortion of foundations, particularly if these are deep trench-fill. This situation can develop if desiccated clay is enclosed between trench foundations when they are laid. It is inevitable that the foundations will sever roots so that no further desiccation can occur. Although water may not be able to reach the clay from above, it can still rehydrate from below. Swelling of the clay will produce an outward force on the foundations as well as upward heave. This lateral pressure often produces cracks through the foundations extending up to d.p.c. level, with the foundations and brickwork below this level being pushed outwards (Figure 16.6). This sort of cracking is particularly likely to occur either if:

i) the tree which produced the desiccation was growing within the area now enclosed by the foundations. Maximum soil swelling will occur within this zone, with little restraint from similar swelling externally.

ii) a tree growing adjacent to the building is retained but the roots are severed by the foundations. This allows the soil outside the building to be maintained in a desiccated (and shrunk) condition, whereas it is able to swell within the confines of the foundation.

Swelling of the clay outside the building will not usually produce inward distortion, as foundations are strong in compression and cross partition walls provide additional restraint.

The horizontal swelling of the clay can also rotate a foundation. If a deep trench-fill foundation extends down into stable soil, the base will be held rigid, but the top can be thrust outwards, causing outward rotation (Case Study 1), whereas maximum swelling near the base of the trench will produce the opposite direction of rotation (Case Study 17).

Strip footings, which have back-fill soil above the footings, will be less vulnerable to this damage. It should not occur if anti-heave precautions, involving lining the foundation trenches, have been taken.

Diagnosis of recovery movements

By definition, recovery can only take place after there has been subsidence associated with development of a persistent deficit. This subsidence must have produced distortion and almost inevitably damage. Although in the past house owners were often prepared to disregard damage and thus permit a significant deficit to establish beneath a building, it is now increasingly rare to find a tree being retained long enough for this situation to develop. In those rare situations where this does occur (Case Studies 4 and 6), investigations should be able to demonstrate initial subsidence followed by recovery. Once again a systematic approach should establish these phases, but the following are of particular relevance:

Removal or deterioration of trees. There must have been a tree which was capable of causing the desiccation to develop in the first place, and something must have happened to that tree to stop or reduce the water uptake. Recovery should be suspected in any situation where trees have been removed in the past.

Level distortion survey. The initial subsidence of the building must have caused distortion. As this subsidence phase will usually be accompanied by dynamic settlement, distortion will almost always be present, even in the final stages of recovery. For this reason, the building will show downward distortion towards the tree, similar to that produced by dynamic

Figure 16.6

Crack below d.p.c. and associated lateral movement of brickwork at d.p.c. level, caused by outward movement of trench-fill foundations. A severe horizontal crack has also opened along the d.p.c, caused by the brickwork being lifted by a ground-bearing floorslab.

settlement associated with seasonal movement, or by subsidence. Conversely, if the building is level, it is very unlikely that recovery can be occurring.

Level monitoring. Monitoring will be invaluable, and should be started immediately. The movements will be progressive, with the direction of movement opposite to the distortion shown by the level survey (Case Study 4). Monitoring may also be needed to determine how long the recovery is likely to continue.

Damage to building. The subsidence phase will have inevitably caused damage, some evidence of which should be present, even if repairs have been made (Case Study 6).

If previous repairs have been primarily cosmetic, subsequent recovery can usually be accommodated by closure of the original cracks. However, if more permanent repairs have been made, the recovery phase can induce different stresses within the structure and the development of a different crack pattern, often at right angles to previous damage.

During recovery, lateral movement of brickwork below d.p.c. level is unlikely to occur, unless the building has been underpinned (in which case, as the foundations are new, the damage should be described as heave rather than recovery) (Case Study 4).

Relevance of determining age of tree and age of building

It is often thought that consideration of the relative ages of the tree and the building is relevant to the diagnosis of heave, or to predicting the risk of heave if a tree is felled. This concept has been fostered by some of the publications of the Building Research Establishment, particularly BRE Digest 298. Table 2 of that Digest provides a detailed analysis, based on whether the tree is older or younger than the house.

It should be apparent that these ages are of no particular relevance; it is the time of development of any persistent deficit which needs to be determined.

Thus, a tree may be present, and of substantial size, when a house is built, but if it has not already created a persistent deficit there can be no risk of heave. Seasonal movements may occur accompanied by dynamic settlement, but there is still no risk of heave.

On the other hand, a tree may have been planted after a house was built and have subsequently grown and created a persistent deficit. This will, of course, have been accompanied by distortion and probably by damage. Subsequent removal of the tree will not cause heave, but it will cause progressive recovery movement of an essentially similar nature to heave; Case Studies 4 and 6 provide examples.

For these reasons it is important to diagnose if and when any persistent deficit developed and relate this, rather than the age of the tree, to the age of the building.

Prediction of risk and duration of heave or recovery if trees are felled

If heave is allowed to occur, the damage is sometimes serious and can be far worse than damage caused by subsidence. The mechanism of heave, and the situations which give rise to problems, are often poorly understood. As a result, consultants and advisers, of all disciplines, are often unwilling to make any recommendations concerning the future management or felling of trees. However, the consequences of any action are usually predictable, and it is essential to make such prediction if the most appropriate preventative or remedial works are to be applied.

The objective of the prediction is to decide whether any soil (and building) movements are predominantly seasonal, or whether there is a risk of rehydration of a persistent deficit, and associated problems of long-term heave or recovery. If there is a risk of heave, in most situations a qualitative assessment is usually sufficient. Will progressive movement occur? If so, will it be sufficient to cause significant damage? How long will the movement continue (2 months, 2 years or 20 years)? Qualitative assessments of this sort can be made comparatively easily, in many cases based solely on visual observation, but if necessary supported by simple site investigations. If these indicate a risk, there are methods for assessing this in quantitative terms - these are described in the next section (page 264).

Predicting heave or recovery is required:

i)   prior to building, when new foundations are being laid, to determine whether there a risk of heave from rehydration of an existing deficit;

ii) if there is an existing building, to determine the consequences of felling or pruning the trees.

In the former situation, prediction must be based solely on the information available on the soil conditions and from the tree. However, if there is an existing building, valuable additional information can be obtained by inspection and by monitoring the performance of that building. Circumstances will dictate the amount of detail which is needed but the information described below can usually be obtained.

Risk from different tree species. Species of tree with high water requirements and the ability to root at depth in clay soils are far more likely to produce a persistent deficit. The worst offenders are poplar, elm, oak and willow, which may produce a persistent deficit extending to a distance at least equal to their height, and some species of cypress which can produce even more extreme deficits but not extending as far radially (not usually beyond 0.5 x tree height).

Most other species of tree will only produce a significant persistent deficit in the close proximity of the trunk. Foundations which are laid directly over the former position of such trees may be vulnerable to heave, but beyond a distance of about 0.2 x tree height, the risk is greatly reduced.

Previous growth of the tree. If the tree is young and the evidence from adjacent buildings indicates that damage has only recently started, or that no damage has yet occurred, it is safe to infer that any influence is only seasonal and that a significant persistent deficit cannot have established. Likewise, trees which have been regularly pollarded in the past are unlikely to have had sufficient influence to produce a persistent deficit; if they have only been allowed to grow a larger crown in recent years it is unlikely that a persistent deficit will have established. The frequency of pruning can be determined either by examining the size of the branch stubs cut during previous prunings, or by study of increment cores taken from the trunk (see Chapter 14, page 228).

Conversely, if a tree shows evidence that it has been very heavily pruned in the past, sufficient to reduce its water uptake significantly for a number of years, and if there is no evidence of damage to an adjacent building at that time, it is unlikely that a repeat of similar pruning, or tree removal, will cause heave (Case Study 2).

Effect of clay permeability. The greatest risk will be associated with clay of low permeability. Such soils normally have high plasticity. A deep-seated moisture deficit in such soils can take several decades to rehydrate. By contrast, clays of lower plasticity such as a

Boulder Clay, tend to be more permeable and even a deep-seated deficit is likely to be eliminated within 5 years or less. (See also Chapter 6, page 95).

A geological survey map can indicate the probable soil type, and with practical experience of that soil in the locality it is possible to make reasonable assumptions about the probable conditions and permeability. However, a more detailed assessment can only come from boreholes to allow proper examination of the soil structure, the extent of soil cracking and the conditions and materials within these cracks, and to check for the presence of any gross features which might aid permeability. The significance of these features cannot be quantified, but must be assessed on the basis of experience. A borehole drilled in spring is particularly valuable, as this can indicate the extent to which the soil can recover in a single winter, and the efficacy of the more permeable features of the soil in allowing moisture penetration.

Soil desiccation. If a borehole is being drilled to assess permeability, it can also be used to assess desiccation, using the techniques described in Chapter 13. Again, boreholes drilled in the spring will be most relevant for this, as any desiccation at that time of year must be associated with a persistent deficit. If necessary, information from soil testing can be used for a quantitative estimate of heave potential (page 264).

Past history of building. The building should be examined to determine the history of any previous distortion and damage; this information can come from a level distortion survey or from examination of previous crack damage and distortion within the building. This condition of the building needs to be assessed in the light of previous growth of any trees.

If there is an old building which was originally built on a persistent deficit so that there is a risk of heave, it is almost inevitable that, while the tree has been present, seasonal movements will have been occurring. Seasonal recovery each winter will have been aided by water penetrating down the sides of foundations, and during the life of the building there will have been sufficiently dry summers to increase the amplitude of seasonal movement and cause damage. These seasonal movements will also have caused dynamic settlement and associated distortion. Alternatively, if there is a vigorous young tree so that a persistent deficit has developed since the structure was built, it must have caused subsidence and associated distortion. In addition, there will have been seasonal movement before and during the development of the persistent deficit. For these reasons, whenever there is a persistent deficit with an old building, distortion and damage will be present. If they are not evident, it indicates that there is no risk of heave or recovery. If they are evident, there may be a risk of heave, or alternatively the distortion and damage may just be caused by the seasonal movement. Level monitoring, as described in the next sub-section, should be able to distinguish these movements.

The younger the building, the less reliable this diagnosis becomes, and on buildings less than 15 years old there may not have been opportunity for distortion and damage to have developed as a result of a pre-existing persistent deficit. However, with the increased awareness of the risk of damage and of building near existing trees, modern buildings will usually have been built on foundations which were designed to cope with any deficit associated with trees which existed at the time of construction. If a persistent deficit has developed since construction, there will be evidence of distortion regardless of the age of the building.

Monitoring for heave prediction. Accurate level monitoring is by far the most precise method for distinguishing between movements which are caused by solely seasonal deficits, and those where there is a persistent deficit and risk of heave. It can also help in predicting the duration of movement. In any situation where heave is suspected, level monitoring should start as soon as possible. The objective of this monitoring is to determine the shape of the recovery curve, and use this information to predict the extent of further movement and how much longer this is likely to continue.

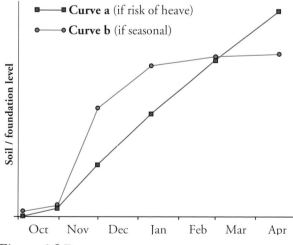

Figure 16.7
Level monitoring provides an essential method for distinguishing between heave and seasonal movement.

If monitoring during the winter months shows the upward movement continuing at a steady rate throughout the winter, it clearly indicates that significant desiccation is still present and that movements are likely to continue (Figure 16.7, curve 'a'). By contrast, if the rate of movement diminishes during the winter, it indicates that any desiccation is being corrected and movement will soon cease (Figure 16.7, curve 'b'). (Obviously, if the trees are left in situ, the direction of movement will reverse in the spring, but such effects will not start to appear until after mid-April).

To allow accurate prediction of this sort, it is essential to have an accurately defined recovery curve, with measurements every 4-6 weeks.

If measurements have been taken during the summer while the tree is present, it will provide a measure of the amplitude of seasonal movement. This can be compared with the recovery movements recorded in the early winter. If there is a risk of heave, the recovery by mid-winter will be less than one half of the seasonal movement. By contrast, if the soil is very permeable and there is no risk of heave, a large proportion, or all, of the movement will occur early in the winter. (With predictions of this sort, it may not be necessary to wait until the spring before reaching a decision on the risk of heave - see Case Study 2).

If trees have already been removed and heave problems have already started, monitoring can help to demonstrate how long the movements are likely to continue. Frequently, by the time the problem is recognized, movements will have already ceased - monitoring can demonstrate if this has occurred. If it shows that movements are continuing, it is necessary to determine the rate, and whether this is diminishing. As previously noted, if heave movements are less than 2mm per annum, there is unlikely to be any significant further damage (although this also depends on the angular distortion, and on the amount of stress which has already developed in the building).

Simple guidelines for heave prediction

The risks of heave discussed in the previous section can be simplified to provide a rough guide on the risk and duration of heave. It relies on determining a score of from 1 to 4 for each of the three factors in Figure 16.8. The scores for these three factors are added, and this score is then multiplied by the plasticity index of the soil divided by 10. This total provides an indication of the risk and possible duration of heave, as shown by Figure 16.8. The risk is shown on a percentage

	Score			
	1	**2**	**3**	**4**
NHBC * "water demand"	Low	Moderate	High	Poplar Oak
Tree height (m)	5 - 10	10 - 15	15 - 20	>20
Proximity †	$1\,^1/_2$ - 1	1 - $^2/_3$	$^2/_3$ - $^1/_4$	< $^1/_4$

* See Chapter 9, page 146 for details.

† Distance from tree expressed as fraction of tree height.

Figure 16.8

"Scores" for factors for assessment of risk of heave.

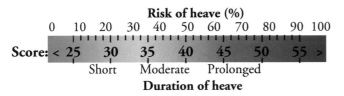

Figure 16.9

Risk and duration of heave, derived by adding the scores from Figure 16.8 and multiplying this by plasticity index divided by 10.

basis, with a 100% indicating inevitable heave. Duration is a qualitative assessment; short is likely to be less than 5 years and long to be more than 10 years. The amount of movement is not necessarily related to duration, but the total movement will usually increase with duration.

This is a highly simplified approach, and should not be used as a substitute for a more detailed assessment. However, it can indicate those situations where additional care and more detailed investigations are particularly justified. The total score might be considered as alarm bells - the higher the score, the louder the alarm and the greater the care which should be exercised.

As examples, a 24m high poplar 18m from a building on a soil with a plasticity index of 45 would score (4 + 4 + 2) x 45/10 = 45, indicating 65% risk of heave, of prolonged duration. A 8m high apple 3m from a building on a soil with a plasticity index of 35 would score (2 + 1 + 3) x 3.5 = 21, indicating a negligible risk of heave.

With an approximate system of this sort, great precision is not called for. The species, height and proximity of a tree can all be assessed quite easily on site.

The plasticity index of the soil, which is being used here as a measure of permeability rather than shrinkage potential, can usually be estimated on the basis of past experience of the subsoil of the locality, as identified off a Geological Survey map. If the soil is known to be variable, the highest values of plasticity index will provide a safer assessment, but obviously this system does not allow consideration of detailed soil structure nor any of the gross features which can be critical to soil permeability.

Quantitative prediction of heave or recovery

In most situations it is sufficient to make a qualitative assessment as to whether the extent and duration of heave will be unacceptable, and whether remedial action is required to prevent this movement. However, in some situations it is desirable to make a quantitative prediction of the amount of this heave.

Methods for assessing desiccation are described in Chapter 13 (page 208). As noted in that chapter, the comparison of moisture content profiles taken from similar locations both within and beyond the influence of the tree can be an unreliable method, as significant differences in profiles can occur even in the absence of soil drying from root activity. Inherent differences in the profiles will usually be accompanied by differences in the liquid and plastic limit; provided these are similar at comparable depths in the two profiles, the moisture content should be similar, but even with a fairly uniform clay there will be some variation. If the liquid and plastic limits in the two profiles differ by more than a few percent, it is inadvisable to attempt any comparison of the profiles, or calculations based on such comparison.

Because profiles can be so variable, it should always be recognised that any estimate of heave potential could be subject to a significant error for this reason alone, irrespective of the accuracy of the method of calculation. It is therefore inadvisable to try to detect and quantify heave potential unless there is a considerable difference between the profiles. For this reason, quantifying heave may be valid in the early stages when large differences are likely to be present, but in the final stages the potential errors are likely to be greater than any residual movement. These limitations should be considered before embarking on efforts to quantify heave.

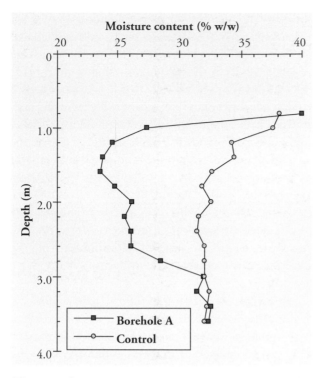

Figure 16.10a

Moisture content profiles (gravimetric) 18m from row of poplars (borehole A), and 34m from trees (control). (see Figure 16.11 for tabulated results)

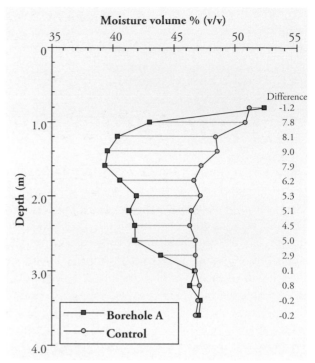

Figure 16.10b

Same moisture content profiles as Figure 16.10a, converted to volumetric values. The difference between the profiles (expressed as a decimal rather than as a percentage) and multiplied by the layer thickness (200mm) gives the layer moisture deficit.

From calculation of soil moisture deficit. At least one borehole should be drilled adjacent to the point where maximum heave of the building is anticipated; the level distortion survey or monitoring of recovery movements should identify this location. The hole must be drilled to sufficient depth to be below the depth of any potential root influence. In most situations 6m is sufficient, but in extreme cases additional depth may be required. For moisture content determination, disturbed soil samples obtained with a small diameter auger are quite sufficient.

Wherever possible a control borehole in a comparable location is required to the same depth. The alternative is to make an assumption that the equilibrium moisture content will be about 0.4 x liquid limit. However, as noted in Chapter 13 (page 211), this relationship is only valid for overconsolidated clays of high plasticity, and down to depths of about 3m; below this any assumptions about a control profile will become increasingly inaccurate.

Boreholes drilled in the autumn will be liable to be suffering from seasonal soil drying. If the soil is desiccated, it is necessary to predict, on the basis of experience of the extent of any deficit and soil permeability, whether full rehydration will occur in a single winter,

or whether long-term movements will occur. These problems can be avoided if the boreholes are drilled in the spring when only persistent deficits will be present.

Moisture content profiles should be accurately defined by sampling at intervals not greater than 0.25m, and the comparability of the soil in the boreholes should be checked by classification tests at intervals of 1.0 to 1.5m. As previously noted, if the soils are not comparable, the potential error of any result will be greatly increased.

The procedure for calculating the soil swelling is illustrated using data from a site on London clay for boreholes drilled in January 1977. Borehole A was 18m from a row of 20m high hybrid black poplars, with the control borehole on the opposite side of a block of flats, 34m from the trees. The moisture content profiles for soil samples taken at 200mm intervals from these two boreholes are shown in Figure 16.10a, and the actual values are shown (as decimal, rather than percentage, values) in columns 2 and 3 of Figure 16.11 (overleaf).

Before moisture deficits can be calculated, these gravimetric moisture values must be converted to volumetric moisture values, as described in Chapter 4 (page

57). This normally requires assumptions that the soil is fully saturated, and also for the specific gravity of the soil particles (commonly assumed that G_s = 2.75). With these assumptions the volumetric moisture content is:

$$m_V = \frac{m}{\frac{1}{G_s} + m} \quad \text{or} \quad m_V = \frac{m}{0.3636 + m}$$

where m = gravimetric moisture content. These volumetric values are shown in columns 4 and 5 of Figure 16.11, and as moisture content profiles in Figure 16.10b; these profiles are, of course, very similar to Figure 16.10a, but with higher moisture values and slight differences in shape of the profiles. The moisture deficit in each layer of borehole A is then calculated from the difference between columns 5 and 4, multiplied by the layer thickness, which in this case is 200mm, i.e. at depth 1.2m, 0.485 - 0.404 x 200 = 16.2mm (column 6). The layer deficit can then be summed from the base of the borehole, to provide the soil moisture deficit at any depth (column 7). This follows exactly the same procedure as the calculation of soil moisture deficits, as described in Chapter 4 (page 52).

The traditional calculation of soil shrinkage involves dividing the layer moisture deficit by the water shrinkage factor (see Chapter 4, page 52). For most highly shrinkable clay soils, including London Clay, BRE Digest 298 advocates WSF = 4; column 8 is calculated on that basis, with column 9 summing the shrinkage of each layer from the base of the borehole to provide the soil shrinkage below any depth. As discussed in Chapter 4, isotropic shrinkage of soil within the normal shrinkage range should produce a value of WSF = 3. However, few soils maintain shrinkage within the normal phase, and within the residual phase there will be a variable and increasing value for the WSF. There is no reliable guidance on appropriate values of WSF for less highly shrinkable soils, but any value is likely to vary depending on the shrinkage curve for the soil. As a result, deriving a value for soil shrinkage from the moisture deficit is liable to considerable error.

As further noted in Chapter 4, recent work by Crilly, Driscoll and Chandler (1992) in measuring actual ground movement of a highly shrinkable London Clay soil has suggested that the value of WSF varies with depth. They suggest that WSF = 5 down to 2m depth, WSF = 2 between 2 - 3m depth, and WSF = 1 below 3m. These values may be applicable to the particular site where this research was undertaken where the soil has exceptionally high values of plasticity, but should be applied with discretion to other situations until further information is available. Columns 10 and 11 of figure 16.11 are calculated using this variable WSF.

Depth (m)	Gravimetric moisture content		Volumetric moisture content		Layer moisture deficit (mm)	Cumulative moisture deficit (mm)	WSF = 4		Variable WSF	
	Borehole A	Control	Borehole A	Control			Layer shrinkage (mm)	Cumulative shrinkage (mm)	Layer shrinkage (mm)	Cumulative shrinkage (mm)
Column 1	Column 2	Column 3	Column 4	Column 5	Column 6	Column 7	Column 8	Column 9	Column 10	Column 11
0.8	0.400	0.381	0.524	0.512	-2.4	122.2	-0.6	30.5	-0.5	38.8
1.0	0.274	0.376	0.430	0.508	15.7	124.6	3.9	31.2	3.1	39.3
1.2	0.246	0.342	0.404	0.485	16.2	108.9	4.1	27.2	3.2	36.1
1.4	0.238	0.344	0.396	0.486	18.1	92.7	4.5	23.2	3.6	32.9
1.6	0.236	0.326	0.394	0.473	15.8	74.6	4.0	18.6	3.2	29.3
1.8	0.248	0.318	0.405	0.467	12.2	58.7	3.1	14.7	2.4	26.1
2.0	0.262	0.325	0.419	0.472	10.6	46.5	2.7	11.6	5.3	23.7
2.2	0.256	0.315	0.413	0.464	10.2	35.9	2.6	9.0	5.1	18.3
2.4	0.261	0.314	0.418	0.463	9.1	25.7	2.3	6.4	4.6	13.2
2.6	0.261	0.320	0.418	0.468	10.0	16.6	2.5	4.1	5.0	8.7
2.8	0.285	0.320	0.439	0.468	5.7	6.5	1.4	1.6	2.9	3.7
3.0	0.319	0.320	0.467	0.468	0.1	0.8	0.0	0.2	0.2	0.8
3.2	0.314	0.324	0.463	0.471	1.6	0.6	0.4	0.2	1.6	0.6
3.4	0.325	0.322	0.472	0.470	-0.46	-0.9	-0.1	-0.2	-0.5	-0.9
3.6	0.323	0.320	0.470	0.468	-0.46	-0.5	-0.1	-0.1	-0.5	-0.5

Figure 16.11

Calculation of soil moisture deficit and soil shrinkage based on moisture content values

It will be noted that the results below 0.8m depth using WSF = 4 and using the variable WSF are similar (30.5 and 38.8mm respectively) Similar results of this sort will usually be produced by the two methods where much of the deficit is at shallow depth, but major differences will be produced if a considerable deficit extends below 3m and WSF = 1 is adopted.

Using soil suction values. Chapter 13 (page 210) has noted the potential value of soil suction tests for the identification of desiccated soils, and these tests are becomingly increasingly commonplace as part of site investigations. It therefore seems logical to use these results for calculating heave potential, and Chandler *et al* (1992) have proposed that total ground heave can be derived from:

$$\text{Total ground heave} = \sum \frac{\Delta P_k}{K'} \Delta h$$

where P_k = soil suction
  K' = soil effective bulk modulus
  Δh = layer thickness

For application of this expression, the soil bulk modulus must be obtained; this can be derived from the slope of the line which plots moisture content against suction. As can be seen from the paper by Chandler *et al*, the correlation of this relationship is poor, and so any value for K' must be subject to a considerable potential error. Furthermore, the suction test measures the mean effective stress in the soil sample, whereas heave should be related to the vertical component only. In addition, this estimate of heave does not consider the effect of desiccation cracks or the partial saturation of the soil. For this reason, just as estimates of vertical soil swelling based on moisture content must be divided by a WSF of about 4, the result calculated from the suction values must be divided by an arbitrary value of about 4. At present there is far less experience of the appropriate value, and the poor correlation for deriving the soil effective bulk modulus introduces additional errors. These problems make this method far less reliable, and for the present it is recommended that calculations based on moisture content should be preferred.

Figure 16.12 shows the results obtained by an engineer using the various methods in respect of a property on Gault Clay and illustrates the problems of calculating heave potential. He obtained the different values for K' using different methods. The range of possible results, from 18 to 132mm, demonstrates the inadequacy of these techniques. Results of this sort are of most dubious value. It was more practical to consider the results of level monitoring. This revealed recovery, at a rate of about 1mm per month over the

winter period, of the corner of the building closest to the borehole used for these predictions. If this rate of movement were maintained, and if the heave predictions were accurate, it would imply that stability might eventually be achieved in anything between 1.5 years and 11 years. In practice, the building stabilised after the first winter and the calculated heave never materialised after the offending trees were felled.

	Potential heave (mm) where WSF	
	= 4	Variable
Derived from moisture contents	41	122
Derived from suction tests:		
if K′ = 2Mpa	46	132
if K′ = 5Mpa	18	53

Figure 16.12

Variation in results for potential heave movements, using different methods.

Measurement of swelling potential

Chapter 4 (page 54) has noted that the most direct method of measuring soil swelling involves use of the oedometer (Figure 16.13). In this equipment a brass ring is used to cut and mount an undisturbed sample of soil. Porous plates are placed above and below the sample and can be used to flood the sample with water. The brass ring confines any soil swelling to vertical movements only, and a micrometer gauge is used to measure the amount of swelling which occurs.

Correct application of this method requires a control borehole away from potential root activity. Samples from appropriate intervals down the control borehole are mounted in turn in the oedometer, and water

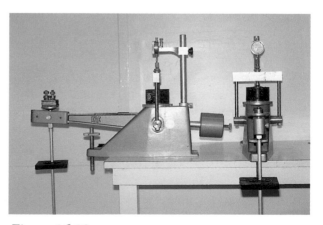

Figure 16.13

Oedometer (side and front views) used for direct measurement of soil swelling potential.

267

is made available. As the sample tries to swell, weights are added to the balance arm to counterbalance the swelling pressure; weights continue to be added to exactly counteract the swelling pressure until equilibrium is reached. Once this equilibrium pressure which is produced by the soil overburden has been determined for samples down the control profile, samples from the desiccated profile are mounted, and the process is repeated, in this case balancing against the swelling pressure of the desiccated soil, which should be substantially higher. Once equilibrium is reached, the pressure on the sample is reduced to the natural overburden pressure as determined from the control borehole, and the swelling of the sample is recorded. This movement of the sample is then multiplied by a factor obtained from the relative thickness of the test sample and the layer thickness. As each sample can take several days to test, the process is lengthy, and even this result may be subject to errors because the confinement of the sample does not allow the horizontal swelling which could occur if there are desiccation cracks in the soil. Tests which omit to determine the overburden swelling pressure will be unreliable, and will be a gross overestimate if no overburden pressure is applied.

Remedies for heave damage

Remedial action against heave is considered in the next chapter.

Summary

1.   When a desiccated clay soil is allowed to rehydrate it will swell. The swelling forces which can be generated are capable of lifting a multi-storey building. If the soil has been desiccated prior to laying the foundations and is allowed to swell, it will lift the building to above its originally constructed level; this is **heave**. If the desiccation occurs after foundations are laid it will cause shrinkage and subsidence. Subsequent rehydration will take the building back towards its original level; this is **recovery**.

2.   Seasonal heave or recovery can occur each winter associated with seasonal changes in moisture content. However, the terms are best restricted to the long-term movements associated with rehydration of a persistent moisture deficit.

3.   Decisions on the type of remedial action should be dependent on whether there is a risk of heave or recovery (see Chapter 17). Vegetation control (tree felling or pruning) will not be effective in stabilising a

building if there is a persistent deficit sufficient to allow unacceptable heave or recovery to occur. In these circumstances underpinning is essential, but underpinning against heave must incorporate special precautions (considered in Chapter 17). For these reasons, correct diagnosis and prediction are essential.

4.   The amount and duration of heave or recovery is dependent on the depth and extent of the persistent moisture deficit, and on the permeability of the clay. In extreme and rare cases the process of rehydration may take 2 - 3 decades; far more commonly it is no more than a slight extension of seasonal recovery.

5.   Heave or recovery can be initiated by any action to a tree which allows an existing persistent deficit to rehydrate. Most commonly this is the felling of a tree, but any other action which reduces the water uptake can start the process. Pruning the crown, root damage (whether intentional or accidental, for instance from soil compaction during construction work), or the natural decline of a tree in over-maturity, can all initiate the process.

5.   The relative age of a tree and building does not form a reliable basis for predicting situations where heave might occur. The relevant factor is the time of development of the persistent deficit. By definition, heave can only occur if the deficit predates the building, but there are many situations where there was no persistent deficit when a house was built, and therefore no risk of heave. Conversely, a tree may be planted after a house has been built and develop a persistent deficit (and cause subsidence); subsequent felling can cause long-term recovery (Case Studies 4 and 6).

6.   Diagnosis requires evaluation of all available data, but a level distortion survey and level monitoring are particularly valuable. The most relevant information to be gleaned from soil investigation is in respect of the permeability of the soil.

7.   If there is a large persistent deficit, soil analysis (either of moisture contents or suctions) can provide a very rough prediction of the extent of potential heave movement. However, as there are so many uncertainties and assumptions, any quantitative estimate of heave will, at best, be liable to considerable error. In most situations the potential error will be greater than the potential movement, making any such exercise pointless.

8.   Level monitoring, to study changes in the rate of movement, provides a valuable technique for predicting the duration and eventual extent of movement.

CASE STUDY 16

Seasonal movements of reinforced raft on piles – Defective piles –
Estimate of major heave potential – No allowance for heave in foundation design –
Engineer liable for defective design – No options for tree management.

Background

The site is in north Kent, on London Clay. I was instructed in late 1985 by loss adjusters acting for the property owners. They sought advice on the management of adjacent trees to prevent further damage, and to pursue a claim against the owners of adjacent trees for the cost of remedial works for damage which had occurred.

The trees

The only relevant trees were a row of Monterey cypress (*Cupressus macrocarpa*) on the neighbouring property, 1.0m from the boundary. Their estimated age was at least 25 years old (i.e. planted 1960 or earlier). They had been planted at 1.2m spacing and as a result some were very suppressed. The height of the surviving trees varied from 9 - 11m. Two of the trees were showing early signs of infection by Coryneum canker (*Seiridium cardinale*) which is a debilitating and often fatal fungal disease which is very common in this species.

History of building

The property, a small detached house on an estate, was built in 1976 (CS Figure 16.1). It has gable walls on the two side elevations. The rear wall was 3.0m from the boundary with the trees (4.0m from the trees). No special precautions were taken with the foundations, except for those at the front which were increased to 1.8m because of an adjacent sewer. At that time the trees were probably at least 6m tall. Aerial photos indicate that some trees were present on the site in 1972 prior to construction.

By 1979 there was some damage, and as a result it was underpinned by the original builders. This extended the foundations to 1.8m beneath all external walls,

In spring 1982 my clients purchased the property. By autumn of that year further damage was apparent, and engineers were instructed. The main damage was to the rear elevation, and an engineer at that time recorded:-

> "the brickwork beneath damp course level has rotated in an outwards direction causing a step to appear at d.p.c. level. The maximum movement is at the centre of the wall and measures 20mm and it tapers to approximately 5mm at each end. The wall above the d.p.c. is leaning outwards slightly by some 15mm in its height throughout the first storey. Beneath d.p.c. level the wall is leaning outwards which accounts for the bowing."

There was also cracking around the windows in the rear of the house on the two side elevations.

It was decided that further underpinning was required. After some delay this took the form of a ringbeam within the existing foundations, and 6 pads to a depth of 4.0m around the periphery. 3 of the pads were on the front elevation, and 3 on the rear. There were an additional 2 pads to similar depth beneath the central partition wall.

At the same time an extension was built on the rear elevation to within 0.3m of the rear boundary (1.3m from the trees). The potential problems of the site were recognised, at least partially, and this was built off 5 x 9.0m long reinforced bored piles.

These piles, and the underpinned foundations of the rear wall of the original house, supported a reinforced raft. This raft was laid directly on the underlying soil. The external walls of the extension were butt-jointed to the house, with a mastic movement joint. To enable the extension to be built, the overhanging branches of the trees were pruned back to a height of 6m.

Case Study Figure 16.1

The west gable wall of the house and rear extension, with adjacent row of Monterey cypress.

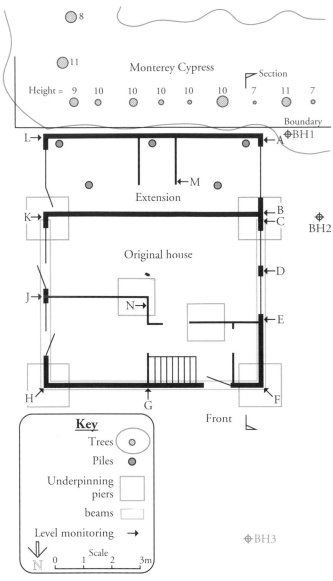

Case Study Figure 16.2

Site plan of house and adjacent trees in 1984 after construction of extension.

The underpinning works were completed in 1984, and the extension in early 1985. A plan of the house at this stage is shown in CS Figure 16.2, and section through the various foundations in CS Figure 16.3.

By the time of my preliminary visit in February 1986, further damage was apparent, particularly at the junction between the house and extension. Although there was an external movement joint, there was no provision for internal movement either at the first floor doorway connecting the house and extension, or where the internal plaster work of the extension abutted the original rear wall. The pattern of cracking indicated that the extension had moved up relative to the house, and also rotated outwards, sufficient to create a 5 - 8mm gap at high level. This was beyond the scope for the movement joint, and a noticeable draught entered at first floor level. There was also minor cracking throughout the original house.

Investigations

The results of a level distortion survey are shown as an isometric diagram in CS Figure 16.4.

In February 1986 I attached level monitoring markers around the outside and inside of the property. Initial readings were taken, plus three further sets later that year, and a fourth set in the autumn 18 months later. The results are shown as isometric diagrams in CS Figure 16.6. Cracks at the junction between the house and extension were also monitored (CS Figure 16.10).

I drilled three 50mm boreholes on 29th and 30th April 1986, each to a depth of 5.0m at the locations shown on the site plan. Borehole 1 is thus closest to the trees and the rear corner of the extension, borehole 2 close to the rear corner of the original house, with borehole 3 a control. The soil was a fairly uniform clay with bands of silt, typical for London Clay, except for borehole 3 which encountered pea gravel with clay between 1.8 - 2.3m, probably from a drain surround, and the soil above this level included sand and was possibly backfill. Samples were taken at 0.25m intervals for determination of moisture content, and at 1.5m, 3.0m and 4.5m for soil classification tests. The moisture contents are shown as profiles in CS Figure 16.5, and values in CS Figure 16.8, and the soil classification tests in CS Figure 16.9.

While drilling the borehole I noted the relative abundance of fine root activity. This is included in CS Figure 16.8. Identifiable roots were taken from 2.7m and 3.0m in borehole 1 and from 2.7 and 3.5m in borehole 2; all were alive and from *Cupressus*.

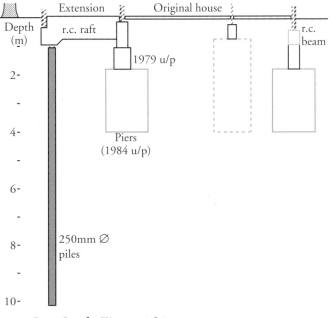

Case Study Figure 16.3

Section through foundations of house after 1984 underpinning and construction of extension.

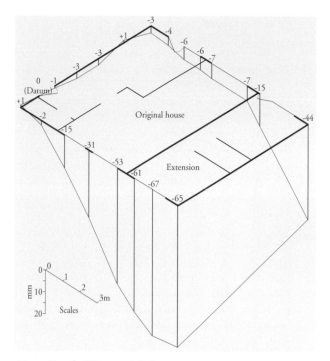

Case Study Figure 16.4

Level distortion survey. The apparent distortion of the extension is probably because the brickcourses were laid to match the previously distorted courses of the house.

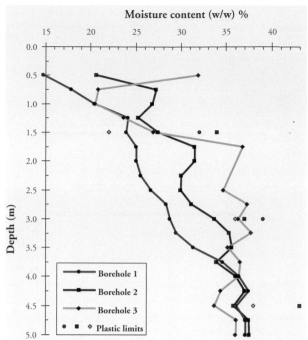

Case Study Figure 16.5

Moisture content profiles for the three boreholes drilled April 1986.

DISCUSSION

Cause of damage

It is probable that the original damage in 1979, and again prior to the underpinning in 1984, was caused by the root activity of the Monterey cypress. Heave associated with the trees which had been felled prior to development may have contributed. The effect of one, or both, of these factors can be seen in the distortion of the original house, as shown by the level survey.

The lateral movement of the rear wall following the 1979 underpinning was probably caused by severance of the roots during the underpinning, which allowed the soil contained within the underpinning to swell. Continued root action below the foundations would have allowed this deeper soil to carry on drying and shrinking.

Although the boreholes were drilled in April 1986, some time after the damage in 1982 - 1984, they provide the best available indication of the earlier soil conditions. Borehole 2 is at a similar distance from the trees as the rear of the original house. The moisture content in this borehole can be compared with borehole 3 which should be clear of the trees. However, borehole 3 is affected by the fill for the adjacent drain; for this reason a moisture content of 36% was assumed for this borehole above the gravel at 2.3m. Column 10 of CS Figure 16.8 shows the moisture deficit of each 0.25m thick layer of soil in borehole 2, derived from the difference between the moisture contents in BH2 and

BH3, as calculated by the method described on page 265. Column 11 sums these values from the base of the borehole to derive the soil moisture deficit.

Using these values, it can be seen that the soil moisture deficit below the 1.8m deep underpinning installed in 1979 was about 124mm. Assuming WSF = 4, the soil shrinkage would be about 31mm. Prior to the underpinning there would have been additional shrinkage of the soil between the underside of the original foundations and 1.8m. These combined effects would be sufficient to account for the observed 50mm distortion.

When the extension was built, the rear elevation was already distorted. The bricklayer matched the brickcourses; as a result the extension also appears to be distorted.

The upwards movement of the extension relative to the main house, which I observed at the time of my initial inspection in February 1986, was probably caused by a combination of:-

i) settlement of the new underpinning bases of the original house;

ii) swelling of the clay beneath the raft of the extension developing as a result of:-

a) normal seasonal recovery;

b) reduced water uptake by the trees as a result of pruning to allow construction.

The cracking in the main house was probably caused by initial settlement of the new underpinning bases. Subsequent level and crack monitoring has shown negligible further movement.

Prognosis

The monitoring of level (CS Figure 16.6) showed a pronounced pattern of seasonal movement of the extension, particularly in 1986. The reduced movement in 1987 may reflect the pruning which was applied to the trees prior to that summer. Although the amplitude of movement was not great (2.2mm at station L), as the extension was pivoting on the raft, it was sufficient to open the joint on the east flank by 2mm.

More importantly, this monitoring confirmed that it was the raft which was moving, and to cast serious doubt on the integrity of the piles and/or their junction with the reinforced raft. Peter Kelsey & Partners, Engineers who were also now acting on behalf of the clients' insurers, dug a trial hole to expose the pile at the rear left corner of the extension. This revealed:-

i) a clear 50mm gap between the top of the pile and the underside of the raft (CS Figure 16.7);

ii) gravel blinding laid across the top of the pile in this gap;

iii) 3 x 12mm reinforcing bars in the pile projected only 75mm from the top of the pile. They were bent through 90° and did not enter nor were linked in any way with the reinforced raft;

iv) the raft was laid on gravel blinding directly on the clay without any void former;

v) the trial pit was extended by auger adjacent to the pile; this confirmed the base of the pile to be below 10.2m.

A second trial hole adjacent to the other rear corner revealed similar conditions. There was a similar gap between the top of the pile and the raft, but the bars at this position did enter the raft. The pile was cracked.

The condition of the piles and their junction (or lack of) accounted for the vulnerability of the raft to seasonal movements.

If the slight seasonal movements were the sole problem, it might have been possible to tolerate them, provided appropriate decorative measures were taken to mask the cracks.

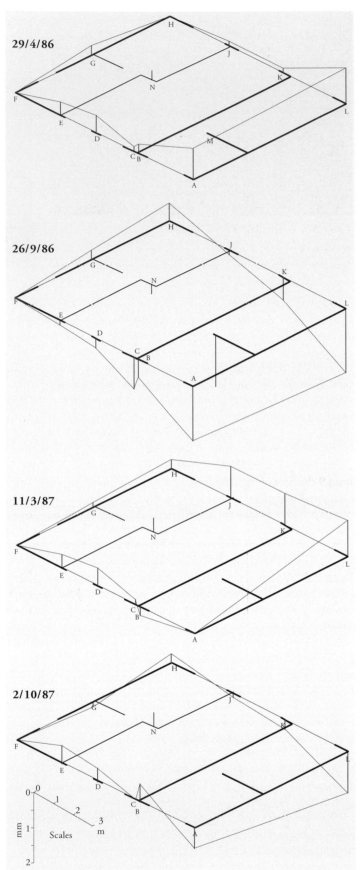

Case Study Figure 16.6

Results of level monitoring, compared with initial readings on 25/2/86, relative to station F as assumed datum.

(The high values along the east elevation on 11/3/87 suggest an error in the transfer at station H; it was not possible to check the closing error through the extension at station M on that date.)

Case Study Figure 16.7

Reinforcing bars exposed and projecting from top of pile, with gap between the pile and underside of the reinforced concrete raft. Note also many large roots. (Photo: P. Kelsey).

Depth (m)	Plastic limit	Liquid limit	Plasticity index	% linear shrinkage
Borehole 1				
1.5	32	90	58	14.6
3.0	39	96	57	19.5
4.5	36	89	53	19.6
Borehole 2				
1.5	34	90	56	16.1
3.0	37	98	61	19.8
4.5	43	95	52	20.4
Borehole 3				
1.5	22	53	31	14.4
3.0	36	96	60	18.1
4.5	38	88	50	18.2

Case Study Figure 16.9

Soil classification tests.

However, this would have been a short-sighted approach. The long-term survival of the trees could not be assured, particularly as this species is so vulnerable to *Coryneum* canker and this fungus was already present. If the trees died, or were removed, for any reason, there was the potential for considerable heave.

Borehole 1 shows the moisture content in a position comparable to the rear of the extension. Column 8 of CS Figure 16.8 shows the layer deficit at each depth, and column 9 the sum of these deficits from the base. The underside of the raft was at 0.8m, indicating a total moisture deficit of about 515mm. Assuming WSF = 4, the heave potential was about 129mm.

Even allowing for the uncertainties of the assumptions in these calculations, there was a massive potential for heave, and the foundations included no precautions against such movement.

A surprising claim was made by the engineer acting for the builders. The basis of his calculations was essentially the same, but he then sought to discount 65mm of the heave potential. This opinion was based on the results of the BRE research at Chattenden, which demonstrated 65mm of seasonal movement for a raft of comparable depth (Crilly, Driscoll and Chandler, 1992). Quite apart from the dubious relevance of such a different site (albeit on London Clay of similar plasticity), my boreholes were drilled in the spring

Depth	Borehole 1		Borehole 2		Borehole 3		SMD Borehole 1		SMD Borehole 2	
(m)	mc% (w/w)	Root[1] activity	mc% (w/w)	Root[1] activity	mc% (w/w)	assumed e.m.c.	Layer deficit[2]	Total deficit	Layer deficit[2]	Total deficit
Column 1	2	3	4	5	6	7	8	9	10	11
0.5	14.7	**	20.6	*	31.9	32	84.7	624	50.0	332
0.75	17.9	**	27.2	**	20.8	32	65.0	529	18.9	273
1.0	20.4	***	26.8	***	20.5	36	68.7	456	36.4	247
1.25	24.1	***	25.2	***	23.6	36	49.2	384	43.9	206
1.5	23.9	****	27.4	***	26.9	36	50.2	331	33.7	157
1.75	25.0	****	31.5	***	36.8	36	44.8	281	16.6	124
2.0	25.0	****	31.5	***	-	36	44.8	236	16.6	107
2.25	25.5	***	30.0	**	-	36	42.4	191	22.6	91
2.5	26.6	***	29.9	**	34.7	34.7	32.2	149	18.1	68
2.75	28.3	***	31.1	**	37.3	37.3	34.8	117	23.0	50
3.0	28.7	***	33.7	**	36.3	36.3	29.2	82	9.3	27
3.25	29.4	**	35.3	**	37.7	37.7	31.6	53	8.4	18
3.5	31.3	**	35.6	**	35.2	35.2	14.4	21	-1.4	9
3.75	34.6	*	33.9	*	36.5	36.5	6.7	7	9.3	11
4.0	36.4	*	36.0	-	36.4	36.4	0	0	1.4	1
4.25	37.4	*	37.0	-	34.4	34.4	-10.2	-	-8.9	-
4.5	36.1	-	35.8	-	33.7	33.7	-8.3	-	-7.3	-
4.75	37.1	-	37.4	-	36.1	36.1	-3.4	-	-4.4	-
5.0	37.1	-	37.5	-	36	36	-3.7	-	-5.1	-

[1] Root activity (fine roots only) assessed on scale ***** = very abundant to * = very occasional, - = absent.
[2] Layer deficit calculated using assumed deficit (column 7), layer thickness = 0.25m, and G_s = 2.75

Case Study Figure 16.8

Soil moisture content, fine root activity and estimated soil moisture deficits in boreholes drilled in April 1986.

Crack movements (μm) compared to 29/4/86:				
		26/9/86	11/3/87	2/10/87
West flank				
High level:	Horizontal	+534	+276	+450
Low level:	Horizontal	+706	+351	+462
	Vertical	-180	-200	-327
East flank				
High level:	Horizontal	+2075	+1592	+1996
Low level:	Horizontal	+1447	+1312	+1450
	Vertical	-15	+142	+63

Case Study Figure 16.10

Monitoring of crack movements at junction of house and extension.

and therefore had already taken account of any seasonal recovery which might occur. If his claim of 65mm seasonal movement was correct, it would have been in addition to, rather than as a subtraction from, the calculated heave potential.

Remedial measures

It was considered that the only viable solution to prevent future heave was to break out the existing raft in sections within the existing edge beam (CS Figure 16.11), drill new piles with sleeves and proper caps, and re-lay the raft, with all of these new works incorporating full anti-heave precautions.

These works were undertaken in 1989, supervised by Peter Kelsey & Partners. In the course of the work the inadequacy of all except one of the original piles was confirmed.

The cost for these remedial works, including fees, totalled £55,600. A claim alleging professional negligence against the engineer who designed and supervised the 1984 underpinning and extension was settled out of Court for 73% of these costs.

There were no practical steps which could be taken with the trees. Any action would have merely precipitated the problems of heave. No claim was pursued against the tree owner. She was clearly entitled to believe that foundations designed by an engineer in full knowledge of the existence of the trees should not be subject to failure.

Case Study Figure 16.11

Original reinforced raft and pile cap being broken out during remedial works, preparatory to drilling new piles and casting new raft.
(Photo: P. Kelsey).

Lessons to be learnt

- If the foundations had been properly designed from the outset, these problems would never have occurred. Alternatively, if the involvement of the trees had been recognized at the time of the initial problems in 1979 and they had been removed at that stage, all of the further problems would not have occurred.

- Even in 1982, when the 1.8m deep underpinning failed, it might have been possible to restabilise the foundations by felling the trees. However, this would not have been practical if the extension was also being built, unless these works were delayed until all soil recovery was complete.

- The 1983 underpinning and foundations of the extension were placed into highly desiccated clay, and should have included full anti-heave precautions. In the absence of such precautions, no form of tree management could have prevented problems.

- The level distortion survey could demonstrate the extent of movement which had occurred, and be correlated to estimates of soil shrinkage.

- The seasonal movements which were affecting the raft were small, but could be detected by the level monitoring. The incomplete traverse and lack of closing error in the readings on 11/3/87 cast doubt on the interpretation of the results on that date.

This chapter is concerned solely with dealing with the problems of structural damage after they have occurred - the prevention of damage is considered in Chapter 18.

When damage has been caused by tree root activity, there are various options:-

i)   Tolerate the damage.

If this is not acceptable, restabilise the foundations by:

ii)   controlling the water uptake of the tree so as to prevent soil drying and movement.

iii) controlling root spread so as to prevent soil drying and movement.

iv)   supplementary watering to prevent soil drying.

v)   accelerated recovery by watering-in, or allowing natural recovery.

vi)   the engineering option of underpinning.

The choice of remedy should depend on the circumstances of the particular case: this decision can only be taken with knowledge of the exact cause of the problem derived from the site investigations and monitoring of movements, as described in Chapters 11-13. Before deciding on which method to adopt, it is necessary to consider these options in greater detail.

Tolerating the damage

This suggestion, particularly if made to a householder who is complaining of damage to his property, may be met by indignant ridicule. However, the problems of damage to buildings are not new. Essentially similar problems have occurred for many years, but previously such damage was ignored unless it was causing severe cracking and problems. It used to be accepted that buildings founded on clay soils were liable to suffer seasonal movements and damage, and the attitude was simply to repair any minor damage whenever necessary.

Attitudes changed with the introduction of subsidence insurance cover in 1971, and the subsequent expansion of this cover to include both subsidence and heave. Householders became aware that they could claim for the costs of repair and redecoration, albeit with a substantial excess on their policy. As neither the householder nor the insurance company wanted a repetition of the claim, they sought to prevent further problems, usually by relying on underpinning. In order to recoup their losses, insurers then tried to claim the cost of the repairs from an adjacent tree owner, or from a surveyor for failing to draw attention to the risk. Surveyors have protected themselves against such allegations by recording any defect however insignificant, which often causes difficulties in obtaining a mortgage and problems in selling a property. All of this, combined with alarmist press reports, has led to increased public awareness and a continual escalation of the attitude that cracks in a building are unacceptable and that immediate remedial measures are required.

This situation can only be resolved by a change in public and professional attitudes to minor levels of damage. It must be emphasised that the majority of damage caused by foundation movement is not significant to the performance, still less to the safety, of the buildings, although it might require periodic cosmetic repair whenever the damage becomes too obvious. This was the attitude which prevailed prior to 1971, and there is no reason why all professionals involved in these problems should not seek a return to this previous situation, provided the damage is minor.

Tolerating damage will only be acceptable if it is an occasional problem. If similar damage reappears every year, positive remedial action will become essential, but if it only occurs every few years, for instance during extreme drought conditions, tolerating the damage may be considered. However, if one is to tolerate damage, one must be confident that there is no risk of the movements increasing or becoming more extensive. This implies that the tree is already mature, and that the damage is only occurring as a result of additional soil drying which develops under extreme drought conditions.

Under these circumstances any soil drying is almost certainly seasonal, or at worst associated with a semi-persistent deficit during a prolonged dry period, and so there should be no risk of development of a persistent deficit and associated subsidence. However, if seasonal movements are being tolerated, there is the possibility of distortion slowly accumulating as a result of dynamic settlement (see page 108). The possibility of this can be determined from a level distortion survey; if a mature tree and building have been co-existing for some time but there is little distortion, say less than 1mm per year during the life of the building, further similar movement might be deemed acceptable.

Where damage is being tolerated, there are simple practical steps which can be taken to mask the damage. For instance, the use of quality wallpapers, particularly the more elastic vinyl papers, will cover minor cracks, whereas a painted plaster surface will reveal the slightest crack. If there is movement at the junction of two walls, or between wall and ceiling, the edge of the paper can be lapped over the corner, but not pasted down. This will allow the crack to move, without creasing the paper or revealing the crack. If movements cause doors to jam seasonally, the door or the frame can be planed to allow greater freedom, and a flexible draught excluder used to cover the larger gap.

Where seasonal movements are being tolerated in this way, the cracks usually keep recurring in the same position. Alternative methods for covering the crack can be considered, e.g. vertical cracks at the junction of an extension can be covered with a decorative wood strip attached to one side only, or furniture can be moved to hide a crack.

Where minor external cracks are occurring, rather than repair by restitching the brickwork, an elastic mastic can be used. This will ensure that the crack remains watertight. Obviously such remedy should not be considered if the severity of cracking is liable to affect the integrity or safety of the structure.

It is a regrettable trait of some house owners to draw attention to damage which would be ignored by any reasonable person. Regardless of whether the damage is caused by trees, by the time they have waged a campaign against insurers for ignoring their claim, notified the local press, refused to carry out normal decoration in case it "hides the evidence" and generally tried to exaggerate a non-existent problem, they end up, not surprisingly, with a blighted property. These comments might only apply to a few extreme cases, but it is surprising how many householders have "hypochondriac" tendencies of this sort.

Restabilising the soil and foundations by controlling the water uptake of the tree

The rationale for this is simple - if the foundations movements are caused by the soil movements induced by water uptake of the tree, if the water uptake is stopped the movements will cease. If the foundations can be restabilised in this way, there can be no justification for underpinning.

Unfortunately the concept has been misunderstood in the past and this has given it an undeserved bad reputation. The usual reason why it has not been successful is because of failure to identify and eliminate the cause of the movement. For instance, cracks may be monitored and show that they are closing through the winter, and there may be negligible movement in the following summer provided it is wet. Movements are then assumed to have ceased and so remedial works are put in hand. However, if no positive action has been taken with the tree to prevent further seasonal movement, when the next dry summer comes there is likely to be excessive movement and damage, leading to the conclusion that the method does not work. **If the foundations are to be stabilised, it is essential to identify and deal with the cause of the movements.**

As the objective must be to restabilise the foundations in an acceptably short period, it must be emphasised that this method will not be viable if there is a significant persistent deficit and associated risk of long term heave or recovery, unless these movements can be tolerated. **Controlling the water uptake should therefore only be used if movements are entirely, or predominately, seasonal.** (An exception to this is if the tree is removed and the persistent deficit eliminated by watering-in; this specialist technique is considered on page 291).

Before embarking on this remedy, investigations are needed to confirm:

i) that movements are seasonal, with no risk of unacceptable heave or recovery;

ii) whether, and if so which, tree or trees are the cause of the movement;

iii) that the foundations are adequate to cope with other causes of soil drying or movement.

Methods for predicting the risk and duration of heave or recovery movements have been considered in Chapter 16 (page 261). The investigations should be sufficient to ensure that movements are entirely seasonal (Case Studies 2 and 6), or else of short duration (Case Studies 9, 11 and 13). Level monitoring, particularly during the recovery phase in the winter months, is particularly valuable.

If seasonal changes in level are demonstrated, it clearly implicates a shrinkable soil and some kind of vegetation (unless the foundations are so shallow as to be vulnerable to moisture evaporation from the surface). The distribution of movement throughout the building will usually identify the vegetation which is involved. If the greatest movements are in a part of a building close to a tree, it provides a clear indication of the probable involvement of that tree. If movement is more widespread, it may indicate that a single tree is influencing much of the building (e.g. Case Studies 7 and 15, both of which involve an oak tree affecting the whole building), or that more than one tree, or some other vegetation, is involved (e.g. Case Studies 5, 9 and 11). Where more than one tree may be involved, assessment of the probable influence of each tree is required. This will depend on their species, vigour (as indicated by growth rate) and crown size. Information on the probable influence of the different trees, and also on the distribution of movement and the history of damage, should identify the role of different trees. In some circumstances root identification may be required, but the potential problems associated with this must be recognized (Chapter 14, page 220).

It is a common practice to try to identify the role of different trees by defining a radial "zone of influence", based on guidelines such as NHBC Standards Chapter 4.2. This approach can be very misleading, particularly if the nominal mature height of the trees is used for defining the zone. If guidelines are required for determining the relative influence of different trees at different locations, it would be preferable to use the system of risk assessment described in Chapter 18 (page 312), as it takes proper account of the species, size and

vigour of the tree. However, as emphasised in Chapter 11, each site should be treated on its own merits. Any form of general risk assessment cannot take proper account of the inherently variable nature of the soil and the interaction between the tree and soil.

If foundations are very shallow (less than 0.6m) on a highly shrinkable clay, virtually any vegetation including grass or weeds, or even direct evaporation, could cause sufficient movement to produce minor damage. Underpinning may provide the only remedy for foundations of this sort. Foundations which are at least 0.8m deep are sufficient in most conditions to counteract the effect of shallow rooted vegetation, and foundations more than 1.0m deep will cope with most root activity except that from trees or very large shrubs.

If movements are **predominantly seasonal** and the foundations would be adequate in the absence of the tree, water uptake can be controlled by:-

   i) controlling transpiration loss of water:
      a) totally, by felling the tree so as to eliminate all soil drying and movement;
      b) partially, by pruning to reduce the leaf area so as to reduce the amplitude of movement caused by soil drying;
      c) tree growth regulators (experimental only);

   ii) controlling root growth by:
      a) root barriers;
      b) root pruning.

Options i a) and i b) are shown diagrammatically in Figure 17.1.

These techniques are considered below. Another option, that of providing sufficient water to the tree to prevent development of deficits, is also considered. Statutory legal constraints on tree felling or pruning are considered in Chapter 19.

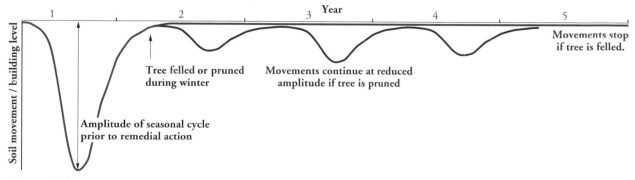

Figure 17.1

Diagram of methods of controlling seasonal soil drying and movement by felling (blue line) or by pruning to reduce the amplitude of movement (purple line).

Tree felling to stop water uptake

Chapter 2 has noted that virtually all water loss is through the leaves as transpiration. To prevent this water loss, one only has to eliminate the leaves. The simplest, and most permanent means of doing so, is to fell the tree; this will stop water uptake instantly and prevent all further subsidence movements.

Although felling the tree will prevent all further subsidence or seasonal soil movements induced by the tree, there are potential disadvantages. It has already been emphasised that rapid stability will not be achieved if there is a persistent deficit. If the recovery from such deficit makes underpinning essential, it may be practical to retain the tree, possibly with some increase in depth of underpinning to allow for any possible future increase in influence of the tree.

It is particular important that **any decision to fell a tree should be taken with due regard to the effect on the landscape and environment.** Is the tree really the cause of the problem? Only accurate diagnosis can ensure that the correct tree is being targeted. If there is uncertainty, it is preferable to limit action to the most likely culprit, and only take additional action if subsequent monitoring demonstrates that it is necessary (Case Studies 5 and 6). Is the value of the tree sufficient to warrant retention, even if this makes underpinning essential? Is felling really justified, or would an alternative remedy such as pruning suffice? These questions are considered in further detail in the section on page 295 of this chapter, which considers the choice of remedial measures.

Time of year for felling. A tree can be felled at any time of the year, but the urgency for felling will vary depending on the time of year. In the autumn, after about mid-October, water uptake by deciduous trees will cease and the ground will be rehydrating until the trees come into leaf the following spring. Felling in late autumn or winter will make no difference to this process; seasonal recovery will occur irrespective of any action which is taken. If there is any doubt about the need to fell a tree, or uncertainty as to which tree or trees are involved, this period should be used to clarify the situation, for instance by level monitoring to check the extent and pattern of recovery movements.

If the tree is in other ownership, it will be advisable to put the owner on notice that the movements are being monitored, and that a request for prompt action for tree felling may follow in the spring when the involvement of the tree, and the risk of heave or recovery, has been established.

Although felling can be postponed until the spring, once the trees come into leaf the annual subsidence movements will start again, at a gradually increasing rate through the summer. Negligible soil drying from tree root activity will occur in April, and, unless there is a long dry spell, any soil drying in May or June is usually at shallow depth and unlikely to influence foundations. By July the rate of subsidence is liable to build up, to reach a maximum in August. Even a brief delay in tree felling during this period can exacerbate the distortion, and require several months of recovery movement to restore the *status quo*. By late September, most of the damage has been done for the year, and another winter of recovery movement will be required.

Emergency treatment in lieu of felling. As any delay in late summer can exacerbate the damage, prompt action is essential at that time of year. If time or lack of facilities prevent immediate felling, an alternative is to sever the water-conducting tissue in the xylem, so as to stop water from passing up the trunk. This requires a cut of any width penetrating about 30mm into the wood tissue around the whole circumference. The cut should not be so deep as to weaken the trunk; for this reason it should not be deeper than about 10% of the radius of the trunk. For safety reasons, the tree should not be left in this condition, but felling completed at the earliest opportunity

Treating the roots and coppice regrowth. Although felling a tree will prevent all further water uptake, the roots will remain alive in the soil for many months, if not years (Chapter 14, page 224). In due course they will die and decay, but in the meantime they are entirely non-functional (where are they pumping the water to?).

Despite the roots being non-functional, there is a common misconception that, in addition to felling a tree, it is also necessary to kill the roots. This often leads to demands from solicitors for injunctions to "fell the tree and poison the roots". Not only is poisoning the roots unnecessary, but it is also impractical. So-called root poisoning typically involves the application of a herbicide to the cut surface of the stump. Even the most effective herbicides will only be translocated a short distance downwards, and so will only kill the tissue for a distance of about 0.5m down the main root buttresses. Stump treatments are of no benefit in killing the rest of the root system.

The objective of stump treatment is not to kill the roots, but to stop the stump from sprouting (shoots developing in this way from a stump are known as coppice shoots). It may be necessary to stop a stump from coppicing, as the regrowth may be sufficient to re-activate seasonal movement in due course. Coppice regrowth is usually most vigorous in young trees. The propensity of different genera to coppice is shown in Figure 17.2.

If it is necessary to prevent the stump from coppicing, correct treatment should involve felling the tree to near ground level. With species liable to coppice vigorously, it is advantageous to make diagonal downward cuts with an axe or chainsaw through the remaining exposed bark (frill-girdling). A solution of herbicide is then applied to the surface of the bark, particularly the bark which has been frilled, and also to the outermost 50-75mm circumference of the stump surface. It is not necessary to apply it to the centre of the cut stump as it is the outer living tissues, not the dead central parts, which require treatment.

The most effective herbicide for stump treatment is ammonium sulphamate (trade names AMS or Amcide). Unfortunately this is not widely available. It is a crystalline solid which absorbs moisture very rapidly from the air. It can either be applied as a 40% solution, or the crystals applied direct to the surface, leaving moisture in the air and stump to make the solution. An alternative herbicide is 2,4,5-T, available in many different formulations and trade names, either on its own or in mixture with 2,4-D. For stump treatment it is preferable to use an ester formulation, and dissolve this 1 part in 40 parts diesel or other light oil (or as instructed on label). Water based solutions give less satisfactory control. 2,4,5-T is the cheaper of these herbicides, but ammonium sulphamate is more effective particularly on resistant species. There are differences in the fungi which colonise the stump; ammonium sulphamate tends to encourage harmless saprophytic fungi, whereas 2,4,5-T can encourage colonisation by the troublesome honey fungus (*Armillaria mellea*), which is then liable to spread to and kill adjacent trees and shrubs. Broadshot™, which is marketed by Shell Chemicals and contains a mixture of triclopyr, dicamba and 2,4-D ester, also provides very effective control. These materials should be applied in accordance with their instructions, taking care to prevent contamination of surrounding ground, particularly with ammonium sulphamate, as any excess which runs off will persist in the ground for several months.

Treatment of suckers. Some species, rather than produce coppice shoots from the stump, will produce shoots off the root system, known as suckers. They are particularly likely to be produced after a tree is felled, but may be produced at any stage in the life of a tree from roots growing close beneath the surface. As they are liable to appear in the middle of lawns, flower beds or breaking through cracks in paving (or on very rare occasions appearing through the floorboards), they can be a source of considerable aggravation. The water requirements of small suckers is inconsequential, but their appearance at a position far from the tree serves to demonstrate the extent of the root system and as a result often gives rise to great alarm. The species which are most prone to produce suckers are shown in Figure 17.3.

Vigorous coppice growth likely		Some coppice growth possible		Unlikely to coppice
Broadleaves				
Alnus	Ilex	Acer	Morus	Fagus
Castanea	Laurus	Aesculus	Nothofagus	Liriodendron
Catalpa	Platanus	Ailanthus	Parrotia	Magnolia
Corylus	Populus	Arbutus	Prunus	Malus
Crataegus	Pterocarya	Betula	Quercus	Pyrus
Eucalyptus	Quercus ilex	Carpinus	Rhus	
Fraxinus	Salix	Carya	Robinia	
Gleditsia	Umbellularia	Cercidophyllum	Sorbus	
		Juglans	Tilia	
		Laburnum	Ulmus	
		Liquidambar	Zelkova	
Conifers				
Sequoia sempervirens		Ginkgo		All other conifers
		Juniperus		
		Taxus		

Figure 17.2

Propensity of genera to produce coppice regrowth from cut stumps. Stumps of young and vigorous trees are far more liable to sprout.

279

Very likely to sucker		Occasional suckers
Ailanthus	*Prunus avium*	*Acer cappadocicum*
Alnus	*Pterocarya*	*Aesculus*
Populus alba	*Rhus*	*Liquidambar*
P. balsamifera	*Robinia*	*Populus* (other species)
P. canescens	*Ulmus procera*	*Zelkova*
P. tremula		

Figure 17.3

Propensity of genera and species to produce sucker growth off the root system, particularly after felling. Other genera, including all conifers, are unlikely to produce suckers.

As herbicide treatments on a cut stump only penetrate a short distance down the root, such treatment will have negligible benefit in controlling suckers. There is no advantage is cutting off the suckers at ground level as this just stimulates fresh sucker growth. Where they are a problem, it is much more effective to use a systemic contact herbicide, applied direct to the suckers. A very effective material for this is glyphosate, obtainable under the commercial trade name of Roundup™, or from retail outlets as Tumbleweed™. It can be obtained in small handy spray applicators. Broadshot™ is also effective for this purpose. Either of these herbicides should be applied to the leaves of the sucker during active growth (it helps to allow the sucker to grow to at least 15cm high to provide sufficient material to treat; on larger suckers just the most recent growth need be treated. The herbicide is absorbed by the sucker, and is translocated down the stem and into the root system. Not only does it kill the treated suckers, but will also prevent new suckers developing from the adjacent length of root. The herbicide produces no apparent immediate effects but shoots will slowly discolour and die. However, the herbicide will have been absorbed down into the root system very rapidly and the sucker can be cut down 24 hours after treatment.

Some caution should be exercised if treating suckers on a living tree rather than a stump, because there is a risk of the herbicide being carried down from the sucker, through the root and into the main tree. If treating only a few suckers off a large tree this would not cause damage, but treating a mass of suckers off a small tree could kill the tree as well. As these are potent herbicides with a very broad spectrum, care is also needed to avoid contamination of leaves of other plants. If necessary, enclose the sucker in a large polythene bag and spray into the bag to prevent any spray drifting onto adjacent plants.

If it is necessary to fell a tree which is very prone to suckering, and if there is sufficient prior notice of the intent to fell, it is possible to stop the suckering by ring-barking the tree prior to felling. This involves removing a complete strip of the bark and phloem about 5cm wide from right around the base of the tree but leaving the underlying wood intact (Figure 17.4). As the sugar needed for root growth and activity is carried to the roots in the phloem, this ring barking will deprive the roots of nutrient. If the xylem (wood) is left undamaged, water will continue to be conducted upwards as long as the roots can stay alive on their available food reserves. Once the reserves are exhausted, the tree will die and these exhausted roots will be unable to sucker. It can take at least 12 months for a tree to die after ring barking, and for real benefit at least 6 months should be allowed, preferably during the summer, before the tree is felled. Killing a root system in this way can also be beneficial for preventing colonisation of the stump by honey fungus.

Figure 17.4

Cherry tree ring-barked prior to felling to exhaust food reserves and prevent sucker growth

Tree felling in stages

There is a popular misconception that trees should be felled in stages. It is apparently thought that this will slow down or prevent heave damage. It results in a proposal that a tree should be pruned by say one third in the first year, pruned by another third after a few years and then finally felled after a further delay.

Regardless of how a tree is felled, if heave is going to occur, the amount of movement is pre-determined by the extent of the persistent deficit and the swelling potential of the soil. Phased removal will reduce the rate of movement, but will make no difference to the total movement or distortion which eventually occurs, nor will it reduce the amount of damage which will occur as a result of this movement. The initial stage of pruning will start the process of rehydration and heave, but as long as parts of the tree are retained, the rate of heave will be slower, or may even reverse in the summer. As a result, felling in stages will extend the time it takes for the foundations to restabilise, and allow a risk of damage to continue throughout this period.

If movements are seasonal and there is no risk of heave, phased removal will prevent immediate restabilisation, and may even result in some continued minor damage until tree felling is complete. It will also result in wasted expenditure on unnecessary tree surgery work.

Tree pruning to control water uptake

Complete removal of a tree by felling is a drastic remedy which should only be used if really justified. As an alternative, in some cases, particularly where movements are small, it is sufficient to restrict the amplitude of seasonal movement by reducing the water requirements of the tree. This can be achieved by pruning to reduce the leaf area, and thus the amount of water lost through transpiration.

As with felling, pruning can only provide a viable remedy if movements are predominantly seasonal. If there is a persistent deficit and associated risk of heave, the reduction in water uptake which occurs as a result of pruning will allow this heave to occur, producing a pattern of seasonal movement, of reduced amplitude, superimposed on progressive heave movement (see Figure 6.20, page 97). It is not possible to "balance the water uptake of the tree", and thus prevent either subsidence (because the tree is too big) or heave (because the tree has been felled).

Chapter 5, page 76, has summarised the results of the experimental pruning of plane trees, and the research experience with other species. Figure 5.15 showed the patterns of soil drying at the end of the summer after the trees were pruned for the first time (in 1984); Figure 17.5 is similar but shows the pattern in 1986, after the trees had been pruned for a second time, on both occasions to a similar severity.

Figure 17.6 shows the even more dramatic contrast in the patterns of soil drying before and after the control plane trees were pollarded.

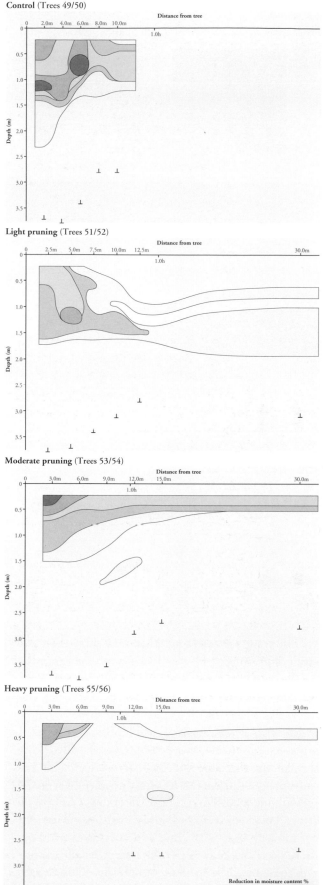

Figure 17.5

Effect of different severity of pruning on patterns of soil drying by plane trees in 1986, after pruning for second time.

281

a) October 1989, prior to pollarding.

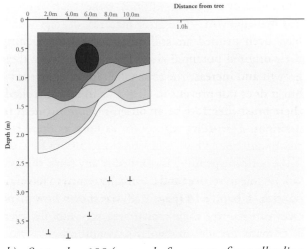

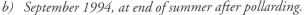

b) September 1994, at end of summer after pollarding.

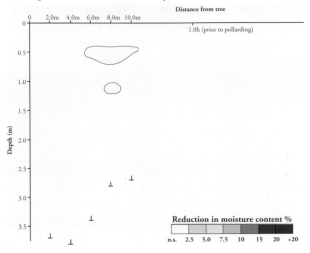

Figure 17.6

Pattern of soil drying before and after pollarding the plane trees used as controls (trees 49/50). Figure 17.10 shows the amount of regrowth in September after pollarding.

The results reviewed in Chapter 5 show that, as a result of pruning, the water deficit is reduced, approximately in proportion to the reduction in leaf area. Although there is some reduction in the depth and radial extent of soil drying, the overall soil volume which is exploited remains fairly similar; the benefit is more a reduction in the intensity of soil drying throughout the large volume. This is probably because conducting roots were already present within the soil volume required to supply water to the full crown area. These roots will continue to function at least temporarily but, with time and successive pruning, those parts of the former root system which are surplus to requirements will eventually die. This dieback will result in the soil volume which is exploited being commensurate with the reduced crown size. If pruning is not continued and the crown is allowed to regrow, the benefits will be temporary and the extent of soil drying will increase again.

Although the experimental pruning and experience goes some way to demonstrating these effects and benefits, the available evidence is insufficient to provide definitive guidelines. However, if combined with consideration of the physiological response which is to be expected from different treatments, it is possible to reach tentative conclusions on how pruning is best applied, and the benefits which can be gained.

Objectives of pruning.   As photosynthesis and transpiration occur through the leaves, any reduction in leaf area by pruning will have an immediate effect on energy production and water loss. The results in Volume 2 merely confirm the previous knowledge that water uptake will be reduced after pruning. It is also widely recognised that pruning the crown of a tree will produce a rapid response in stopping further root growth.

Pruning will upset the natural root:shoot ratio of the tree. It will seek to re-establish this ratio as rapidly as possible, by:

i)   enhanced shoot growth to restore the previous crown size;

ii)   reduced root growth, or dieback of the roots, to achieve a root volume commensurate with the smaller crown size;

iii) a combination of these processes.

Enhanced shoot growth requires the production of additional leaf-bearing shoots, or additional growth on existing shoots, as rapidly as possible. Additional energy requirements for this cannot come from existing leaf area, as this has been reduced by the pruning. Instead, the tree will utilize its energy reserves, particularly the starch which is stored in the root system. As this energy is coming from reserves, rather than from photosynthesis, this additional growth does not involve additional transpiration and associated water uptake; water uptake will remain at a reduced level until the leaf area recovers. Despite this, it is often mistakenly thought that the vigorous regrowth which follows pruning must indicate additional water uptake.

With a vigorous tree with abundant food reserves, regrowth of this sort after pruning can be very rapid. Many trees can produce epicormic shoots from adventitious buds beneath the bark, and these can be stimulated into growth soon after pruning. Other species may have to delay additional growth until the next period of shoot extension growth and leaf development. Whichever the mechanism, it can soon allow the tree to re-establish the original root:shoot ratio. As it recovers, it will return to its original rate of photosynthesis, transpiration and water uptake. Once the tree has recovered to its normal leaf area, it can replenish its food reserves.

Provided the tree has the necessary energy reserves, enhanced shoot growth is the preferred and more efficient option. However, if reserves are inadequate, new shoots can only develop very slowly, utilising any surplus energy from photosynthesis. As the leaf area has been reduced, such surplus is unlikely or limited. Roots which are surplus to requirements and not being used must continue to respire, albeit at a reduced rate, but this is a drain on starch reserves and an inefficient use of carbon resources. It has been emphasised that the root system is highly dynamic, and so, if they remain surplus to requirements, they will soon die.

The tree will re-establish its root:shoot ratio by whichever combination of these processes is the most energy efficient.

If a tree recovers by enhanced shoot growth, pruning can be repeated so as to maintain the tree at the reduced leaf area. Recurrent pruning of this sort will progressively diminish the food reserves and thus reduce the ability and rapidity of recovery. The tree will therefore tend to restore the root:shoot ratio by dieback of the root system.

In this way, with successive pruning to restrict any regrowth which occurs, the water uptake by the tree is reduced, the vigour and ability of the tree to recover is reduced, and the extent of the root system is reduced into a new balance with the reduced leaf area. As the ability to recover diminishes, the interval between recurrent pruning can be increased.

Disadvantages of pruning. Whilst pruning offers a potential alternative to felling, it must be recognized that there are many disadvantages. It certainly does not provide the panacea which is sometimes expected.

Pruning does not eliminate seasonal movement; it merely reduces the amplitude. If the movements which occur prior to pruning are small, for instance if unacceptable movement and damage only develop under drought conditions, it may be quite sufficient to reduce the amplitude, but if movements are large it is unlikely to be effective. Available evidence suggests that pruning will be most effective in reducing movement towards the periphery of any influence of the tree, and is therefore less likely to be effective for a tree in very close proximity to a building.

The size to which a tree will grow at maturity is controlled by the site conditions, rather than its previous management. The great majority of trees which have been pruned are still quite capable of reaching their original potential size. Pruning will slow their growth and increase the time taken to reach maturity, but it does not prevent it. **If size is to be controlled, there must therefore be an on-going commitment to maintain a pruning regime for as long as there is a risk of damage.** This has obvious implications for cost. If the periodic pruning is stopped at any time, the tree will be able to recover and eventually return to its original size. Chapter 14 (page 228) has shown how plane trees can recover their crown area very rapidly, even after many decades of regular heavy pruning.

To many people, a natural growing tree is an object of beauty, both when it is in leaf in summer and the silhouette of the bare branches in winter. Maintaining a tree under a regular pruning regime, however expertly done, produces an artificial shape which diminishes this beauty (except in some very formalised situations). Poorly executed pruning can ruin a tree irrevocably.

There is sometimes a belief that a tree benefits from regular pruning and that it keeps a tree "tidy". This belief possibly originates from the care of shrubs or fruit trees, as flower and fruit production can be improved by appropriate pruning. The public also see the frequent pruning of street trees, which supports the notion that trees should be pruned. These trees usually require this pruning for other reasons, such as clearance of low branches for vehicle passage or to ensure that adjacent properties enjoy sufficient light. The pruning is being applied to fulfil a specific objective. The control of water uptake can also provide a legitimate objective, but pruning should not be thought necessary just for its own sake.

The cuts which are created by pruning increase the risk of entry and spread of decay fungi. The natural defence mechanisms of the tree will ensure that small cuts, which affect only the outer sapwood, are reasonably immune, but large cuts which expose the inner heartwood can be more vulnerable. The heavier the pruning, the larger the cuts and the greater the potential risk.

Many of the new shoots which develop after pruning originate from adventitious buds under the bark, rather than from the normal processes of axillary bud formation. These shoots, which are known as epicormics, are less firmly attached initially, and can be more prone to future storm damage.

Methods of pruning. There are two standard tree surgery techniques for pruning which can be considered for reducing water uptake:

i) crown reduction involves reducing the height and crown spread so as to produce a tree with a smaller crown area (Figure 17.7 shows an oak tree before and after crown reduction, and Figure 17.8b shows it diagrammatically).

ii) crown thinning only reduces the density of the branch structure within the crown, whilst retaining the overall crown dimensions (Figure 17.8c, and Figure 17.9 shows a beech tree before and after crown thinning).

In either case the work should involve cutting the branch which is being removed back to a lateral fork so as to retain a flowing branch line without leaving projecting stubs. The work needs to be carried out in accordance with British Standard 3998, with all cuts made at the correct position relative to the branch collar. Provided the scope of work is correctly specified and then properly executed by skilled tree surgeons, who are capable of working throughout the crown, the appearance of the tree need not be destroyed.

There is no research to determine the relative merits of these methods, but crown reduction is probably the more effective. Reduction has the advantage that it removes much of the fine twig structure and associated leaves, most of which are carried near the branch ends. As a result, quite a small reduction in the dimensions can achieve a major reduction in leaf area. It also removes the most exposed parts of the crown where transpiration of water is most rapid. It will produce a tree with a smaller crown, but subsequent regrowth will usually produce a high density of foliage until a new root:shoot ratio is established.

By contrast, thinning tends to remove larger branches from within the crown, with a smaller proportion of the leaf-bearing twigs. Leaves from the centre of the crown will normally be shaded and transpiring less freely; their removal therefore produces less benefit. As thinning produces a more open crown structure, the leaves which are left will be more exposed and potentially able to transpire more rapidly. In addition, a tree probably recovers its leaf area more rapidly after thinning.

In practice, most tree surgery will involve elements of both reduction and thinning, but the emphasis and severity of each can be adjusted to achieve the desired objective.

Crown lifting, which involves removal of low branches, is another technique but it removes the leaves which are least efficient for photosynthesis, and will be of far less benefit.

Figure 17.7

Large mature oak tree, a) before and b) after, heavy crown reduction by about 50%. The tree has responded to the treatment by producing a mass of epicormic shoots on the remaining branch structure.   *(Photos: R. Finch).*

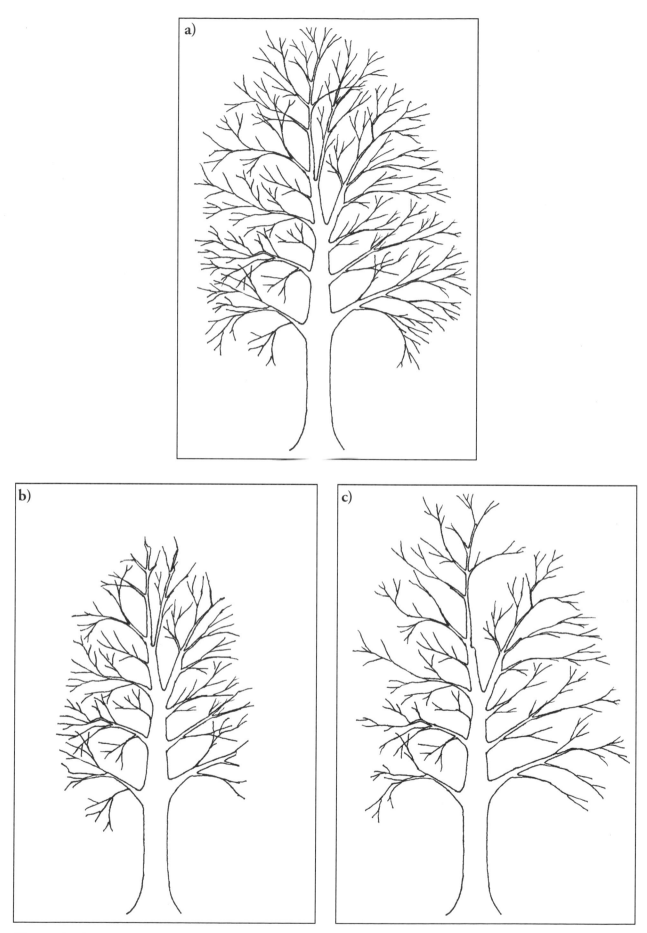

Figure 17.8

Tree surgery techniques for reducing leaf area. a) diagrammatic section through crown before surgery. b) same crown after reduction by about 20%. c) same crown after thinning by similar amount.

The term 'pollarding' is also often applied to very heavy crown reduction, involving 'beheading' the tree in later life, to leave only the trunk, or the trunk and short stub branches (Figure 17.10). Removal of all branches is complete pollarding, but any crown reduction which involves shortening the branches by more than 50% could be described as pollarding. Drastic treatment of this sort leaves major wounds and compounds the problems for future management, and it is questionable whether the resulting object is worth retaining. However, if the tree is capable of surviving the treatment, it can drastically reduce the water requirements and is occasionally justifiable as an alternative to complete felling.

Figure 17.9

Copper beech tree, a) before and b) after, crown thinning by about 20%. Crown reduction, by about 15%, has also been applied.

(Photo: R. Finch).

Pollarding is often advocated, particularly by non-arboriculturists who may not have a proper understanding of the technique. When applied correctly, it should involve heavy crown reduction **early** in the life of the tree, cutting back all of the branches to form a basic framework. Shoots which develop off these branches are then cut right back, usually every year or every second year, although in some cases, for instance with willow, it may be at far longer intervals. Pollarding therefore involves a regime of regular and heavy crown reduction. It has the advantage that the early formation of a framework and regular removal of all regrowth ensures that all of the cuts are small, which minimises the entry of decay and the problems associated with weak epicormic shoots. In due course the repeated regrowth produces a swollen branch end which may require removal, but this should be avoided as far as possible, as it involves cutting into older wood. When used correctly in this way, pollarding provides an appropriate and effective management technique for maintaining a tree at a small crown size.

Figure 17.10

Plane tree with one year of regrowth after pollarding. Although initially pollarded when young, this tree had not been pruned for about 25 years, and as a result had developed a large crown. Repollarding had therefore involved cutting large branches. The pattern of soil drying of this tree (tree 50) before and after pollarding is shown in Figure 17.6.

Reaction of species to pruning. The way in which a tree responds to pruning depends on the species, vigour, and age of the tree, on the distribution and severity of the pruning, and sometimes on the time of year.

A tree which is only subjected to a light pruning will usually produce additional growth on the remaining leaf-bearing shoots, either by extension of existing shoots or from terminal or axillary buds. Growth of this sort will be almost indistinguishable from the normal shoot production, and will usually have minimal effect on the appearance of the tree. Some species, for instance pine, are only able to respond in this way. If these species are reduced too hard, so as to eliminate all of their existing terminal or axillary buds, they will be unable to produce fresh growth and will die. Provided adequate live buds are retained, the tree may be able to redevelop from these, but it can result in considerable deformity in the shape.

If pruning is heavier, the majority of species respond by production of epicormic shoots, developing from adventitious bud initials in the cambium beneath the bark. Some species, for instance oak, can produce particularly dense epicormic shoots, whilst other species, such as birch, will only produce a few shoots, and even these will only develop on young and vigorous trees. If a tree is only lightly thinned, epicormic shoots are usually concentrated around the edges of the cut surface and on adjacent parts of the remaining branch. With heavier thinning or reduction, all the remaining branches are likely to develop a mass of epicormic shoots from along their length, initially producing a dense bottlebrush appearance (Figure 17.7b).

As epicormic shoots are developing from buds just beneath the bark, rather than from the centre of the branch, they may be poorly attached, at least until such time as they become adequately surrounded by fresh annual growth rings laid down on their parent branch. This can create problems in the future management of the regrowth. If a few epicormics develop from around the edge of a small cut, they can appear similar to normal shoot production, and any inherent weakness will soon be overcome by fresh growth rings around the base. However, if there is a mass of growth, the epicormics will need thinning and the contrasting size between thin epicormic shoots and the thicker diameter of the parent branch will appear abnormal for many years.

As the response of a tree can be so variable, specific guidelines for pruning are not practical in this book. However, a skilled tree surgeon can anticipate the type of regrowth, and should be able to ensure that a tree retains as normal an appearance as possible, commensurate with the desired extent of pruning.

A few species, notably plane and to a lesser extent lime, are particularly tolerant of crown reduction or regular pollarding, and it is an acceptable and widespread practice to manage them in this way (Figure 17.11). Different shapes of tree can be achieved (in London you can often tell which Borough you are in by the shape of the plane trees). With these species the tree can be controlled to any size from a small 'lollipop' which is pollarded and reshoots each year, through varying degrees of regular crown reduction, to the full size of a mature tree. Most other species are reasonably tolerant of either reduction or thinning, but the results are often less satisfactory both in terms of the shape of the tree as it regrows and the ease of subsequent management. Species which produce few or no epicormics, such as beech, birch, pine and spruce, must be pruned with extreme care. Some species, of which poplar is the obvious example, regrow so fast that repeat treatments will be needed so frequently as to make the technique of dubious value.

Figure 17.11

Plane trees pruned as part of regular management regime. Regular reduction is required to prevent the crowns from becoming over-bearing in close proximity to the houses, as well as to control the leaf area and water requirements.

Regular pruning, such as that shown in Figure 17.11, is often used to prevent the development of damage in situations where the risks can be identified and are considered unacceptably high. Preventative work of this sort is considered in further detail in Chapter 18 (page 317).

Frequency and severity of pruning. The extent of pruning and the frequency of re-treatment will obviously depend on circumstances. The more severe the pruning, the greater the benefit achieved in terms of reduced water uptake, and the longer this benefit will last. On the other hand, a severely pruned tree is aesthetically less pleasing, and the work inevitably causes more damage and trauma for the tree. Heavy pruning usually involves larger cuts, and these will be more prone to disease and future problems. The species of tree and its branch configuration will also dictate how severely it may be treated, and also its ability to produce fresh leaf-bearing shoots.

The severity of pruning is normally defined in percentage terms. Thus, a 20% crown reduction will involve reducing the length of branches and the crown height (excluding the trunk height) by 20%, whilst a 20% thinning will involve removal of about 20% of the overall branch structure (Figure 17.12). Defining the severity in this way may be ambiguous and it is difficult to check how much tissue has been removed after the work is complete. For this reason, there can

be advantage in defining crown reduction in terms of dimensions of the tree and the branches before and after treatment. The subsequent maintenance of an appropriate size is usually best defined in terms of crown dimensions, i.e. keeping the height and spread within certain limits.

BS 3998:1989 includes various comments on the frequency and severity of pruning, for instance recommending that regular crown reduction may be harmful, that thinning should not exceed 30% of the original coverage, and that pollarding should not be used on trees which have not previously been pollarded. Whilst caveats of this sort are correct for general advice, it is essential to ensure that the work which is undertaken is sufficient to achieve the desired objective. If the means justify the ends, severe pruning, in excess of the ideal, may be required and justified.

In particular, it is often necessary for the initial pruning to be more severe than subsequent work. This will help to ensure that the benefits are seen as rapidly as possible, and minimises the risk of recurrence while a property owner is particularly alert to further damage. As previously noted, a tree will often regrow very rapidly in response to initial treatment, and require further work within a few years. Once the situation has become more stable, it is usually possible to increase the interval between treatments and allow a slightly larger, or denser, crown structure.

It must be emphasised that, if a tree has caused damage and pruning is considered appropriate, there will need to be an on-going commitment to maintain the regime. If the tree is left and allowed to redevelop to its former crown size, the original problems are likely to recur. Pruning should therefore become part of a regular management regime (see Chapter 20, page 353).

Arrangements for surgery work. The decision on the method, severity and frequency of pruning should take account of all of these factors, and also the many other factors which might influence the type and severity of pruning, for instance the general condition of the tree and any defects which might exist, any other problems from shading or proximity which might be ameliorated by appropriate surgery, and also the viability of long-term management if this involves recurrent pruning. It is advisable to seek advice from an arboricultural consultant who can also arrange the work, or from

Figure 17.12

Photographs in Figure 17.7 superimposed to show the extent of an approximate 50% crown reduction.

an experienced tree surgeon who can then undertake the work. The Arboricultural Association maintain registers of Consultants and Contractors who can provide such service; the address of the Association is given at the end of this chapter.

Tree surgery can be carried out at most times of year, although late winter is usually the ideal time. Some species such as birch and sycamore should not be pruned in the spring, and walnut and *Prunus* species should only be pruned in the summer.

Control of size by plant growth regulators

Plant growth is under complex hormonal control. Production of these hormones can be suppressed by some chemicals such as paclobutrazol. In the United States this material is used as a soil drench to the roots, as a drench around the base of the trunk or as implants into the trunk, and apparently provides economical control of growth. There is no information on the effects on water uptake of treated trees, but as growth and leaf area are both reduced, it should be beneficial. However, the treatment can be very damaging to the tree, and at present this material is not registered for use in this way in this country.

Watering tree to reduce damage

The extent to which the soil dries is dependent on the amount of water which is lost from the system by transpiration and the amount which is input, usually in the form of rain. Theoretically, it should be possible to influence the extent of soil drying by supplementing this input by artificial watering. If such water is readily available, it will be absorbed by the tree in preference to the water which is tightly bound to the clay. In theory this should prevent drying of the underlying clay, but in practice there are problems to this approach.

Firstly, the volume of water which is required should be appreciated. Potential transpiration losses in midsummer can exceed 5mm per day. To correct such loss requires 5 litres of water per square metre. If the radial extent of root activity of a tree is 20m, the surface area potentially occupied by roots is about $1250m^2$; the volume of water required per day over this area is therefore about 6250 litres. It must be noted that this does not imply that a tree is removing this much from the soil; water will also be lost from other competing vegetation (grass etc.) and from evaporation from bare surfaces. In addition, tree roots will not be taking the water uniformly from the whole area. Provided one can be certain that the tree roots in a restricted area are capable of absorbing all of the water required by the tree, it would be sufficient merely to supply water to this area. The tree would not go into water stress, and would not need to absorb moisture from the underlying clay. In practice, it is usually difficult to ensure that sufficient water is being made available in this way, but some benefit can obviously be achieved by at least ensuring that excess water is available in the vicinity of the foundation i.e. by providing large volumes of water to the soil adjacent to the house. This can help to minimise any soil-drying occurring below foundation level.

For these reasons, provided a reliable source of water is available, artificial watering may be effective in reducing, or even preventing, damage. However, the times when the water is most needed usually coincides with drought conditions when there is likely to be a ban on all use of hose pipes. In 1976 even the use of baths was discouraged, so one could not even rely on waste water from this source to water trees. Artificial watering for as long as hose pipe use is permitted will ensure that soil moisture reserves are at a maximum at the start of any ban and could thereby reduce the risk of subsequent damage, but these reserves may not be sufficient to last through a prolonged drought. If the regular supply is cut off when it is most needed, the tree will need to turn to new areas of water supply which might, of course, be from beneath the foundations.

Similar comments apply to situations where water has been regularly made available from any source, which is subsequently cut off. This might be from a water course which is culverted, a leaking water main or drain which is repaired, or an underwater aquifer which is disturbed (for instance by drainage works). If the tree has previously relied on this water, the alteration to the water balance could easily lead to changes in the pattern of soil drying and the risk of structural damage.

Root barriers to control root spread

It is logical to think that, as damage is caused by tree roots drying the soil beneath the foundations, it can be prevented by severing these roots and preventing their regrowth by inserting a root barrier. In theory this will certainly work, but there are usually overwhelming practical objections. Unless a barrier can be fully effective, it will merely provide a false sense of security (Case Study 15).

To be effective, a barrier must eliminate all root activity beyond it. If it can be bypassed, either by roots growing round the ends, beneath, over, or through the barrier, the roots will proliferate in the favourable conditions beyond the barrier and again be liable to cause damage. To prevent this, a barrier must be long enough to avoid any risk of roots growing around the end, and also be deep enough and extend right to the soil surface so that roots cannot pass under or over. These dimensions should take account of the potential future growth of the tree. The barrier must also be totally impenetrable to root growth.

The excavation for the root barrier must not be so close to the tree as to render it unstable. As an approximate rule of thumb, for safety the barrier should not be closer to the edge of the trunk than a distance equal to 1.5 times the circumference of the trunk (measured at breast height or 1.5m), but excavation in such close proximity might kill the tree. For this reason, it is always advisable to seek advice from an arboriculturist. Care is also needed to ensure that any trench does not affect the stability of the foundations - advice should be sought from a structural engineer.

Ensuring that a barrier is not undermined is likely to be particularly difficult. Obviously it must be deeper than all root activity, including all fine roots, at the time of construction. However as the soil adjacent to the barrier dries and shrinks, it produces conditions of air and moisture which are conducive to root growth, so that roots will tend to grow down the face of the barrier until they eventually pass right beneath. To minimise such risk, the side of the barrier facing the tree should be a tight seal to the soil, i.e. do not use any backfill in this area. No general guidelines can be given on depth as this must depend on local conditions, but it is likely to be at least 3m, and in many situations considerably more.

Roots can grow over a barrier very easily if there is any soil or moist debris lying on top. Once the root is suberised, it can continue growth in this position. For this reason a barrier needs to be above, or very close to, the soil surface. This creates practical problems. On the side of the barrier nearer the tree, there will be continued root activity and seasonal soil movement, with ground level fluctuating by as much as 100mm under extreme conditions. By contrast, movement on the far side of the barrier is likely to be substantially less. This means that the top of the barrier is likely to protrude above the ground as a visible step each summer, making it unacceptable in a lawn, path, or even a flower bed. Incorporating a barrier into the foundations of a wall is perhaps one of the few practical locations.

If there is any underground service passing through the barrier, it will provide a potential hole for any root to pass through - with even a small hole a massive amount of root proliferation could occur beyond the barrier. It is, of course, inadvisable to seal a service into a rigid barrier, as the differential soil movements between the barrier and service would cause it to fracture. This problem with underground services rules out root barriers in most situations.

The materials most commonly used are concrete (cast direct into a trench excavation) or heavy duty polythene sheet, 2000g or heavier, laid against the face of a trench, and backfilled behind. The Heidemy anti-root screen is a purpose-made woven and coated sheet, with UV resistance, which should be more effective than polythene sheet, while the Reemay Biobarrier™ membrane incorporates pellets of a root growth inhibitor. These materials have the disadvantage of preventing any moisture movement across the barrier. As an alternative, some geotextile membranes will prevent root penetration, but can allow water movement. Terram™ 3000 or one of the heavier grades have proven effective in trials against root growth, but their long-term efficacy remains unknown (Brennan *et al*, 1981). Sheet piling is also sometimes suggested as a material, but the junction between piles, even when they are lipped together, is insufficient to prevent root penetration. Marshall *et al.* (1997) provide further details on the use of barriers and the available materials. Moffat *et al.* (1998) tested various materials and concluded that Biobarrier and a 1mm thick low density polythene membrane gave the most effective control.

Root severance

Root severance is unlikely to provide effective long term control, but may be a temporary expedient in some situations. A severed root can regenerate from the cut end (Figure 3.10), and subsequent root extension growth can be in excess of 1.5m per year. Provided sufficient roots are severed, root severance should be effective, until the roots have regrown. Any roots which exist below the depth of severance can also grow upwards to exploit the soil previously utilised by the severed roots, and so, if the treatment needs to be repeated, subsequent severance would need to extend deeper. If roots are severed, care must be taken not to destabilize or kill the tree.

A method which I have considered, but never had opportunity to try, utilizes a soil sterilant to kill the roots. For this a line of boreholes are drilled at close intervals. These are filled with pea grit, and a chemical soil sterilant such as metham sodium is applied to the full depth of the holes. This material will kill the roots in the adjacent soil, but boreholes must be sufficiently close to ensure it permeates between them (spacing therefore depends on soil permeability). The chemical will kill roots present at the time of treatment, but it is soon inactivated. Alternatively, a narrow trench can be dug to the full depth of the root profile so as to sever all of the roots, and then backfilled with pea grit. Roots can grow back through the barrier, and will even tend to proliferate in the favourable conditions adjacent to the barrier. In due course, roots which have crossed the barrier can be killed by a repeat treatment, re-using the previously drilled holes or trench. The frequency of re-treatment will depend on the proximity of the barrier to the house foundations. As with root severance, care must be taken to ensure that the treatment does not kill the tree, and the use of metham sodium may be unacceptable in some situations.

Accelerated recovery by watering-in

It has been emphasised that restabilisation of foundations by tree removal will only be effective if movements are predominantly seasonal so that recovery can occur within a single winter, or within an acceptably short period. If there is a deep-seated persistent deficit and a tree is removed or pruned, long-term heave or recovery will occur. Under some circumstances these problems can be overcome by artificially enhancing the permeability of the soil so as to accelerate the rehydration of the persistent deficit. Case Study 17 at the end of this chapter provides a practical description of the application of this technique. In that case the permeability was enhanced by drilling boreholes at 1m intervals into the desiccated soil below foundation depth. These holes were filled with sand which was then kept saturated.

A more sophisticated and probably more efficient mechanism has now been developed by Packman Lucas Associates (Figure 17.13). This requires 100mm diameter boreholes drilled through the zone of desiccation. A probe is lowered to the base of a hole. This probe has four tines which are hinged at the base and folded flat against the probe as it is inserted. As the probe is withdrawn the tines are pushed out into the soil, gradually rotating around the hinge, producing four diamond-shaped cuts through the soil. These increase the surface area and effective size of the holes. Further similar cuts can be made at other levels. The holes and cuts can then be back-filled with sand, and connected to a water supply.

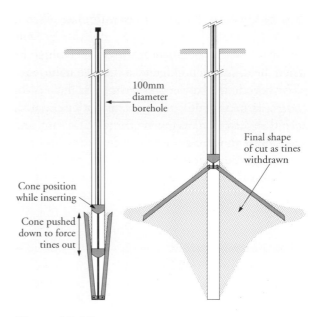

Figure 17.13

Diagram of system devised by Packman Lucas Associates for accelerated recovery by watering-in.

A limitation with any method of accelerated recovery is to ensure a sufficiently uniform rate of rehydration and recovery beneath the whole building. It is easy to ensure recovery beneath the perimeter walls where there is ready access, but if desiccation extends beneath a slab or internal partition walls, there is a likelihood of severe differential movement unless all the desiccated soil beneath the building is treated. With Case Study 17 this problem did not arise as the desiccation and movement was limited to the flank wall.

The Packman Lucas system may have potential for improving the permeability and aeration of the soil, and thus might be used to encourage roots to grow within the treated soil, rather than elsewhere. Treated soil will have an increased potential for seasonal drying, and so must be kept well clear of a building, and, as with artificial watering, it would be necessary to ensure that the soil has adequate water reserves for periods of drought.

Allowing natural recovery

In many cases, by the time it is appreciated that damage is being caused by heave, the majority, or all, movement has already occurred and the foundations are restabilising. Alternatively, the predicted heave or recovery movements are often very slight and complete in a short period (often little more than seasonal movement). In all these cases, provided the foundations are going to stabilise within a reasonably short period, it is preferable to allow this natural recovery and to avoid the cost and inconvenience of underpinning.

Checking the efficacy of remedial action

Whenever any technique has been used which relies either on controlling the water uptake of a tree or on the rehydration of the soil (either naturally or by accelerated means), it is advisable, if not essential, to check that the action has been effective and sufficient to restabilise the foundations.

By far the most effective way of doing this is by level monitoring. This will establish whether there is any continuing foundation movement. For this reason it is recommended that level monitoring should be continued whenever techniques of this sort are used. It should be considered an essential part of the technique (for instance as part of an insurance claim), and should be continued for sufficient period to confirm stability. The duration of this will depend on individual circumstances. If there is some continued recovery, the monitoring should continue through this period. If there are slight continuing seasonal movements, it may be necessary to check the amplitude of these in a reasonably dry summer.

Interpreting this information and deciding whether any slight continuing movements are significant will be far easier if monitoring has been started prior to the remedial action, so that there is information on the previous behaviour of the structure. As noted in Chapter 15 (page 240), this need not involve a full year of prior monitoring; monitoring the recovery movement through the winter after damage has occurred will be sufficient to determine the amplitude and distribution of the previous seasonal movements.

The objective is to ensure that future foundation movements do not reach the amplitude which initiated the original damage, plus a margin of safety to allow for extreme conditions. As shown in Chapter 5 (page 70), the extent of drying and amplitude of seasonal movement is only increased slightly in a drought year.

It is certainly not necessary to seek, or expect, complete stability. It is common to find shrubs or other vegetation causing seasonal movement of 5mm or more without significant damage; this should be acceptable provided the angular distortion is small and less than that which caused the damage.

When level monitoring utilising the unobtrusive methods described on page 241 has been completed, it is usually possible to leave the markers attached to the building. In the event of any problem developing in the future, these markers will provide a valuable starting point for any further investigations (Case Study 3).

Crack monitoring is an additional and viable technique for checking the efficacy of remedial action, but, as with levels, complete stability is not essential. As long as cracks remain, the stresses from any further slight foundation movement will be manifest in those cracks. However, if they are repaired (see page 296), the building will regain its original ability to distribute the stresses more widely, and thus to withstand some movement.

Crack monitoring is usually more obvious than level monitoring, and so it is unusual for the markers to be left *in situ* on completion of the exercise.

Stabilising the foundations by underpinning

This has been the traditional method of dealing with problems of tree root damage to buildings. For the engineer it provides the obvious solution which he understands. However, the methods are generally expensive and not cost effective. Despite this, underpinning has been widely used, which has eventually resulted in much justifiable criticism, particularly in BRE Digest 352 "Underpinning", and in an associated report for BRE by Hunt *et al.* (1991).

The previous sections have emphasised that underpinning can be avoided in favour of other cheaper methods in situations where the soil and foundation movements are predominantly seasonal. Chapter 5 has emphasised that the majority of soil movements caused by trees are seasonal; for this reason, **in the majority of situations, underpinning is avoidable and unnecessary**. However, underpinning should be the preferred method when:

i)   there is a significant persistent moisture deficit and associated risk of heave or recovery which is likely to be unacceptable in duration or extent;

ii) the foundations are so shallow that any vegetation is likely to continue to produce unacceptable foundation movement, irrespective of reasonable efforts at vegetation management;

iii) any trees which might require felling or pruning are of sufficient amenity value as to preclude such work.

BRE Digest 352 advocates that underpinning is only justifiable where movements are progressive. This is correct and would apply if there is likelihood of heave or recovery. However, if the foundations are too shallow or the tree must be retained, any movements should probably be defined as seasonal, rather than progressive. In these situations underpinning would still be justified if the amplitude of the movements are excessive. It should be the extent, not the type of movement, which determines the need to underpin.

Underpinning methods are described in many engineering publications (e.g. Hunt *et al.*, 1991 and the Institution of Structural Engineers, 1994), so that it is unnecessary to describe these methods in detail here.

Although detailed descriptions are not required, it is appropriate to note some general principles in respect of features which are particularly relevant to underpinning against tree root activity.

- Diagnosis must identify the full extent of existing foundation movement to ensure, as a minimum, that these movements are stopped. Level monitoring will identify the lateral extent of movement, as well as confirming the cause.

- In particular, if a building is in multiple ownership (semi-detached or terraced), root activity will not necessarily stop at the boundary. Partial underpinning which stops at the boundary is often a recipe for disaster (Case Studies 2, 7 and 15).

- If a partial underpinning scheme is employed, it must be remembered that this might be effective in stopping existing movement, but if it creates differential foundation depth, it may increase the risk of future problems.

- If underpinning is sufficient to deal with the full extent of existing soil drying, and if the tree is unlikely to grow significantly larger, it may be possible to retain the tree which has caused the soil drying. Consideration should always be given to this option, which can often be achieved with little or no increase in the depth or cost of underpinning.

- Chapter 9 has emphasised the inherent variability between individual trees of the same species. This, compounded by the variability in the soil, makes it impractical to predict the depth and extent of soil drying. Underpinning design should therefore always be based on site-specific soil investigations. (Proper investigations will be required anyway to confirm that there is a persistent moisture deficit, and that underpinning is justified).

- In particular, generalised guidance such as that contained in NHBC Standards Chapter 4.2, is inappropriate and should not be used for design of underpinning. That guidance is intended to be sufficient to cope with the majority of trees (see also Chapter 18). However, the trees which cause damage are likely to be the more extreme individuals, which are capable of causing extra depth or extent of drying. For this reason additional depth or extent of underpinning may well be required.

Underpinning against heave. This should usually be the only situation where underpinning is justified (except for those cases where the foundations are particularly shallow, or the tree is exceptionally valuable).

Heave will not continue indefinitely, and by the time it is apparent and diagnosed, the worst of the movement is often over. Before embarking on underpinning, it is therefore essential to confirm that movements are still continuing at an unacceptable rate, and that they are likely to continue to move for an unacceptable duration. Level monitoring, combined if necessary with quantitative assessment of soil moisture deficit and estimates of potential heave movement, will be required as the basis for this decision. Provided the monitoring has been started from the onset, obtaining the necessary information should not cause any unacceptable delay.

The objective is to transfer the building load to a level below the zone of soil desiccation and swelling, and to isolate the foundations above this level from the upward (and outward) forces exerted by the swelling soil. Boreholes, and careful examination of soil conditions, will normally be required to determine the appropriate bearing level.

Most of the normal systems of underpinning can be used against heave. In practice, because of the depths normally involved, pier and beam or pile and beam is usually employed. With these systems it is essential that:

i) the piers should extend to below the level of soil desiccation;

or ii) the piles should extend sufficiently far into non-desiccated soil to provide the required support;

iii) the pier, or pile, is sleeved throughout the zone of soil desiccation to prevent uplift. Provided the sides of the pier or pile are smooth, a double skin of 1000g polythene is sufficient for this purpose, but if the edges are rough, sufficient friction can be generated to lift the pier or pile (Case Study 4);

iv) piles should be reinforced to below the level of desiccation. There should also be reinforcing at the junction of the piles or piers with the beams (Case Study 16);

v) the underside of the beam should be entirely isolated from the underlying soil, leaving sufficient space to accommodate all of the potential soil swelling. The common practice of casting the beam within the existing foundations and leaving the existing footings *in situ* without creating any gap, is a frequent cause of failure (Case Studies 4, 14, 16, 18);

vi) all floors should be suspended, again leaving sufficient gap to allow for potential uplift;

vii) precautions should be taken against horizontal soil swelling forces on the piers. If desiccation all round the pier is uniform, these forces will cancel out and not create problems, provided the pier is excavated straight into the desiccated soil without leaving an access trench on one side. If such trench is left and the pier formed with shuttering and then backfilled, there will be inadequate constraint on one side of the pier and risk of lateral displacement (Case Study 4). If there is a risk of this, or if the desiccation is asymmetric around the pier, the sides of the pier should be lined with a void former.

If continuous strip underpinning is used, and the soil enclosed within the foundations is liable to swell more than the surrounding soil, (either because it is more desiccated, or because surrounding trees are being retained so keeping external soil at low moisture content) it is advisable to line both sides of the foundations with a void former.

Underpinning shallow foundations. Foundations which are less than about 800mm deep will be vulnerable to seasonal soil movement caused by transpiration from most types of vegetation. Foundations less than 500mm may also suffer movement as a result of surface evaporation of moisture, irrespective of vegetation. These movements will usually be sufficiently uniform for it not to cause significant damage. However, the shallower the foundations, the greater the risk

of differential movement. Shallow foundations of variable depth will be particularly vulnerable. Shallow foundations can also be vulnerable to freezing (ice formation causes the soil to swell).

If foundations are vulnerable to continuing damage irrespective of the effects of tree root activity, underpinning may be required. It is questionable whether the tree should be blamed for the need, or costs, for such work, even if the deeper root activity of the tree has contributed to any existing damage.

Underpinning in this situation is usually only required to provide a modest increase in depth, or to provide a uniform depth. In this situation continuous strip underpinning will usually be the most cost effective.

If underpinning is required because of the inadequate depth of existing foundations, consideration should be given to whether this increased depth is sufficient to allow retention of trees, or whether a slight additional increase in depth is desirable to achieve this.

It is sometimes suggested that continuous underpinning is more effective than a pier and beam system as it also acts as a barrier to root spread. However, in most situations roots will be able to penetrate beneath the underpinning without necessarily causing significant drying below the underpinning, just as roots can extend below foundations without causing significant damage. However, any roots which pass beneath the underpinning may be able to proliferate and exploit the soil beneath the original foundations, if these have been retained on other parts of the building. For this reason, continuous underpinning should not be considered an effective root barrier.

Underpinning to allow tree retention. Although underpinning is expensive, some trees are of sufficient value to warrant such expenditure (Case Study 15). Methods exist for assessing amenity value (e.g. Arboricultural Association, 1990), but these are subjective and not necessarily appropriate as a basis for comparing the relative merits of tree removal or underpinning. For this reason an assessment must be made on an individual basis whether any tree is of sufficient importance to retain.

If a property is being underpinned so that a tree can be retained, it is essential to ensure that the scope of underpinning is sufficient, both in terms of its depth and extent. As previously noted, NHBC guidelines may not be sufficient for this purpose.

The choice of action

It should be apparent from this chapter that there are many potential options for remedial action. In the past there was a near automatic choice to underpin, but it is now increasingly realised that, as vegetation and trees in particular are the chief cause of subsidence, it is logical to consider vegetation management, both as a means of control to prevent damage and as a remedy for any damage.

Although there are a variety of potential remedies, circumstances should usually dictate which of the remedies is most appropriate. The correct decision should seek to achieve stability of the foundations in the most cost-effective manner. In this context, there should be an appropriate balance between the financial cost of the action and any environmental cost in terms of tree removal or pruning. Thus, an extensive and deep underpinning system, provided it is correctly designed and implemented, should ensure stability but the expense may be prohibitive, and would be totally unjustified if the same stability could be achieved at minimum environmental cost by felling or pruning one, or a few, trees, unless these trees are of exceptional value.

As circumstances can vary so widely, it is inadvisable to stick too rigidly to a decision flowchart, but Figure 17.14 provides a basis which may be applicable in many situations.

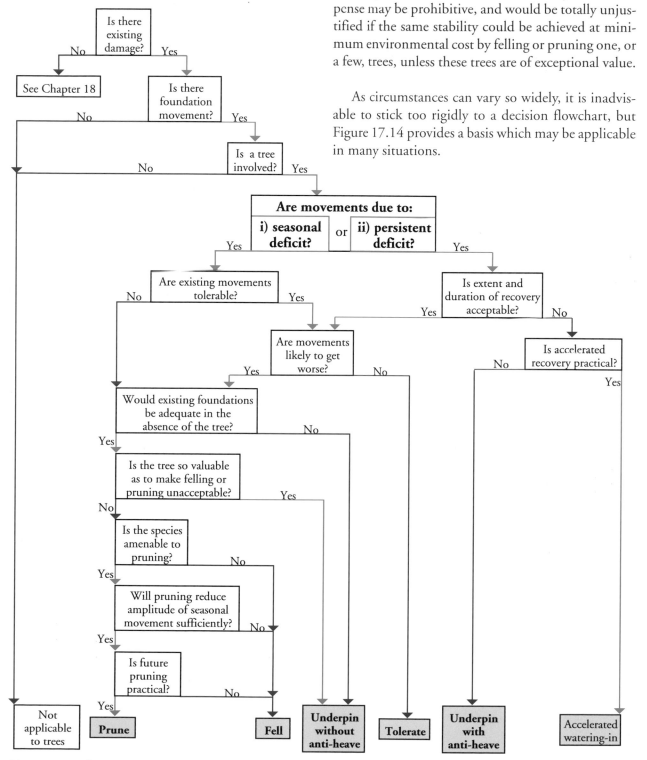

Figure 17.14

Decision flowchart for remedial works

Assuming that the investigations confirm that a tree, or trees, are involved, the crucial factor for determining the remedy is whether a significant persistent deficit is present. If it is, and the recovery or heave movements cannot be tolerated, underpinning is essential. However, if the movements are predominantly seasonal but of unacceptable amplitude, felling or pruning should be the preferred option, provided this does not involve excessive environmental damage and the existing foundations would be adequate after this action has been taken. The choice between felling and pruning is dependent on whether it is sufficient merely to reduce the amplitude of seasonal soil movements or whether more radical action is required, and also on whether the tree is amenable to pruning. Any action with the trees or other vegetation should be part of an overall management plan, which should consider appropriate replanting as well as tree removal.

Superstructure repair

Once the foundations are stabilised sufficiently and there is reasonable certainty that unacceptable movements will not recommence, cracks can be repaired and redecorated In the past, this work was often undertaken without appropriate action to trees to ensure adequate stability, with inevitable consequences in the next dry period. If a building has been underpinned, it is necessary to allow time for the new foundations to settle.

The extent and method or repair should be specified by an engineer or builder, and is outside the scope of this book. However, if cracks are repaired using modern techniques such as resin bonding which restore the structural integrity, the building will regain its original ability to withstand some movement. If complete stability has not been achieved and there is a risk of further minor damage, the practical steps described on page 276 can help to ensure that any further damage is masked.

Summary

1.   Remedial works should aim to provide sufficient stability of the foundations so as to ensure that unacceptable superstructure movements do not occur.

2.   Most buildings are able to tolerate some movement. A greater willingness to accept this, both by the house owner and also by all professionals who assess the significance of damage and provide advice, should be encouraged.

3.   Cost-effectiveness should be the basis for deciding on the most appropriate remedial action. This must include consideration of environmental costs of tree felling or pruning, as well as financial costs.

4.   Where movements are **predominantly seasonal**, or the extent and duration of heave or recovery is acceptable, **tree felling** can eliminate all deep-seated soil drying and thus restabilise the foundations, provided the foundations are deep enough to prevent movement from drying by short-rooted vegetation and evaporation from the surface.

5.   Where movements are predominantly seasonal, pruning can reduce the amplitude of the seasonal movement to an acceptable level. In some circumstances it can provide a viable alternative to felling, but there must be a commitment to a continuing pruning regime.

6.   Where there is a **persistent deficit** and risk of heave of unacceptable extent or duration, **underpinning** is usually the only method of restabilising the foundations. Such underpinning must include **anti-heave precautions**.

7.   In rare circumstances, accelerated recovery by watering-in may provide an alternative where there is a persistent deficit.

8.   Root barriers and other methods of trying to control root growth are unlikely to be practical or reliable.

9.   The efficacy of any form of vegetation management or soil recovery should be confirmed by a period of level monitoring to demonstrate that all movement has been reduced to an acceptable amount.

Additional reading

Hunt, R., R.H. Dyer and R. Driscoll (1991). Foundation movement and remedial underpinning in low-rise buildings. Building Research Establishment Report.

Address

Directories of Registered Arboricultural Consultants and Contractors:

Arboricultural Association
Ampfield House
Ampfield
Nr. Romsey SO51 9PA
Tel: 01794 368717

Block of flats with independent deep foundations for flank wall – Severe subsidence from closely adjacent trees – Polythene around foundations preventing seasonal recovery – Trees felled and recovery accelerated by watering-in, providing rapid and effective remedy.

Case Study Figure 17.1

Front elevation of block of flats showing vehicle access beside left flank.

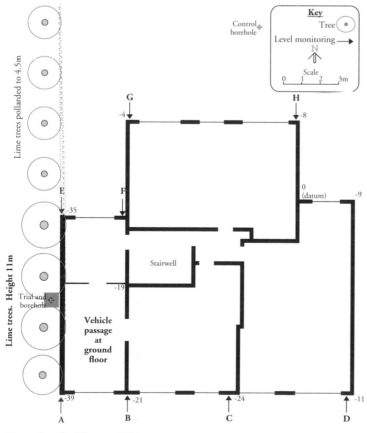

Case Study Figure 17.2

Site plan including location of level monitoring markers and results of engineer's level distortion survey (mm) in March 1983.

The Building

The building comprises a three storey block of flats (CS Figure 17.1), built in late 1976 / early 1977. In order to provide access to garages at the rear of the site, the design omitted the ground floor rooms adjacent to the left flank, but provided an archway for vehicle access at this position. The base of this left flank wall was constructed of solid 35cm thick brickwork, reducing to a 25cm thick cavity wall at first and second floor levels. The layout of the site is shown in CS Figure 17.2; it is in north east London, on London Clay.

The trees

In the adjoining property to the left, 1m from the boundary, was a row of lime trees; four of these trees were directly adjacent to the left flank wall of the flats. When young these trees had been regularly and heavily pollarded to a height of 2.5m, but prior to 1976 they had been allowed to sprout and were recorded as being 4.5m high at that time. After the flats were built the trees to the rear had been kept regularly pollarded, but those beside the flank had been allowed to grow to screen the blank wall. By 1983 they each consisted of 2 or 3 long stems which supported the crown extending above the building to a height of 11m. In addition to these lime trees, there was a large copper beech in the adjacent garden in front of the flank.

Previous history and investigations

Construction was completed in June 1977, with engineer-designed foundations.

In January 1982 the tenant in the 2nd floor flat above the arch reported cracking but took no action at that stage. By August 1982 the cracking was worse and structural engineers were instructed. At the same time a new tenant occupied the first floor flat directly over the arch and redecorated. In March 1983 it was considered that there had been further deterioration since August.

Trial pits were excavated at the front and rear of the flank. These confirmed that the foundations were 750mm wide trench fill, extending to 2.4m below ground level at the front and 2.1m at

297

the rear. On the opposite side of the archway the foundations were 2.0m deep. All of the foundation trenches were lined with a double skin of polythene. The subsoil was a stiff brown fissured clay, typical of London Clay. Fine lime roots were identified adjacent to the base of the foundations, and roots of other trees were identified at shallow levels.

The results of a level distortion survey by the engineer are shown in CS Figure 17.2; they show a general tilt with an additional 18mm distortion of the flank wall.

Further investigations

I first visited the property in May 1983, and was sceptical that foundations in excess of 2m depth would be affected. I was also dubious about the involvement of the trees in view of the damage first being recorded in January (1982), and the alleged deterioration between August 1982 and March 1983.

Level monitoring was started on 6th May. The position of the stations is shown on the site plan. There were two independent sets of readings on the front and rear elevations, in each case using the stations on the right flank as the datum (i.e. stations D and H), with no attempt made to relate these to each other. Stations C, B, F and G on the main building showed negligible differential movement throughout the period of monitoring; the results for station B are included in CS Figure 17.3 but are otherwise omitted for clarity. Movements of the front and rear of the flank were considerable; the readings up to September 1984 when the trees were felled are shown in CS Figure 17.3.

It will be noted that there was no recovery between 30th September and 6th December 1983, which increased my scepticism about the involvement of the trees. By that time, just over 20mm of subsidence of the flank had been recorded.

By 2nd May 1984 slight recovery (2.9mm at the front, 1.6mm at the rear) had been recorded. A further trial hole was dug adjacent to the foundations. At this point the foundations were 2.5m deep, with the same double skin of polythene observed in the previous holes. Roots, identified as lime, were observed growing down the interface between the polythene and clay. Despite the hole being dug at the end of the winter and a wet spring, the ground was very dry. The reason for this became apparent when it was observed that the polythene lining of the foundations was acting as a water-filled bag, preventing water seeping down any gap between the foundations and soil and reaching the adjacent ground. Large volumes of water had been trapped and poured out when the bag was punctured. The soil below the foundations was moist in only a localised area beside a joint in the polythene.

I drilled a borehole into the base of the trial pit and took samples for moisture content determination; the results are shown in CS Figure 17.4.

While drilling this borehole, abundant fine roots were observed to 3.35m and occasional roots to 3.75m (i.e. to 1.25m below the base of foundations).

Damage

Damage was entirely restricted to those parts of the two flats directly above the archway adjacent to the flank. Crack widths increased dramatically during the summers of 1983 and 1984, with these cracks particularly apparent on the front wall (CS Figure 17.5a and b) and rear wall (CS Figure 17.5c). The flank wall rotated outwards causing gaps around the door in the central partition wall (CS Figure 17.5d), and there was also lateral movement of the flank wall at d.p.c. level (CS Figure 17.5e). Movement was sufficient to fracture some service pipes, and to require evacuation of the flats in April 1984.

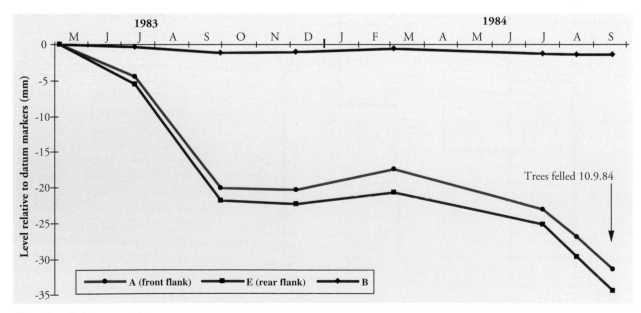

Case Study Figure 17.3
Results of level monitoring prior to felling trees in September 1984.

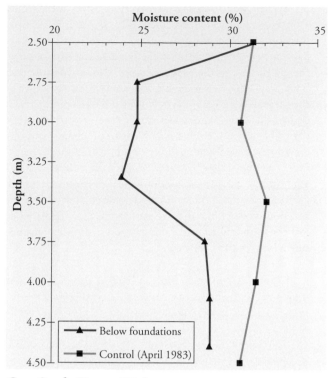

Case Study Figure 17.4

Moisture content profile (2/5/84) beneath 2.5m deep foundations of flank wall. Control profile by engineer (April 1983).

DISCUSSION

Cause of damage

Although the lack of recovery during the initial winter made me sceptical about the involvement of the trees, the condition of the polythene liner in the foundation trench provided a logical explanation. Normally water can flow down the face of the foundations in the gap which develops as the clay shrinks away from the foundations. However in this case this water was trapped by the polythene, with this polythene maintaining a tight seal to the soil. The only water penetrating to the underside of foundations was very localised at a joint in the polythene, although large volumes were present in the bag. As a result of this, negligible rehydration and recovery had occurred.

The borehole confirmed the presence of fine root activity from the lime tree below the foundations of the flank wall. On the basis of this root activity and the low values of moisture content down to 3.75m compared to the control which had been drilled previously by the engineer, the soil appeared to be desiccated, with a calculated soil moisture deficit of 144mm. Assuming a water shrinkage factor of 4, this would suggest shrinkage of 36mm. This correlates closely with the 18mm subsidence recorded by the level monitoring plus the 18mm distortion prior to the commencement of monitoring = 36mm.

Engineering calculations confirmed an acceptable factor of safety for the foundation load and that settlement should not be significant.

All of this information confirmed that the trees were the sole cause of the subsidence.

a) front wall beside flank.

b) front wall below window.

c) rear wall beside flank.

d) cross partition wall.

e) d.p.c. at rear of flank wall.

Case Study Figure 17.5

Cracks (September 1984) in first floor flat, showing location of some of demec monitoring studs.

Remedial action

The estimated 144mm soil moisture deficit was recorded in the spring, indicating that it was a persistent deficit. It was apparent that the low permeability of the clay, combined with the tight seal between the polythene and the clay which prevented the foundations acting as a sump, was greatly restricting the amount of seasonal recovery; as a result the recovery recorded during the winter was only 3.0mm at the front and 1.6mm at the rear. As the potential for recovery was estimated at 36mm, it was apparent that movement would continue for many years if the trees were felled, whilst retention of the trees would aggravate the subsidence still further.

The depth of the existing foundations made conventional underpinning impractical. Furthermore, the adjacent owner would not allow access from outside the flank wall, and working from inside would have blocked vehicle access which was essential for the other residents and for safety. For these same reasons, a piled underpinning solution was not practical. Consideration was therefore given to demolishing the two flats above the archway, and rebuilding on new piled foundations. The costs of this would obviously be considerable, and the works would cause disturbance and inconvenience to the other residents.

As an alternative, I suggested that consideration be given to felling the trees and accelerated recovery by watering-in. The situation lent itself to such treatment, as only the flank wall was affected, and the strength and stiffness of the wall would minimize problems from differential rates of recovery.

This course of action was agreed at a meeting in March 1984, and the co-operation of the neighbours was sought for the immediate felling of the trees. Procrastination by the tree owners, (and their ridiculous claim that the damage was being caused by heave, not subsidence!) meant that the trees were not felled until 10th September 1984.

Case Study Figure 17.6

Mini drill-rig boring holes at angle beneath foundations for accelerated recovery.

During that summer, a further 14mm of subsidence occurred (CS Figure 17.3), so that total subsidence during the period of monitoring was 34.4mm at the rear and 31.3mm at the front of the flank. Associated with this was serious deterioration in the condition of the two flats above the arch so that by September 1984 the damage was assessed as Category 4 "Severe"; CS Figure 17.5 illustrates the condition at that time, with cracks up to 20mm wide.

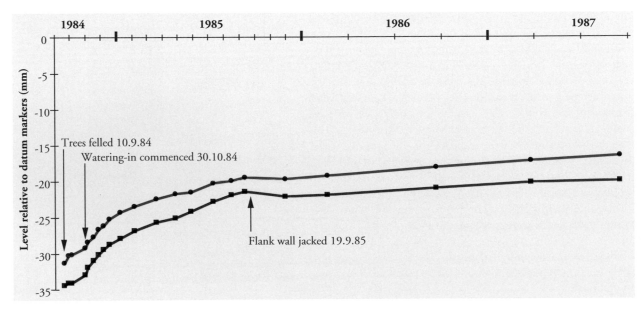

Case Study Figure 17.7

Monitoring accelerated recovery after trees felled (excluding movement during jacking)

Once the trees were felled, the watering-in system was installed. A mini drill rig with continuous flight augers was used to bore 100mm diameter holes to a depth of 5m (CS Figure 17.6). There were 11 such holes at 1m intervals adjacent to the wall, drilled at a slight angle so that the base of the hole was directly below the foundations. The holes were filled with coarse sand to within 2m of ground level, with a polypropylene pipe installed in the sand. The top of the hole was then sealed with concrete, and the pipes connected together and fed from a watertank with a ball valve control.

Monitoring of recovery movements

I continued the level monitoring, using the markers previously attached. CS Figure 17.7 records the movements.

In addition, demec strain gauge studs were attached across a selection of the external cracks and internal cracks in the first floor flat. Many of these were later changed for reading by vernier calliper. CS Figure 17.8 summarises the crack movements which were recorded (for clarity, only a selection are shown). With the exception of station M, all of the cracks showed a similar pattern with rapid closure after the water was switched on and a diminishing rate after a few months. Station M recorded a steady rate of movement throughout; this was recording the lateral movement at d.p.c. level, with the wall apparently moving out below d.p.c.. This was probably caused by the lateral swelling of the clay pushing the base of the foundations inwards, with the concrete drive acting as a fulcrum. This lateral swelling was being resisted by the clay on the opposite face, and so could only occur slowly as this clay consolidated under load.

The levels showed slight recovery even while the boreholes were being installed, presumably because water was needed to lubricate the drill. During October the water supply was not properly connected, and only limited movement occurred, but at the end of October the water was switched on permanently and the recovery accelerated. By January the rate of movement was starting to slow down, and provision of water was stopped after April.

Recovery by the beginning of February 1985 was 7.7mm; and by extrapolation of the recovery curve it was clear that the total recovery movements would only be about 14mm. As this was going to leave the building considerably distorted, it was decided that the flank wall should be jacked.

This jacking was eventually carried out by Pynford South Limited. Jacks were installed immediately above the concrete of the trench fill; it was also considered necessary to build in a reinforced beam for the jacks to bear on. Once this was cured, the flank wall was lifted by the jacks on 19th September 1985. Just prior to the jacking, the total natural recovery of the front of the flank was 12.3mm and at the rear it was 13.4mm; the jacking produced a further lift of 35.3mm at the front and 35.0mm at the rear, taking the flank wall back to its original level as determined from the initial distortion survey.

The level monitoring after the jacking showed a brief downward trend as a result of consolidation under the increased load imposed on the foundations by this realignment of the superstructure. Thereafter recovery continued slowly, with a further 3.3mm at the front and 2.2mm at the rear over a 22 month period, i.e. a rate of less than 2mm per annum. Movements of this rate are unlikely to cause any significant cracking.

The jacking produced dramatic closure of the cracks. The worst cracks around the rear window and the doorway in the cross partition, which had closed naturally by nearly 4mm, showed a further 11mm of closure. All other cracks also closed.

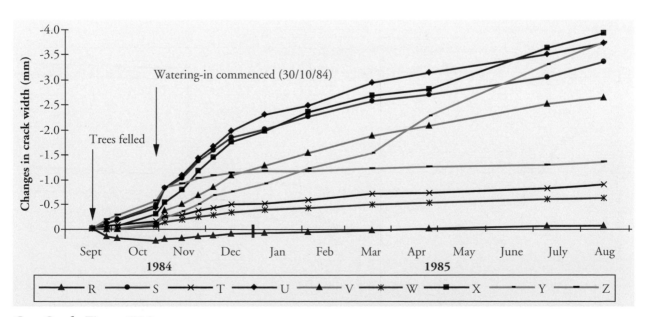

Case Study Figure 17.8

Monitoring crack widths during accelerated recovery prior to jacking (for location of demec studs, see Figure 17.5)

Full reinstatement of the superstructure was carried out soon after the jacking and the flats re-occupied. It is understood that no further damage has occurred.

Various legal claims were successfully pursued, primarily against the engineer involved in the original design, as the depth of foundations did not accord with guidelines in force at that time (the 1974 edition of NHBC Practice Note 3), although it should be noted that they would have complied with the current guidelines in NHBC Standards Chapter 4.2. A claim was also made against the owners of the tree in respect of the additional costs incurred as a result of his delay in abating the nuisance after he was notified.

Lessons to be learnt

- The effect of these comparatively small lime trees had gone surprisingly deep. However, the trees were in very close proximity, and some of the research into the effects of this species has also shown a localised very deep influence.

- The polythene around the foundations provided a very effective seal with the clay. This prevented the foundations acting as a sump. As a result, there was very little seasonal recovery, thus allowing the development of a considerable persistent deficit.

- The damage would have been prevented, and the trees could have been retained, if the original foundations had been piled to a greater depth.

- This building was particularly suited to the watering-in exercise. Only the flank wall was affected, with no cross walls, and this wall had strong foundations to resist any differential movement.

- The watering-in process was very effective and achieved the desired result of restabilising the foundations. However, even with the boreholes at 1m intervals and a regular supply of water, there was a years' delay between when the trees were felled and eventual reinstatement. This might be considered unacceptable, but it should be noted that most of the movement occurred within a brief 3 month period. The 12 month delay could have been shortened if watering-in had commenced immediately after the trees were felled, and if the jacking had been undertaken at an earlier stage.

- Even more time could have been saved if the trees had been felled promptly when the original request was made in April 1984. Prompt action would also have prevented the severity of damage increasing from Category 3 to Category 4.

- The total recovery was only 15mm, which was just under 50% of the recorded subsidence and less than 30% of the total subsidence. It was also considerably less than the predicted movements. This lack of recovery was probably due to additional consolidation settlement combined with dynamic settlement.

- Any other method of reinstatement would have taken as long, if not longer, as well as being far more expensive and disruptive.

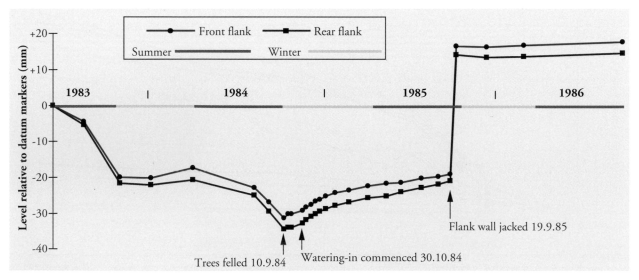

Case Study Figure 17.9
Overall movements of flank wall throughout period of monitoring. Jacking lifted to above datum to take account of distortion prior to commencement of monitoring.

"In open country situations, during drought it [strong clay] is apt to split and cause fracture to the building unless the foundation be laid below the range of fissures which occur in it" (Bartholomew, 1841)

There is nothing new in guidelines for preventing damage.

Introduction

The means exist to ensure that trees do not cause damage to any building. There are two options for this:

i) provision of foundations of sufficient depth to ensure that foundation movements cannot occur, combined with the use of materials for underground services which are sufficiently flexible.

ii) spatial separation between trees and structures sufficient to ensure that movements cannot occur.

Whilst either of these options could be fully effective and might conceivably be adopted, their implementation in full, sufficient to stop all damage, would involve financial or environmental costs which are generally considered to be unacceptable. The most economical deep foundation is to pile, but the costs of this are greater than traditional shallow trench fill foundations and would be difficult to justify. Spatial separation could either involve decreasing the density of housing, which has implications for housing costs and land availability, or alternatively elimination of trees from most urban locations, which is unacceptable in environmental terms. Even if these options were to be adopted in future, they do not address the problems created by the existing housing stock, most of which have shallow foundations, nor the existing trees, many of which are close to buildings.

Although damage might be prevented by adopting these options, the costs of doing so needs to be compared with the cost of correcting damage if it occurs. In general terms prevention may be better than cure, but the costs and implications of both deserve consideration, so as to achieve a sensible compromise.

There are three main situations where action may be appropriate to prevent damage. The approach, and the balance between the options for preventing damage, may differ in these situations. These situations are:

i) construction of new buildings:
    a) near existing trees;
    b) without existing trees;

ii) where there are existing buildings with existing trees in their proximity;

iii) planting trees near existing buildings.

The methods for dealing with these situations are considered in later sections of this Chapter, but before doing so it is relevant to consider our ability to predict how trees and buildings interact, as this should be fundamental to any guidelines on preventing damage.

The prediction of damage

There are two potential methods for predicting situations where damage is likely to occur:

i) by analysis of data from existing situations where damage has, or has not, occurred.

ii) from knowledge of the interaction of the tree, soil and building.

Prediction from data analysis. There are very extensive data on situations where damage has occurred. For instance, the Kew Root Survey (Cutler and Richardson, 1989) includes data on the proportion of cases where damage has occurred on shrinkable clay soils at varying distance of trees from buildings; the results for oak are reproduced in Figure 18.1.

Cases of damage (%)	Distance from damage (m)
0	over 30
10	18 - 30
15	13 - 18
25	9.5 - 13
25	6 - 9.5
25	1.3 - 6

Figure 18.1

Data from Kew Root Survey on the proportion of cases of damage occurring within certain bands of distance from oak trees on shrinkable clay soils.

(from Cutler and Richardson 1989)

Whilst this tells us about the proximity of oak trees to buildings in cases where damage has occurred, it provides no information to relate this to the overall tree population. This published data also contains no information on important aspects such as the characteristics of the clay, the depth of foundations, the construction of the building, the extent of damage, or the growth and condition of the tree. Additional data of this sort may be available on their original record cards, and there are undoubtedly other records, particularly in the files of insurance companies, with data of this sort where damage has occurred. However, to the best of my knowledge, there is no data, nor reliable means for determining, those situations where damage has not occurred. **For this reason this data should not be used for predicting the risk of damage occurring.**

The analysis above is based on sample cards for 293 cases where oak trees have caused damage; one can therefore deduce that the Survey recorded 73 cases of damage where the tree was between 9.5 to 13m from the building. However, there must be many thousands of oak trees growing on shrinkable clay soils within this range of buildings. Some of these other trees will also be causing damage, but without information to relate the sample to the overall population, it is not possible to make an assessment about the risk of a tree causing damage.

Although no extensive analyses have been undertaken on the incidence of damage, I have analysed the record of insurance claims involving plane trees growing in the pavements of part of one of the London Boroughs. This was in connection with a claim involving a plane tree 5.3m from a building on London Clay. The tree had a history of pollarding, but after the mid 1960's had been allowed to grow larger with only intermittent crown reduction, so that it had reached a height of 18m by 1989. The computer records of the local authority show that there were 1305 plane trees with a similar history, growing in compa-

rable locations in that part of London. The number of subsidence claims in which these trees were alleged to be involved during the period 1975 to 1989 is shown in Figure 18.2. During this period there is little indication of the number of claims increasing as the trees grew. The total number of claims during this 15 year period was 54, or 4.1% of the population. This represents a rate of less than 0.3% of the trees being involved in a claim per year.

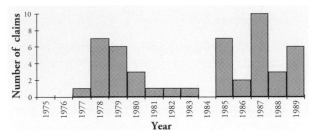

Figure 18.2

Number of claims for subsidence damage within a population of 1305 comparable plane trees in a London Borough during the period 1975 to 1989.

A far wider-ranging estimate of the incidence of damage might be derived from the total number of insurance claims per year. As shown in Figure 1.3, in recent "bad years" such as 1995 or 1996, there were about 45,000 claims. It has been estimated that, as a conservative figure, there are likely to be at least 100 million amenity trees in urban areas of Britain (Forestry Research Co-ordination Committee, 1988). If 80% of subsidence cases involve a tree (see page 5), even in a bad year the number of subsidence claims only involves 0.036% of the amenity tree population. Obviously, even in urban areas, a proportion of the trees will be well clear of buildings, but this does support the concept that only a small proportion of trees are the cause of damage.

The Kew Root Survey also presents graphs showing "the reduction in percentage of cases of damage recorded as the distance of trees from buildings increases (for shrinkable clay soils)"; the blue lines in Figure 18.3 show this graph for oak. It shows the distance within which 50% of cases of damage occurred (i.e. the median distance), but provides no indication of the shape of the graph within this range close to the building. There are many misunderstandings about the interpretation of these graphs, for instance it is often believed that the curve should be extrapolated upwards. The method of their derivation is described in Cutler and Richardson (1989), and Figure 18.3 includes a histogram, derived as they describe from the original data for the oak trees, on which the blue lines are superimposed. This shows that, if the complete curve is presented, it has a positive skew distribution.

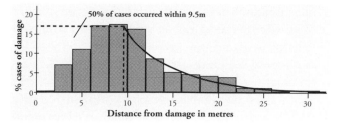

Figure 18.3

Method for derivation of graphs presented by Cutler and Richardson (1989). The red histogram shows the actual number of cases of damage at different distances of trees from buildings, with the blue lines showing the results as presented by Cutler and Richardson. The data are for oak trees.

The derivation of this curve must be appreciated when interpreting these results. Its overall shape provides some indication of the inherent variation in the results; the wider and straighter the curve, the greater the standard error and the more variable the distance within which damage occurs. Inspection of the results for other species, for instance for cherry, shows a very narrow curve but with a long tail, indicating that most cases of damage occur within a close distance (50% within 3m and 90% within 7.5m), but a few extend up to 11m. The maximum height of the curve and the horizontal intercept of the dashed line is not relevant, except in so far as low values indicate a wide curve, and vice versa. The shape of the curves provides no information on the risk of damage.

As noted in Chapter 9 and shown in Figure 9.5, (page 143), the Kew Root Survey also provides information on the **maximum** recorded distance where damage has occurred (for oak the distance is 30m.) This maximum distance was used by The Institution of Structural Engineers (1994) as the basis for Table 6 of their report on subsidence of low rise buildings, but the caption to that table refers to "**minimum** distance to trees" and the table also refers to "safe distance". If it is intended to adopt a policy of spatial separation to stop any possibility of damage, these distances might be relevant. However, the risk of a tree causing damage at any lesser distance must be only a small fraction of 1% (once again, without data the exact percentage cannot be specified). **If these distances were to be enforced, it would eliminate the vast majority of trees from the urban landscape.**

These same distances also appear in an influential report of the Loss Prevention Council (1995); in this case the heading to their table is more accurate by referring to "typical safe distance to tree, outside which the tree is unlikely to affect subsidence (or heave) of the building." If this type of information is used solely in this way, that is to denote distances beyond which

the tree is very unlikely to ever have any influence, it would be appropriate and reasonable, but the information is almost inevitably misinterpreted. Even the Loss Prevention Council, in referring to this table, interpret it as the "influencing distance".

Gasson and Cutler (1998) also consider that the maximum distance is a misuse of their data. They suggest the adoption of the 75% distance for all trees, except those with the potential to grow very large, for which the 90% figures are more appropriate. They further advocate that should be applied to new planting only, and not for existing trees which may have grown for many years without causing damage.

Prediction based on knowledge of interaction of tree, soils, and building. If it is possible to define with reasonable accuracy:

i)   the patterns of soil drying which are likely to occur in the vicinity of trees;

ii) the extent of soil movement produced by this soil drying;

iii) the ability of the building to tolerate movement;

it should be possible to predict situations where there is an unacceptable risk of movement and damage.

Chapter 9 has emphasised the variation in patterns of soil drying, not only between different species but also between individuals, even if these are genetically identical. Likewise Chapter 5 which describes the patterns of seasonal soil drying and Chapter 6 which describes persistent moisture deficits, emphasise the variation in results of the research which is described in Volume 2. That research sought out sites where the conditions were expected to be as uniform as possible, so as to try to minimise this variation, but despite this the results are very variable and unpredictable. On less uniform sites and with less homogeneous clay soils it can be anticipated that the variation between trees will be even greater.

In the urban situation even greater variation in patterns of soil drying will be imposed by:

• the condition and previous management of the tree.

• excavations for drainage and other services. These influence soil permeability and might also serve to either introduce or remove water from the system.

- artificial sources of water, such as leaking drains or water mains.

- the condition of the soil, e.g. the soil structure which influences permeability, or compaction which can restrict the ability of roots to exploit the soil.

- impermeable surfaces which can prevent ingress of moisture.

- transpiration by other surface vegetation or evaporation from the soil surface.

The very variable patterns of soil drying will interact with:

- foundations of the building, which can vary in their depth, design and construction.

- the design and materials of the superstructure, which influence the flexibility of the building and its ability to tolerate some movement.

All of these factors combine to produce a system which is inherently variable and unpredictable. Any attempt to predict the amount of movement which will occur in specified circumstances will be subject to a massive statistical error, sufficient to make any such prediction virtually meaningless.

This need not preclude attempts to predict and prevent the risk of damage, but we must appreciate the inevitable and major limitations. We must also appreciate that **there is no advantage in trying to predict and prevent damage if the costs of doing so, either in economic or environmental terms, outweigh the benefit.**

Prevention of damage
i) a) for new buildings near existing trees

The National House-Building Council (NHBC) provides detailed guidelines for foundation design in the proximity of existing trees.

These guidelines were first produced in 1969 as Practice Note 3, (NHBRC, 1969), with this initial guidance advocating spatial separation between buildings and existing trees. These distances for clay soils were equal to the height of the tree for poplar and willow, and two-thirds of the height for all other species. On all other soils a distance of one-third height was specified for all species. These distances were to be

increased by 50% for rows or groups of trees. As an alternative to this spatial separation, the Practice Note referred to special precautions for foundation design, but it provided no details of these precautions.

In 1974 this Practice Note was revised (NHBC, 1974), and for the first time provided guidance on the necessary increase in foundation depth near all on clay soils trees to prevent damage. Greater depths were specified for poplar, elm and willow, and 50% extra depth for trees in rows and groups.

The research which is described in Volume 2 was partially funded by NHBC to provide a basis for a further revision of this Practice Note, and in 1981 I was commissioned to advise on this revision. My report (Biddle, 1981) formed the basis of the subsequent 1985 revision (NHBC, 1985). This advocated a three-stage classification of clay soils, dependent on their plasticity index, and a three-stage classification of broad-leafed tree species and two-stage classification for conifers, dependent on their "water demand". Foundation depths were defined on the basis of this 3 x 3 classification of clay and trees, and on the proximity of the tree, with some allowance made for climatic variation dependent on the geographical location. The presentation of this information was altered in 1992 (NHBC, 1992) to bring it into line with other NHBC documents, and the name was altered to Standards Chapter 4.2. Apart from minor changes and greater emphasis on precautions against heave damage, the technical content remained the same as the 1985 version.

The depths for foundations of new buildings which were being laid in proximity to existing broad-leafed tree species, as specified in the 1985 revision, are summarised in Figure 18.4.

In deciding on these depths, all available sources of information were considered. This included my own research and practical experience, information (both published and unpublished) from the Kew Root Survey, other published data from Britain and overseas, and also the previous experience of NHBC in the implementation of the 1974 version of the Practice Note.

It should be apparent from Figure 18.4 that there is intentionally a mathematical simplicity in these recommendations. The lines for the high water demand species are spaced 0.5m apart at zero D/H, and all terminate at a distance of 1.25 D/H for their relevant minimum foundation depth. Likewise the moderate water demand are 0.4m apart and all terminate at 0.75 D/H, and the low water demand are 0.3m apart and

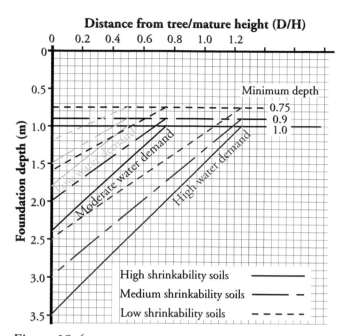

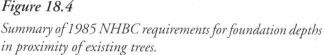

Figure 18.4

Summary of 1985 NHBC requirements for foundation depths in proximity of existing trees.

terminate at 0.5 D/H. One should not be so naive as to believe that the influence of trees would actually follow such simple guidelines. As strongly emphasised in the previous section, the influence of trees and the patterns of soil drying and movement are very unpredictable, and so it is unrealistic to expect simple guidelines to define such influence. Despite this, one frequently sees reports which seek to describe the influence of a particular tree on a building, based on circles derived from these guidelines, or even worse, a claim that the root system of a tree has a shape which accords to these guidelines.

These NHBC guidelines have merely sought to consider the potential influence and provide a recommendation on the amount by which the foundation depths should be increased in the proximity of trees. **They seek to provide a compromise between the benefits of increasing the depth so as to minimise the risk, against the costs incurred as a result of such increase.** They are intended for application for low-rise housing built under the aegis of NHBC, and as such are heavily dictated by practical building considerations, rather than any definable influence of the tree.

Obviously they are intended to provide sufficient protection and to ensure that the incidence of damage is acceptably low. Although the guidelines do not overtly acknowl-

edge it, the remit on which they were originally produced recognized that under some circumstances, particularly with an exceptional tree, soil or climatic conditions, or combination of these factors, damage will still occur. Such risk could be reduced by a further increase in foundation depth, but the cost of doing so for all new foundations would not be justified.

It is recognized that the influence of many trees goes far beyond the depth or distance suggested by these guidelines. For instance, Figure 18.5 reproduces one of the graphs included in my report to NHBC to show the depth to which I had recorded a significant soil moisture deficit during various investigations of damage to buildings in 1976/77. For these purposes a significant deficit was considered to be in excess of about 25mm (as calculated by comparing deficits close to the tree with a distant position), with all cases being on London Clay with a plasticity index in the range 35 - 55. Species which are classified as high water demand and moderate water demand are distinguished by their colour, and to aid interpretation the figure includes the lines showing the required foundation depths which were adopted in the 1985 guidelines for such species. It is apparent that, for these examples, the required foundation depths would be inadequate for deficits of this amount. This is particularly apparent for the high water demand species, as every example has a significant deficit extending well below the specified foundation depth.

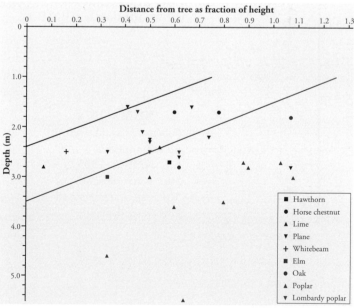

Figure 18.5

Depths to which significant moisture deficits (>25mm) were recorded during investigations of damage in 1976 and 1977 in proximity to various trees on London Clay, and also NHBC guidelines (1985) for high and moderate water demand species.

The apparent inadequacy of the foundation depth demonstrated by Figure 18.5 does not indicate that the guidelines are flawed. In all of these examples damage had already occurred, and they therefore probably indicate the extreme, rather than the average, conditions. I have no doubt that other investigators could add immensely to this data in cases where damage has occurred, but there are scant records for cases where damage has not developed.

In recognition of these many examples where site investigations indicated that significant deficits were extending to considerable depth and distance, the 1985 revision of the guidelines imposed more rigorous requirements than the 1974 version, particularly for the high water demand species on clays of high plasticity. The modest increase which was imposed reflected the experience of NHBC that the 1974 guidelines had generally been adequate for these situations. For species of moderate water demand the requirements remained essentially similar to the previous requirements for "all other species", but the inclusion of a low water demand category allowed less onerous requirements for these species. A comparison between the 1974 guidelines and the 1985 guidelines applicable to high shrinkage clays is provided by Figure 18.6.

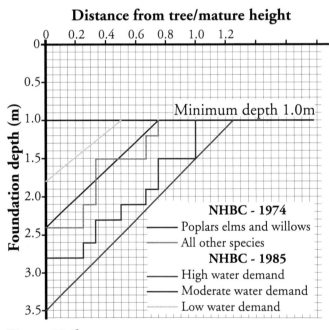

Figure 18.6

Comparison between NHBC guidelines in 1974, and in 1985 for trees on high shrinkability soils.

One of the criticisms of the 1974 version of NHBC Practice Note 3 was its failure to distinguish between clays of different characteristics. It was based primarily on information derived from more highly plastic clay soils, but was applied to all types of clay. For the

1985 revision I recommended that the plasticity index of the soil should be used as a means of distinguishing between clays, as this was deemed to be the most appropriate criterion at that time. BRE Digest 240 (1993 revision) advocates a similar, but four-stage, classification. Although plasticity index is used, as noted in Chapter 4 (page 55), it is poorly correlated to the amount of shrinkage which will occur as a result of changes in moisture content over the range of available water. I would therefore suggest that in future, when more information is obtained on the behaviour of different soils, it may be desirable to use a method which is based on the actual shrinkage characteristics of the soil.

For the soils in the high shrinkage category (plasticity index > 40) there was a lot of data on the size and proximity of trees to buildings which had suffered damage. However, for other soils there continues to be scant information on which to base recommendations, and as a result the depths which were adopted in the 1985 revision were, and remain, fairly arbitrary. As previously noted in Figure 18.4, they follow a simple mathematical progression, rather than any evidential basis.

There was also criticism that the 1974 version of Practice Note 3 lumped together all tree species, with the exception of poplars, elms and willows. A broader three-stage classification was considered desirable, but, as noted in Chapter 9 (page 147), there is scant information for deriving definitive lists. There is some information on those species of tree which occur very commonly, and also those which are particularly liable to cause damage, but there is little information on the less common species and those which rarely cause damage. For this reason the foundation depths advocated for species of low water demand are also fairly arbitrary, and also based on an assumed mathematical progression rather than evidence.

There are many other aspects of the NHBC guidelines which are highly simplified and not necessarily based on scientific facts. For instance, the reduction in foundation depth which is allowed on the basis of geographical location merely recognizes that soil moisture deficits generally diminish in the north and west of the country, and that it is reasonable to make some allowance for this.

These guidelines also provide a table of mature heights of trees. This was not intended to imply that a tree will grow to a specified height, but was dictated by the need for an unambiguous method for defining the requirements. On some sites with clay soils trees might be capable to attaining their "mature height", but in the majority of situations it will be substantially less. The guidelines are intended for builders, and it was considered inappropriate that they should form judgements on the future growth potential of a tree. However, the guidelines allow such judgement to be provided by arboriculturists, if working in conjunction with an engineer on purpose-designed foundations.

Another simplification in the NHBC guidelines is the use of the term "water demand" of trees. As noted in Chapter 9 (page 145), this term is biologically mis-leading, and has been correctly criticised by some (Lawson 1993). I proposed its use in the guidelines as being a simple term to convey the concept that different species can differ in terms of the depth, extent or intensity of soil drying which they can cause; it should not be taken as indicating any specific physiological distinction between species.

The preceding comments should not be taken to imply criticism of NHBC Standards Chapter 4.2. As noted in its introduction, it "gives the technical requirements and recommendations for building near trees, particularly in shrinkable soils". Provided it is used for this purpose, it provides admirable guidelines. However, its origins and limitations must be appreciated, particularly if one tries to extend its use to other purposes. Thus it may be inappropriate and misleading if used as:

- a model for the extent of a root system.

- a model for the influence of roots on the soil.

- a model for where damage may occur.

- guidance for tree planting.

- guidance for tree pruning.

- guidance for the design of underpinning (page 293).

- risk assessment for buildings near trees (except if using the modified system on page 312).

The emphasis in the NHBC guidelines on increasing the depth of trench or strip footings makes it easy to forget that a pile and beam foundation has many advantages on clay soils. Provided the piles are taken to sufficient depth (the effective length of the pile should ignore the section of the pile above the depths specified in the NHBC guidelines), and provided they are properly designed and installed, piles are very effective against subsidence. If they are installed in soil with a persistent deficit, appropriate precautions can be taken against heave. Piles are generally cheaper to install than trench foundations in excess of 1.5m depth, and the cost benefit will be even greater if the spoil from trench foundations needs to be removed from site and be subject to tax for waste disposal.

Prevention of damage
i) b) for new buildings without existing trees

Requirement A2 of the Building Regulations requires that:

> "The building shall be so constructed that movements of the sub-soil caused by swelling, shrinking or freezing will not impair the stability of any part of the building."

Part E provides guidance on the width of foundations required for different loads and sub-soils, but gives no guidance on depth. BS 8004:1986 "Foundations" advocates a minimum depth of 450mm as protection against frost, and on clay soils a minimum depth of 900mm below finished ground level in order to protect against the seasonal effects of grass and other vegetation. BRE Digest 298 suggests that this minimum should nowadays be increased to 1.0m.

A minimum 1.0m should be sufficient to protect against grass and similar vegetation, but will be vulnerable to damage from vegetation such as trees and shrubs which can extract moisture to greater depth. If a minimum depth is adopted, the building will remain vulnerable to tree root damage throughout its life. Such an approach is unrealistic in most situations; for instance BS 5837:1991 states (para. 10.1.1) that:

> "many buildings are likely to come into close proximity with planted or self-sown trees during their useful life, so they should be constructed to allow for future tree growth".

One has only to look at trees in proximity to existing houses to realise the truth of this, and that the public want, and expect, trees to be able to grow in reasonable proximity. In my opinion this should be interpreted as any distance in excess of half the mature height of the tree. Trees are generally appreciated and enjoyed when at distances greater than half their height from the building, but at closer distances there is often increasing concern about their proximity and stability, or annoyance at the extent of shading or from leaves falling into gutters.

In my opinion foundations should be designed to ensure a minimum risk of damage from the planting of most species of tree within this distance. The appropriate depth can be derived from NHBC Standards Chapter 4.2, using the depths applicable to moderate water demand trees. The depth will depend on the plasticity index of the soil, and will be:

Soil PI	Depth of foundation (m)
>40	1.5
20 - 40	1.25
10 - 20	1.0

This approach is advocated in BS 5837 (para. 10.4.3) and NHBC Standards Chapter 4.2 (para. D5 (d)). If these depths are used, it should ensure minimum risk to a building from a moderate water demand tree at a distance of 0.5 times its mature height, from a high water demand tree at 1.0 times its mature height, or from a low water demand tree at 0.2 times its mature height. The universal application of these depths would overcome the existing uncertainty about foundation depths and the risk of damage. **The universal use of pile foundations on clay sites would provide an even better solution.**

It is regrettable that NHBC also allow two other approaches. One allows foundations to be designed in accordance with a specified planting schedule. This will ensure that the foundations are appropriate for the initial planting scheme. However, with time the original foundation depths may be forgotten, and other trees may be planted in locations which create uncertainty about the adequacy of the foundations. The other approach allows a minimum foundation depth, but then advocates that planting should be restricted from proximity to the building. This may be reasonable in situations where tree planting is extremely unlikely, for instance in high density town housing, but should not be allowed as a means of opting out of providing deeper foundations where tree planting may be required. Allowing alternative depths will create uncertainty in the future about the risks of damage from trees.

BS 5837 has a sensible additional recommendation (para. 10.4.5) that foundation depths should be increased in any situation where trees are likely to be planted closer than half their mature height, e.g. adjacent to gable walls without windows, where trees play a valuable role in screening the wall, and are less likely to be a cause for concern (Figure 18.7).

Increasing the depth of all foundations in this way will increase the building costs and for this reason may be ignored by builders, particularly as the NHBC

Figure 18.7
Featureless gable walls and similar locations can be enhanced by tree planting, but on clay soils this is only possible if foundation depths have been increased.

guidelines allow the option of a lesser depth. For this reason appropriate planning conditions may be required when planning consent is granted for any development. The means for this exist, indeed section 197 of the Town and Country Planning Act 1990 states:

> "It shall be the **duty** of the local planning authority to ensure, whenever it is appropriate, that in granting planning permission for any development, adequate provision is made, by the imposition of conditions, for the preservation or planting of trees."

Such conditions should not only impose a required landscape scheme, but also a condition requiring foundation depths appropriate to the soil conditions. The use of planning conditions is considered further in Chapter 19, page 336.

Prevention of damage
ii)   for existing buildings with existing trees

Although increasing the depth of foundations is an option for new buildings, the vast majority of houses were built before there was awareness or concern about damage from clay shrinkage. The majority of these have shallow foundations, in many cases substantially less than 0.9m deep. Trees have been planted, usually with no regard to possible consequences, or have been self-sown, and have grown in proximity of these buildings. One has only to look at the majority of these buildings to appreciate that they have trees growing substantially closer than is advocated in general guidelines such as BRE Digest 298, or which might be inferred from NHBC Standards Chapter 4.2.

Until the last few years this had not been considered a particular problem. Damage occasionally occurred, and with increased public awareness there were increasing numbers of insurance claims. The reaction of the insurance industry was to underpin the buildings, often combining this with quite understandable demands for removal of the offending trees (although perhaps unnecessary if the underpinning was adequate). The costs of this underpinning were prohibitive (Figure 1.3) and so, rather belatedly, the insurance industry has woken to the alternative and far more sensible remedy of dealing with the offending trees.

If a building is underpinned, typical costs might be about £20,000. With costs of this magnitude it is understandable that insurers should try to avoid such expenditure by seeking the removal of all trees which might possibly cause damage in the future. However, these costs are not relevant if underpinning can be avoided by the prompt removal of those trees which have been shown to have caused damage. The cost of felling a tree, even from an awkward location, is unlikely to exceed a few hundred pounds, with similar costs for the essential monitoring of the building. In addition there will be a need for some redecoration and possible superstructure repairs but, provided prompt action is taken, these should be modest. In many situations the total cost should be less than the insurance excess. If approached in this way, most problems of tree root damage could, and should, be of little concern to the insurance industry (although perhaps remaining a justifiable concern for the house owner who may have to bear the remedial costs).

Regrettably, and illogically, insurers do not see the problems this way. Their fingers have been burnt in the past by the costs of underpinning, and they continue to equate problems of tree root damage with similar heavy losses. As a result they have been applying increasing pressure for the removal of trees in proximity of buildings, regardless of whether the tree has caused damage. This occurs most commonly when properties are sold and valued for mortgage purposes. The surveyor who undertakes the valuation is now expected to comment on any tree in proximity to the building. The surveyor will not usually have any information on sub-soil conditions or foundation depth, nor knowledge about the past or future influence of the tree on the soil, and so cannot assess the significance of the tree. However, to protect his interests, the existence of the tree is reported. If it is within the "safe distances" quoted in table 6 of the report by The Institution of Structural Engineers (1994), or table 1 of the report by the Loss Prevention Council (1995),

it is highlighted in the report. This alone may be sufficient for a mortgage to be refused unless the tree is removed - few trees are likely to survive such pressure.

If the tree is not removed on the basis of the Surveyor's report, an arboriculturist is frequently asked to report. Typically it is required that this report includes an assessment of the influence of the trees on the property at the present time and in the future, especially with reference to the risks of subsidence and/or heave.

Such requirement would be quite understandable and reasonable if:

either i) the chance of damage is so high as to justify the elimination of all trees which pose this threat;

or ii) the trees which are going to cause damage could be distinguished from the remainder;

and iii) there is reasonable action which could be taken to minimise any risk which is identified.

However, none of these circumstances will usually apply. The patterns of soil drying and movement are far too variable and unpredictable to allow accurate prediction as to which individuals are going to cause damage. Even with the benefit of detailed site investigations, accurate prediction is not possible, still less with the amount of information which is normally available as a basis for any judgement. If the individuals cannot be identified, the alternative is to deal with all of the population which might cause damage. However, as emphasised at the start of this chapter, in most situations the incidence of damage is very low, and so any such policy will inevitably cause massive and unnecessary environmental damage.

In my opinion most of those who ask for these arboricultural reports are under the misapprehension that there are effective and reasonable steps which could be taken to mitigate the risk of damage, apart from felling the tree. For instance, they instruct that the trees "be lopped to maintain their present size". This idea has probably been fostered by the regular pruning of some trees, for instance plane trees growing in pavements in close proximity to buildings, where there is a well-recognized risk of damage and pruning provides a viable preventative measure. Preventative pruning of this sort is considered in a later section (page 317). However, **pruning is unsuitable for the majority of species and in the majority of circumstances, and should not be considered the panacea for all cases of potential risk.**

It is also pertinent to re-iterate the comment in the introduction to this chapter that the costs of preventing damage need to be considered in the light of correcting damage if it occurs. The costs of prevention need to include the costs of site investigations on which to base any judgement of risk. These costs will apply to all trees which need to be investigated. In addition, there will be the financial and environmental costs of any remedial action which is deemed necessary on trees which are identified as posing an increased risk.

For instance, if there are 100 trees which require investigation because they have been identified by surveyors as being within their "safe distance", perhaps 10% (i.e. 10 trees) might be identified as posing sufficient risk to warrant preventative action. If the cost of investigating each tree is £150, the cost of this exercise alone is £15000, with say a further £200 x 10 = £2000 for the trees requiring preventative action; i.e. a total expenditure of £17,000. One should also heed the environmental damage to the trees which suffer preventative action. As noted on page 304, less than 1% of the trees are likely to actually cause damage, indicating that all this expenditure is required to prevent less than a single case of damage. As we shall see in a later section (page 315), even sophisticated investigations may not be effective in identifying those trees which pose an unacceptable risk, indicating that the cost of preventing each case of damage might be in excess of £50,000. Against these costs of preventing the damage one must balance the costs of remedial action - as previously noted, provided prompt action is taken, these would normally be less than the excess on an insurance policy, and certainly far less than the financial and environmental costs of trying to prevent the damage from occurring.

For these reasons I have expressed the opinion that it is inappropriate and unwarranted to attempt to predict and prevent damage (Biddle, 1995). There are sufficient other factors which influence and control the proximity of trees to buildings, and it is sufficient to rely on these. It will cause excessive environmental harm and be a waste of effort to try to further reduce the existing incidence of damage.

A method of risk prediction

Although it is my opinion that it is inappropriate to attempt risk prediction, and despite representations to this effect made to the Association of British Insurers and the Council of Mortgage Lenders, most insurance companies, building societies and other lenders continue to seek an assessment of the risk, and also require remedial action to trees where this risk is deemed unacceptable. In the absence of any published guidelines (except the totally inappropriate tables of distances from the Institution of Structural Engineers and the Loss Prevention Council), I have collaborated with the Arboricultural Association in the development of the method of risk assessment which is described in this section. It has been developed to take account of all of the factors which are believed, on the basis of existing knowledge, to influence the risk, and should provide the best available guidelines for assessing risk.

NHBC Standards Chapter 4.2 is a method of risk assessment relevant to foundation design. The principles which underlie that method provide an appropriate basis for developing a more detailed system for assessing the risk of subsidence. However, the NHBC model requires modification to recognise:-

i) that its recommendations are based on a cost : benefit analysis, which considers the cost of increasing foundation depth against the benefit of tree retention (and obligations imposed by planning consent). Such analysis may need modification if used in other situations;

ii) the NHBC model uses a 3-stage classification of soil shrinkage based on the plasticity index (PI) of the soil. This produces sudden steps - it would be preferable to avoid these steps by inputting actual PI values;

iii) the NHBC model uses a 3-stage classification of "water demand" of different trees. There is now more information on the behaviour of different species, particularly those which are only rarely associated with damage, so that a 6-stage classification is now suggested;

iv) the NHBC model assumes that a tree will grow to a theoretical mature size. Many trees never reach this size - actual size relevant to the site is more appropriate;

v) the NHBC model assesses size on the basis of height. It assumes a worst-case scenario, with the tree having a large crown size for its height. It makes no allowance for many trees having a small crown relative to their height (or conversely for the tree of truly exceptional size);

vi) that trees which are growing very rapidly have a greater effect on moisture abstraction than a slow-growing tree of comparable size - allowance should be made for this;

vii) a more sophisticated method is needed to take account of climatic variation across the country;

viii) consideration should be given to the vulnerability of the structure;

ix) any decision and management recommendations for trees should take account of the amenity value of the tree.

The method which is proposed is based on a mathematical expression which is derived from the NHBC recommendations. In order to derive the expression, one has to assume appropriate values of PI to correspond to the median value for the three categories of soil shrinkage which are used in the NHBC procedure. For this purpose it is assumed that the average high shrinkage soil (defined by NHBC as PI >40) has a PI = 50, and the average low shrinkage soil (defined by NHBC as PI <20) has a PI = 15. If these values are used, it can be derived that a medium shrinkage soil (defined by NHBC as PI 20 - 40) has a PI = 34.

Likewise NHBC has a 3-stage classification of water demand; the proposed method uses a 6-stage classification of tree species and allocates a species factor score to each of these categories (Figure 18.8; note that the classification reflects my recommendations in Figure 9.13). To derive the expression, it is considered that the appropriate species factor score for the NHBC

"High water demand" species = 8, and for "Low water demand" = 4.5. On this basis, it can be derived that "Moderate water demand" species = 5.6; this appears to be an appropriate value. Thus, species with a factor of 6 (*Aesculus*, etc.) have a slightly higher factor than the average for NHBC "Moderate water demand", whereas *Acer*, etc., have a slightly lower factor. Those species with a factor of 3 are considered to pose a lower risk than any of those specified by NHBC - it includes species which rarely occur in root identification or other records. Little is known about their influence, but by implication they pose a particularly low risk. Species which are not listed are assumed to have a factor of 4.

Using these values for the soil PI and species factor, one can define the ideal depth of foundations (*C*) which would be stipulated by the NHBC model for broadleafed trees as:

$$C = -0.496 - 0.293P + 0.319T + 0.00375S - 0.103PT - 0.0174PS + 0.00308TS$$

and for conifers as:

$$C = -0.518 - 1.054P + 0.322T + 0.00588S - 0.153PT - 0.0377PS + 0.00281TS$$

where:

P = the ratio of 'Distance of tree from building / tree height'.
T = the tree species factor.
S = the soil's plasticity index.

Species factor					
8	**7**	**6**	**5**	**4**	**3**
Broad-leafed genera					
Eucalyptus	*Crataegus*	*Aesculus*	*Acer*	*Ailanthus*	*Catalpa*
Populus	*Salix*	*Fraxinus*	*Castanea*	*Alnus*	*Corylus*
Quercus	*Sorbus aria*	*Platanus*	*Fagus*	*Betula*	*Ficus*
	Ulmus	*Tilia*	*Malus*	*Carpinus*	*Liquidambar*
			Prunus	*Gleditsia*	*Liriodendron*
			Pyrus	*Ilex*	*Magnolia*
			Robinia	*Juglans*	*Morus*
			Sorbus aucuparia	*Laburnum*	*Sambucus*
Coniferous genera					
Cupressus	*Chamaecyparis*	*Sequoiadendron*	*Cedrus*	*Juniperus*	*Abies*
	X Cupressocyparis		*Thuja*	*Taxus*	*Araucaria*
				Tsuga	*Ginkgo*
					Larix
					Picea
					Pinus
Shrubs			*Cotoneaster*	Other *Rosaceae*	All other shrubs
			Pyracantha		

Figure 18.8
Allocation of scores for species factor.

These formulae provide a very accurate fit to the foundation depths specified in the graphs in NHBC Tables 4, 5 and 6; the calculated depths are generally within ± 2% of the NHBC depths. They allow the ideal foundation depth (*C*) to be calculated for any value of soil plasticity and for a much wider range of species.

The formulae require input of the distance of the tree from the building, and the height of the tree. The distance can be directly measured, but the proposed method allows more detailed consideration of the height.

"Mature height" was used in the NHBC procedure as a method of defining crown size and leaf area. It assumes that a tree will reach a specified mature height, and that its size will not be influenced during its life either by environmental factors or by tree management. Whilst this provides a simple system which is suitable for builders, it does not reflect the reality of tree growth, nor the factors which influence water uptake by the tree. Ideally the total leaf area should be determined, but this is not practical; instead it has been suggested that the two-dimensional crown area provides an adequate approximation for comparing leaf area (Wilkinson, 1995).

Although NHBC only refers to height, it is suggested that, when the NHBC guidelines were being prepared, it was assumed that a mature broadleafed tree was of the shape shown in Figure 18.9. A conifer is assumed to have the same general shape, except the crown width would be 1/3 x H.

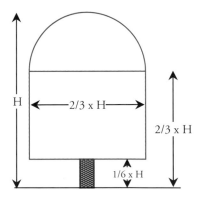

Figure 18.9

Assumed shape of NHBC model tree.

For trees of this shape, the relationship between height (H) and crown area (A) is:

for broad-leaf: for conifer:

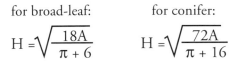

When the system is being applied, the actual crown area of the tree under inspection is determined. For this purpose the crown is considered to be one of four simplified shapes: rectangular with semi-circular top, ellipse, circular, or triangular. The crown area (A) is determined from an expression appropriate to the relevant shape, using values of crown height and crown spread which have been measured on the tree. The crown area is then adjusted, by multiplying by an appropriate factor, to make allowance for the vigour (rate of growth) of the tree; the resulting value provides a measure of the effective crown area of the tree. The factors range from 2.0 for a tree of exceptional vigour and growth rate, to 1.0 for a tree of average vigour, and 0.4 for a tree of very low vigour with extensive dieback. A tree of exceptional vigour is therefore considered to have an effective crown area twice the size of an average tree. In all cases, vigour is compared with an average healthy mature tree of that species.

This effective crown area is then used to calculate the height of the "NHBC-shaped tree" which would have an equivalent crown area. One then uses this equivalent height tree for calculating the value of *P* (distance of tree from building / height) and use this value of *P* in the mathematical expression. In this way the expression takes account of the actual tree size, with appropriate allowance for vigour and growth rate, rather than an arbitrary specified mature height.

The model therefore calculates the ideal foundation depth (*C*) which would be required in accordance with the NHBC method (with the added refinements of taking account of actual crown area, the actual plasticity index, a wider range of tree species and the vigour of the tree). This calculated value of foundation depth can then be compared against the actual foundation depth (*F*) to determine the foundation depth ratio (*W*), from *W* = *F/C*.

Although the actual foundation depth is of fundamental importance when assessing risk, it will often be unknown and must therefore be based on an assumed value, dependent on the age of the property. However, where the actual depth has been measured, obviously this value can be used.

The foundation depth ratio (*W*) is then used to determine the **subsidence risk factor** (*R*). There are various possible ways for deriving a risk factor from the foundation depth ratio, but it is suggested that a suitable expression for this purpose would be:

$$R = \frac{750}{11W - 1}$$

This expression gives a value of 75 if the actual foundation depth is the same as the ideal depth, calculated in this way. A higher value will be given if the foundations are shallower than the ideal, and vice versa. For instance, if the actual foundations are 1.0m deep but the calculated ideal depth is 3.5m (an extreme example, only applicable in exceptional circumstances), it would give a factor of 350. This factor would reduce to 220 if the calculated ideal depth is 2.5m. Conversely, if the actual depth is 1.5m, but the calculations indicate that 1.0m would be sufficient, the factor would reduce to 48.

As final refinements, this value of R is multiplied by a factor which takes account of the climatic conditions of the locality, and also any other special factor. The climatic factor was derived from the SMD values for each of the 40km MORECS squares in the country (Chapter 8, page 123). It varies from 1.0 around the Thames estuary, to a minimum value of 0.14 in parts of the Lake District. Most values in central and southern England are in excess of 0.8. The special factors recognise that buildings differ in their vulnerability to damage, with extensions and bay windows particularly vulnerable, whereas it is reasonable to accept a higher level of risk with some structures, such as garages. A wide variety of factors are advocated, varying between 1.1 to 0.5, to reflect these differences.

Efficacy of Subsidence Risk Factor (SRF) for predicting damage

The Arboricultural Association, following their discussions with the Association of British Insurers, propose that the risks associated with a subsidence risk factor derived in this way should be defined as:

SRF	Description of risk
less than 100	Insignificant
100 - 140	Low
141 - 200	Moderate
greater than 200	High

If the subsidence risk factor is an effective method for predicting the risk of damage, one should expect that situations where foundation movement and damage has occurred would be associated with high factors. However, analysis of cases indicates that this is not so. For instance, Figure 18.10 plots the seasonal foundation movements recorded by level monitoring, against the subsidence risk factor for the tree which is considered to be the cause of those movements. It uses data obtained from the investigations which are illustrated in the Case Studies in this book, but supplemented by additional cases where foundations movements have been monitored. In each case the SRF has been calculated for the level monitoring

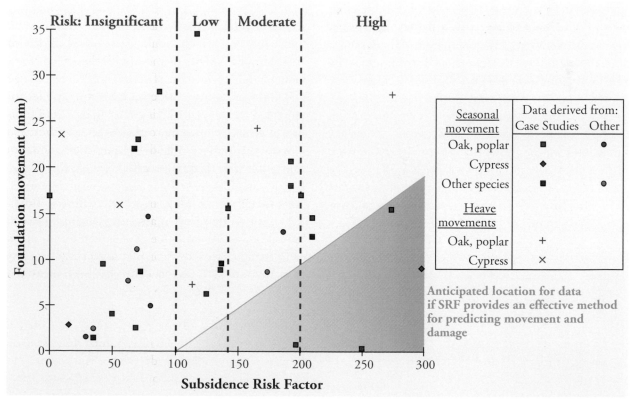

Figure 18.10

Seasonal movements (plus some progressive heave) recorded by level monitoring, plotted against the subsidence risk factor for the trees causing the movement.

315

marker closest to the tree, with this plotted against the amplitude of seasonal movement at that marker. A few cases of progressive heave movement are also included. If the SRF was an effective prediction tool, one would expect to see the data concentrated in the high risk area towards the right-hand part of the graph, and also the extent of seasonal movement increasing in the right-hand part. In other words, the data should be concentrated in the shaded area. Quite clearly there is no such relationship. Very considerable foundation movements can occur even in situations where the SRF indicates an insignificant risk.

An alternative analysis is provided by Figure 18.11. This provides a frequency distribution histogram for the SRF of the trees involved in my last 50 investigations. It only includes cases where I consider that a tree has been correctly implicated as a cause of damage, and for which I have sufficient data to calculate the SRF. It provides a positively skewed distribution, with occasional cases of damage at very high values, but the majority occurring in the range from 30 - 140, and a median value of 99. In other words, in half the cases where damage has occurred, the SRF would indicate an insignificant risk.

It might be suggested that the method is valid, but it is the definitions of risk which are at fault. For instance, if the boundary between insignificant and low risk were to be set at 30, Figure 18.11 indicates that 95% of cases would have an identifiable risk. Assessing the risk and setting the appropriate boundaries requires an analysis of the frequency distribution of the SRF in situations where damage has not occurred. Just as there is no data on proximity of trees where damage has not occurred (page 304), there is also no data on the SRF where no damage has occurred. However, simple observation shows that a very high proportion of trees in urban situations will have a SRF well in excess of 30. **The objective of a method of this sort is to identify and predict those situations where damage is likely to occur; it clearly fails to achieve this.**

These analyses should not be taken as indicating a criticism of the method of subsidence risk assessment. The method takes account of all of the relevant factors such as the species, size and vigour of the tree, the proximity of the tree to the building, the foundation depth and other special features of the building, the shrinkage characteristics of the soil, and the weather conditions of the locality. It is based on the most widely used model for considering the influence of trees on buildings, and in my opinion it should provide the best available method based on current knowledge.

The problem lies, not in the method, but in the inherent variability of the whole interacting system of trees, soils and buildings. **The analyses demonstrate that, within the range where damage may possibly occur, the actual development of damage is unpredictable.**

Implications of subsidence risk assessment

It has been noted (page 312) that the method of subsidence risk assessment was developed in response to the demand from insurers and mortgage lenders for an arboricultural report on the risk of trees causing damage of this sort. In addition to assessing the risk, insurers normally expect arboriculturists to provide recommendations for immediate and/or future action/treatment to any trees or woody vegetation which are considered likely to pose a subsidence risk to the building or outbuildings.

In response and in an attempt to comply with this demand, the Arboricultural Association have provided guidelines on the type of action which might be contemplated for trees which have been identified as having a low, moderate, or high subsidence risk. As noted on page 311, action would be reasonable if it was possible to identify those trees which are going to cause damage, and if there was any reasonable action which could be taken to minimise any risk which is identified. It is clear that even sophisticated techniques such

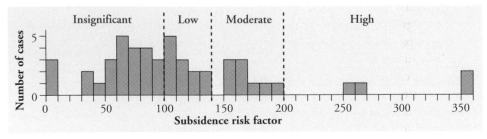

Figure 18.11

Frequency distribution of the subsidence risk factor for trees which are known to have caused damage in 50 of my recent investigations.

as subsidence risk assessment cannot identify the risk situations. If existing levels of damage are to be reduced significantly, it would be necessary to apply preventative action to a massive proportion of the tree population. As emphasised on page 311, pruning is not a panacea for all cases of potential risk, still less if it needs to become a near-universal treatment. Likewise, tree felling as a preventative action would have devastating consequences for the urban landscape and quality of life.

It is better, both on economic and environmental grounds, to accept that damage will be caused by a very small percentage of trees, whilst ensuring that prompt remedial action will then be taken to deal appropriately with those trees which have caused this damage. The implications of this for all professionals are considered further in Chapter 20.

Preventative pruning in identifiable high risk situations

The preceding sections have emphasised that, in most situations, the risk of damage is remote and that it is not possible to identify those trees which pose an unacceptable risk.

However, in some situations it is recognized that, if trees are allowed to grow to their full potential size, there is a particularly high and unacceptable risk. It is appropriate to apply different criteria and management techniques to these trees. Chapter 17 (page 281) has indicated that pruning a tree will reduce its water uptake and, in some circumstances, can provide an effective remedy. In the same way, recurrent pruning can **sometimes** provide an appropriate system of management to prevent damage, or at least reduce the risk.

It is usually easiest to identify high risk situations where there are a number of trees growing under similar conditions, particularly if all of these trees are under the same management, as this provides knowledge of the history of any damage. Trees in local authority ownership, such as those growing in pavements where they are often in close proximity to buildings, provide an obvious example of situations of this sort. Subsidence risk assessment, as described on page 312, becomes irrelevant if practical experience has demonstrated an unacceptable incidence of damage in the past from trees of comparable size growing under comparable conditions. A high SRF (in excess of 200) does not necessarily indicate an identifiable risk, particularly if a tree and building have co-existed for many years.

The decision on how much damage should be tolerated before instigating preventative action should depend on individual circumstances. Chapter 19 (page 341) suggests that the scope of duty to prevent damage should consider the foreseeable consequences (for instance the cost of remedial action if damage occurs), balancing these against the practicable measures which can be taken to minimise the damage and its consequences. The cost of remedial action will depend on whether underpinning is deemed to be essential, or whether vegetation control and cosmetic repairs of the building will be effective. In the latter situation it might be deemed reasonable to take a greater risk.

Figure 18.2 has shown the number of claims for subsidence damage associated with a population of 1305 plane trees growing in pavements in close proximity to buildings on London Clay. Throughout the period shown on that histogram (from 1975 to 1989) the average number of trees growing in those circumstances which were involved in claims each year was 0.3% of the population. Throughout this period the trees were being pruned periodically, but were slowly developing a larger crown area. The risks associated with this management policy might (or might not, depending on circumstances) be deemed acceptable. However, in subsequent dry years the number of claims escalated very considerably, indicating a need for a more rigorous pruning policy. This illustrates how feed-back from practical experience can help to refine an appropriate policy.

It is impractical to provide definitive guidelines for all of the circumstances where preventative action may be justified. Decisions on the scope and frequency of any pruning must be taken in the light of individual circumstances, and will depend on:

i)   the species of tree which is involved, and its ability to tolerate periodic pruning;

ii) proximity of the tree to the building, and any other factors affecting the risk of damage, such as the vulnerability of the building;

iii) whether other factors dictate a need for pruning, for instance to improve light to adjacent buildings or to provide clearance for vehicles;

iv) soil conditions;

v)   past experience of damage;

vi) ability to respond promptly if damage occurs.

It is possible to adopt an cautious approach. For instance, Figure 18.12 shows lime and horse chestnut trees growing in a pavement in Grimsby, where the underlying soil is a very soft alluvial clay. The trees stand well clear of the buildings and are being regularly and heavily reduced to provide a small spherical crown. The visual impact of the individual trees is reduced, but management is simple and the risk of damage will be extremely low.

Figure 18.13 shows a contrasting situation, still on very soft alluvial clay, but across the River Humber in Kingston-upon-Hull. The lime, sycamore and horse chestnut trees have been pruned in the past, but have been allowed to develop large crowns. Extensive damage had occurred to at least one of the properties in the photograph, and elsewhere in the proximity. The risk associated with these trees might be considered excessive.

Figure 18.14a shows the annual radial growth rate derived from an increment core for the sycamore tree in the centre of Figure 18.13. This suggests very rapid growth until about 1920, and a slight increase after 1970. However, if this radial growth is expressed as basal area increment (see Chapter 14, page 230), as seen in Figure 18.14b, it provides a better picture of the growth rate of the tree throughout its life. This shows that the rate of wood production, and thus pho-

Figure 18.13

Lime, sycamore and horse chestnut trees which have been allowed to grow to large size after previous regime of regular crown reduction. See Figure 18.14 for growth rate of central tree.

Figure 18.12

Lime and horse chestnut trees subjected to regular heavy crown reduction to limit crown size and water uptake.

tosynthesis and water uptake, was increasing progressively until about 1920, followed by a prolonged period until the mid 1960's with a reduced and fluctuating growth rate. Examination of the crown structure indicates that the tree was being crown reduced on a regular basis throughout this period. After 1965 the growth rate again increases and exceeds the previous

growth rate by the mid 1970's. Basal area increment throughout the 1980's is approximately double that between 1920 and 1965. The associated increase in damage in adjacent properties indicates that a return to a far more rigorous pruning regime is overdue.

Where trees have been pruned like this in the past, it is usually possible, by examination of the crown and increment cores, to estimate how large the crown has been throughout its life. The different heights to which the lime tree in Figure 18.15 has been pruned are readily apparent, and shown by the lines A, B and C. The annual radial growth is shown in Figure 18.16.

The tree would have been pollarded when young to level A (removing the complete top of the tree); prior to this it would have had the typical small crown of a young tree. The drop in growth rate in 1927 was probably caused by this initial pollarding. It would have responded to this treatment by the production of multiple branches; it is these which now form the main branch structure between levels A and B. From about 1935 through to 1970 the

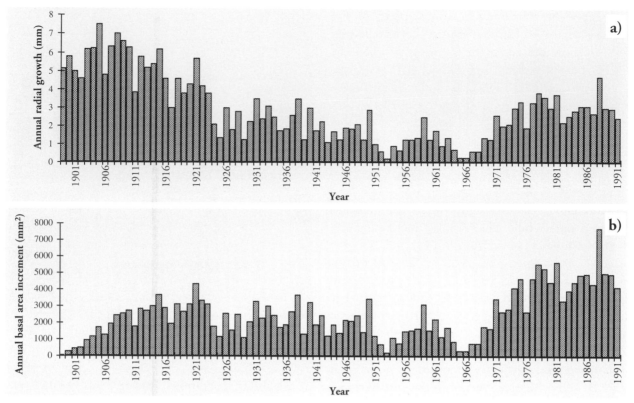

Figure 18.14

Growth rate of sycamore tree in centre of Figure 18.13. a) Expressed as annual radial growth. b) Expressed as basal area increment, derived from radial growth rate.

Figure 18.15

Lime trees subjected to typical pruning regime, indicating level of pruning at various times.

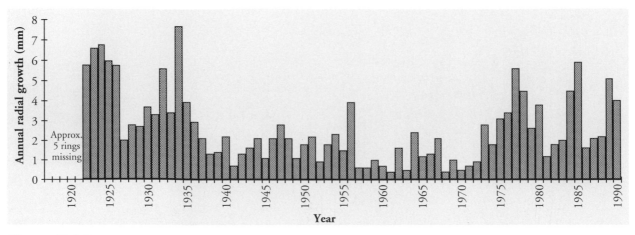

Figure 18.16

Annual radial growth of lime tree in Figure 18.15, used to determine date of previous pruning

growth rate is generally slow but with a regular pattern, building up over a period of three or four years and then dropping back. This is the typical pattern where trees are being regularly pollarded or heavily reduced, and was associated with recurrent reduction to level B. The shape of the tree during this period is shown diagrammatically in Figure 18.17, and its appearance would have been similar to the trees in Figure 18.12.

In about 1970 this pruning was stopped, and multiple branches were allowed to develop above level B. As these branches develop, the growth rate progressively increases over a 10 year period, until there is a sudden drop in 1980. This was probably caused by

the reduction of this regrowth for the first time to level C. New shoots would have developed above level C, with these being reduced again in 1986. A further repetition of this treatment was imminent when Figure 18.16 was taken. The recent management of the tree is shown diagrammatically in Figure 18.18.

The change in management between the small crown shown in Figure 18.17 and the far larger crown in Figure 18.18 would have been accompanied by a considerable increase in water uptake. If it is consid-

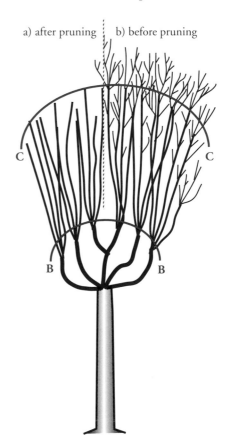

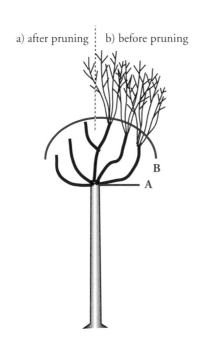

Figure 18.17

Diagram of crown structure of tree during period of heavy crown reduction between 1935 - 1970

Figure 18.18

Diagram of same tree during the 1980's, after the development of larger crown

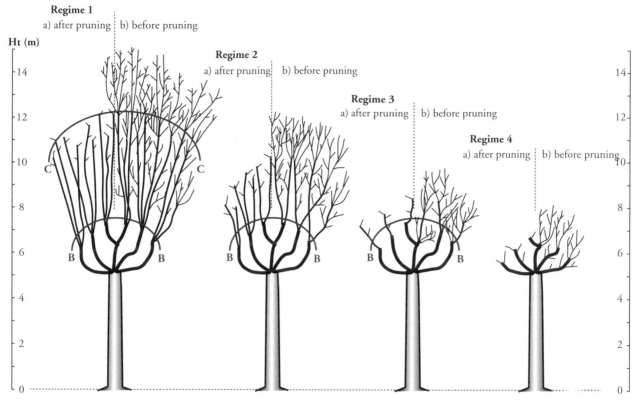

Figure 18.19

Variations on a theme for pruning trees such as plane or lime, to produce different crown sizes.

Regime 1   Common existing shape, generally involving shortening regrowth on 3 - 4 year cycle.
Regime 2   Reduce number and length of rising stems above level B, and prune on 3 year cycle to 12m height.
Regime 3.   Further reduction in number and length of risings stems above level B. 2 - 3 year cycle. 9m height.
Regime 4   Re-instigate pre-1970 policy, cutting right back to original branch structure on 2 yearly (or if necessary 1 year) cycle. Small compact crown.

ered that this larger crown area poses an unacceptable risk, it is often possible to instigate a heavier pruning regime. Various options for this are shown in Figure 18.19. Obviously one could have variants of this basic shape with a considerably larger crown than regime 1, or it would be possible to remove all branches and allow only one year of regrowth, to produce a crown which is even smaller than regime 4. These figures illustrate one very common shape which is used for the management of species such as plane and lime, but there are many others which can be equally effective and can be varied to provide a similar range of crown size.

When deciding on an appropriate regime, crown size is only one of the relevant criteria. In general terms, the larger the crown size, the greater the visual impact and amenity which is provided, particularly with larger buildings for which a large tree provides better scale. However, trees with large crowns are more likely to obstruct adjacent windows, but this will depend on the height and proximity of adjacent buildings. In some situations there is less light restriction if the crown is carried above the windows on a long clear stem. The cost of recurrent pruning will be influenced by the accessibility of the branches for surgery. For instance, the small branches which are removed on regime 3 and 4 can be reached easily from the main branch structure, whereas the regrowth on the long stems on regime 1 are far harder to reach and may require working from a high-lift or far more laborious climbing by a tree surgeon. Many of our street trees are becoming increasingly awkward, and therefore expensive, to work on. The resumption of a heavier pruning regime would involve cutting into large branches, which could accelerate decay and the decline of the tree. All of these factors need to be considered to reach a balanced judgement, but in general the resumption of a more rigorous regime could have practical and financial benefits, as well as reducing the incidence of damage.

The interpretation of the increment cores postulated above are based on cores taken from a convenient height on the trunk. If required, more reliable details can be obtained if cores are taken from the branches at different levels, to determine their exact age. In any such analysis it must be remembered that a branch may be cut to below the level of previous pruning, destroying all regrowth which has developed in the intervening period. The size of the branches above and below the pruning level can provide an indication of this.

Figure 14.15, and the accompanying histograms in Figures 14.14 and 14.16 (pages 228 - 230) provide a similar picture, which is very typical of many of the street trees throughout England.

Prevention of damage
iii)   if tree planting near existing buildings

When trees are being planted, it is obviously sensible to locate them carefully and to use species which will avoid the creation of problems in future.

The location is often dictated by other factors, such as suitable space within the garden landscape design. This may also dictate the size, shape, colour or other characteristics of the tree. However, with the enormous range of species which are available (Chapter 14, page 217) there should be a choice of species for most locations.

It is preferable to choose aesthetically suitable species, before considering the implications of possible future damage. It has been emphasized in this chapter that the risk of any tree actually causing damage is very remote. There will be a similar remote risk with new planting. Many of the trees which have caused damage in the past would not have been the ideal choice because their size and proximity were also causing excessive shading and loss of light. If unsuitable trees are avoided for these reasons, it would also ensure a reduced risk of damage in future.

If one has a short-list of species chosen on the basis of their appearance and general suitability, any of which would be equally suitable, consideration can be given to selecting the species which poses the least risk. Selection of species from the right-hand columns of Figure 18.8 will be most suitable in this respect. Conversely, it is sensible to avoid species from the left-hand columns if planting in particularly high risk situations, for instance where it is known that the foundations are particularly shallow.

Although it must be recognised that some trees cause damage, the complete avoidance of damage could only be achieved by eliminating all trees within the distance where damage might possibly occur (i.e. the maximum distance from the Kew Root Survey (Figure 9.5, page 143). If it is unrealistic to fell all existing trees which are a lesser distance, it should be considered equally unrealistic to stop planting within these distances. It is only by maintaining previous planting policies that the existing landscape can be conserved in the long-term. As emphasised at the start of Chapter 1 (page 1), trees have an important role in environmental improvement, which also provides knock-on benefits in economic and social improvement.

If, despite this plea that planting should not be restricted by concerns for possible future damage, specific guidance on planting distance is sought, Gasson and Cutler (1998) have provided suggestions based on the data from the Kew Root Survey. They propose that, when planting urban trees, the "75% distance" from the Kew Root Survey is suitably cautious if the tree is expected to grow to its maximum size. For most *Rosaceae*, birch, the smaller *Acer* and small cypresses, the 50% figure could be more suitable. The 90% figure should only be applied in the case of potentially very large trees. Note that they only advocate these distances in respect of new planting, and if it is expected that the tree will grow to its maximum size.

These caveats are important. Just because a tree is planted, it does not necessarily mean that it must be grown to maturity. Some trees are at their most attractive when young and may be planted close to a building with the intention that they be replaced long before they reach maturity. As trees mature, their suitability within the landscape will need periodic reappraisal. The risk of damage as perceived at that time may be one of the criteria which form the basis of future decisions, particularly if more accurate methods of risk assessment are developed in the future. In the meantime, we should not deny future generations the advantages of trees, by stopping a reasonable policy of tree planting.

Implications of future changes in risks of damage

The analysis of the prediction of damage at the start of this chapter is based on historical data. However, during the past 25 years, since the inception of insurance cover for subsidence damage, there is no doubt that there has been a major change in the public's perception of damage (Chapter 1, page 6). Levels of damage which were tolerated in the past, now give rise to claims of damage. It is therefore possible that the risks of damage in future have been under-estimated.

Improved methods of investigation, particularly level monitoring, now make it possible to identify the influence of trees with greater accuracy, and thus confirm their involvement even in very minor levels of damage. A wider application of these techniques, or further improvements, may further increase the number of claims of damage.

One reason for the change in perception is the lack of any guidelines on what constitutes damage, or on a definition of the threshold of damage. BRE Digest 251 provides a 6-stage classification of damage (see Chapter 12, page 187, and Figure 12.8), and suggests that categories 0 - 2 are 'aesthetic', categories 3 and 4 are 'serviceability' damage, and category 5 is 'stability' damage. The suggested boundaries are often criticised, particularly the description of category 2 damage as 'aesthetic', but this does not alter the fact that even category 1 damage, with cracks no more than hairline, now give rise to complaints and claims. These very minor levels of damage may be caused by many factors, but if trees are contributing, it gives rise to demands for remedial action with the tree. The implications of this are considered further in Chapter 20 (page 346).

In addition to the past and possible future changes in public perception, it is possible that the actual risk of damage may alter. Chapter 8 (page 132) has noted the natural fluctuations in climate, and that man-made trends for global warming may increase the extent of soil drying. After 1976 it was reckoned that, for parts of the country, the 16 month period starting in May 1975 had been a 1:1000 year event (Wright, 1976), but this occurrence had greatly reduced the odds for a similar event in the future. The further drought in the period 1988 - 1992 exemplified the occurrence of similar, if less extreme conditions. For England and Wales, the 28 month rainfall total from March 1990 to June 1992 was eclipsed only by the drought during the mid-1850's and late 1780's (Marsh and Monkhouse, 1993). Note that when describing extremes of this sort, it is essential to define the criteria (such as duration and location) on which they are based. For instance, a shorter period than 28 months would be far less exceptional, and in Scotland the rainfall was significantly above average over this period.

These droughts may have been accentuated by global warming, but at present are indistinguishable from the natural fluctuation in weather. However, if there is a significant increase in global warming in future decades, the risks of tree root damage may increase (although increased rainfall may mitigate any effects of increased evaporation). As trees take many decades to mature, it is essential to ensure long-term strategies and to plan now for the future. The potential risks may already be sufficient to indicate that existing guidelines for preventing damage should be revised, for instance by requiring an increase in the depth of foundations, or the universal use of piles, for all new buildings on clay soils. A change in policy now could reap immeasurable benefit in the future, particularly as the value of trees for shade and for carbon dioxide absorption is likely to increase.

Summary

1.   Theoretically all damage could be prevented by ensuring that the foundations of all properties are at sufficient depth to avoid all risk. Alternatively, the spatial separation between trees and buildings could be increased, sufficient to ensure that there is no risk. Implementation of such policies would have major repercussions on housing costs, and/or on the important environmental benefits provided by trees. These costs and benefits need to be balanced against the risk of damage occurring, and the costs of correcting the damage if it does occur.

2.   Existing data on the incidence of damage, such as that contained in the Kew Root Survey (Chapter 9, page 141), describe the proximity of trees in situations where they have caused damage. However, there is negligible data on comparable situations where damage has not occurred. The scant data which is available suggests that, in most situations, the actual risk of damage is very low. In most situations, even on clay soils, the risk of a tree causing damage is less than 1%.

3.   The interacting system of trees, soils and buildings is so inherently variable as to make any accurate prediction of the risk of damage impractical.

4.   Even a detailed method of subsidence risk assessment, such as that developed by the Arboricultural Association, does not manage to target those trees which are most likely to cause damage. **Within the range where damage may possibly occur, the actual development of damage is unpredictable.**

5.   In the past the cost of remedying tree root damage may have been deemed unacceptable. Such judgement was based on the cost of underpinning properties which had suffered damage. It is now recognised that vegetation control provides a viable and far cheaper alternative for remedying damage. Assessing the costs

and significance of damage should therefore now be on the basis of remedial action by vegetation control, rather than on the basis of the cost of underpinning.

6.   In the majority of situations, where the development of damage is unpredictable, it is recommended that the costs of remedying damage by vegetation control should be deemed an acceptable price to pay for the benefits conferred by trees.

7.   If these costs are considered unacceptable, any alternative would involve very widespread tree felling or implementation of a regular policy of pruning. The circumstances where pruning is a viable treatment are very limited. It may be advocated in some situations where damage has occurred, but should not be considered a routine panacea for the prevention of damage, unless the need for pruning is dictated by other constraints.

8.   It is therefore recommended, both on economic and environmental grounds, that **in most situations it is better to accept that damage will be caused by a small percentage of trees, and to deal with these by prompt and appropriate remedial action.**

9.   In a few situations, for instance with some species such as plane trees and lime trees growing in pavements in close proximity to buildings, there is sufficient data to indicate an enhanced risk of damage. In these situations it is reasonable to consider a programme to prevent damage, particularly as routine pruning of many of these trees is required to prevent other problems, such as loss of light.

10.   Just because a preventative policy is justifiable in these identifiable circumstances, it does not justify a similar policy in other situations where the risks are less clearly defined.

11.   The risk of damage to new buildings can be minimised by ensuring that the foundations are of sufficient depth. Where there are existing trees, the guidelines in NHBC Standards Chapter 4.2 (National House-Building Council, 1992) should ensure that such trees do not cause damage in future.

12.   All new buildings on clay soils should have foundations at sufficient depth to ensure that trees can be planted in reasonable proximity, whilst minimising the possibility of damage in future. It is recommended that, if trench foundations are used, they should have a minimum depth of 1.5m if the soil has a plasticity index greater than 40, a minimum of 1.25m if the plasticity index is between 20 - 40, and a minimum of

1.0m if the plasticity index is less than 20. These depths should be reduced only if there is no likelihood of any tree planting in proximity at any time in the future. They should be increased if there is a likelihood of trees being planted in particularly close proximity.

13.   In most situations where an increase in foundation depth is required, pile foundations may provide a more effective and cheaper solution than increasing the depth of trench fill foundations.

14.   Long-term predictions of global warming suggest that consideration should be given now to a further increase in the minimum depth of trench foundations (in excess of those specified in paragraph 12 above), or the universal use of pile foundations on clay soil

15.   Consideration of other constraints, such as shading and the physical size and proximity of trees, should be sufficient to ensure that trees which are planted are in appropriate locations and do not pose an unreasonable risk of future damage. Special precautions when planting are not justifiable, except to avoid locating trees with known particularly high risks in close proximity to buildings.

Bungalow, on sloping site with extensive fill, suffered extensive damage in 1980 –
Insufficient funds for full remedial scheme – Partial underpinning – Further damage –
Level monitoring confirms continued movements including underpinned areas –
Lack of datum prevents distinction between heave or slope instability.

Background

The subject property is a bungalow, located on the Bembridge Marls towards the eastern end of the north shore of the Isle of Wight. It was built in the 1950s, with a bedroom added to the rear soon after construction. The layout is shown in CS Figure 18.1, and the front elevation in CS Figure 18.2. Construction included a ground-bearing floor slab throughout, except in the bedroom extension. The bungalow stands on ground which slopes steeply down towards the north, particularly near the front, with a step down of approximately 1.2m at the northern (right) boundary.

In 1976, during previous ownership, it suffered significant subsidence damage around the south elevation of the lounge. As a result, this south elevation was demolished and rebuilt on a new pile and beam foundation, with the piles reported to extend to a depth of 3.0m.

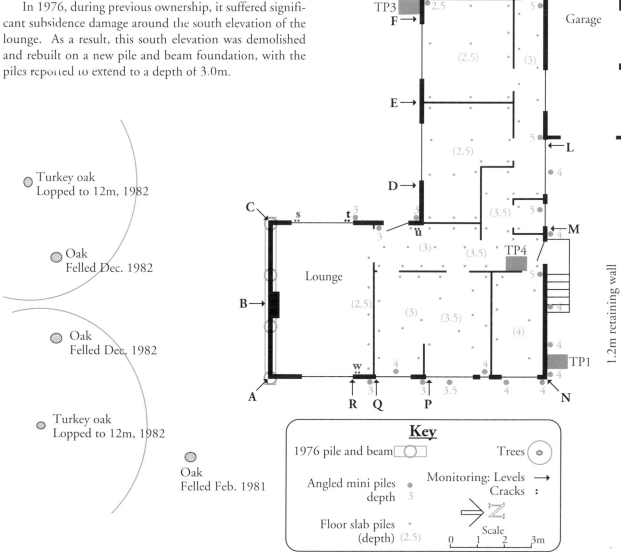

Case Study Figure 18.1
Site plan, including previous underpinning and location of monitoring markers.

Case Study 18.2

Front elevation of bungalow and adjacent oak trees remaining in 1984.

The property was purchased in summer 1977 by my clients. In September 1979 cracking was observed on the front elevation and an insurance claim was notified. A structural engineer was appointed, and he made various visits in early summer 1980. His report at that time recorded:

> "Cracking was observed over the whole of the interior of the property, but was particularly severe around the north east corner and a large area close to it. The other area of severe cracking was in the rear bedroom."

> "Severe subsidence of the ground floor slab has occurred, particularly around the north east corner and along the north elevation."

Three trial pits were dug at the location shown on CS Figure 18.1. Trial pit 1 showed the foundations to be to a depth of 1.35m below ground level. They had been taken through fill consisting of a mixture of clay, topsoil and chalk, and rested on a soft to firm clay only just below the level of the original organic topsoil. This topsoil contained several large roots, and there was a large inflow of water into the trial pit. Trial pit 2 showed the foundations of the rear extension to be 0.62m deep, situated on firm brown grey mottled clay. A single soil sample taken from this trial pit had a plasticity index of 33. At trial pit 3 the foundations were again in similar clay, but to a depth of 1.2m.

The engineer concluded that there were four main causes of damage:

> "1.   Subsidence due to soft ground containing decaying roots, together with passage of ground water. This type of subsidence damage has affected the north east corner in particular and the effect extends along most of the north elevation and part of the east elevation. The original ground level in the north east corner was approximately 1.2m below the present level. Foundations were only taken to just below this level. The presence of large roots suggests there were several trees in this area that were removed during construction"

> "2.   Subsidence due to shallow foundations on a highly shrinkable clay. The foundations to the rear extension were proved to be at extremely shallow depth. This subsidence has caused rotation of the extension and resulted in it tearing away from the original part of the property."

> "3.   Subsidence damage due to moisture abstraction from vegetation on highly shrinkable clay. There are many large oak trees very close to the south elevation of the lounge. The cracks suggest that the new foundations, which consist of short bored piles taken to a depth of approximately 3m, may not be adequate. It is suggested that underpinning using short bored piles of this diameter should have been to a depth of 5 - 6m. The future of the trees will be very important. The removal of the large oak tree close to the south east corner is advisable. The remainder of the trees are on the adjoining property, but if possible these should be lopped but not removed to reduce their effects."

> "4.   Subsidence of the concrete ground slab. Severe subsidence of the ground slab has occurred over the north eastern half of the property. This has clearly being caused by compaction of a large quantity of fill under the slab together with deterioration and compression of the deep peaty topsoil and roots below."

Subsequent further investigation with trial pit 4 through the floor slab revealed a loose chalk fill consisting of small lumps, below which was a loose fill of friable creamy clay with chalk lumps. Beneath this fill, and presumably representing the original topsoil, was 170mm thick layer of very soft silt containing some well decayed large roots. The internal walls were found to be supported directly off this ground slab, with no underlying foundations. There were gaps between the walls and slabs, showing that the walls were supported by interaction between the various components of the building.

The engineer recommended an extensive underpinning scheme, but insurance cover was insufficient to fund these works. As a result, a more limited scheme was undertaken involving 95mm angled piles through the foundations to the depths and locations shown in CS Figure 18.1. The floor slab was supported by 75mm vertical mini-piles, again to the depths and location shown in CS Figure 18.1. The floor slab was also pressure grouted.

These works were completed in early 1981 but by the beginning of 1982 the cracks were appearing again. The engineer who had supervised the underpinning re-inspected and reported:

> "Significant movements were observed in two areas of the property as follows:
>
> 1. The lounge. Cracking on the front and rear elevations of the joint of the lounge structure with the remainder of the property that was treated by us is continuing as we would expect.... The maximum cracks occur immediately over the last piles put in by us as this is the strong point about which the lounge structure is rotating.
>
> 2. Movements around the rear bedroom, particularly in the south east corner of the join of the internal wall with the external wall. The internal wall has moved upwards in relation to the external wall. This is again movement caused at the change between the work that was carried out by us and the work that was not. The movement would appear to be caused by ground recovery following the removal of the oak tree on the adjoining property.
>
> The whole property was inspected and no signs of significant movement were observed in any of the areas that had been totally treated by our works. There would seem to be no doubt that the works carried out under our supervision are performing satisfactorily. The areas that are causing problems are those ar-

eas that were not treated, and as you know the reason for this was that the property was considerably under-insured at the time of the claim.

There is no doubt that the property requires full treatment of the areas not treated by our works in order to prevent further movements. This work would cost a considerable sum of money, hence the first item is to agree with insurers that the property is still covered and that they are prepared to pay for the works.

The insurers denied liability for the further damage, apparently on the basis that it was a continuation of the previous damage which had been excluded from the previous insurance claim. There was also dispute whether subsidence cover had been maintained. I was instructed in autumn 1983 by solicitors acting for the owners to provide an independent report on "What is happening to the property". I was requested to keep further costs and site investigation to a minimum.

The trees

The significant trees in proximity to the property are shown in CS Figure 18.1. The oak tree 4.2m from the south east corner was felled in February 1981 on instructions from the engineer. The remaining trees were in the neighbouring property. Following negotiations by the engineer, two oak trees had been felled and the two Turkey oak trees lopped in December 1982. At the time of my inspection they were about 12m high with dense regrowth on the lopped branches. From the size of the cut surfaces, they were probably originally about 18m high, and had been growing vigorously.

Further investigations

During my initial visit I carried out a level distortion survey. The results are shown in the isometric plan in CS Figure 18.3. They show a significant tilt to the whole building, including the bedroom extension, with the lowest point in the north east corner. The only divergence from this trend was in the lounge, which shows a tilt down to the south. The maximum difference in level was 92mm.

During my initial visit I set up level and crack monitoring; the location of these markers is shown in CS Figure 18.1. Subsequent readings were taken on two occasions through that winter and at the end of the following summer to provide the basis for my report. A further set of readings was taken 18 months later out of personal interest; all these results are presented in CS Figure 18.4, and each set of results are shown diagrammatically in isometric view in CS Figure 18.6. The level monitoring is presented relative to a marker on the adjacent building to the north as an assumed stable datum; this modern building was apparently not suffering any damage.

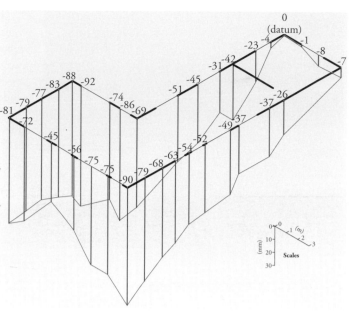

Case Study Figure 18.3

Level distortion survey (17/11/83), presented relative to highest point on brickcourse.

Changes in level (mm) compared to 7/11/83, relative to adjacent property as datum:-				
Station	29/2/84	21/5/84	21/9/84	11/4/86
A	+1.2	+3.2	-2.7	+6.8
B	+1.4	+3.0	-2.6	+9.3
C	+1.6	+2.8	-2.1	+11.5
D	-0.8	0	+1.0	+5.0
E	-0.7	+0.4	+1.3	+5.9
F	+0.5	+0.7	+2.6	+8.1
G	+0.9	+1.2	+2.4	+7.0
H	-	-0.8	+1.0	-
J	+1.7	+1.6	+2.9	+8.6
K	+0.5	-0.5	+1.5	+4.8
L	+0.9	+0.6	+0.9	+0.8
M	+0.8	-0.5	-0.5	-1.0
N	-0.4	-0.8	-1.0	-2.3
P	-0.4	-0.8	-1.6	0
Q	+0.2	0	-0.9	+1.4
R	0	-0.2	-1.8	+1.1
Changes in crack width (μm) compared to 7/11/83:-				
s	c-1000*	c-1500*	+2821	+1143
t	-683	-1316	+1384	-980
u	-17	+125	+827	+1028
v	+134	+596	+663	+1224
w	-742	-1350	+477	-670

Case Study Figure 18.4

Results of level and crack monitoring. See CS Figures 18.6 and 18.7 for diagrams.

By the time of my involvement the cracks at both ends of the window on the west elevation of the lounge (demec markers s and t) were up to 10mm wide (CS Figure 18.5), with a 4mm wide crack over the adjacent door (demec u). Corresponding cracks on the east elevation (demec w) were up to 6mm wide. Cracks at the junction of the bedroom extension and house (demec v) were up to 5mm wide. The rest of the property showed little evidence of movement.

Case Study Figure 18.5

Crack above rear window of lounge with demec marker t.

DISCUSSION

The level monitoring during the initial 10 month period showed a clear pattern of the south flank wall of the lounge recovering during the winter and subsiding during the dry summer of 1984. The amplitude of these movements was 5.9mm at station A on the south east corner, with this movement causing the cracks in the lounge to open by about 4.3mm. These movements were clearly consistent with the involvement of the remaining oak trees opposite this flank wall. The remaining Turkey oaks were very vigorous, with the regrowth which had developed sufficient to produce this amount of movement.

This wall which was moving had been rebuilt on new foundations in 1976, but these works were obviously inadequate. The pile foundations were installed in autumn 1976, probably while the ground was still desiccated. There was no information whether anti-heave precautions were included, but, if they were omitted, seasonal recovery could have lifted the building off the piles, or else lifted the whole pile. Once they had failed, their depth became immaterial as their effective depth would have been no more than the ground beam.

The damage which developed in the lounge in 1980 had been comparatively minor, with most cracks only hairline. In the absence of definitive information about the building movement at that time it is not possible to be categorical about their cause, but it is relevant to note that the previous cracks were in different positions to the later damage. It is possible that the seasonal movement were previously more extensive but sufficiently uniform so as to prevent differential movement and damage.

Although the engineer had implicated the oak trees as a cause of the damage, the remedial works which he had implemented had made matters worse. Furthermore, the removal of the nearest oak tree and lopping of the other trees had all been to his specification and satisfaction. On completion of the work he had given no warning that they might not perform satisfactorily, still less that the situation would deteriorate.

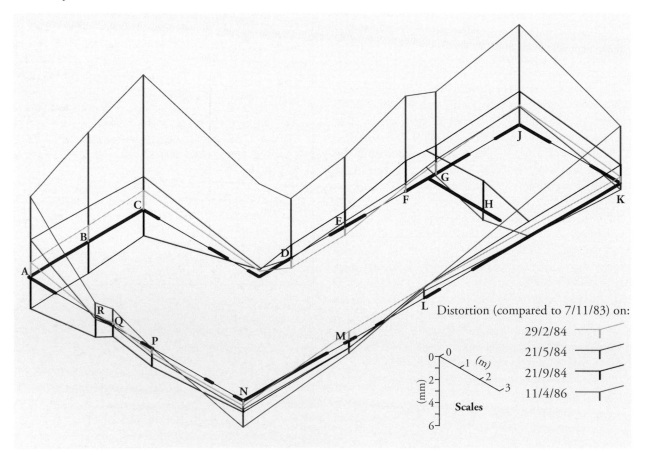

Case Study 18.6

Distortion recorded by level monitoring, compared with initial readings on 7/11/83, and with datum on adjacent house.

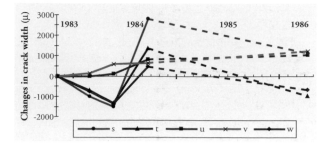

Case Study Figure 18.7

Results of crack monitoring (note no readings during 1985).

The level monitoring also demonstrated significant movement elsewhere in the building. The greatest differential movement was across the diagonal between the south west corner (station J) and the north east corner (station N). These two points showed a difference in level of 2.1mm by February, 2.4mm in May and 3.9mm in September. By April 1986 this had increased to 10.9mm. This pattern of movement, which was present to varying extent throughout the building, was clearly progressive and did not show the reversal in trend which was apparent in the lounge. Likewise, the crack monitoring at demec s and v showed progressive opening.

Most importantly for my client, this monitoring was sufficient to establish that differential movements were affecting those parts of the building which had been underpinned. This thus refuted the engineer's claim that "the areas which are causing problems are those areas that were not treated". Indeed, to the contrary, some of the greatest differential movement was in those parts which had been underpinned, with only small movements along the south elevation of the rear wing which had been omitted from the work in 1981.

The cause of this movement was difficult to resolve on the basis of the available information. The pattern was consistent with an increase in the historic distortion recorded by the level distortion survey. Furthermore, if it was a continuation of the same cause, it implied that the rate of movement had increased (90mm in 30 years = 3mm/annum, increasing to 10mm in 2.5 years = 4mm/annum). Two mechanisms were proposed:

i) slope instability, causing subsidence of the north east corner. Although the slope at ground level was modest, the trial holes implied that the underlying original soil level was at a far steeper angle (of about 12°), which might be above the angle of repose. Furthermore, this slope was surcharged by the weight of fill, and the trial pit showed that this fill was saturated. If a tree had previously grown in this location (as implied by the large roots in the topsoil) these roots could have helped to stabilise the soil previously, and a lower moisture content would have increased the cohesion. Removal of the tree when the bungalow was built would have eliminated any such benefit. This explanation was not consistent with the upward movement of the rear corner relative to the datum, but this might merely have been caused by movement of the datum (the adjacent building used as the datum was also on the slope and could thus have been subject to similar movements as station N).

ii) heave of the rear (south west) corner. This explanation was consistent with the movement relative to the datum. However, the pattern of movement was not related to the proximity of trees which had been felled in 1981/82. Furthermore, these trees could not have been involved in the previous movement, nor could heave account for the recent pattern of movement being similar to the historic movement recorded by the level distortion survey, nor the possible acceleration of such movement.

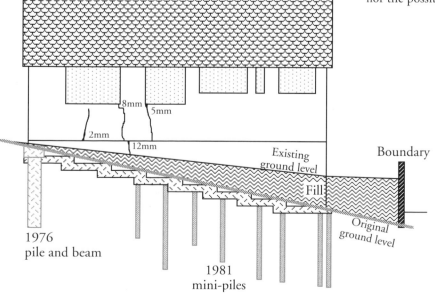

Case Study Figure 18.8

Diagram of front elevation showing underpinning and original ground level.

An independent engineer instructed by insurers quite reasonably criticised the adequacy of the datum, but went on to suggest:

> "It is probable that, since the north east corner can neither be affected by heave or settlements due to trees nor is likely to be consolidating or creeping downslope following the introduction of 4m long mini-piles, level station N must remain reasonably fixed in space. By correcting to a datum at N, stations E, F, G, J, and to a much lesser extent K, indicate that heave movements are probably affecting them. These latter small movements probably being due to the removal of trees adjacent to the south boundary."

These comments were made in 1985 without benefit of the later readings, and are only valid if one ignores the small movements affecting other parts of the building. By the time of the readings in 1986 the variations in level throughout the building were far more apparent and show that movements were also affecting the north east corner (3.1mm between N and L, and 3.7mm between N and Q). The efficacy of the mini-piles, whether against heave or settlement, must be questioned.

Further investigation would have been needed to resolve these issues but could not be warranted within my limited remit. Such investigations might have included installation of a reliable deep datum, and possibly study of aerial photographs to see if trees had been removed prior to my client's purchase of the property.

Regardless of the cause, not only was it established that differential movements were affecting those parts of the building which had been underpinned in 1981, but neither of the explanations (by myself or the insurer's engineer) supported the claim by insurers that this aspect of the movement was a continuation of the previous cause. Furthermore, as previously noted, damage resultant upon the seasonal movements of the lounge had been made worse by the underpinning, nor had they been remedied by the engineer's action with the trees. On this basis the insurance claim by my client was accepted, and eventually settled on the basis of diminution in value. The monitoring readings in 1986 were taken just prior to his disposal of the property.

Lessons to be learnt

- Level monitoring provided a simple and reliable method of establishing the extent of differential movements occurring in the building.

- This was sufficient to provide the information to support my client's claim and to reinstate insurance cover.

- In this case, with potentially different causes acting in opposite directions, the lack of a deep datum prevented determination of the absolute movements, and thus determining which explanation was correct.

- The extensive mini-piling scheme was ineffective in stabilising those parts of the property which were treated.

- An engineer (or any other professional) who recommends and supervises remedial works might not be the most appropriate choice for investigating their subsequent failure!

Statutory controls on tree work

Introduction

There are three ways in which local planning authorities (abbreviated as LPAs) can exert some control on felling or other work to trees:-

i)   Tree Preservation Orders (TPO) (page 332)

ii) Conservation Areas (page 336)

iii) Planning Conditions (page 336)

Occasionally felling licences, which are administered by the Forestry Authority, may be relevant.

Whilst these controls can restrict freedom to immediately carry out work, it is mistaken to believe that they prevent all work, or that there is little to be done about trees which are subject to such control. There are important exemptions which can override the control, and there are rights of objection and appeal. There are also provisions for compensation which may need safeguarding and utilizing. It is therefore important to understand the processes and the actions which should be taken.

The law relating to TPO's and Conservation Areas is contained in Part VIII of the Town and Country Planning Act 1990 (T&CPA 1990), which should be read in conjunction with section 23 of the Planning and Compensation Act 1991. The law relating to Planning Conditions is scattered through Part III of T&CPA. There are also a number of Regulations made under the T&CPA, notably

i)   Town and Country Planning (Tree Preservation Order) Regulations 1969. (SI 1969 No. 17).

ii) Town and Country Planning (Tree Preservation Order) (Amendment) and (Trees in Conservation Areas) (Exempted Cases) Regulations 1975. (SI 1975 No. 148).

iii) Town and Country Planning (Tree Preservation Order) (Amendment) Regulations 1981. (SI 1981 No. 14).

iv) Town and Country Planning (Tree Preservation Order) (Amendment) Regulations 1988. (SI 1988 No. 963).

All of the above references are in respect of England and Wales; details differ for Scotland.

There are three relevant sources of guidance produced by the Department of Environment, Transport and Regions (DETR):-

i)   Circular 36/78 (64/78 by Welsh Office) "Trees and Forestry". As its title implies, this was issued in 1978, and is now out-of-date in many details, but still provides the definitive government guidance.

ii) "Tree Preservation Orders. A Guide to the Law and Good Practice", issued by the Department of Environment in October 1994. This is primarily intended to suggest ways in which LPAs can administer the TPO system in accordance with good practice, but also provides helpful advice for anyone affected by TPO's.

iii) Circular 11/95 (35/95 by Welsh Office) "The use of Conditions in Planning Permissions".

These various powers are exercised in the public interest and it is inevitable that this may diverge from a private interest. Because felling trees and most other work is irreversible there is an understandable (if frustrating) tendency on the part of a local authority to adopt a defensive approach. The making of a TPO should not be, nor be interpreted as, a complete block to action in respect of a tree; instead it should provide a means to control appropriate work and to prevent ill-advised work. This may ultimately be in the best interests of the owner as well as the tree. In most situations LPAs exert their control in a reasonable and proper fashion. However, there are situations where, either through ignorance or laziness, or regrettably in a few cases by deliberate action, the systems are abused. If this occurs, the systems include safeguards to protect the rights of the tree owner, and also of a house owner affected by trees, but these safeguards will only work if properly utilised. The subject is extensive and cannot be covered in detail in a brief commentary. This chapter therefore confines itself to aspects which are particularly relevant to problems of tree root damage to buildings.

The objective of TPO's

TPO's are made in the interests of amenity. This has a wide interpretation, but in general

> "... Orders should be used to protect selected trees and woodlands if their removal would have a significant impact on the environment and its enjoyment by the public. The Secretaries of State consider that authorities ought to be able to show that a reasonable degree of public benefit would accrue before Orders are made or confirmed. The trees - or at least part of them - should therefore normally be visible from a public place (such as the road or footpath), although exceptionally, the inclusion of other trees may be justified. The benefit may be present or future (for example, when proposed development is taking place). Trees may be worthy of preservation for their intrinsic beauty or for their contribution to the landscape; or because they serve to screen an eyesore or future development; the value of trees may be enhanced by their scarcity; the value of a group of trees or woodlands may be collective only. Other factors (such as importance as a wildlife habit) may be taken into account which alone would not be sufficient to warrant an Order." (Circular 36/78, paragraph 40).

It often helps to keep these objectives in mind when dealing with TPO's.

Orders can be made in respect of:-

i)   individual trees

ii)   groups of trees

iii) trees growing within an area

iv) trees in woodlands

There are important differences between these methods of specifying trees. With many Orders the circumstances have changed radically since an Order was made, for instance by development within a woodland. This does not prevent remaining individual trees being covered by a 'woodland' Order.

An Order has the effect (subject to various exemptions) of "prohibiting the cutting down, topping, lopping, uprooting, wilful damage or wilful destruction of trees except with the consent of the local planning authority, and for enabling that authority to give their consent subject to conditions." (T&CPA 1990, Section 198 (3)(a)).

Objecting to a TPO

A TPO must be served on the owners and occupiers of the land affected by the TPO, and must fulfil a number of statutory requirements. An Order usually takes effect on the day it is first served, but must be confirmed by the local authority within a period of 6 months. Before it is confirmed there is a right of objection; this must be made in writing to the LPA within 28 days. Such objection may be on any grounds, such as that the tree is causing damage to property. If there is such damage, it is advisable to object, but at the same time appreciate that, as the primary consideration for making a TPO is the amenity value of the tree, objections relating to other issues, particularly if unsubstantiated, may not be sufficient to result in the Order being modified or not confirmed.

Once an Order has been confirmed there is a very restricted right of challenge in the High Court, but even this is only within 6 weeks of the date of confirmation. Thereafter an LPA has the power to revoke or modify an Order, but very rarely exercise this power. If an Order is incorrect, it is probably invalid, but disputing an Order in these circumstances should be undertaken with caution and competent advice.

Determining whether a tree is covered by a TPO

When an Order is made a copy is sent to the District Valuer. When properties are sold, the existence of the Order should be disclosed during the search of the title deeds. A property owner should therefore always be aware of the existence of an Order.

A certified copy of the Order must also be kept by the LPA at a convenient place, usually the offices of the Planning Department, and be available for inspection at any reasonable time. This allows anyone to check whether or not a tree is covered by an Order.

Although some towns have a virtual blanket coverage with TPO's, overall only a small proportion of trees are covered. If a tree is not covered, there is nothing to stop an Order being made and served, consequent upon an enquiry about the tree. Once it is made, the tree is then protected. In order to guard against this, if you are anxious to ensure prompt removal of a tree, it is advisable to be circumspect when enquiring about the existence of an Order on a site and not disclose the precise location, nor submit a written application which might allow the LPA to prevaricate until an Order is made. Most local authorities have some form of map or index of all of their Orders, and a proper search of this at their offices should determine whether any Orders are relevant to the site. If there is no Order and the LPA are aware of the intention to fell, it is advisable to take prompt action with the tree (if necessary ring-barking (see page 280) so that it is no longer suitable for retention). Such action may be deemed improper by some, but the alternative may be to find that an Order has been made and served, even after the owner has been advised that there is no Order.

Exemptions to a TPO

There are a number of situations where it is not necessary to seek consent of the LPA. The most relevant are in section 198(6) of the T&CPA 1990, which states:-

(6)   "Without prejudice to any other exemptions for which provision may be made by a Tree Preservation Order, no such Order shall apply -

(a) to the cutting down, uprooting, topping or lopping of trees which are dying or dead or have become dangerous, or

(b) to the cutting down, uprooting, topping or lopping of any trees.... so far as may be necessary for the prevention or abatement of a nuisance."

The burden of proof lies with the tree owner to establish that any action which is taken is covered by these exemptions. If in doubt, try to agree with the LPA whether these exemptions apply, but, failing this, unilateral action may be the best course. Removal of dead branches is normally considered to be exempt, but determining whether a tree is dying, dead or dangerous is usually best left to an arboricultural consultant.

Action which is necessary for abatement of a nuisance is particularly relevant to problems of tree root damage. The term 'nuisance' is used here in its legal sense. Under common law roots or branches which cross a boundary are considered a nuisance and may be cut off at the boundary, whether or not they have caused any damage. What is not clear is whether this right can be exercised on trees which are covered by a TPO. In the case of *Sun Timber Co. Ltd. -v- Leeds City Council* (unreported, Leeds Crown Court, 10th October 1980) it was held that the exemption only applies where the nuisance is actionable, i.e. where there has been, or there is, an immediate risk of damage. This is a matter which may need to be resolved in a higher court. It is also normally considered that, for this exemption to apply, the damaged property must belong to a third party and that you cannot claim that your own tree is causing a nuisance to yourself, but this may also need to be resolved in court.

As the exemption only allows work "so far as may be necessary ..." it does not give freedom for any action. For instance, if seasonal movements could be curtailed by pruning, this exemption would not allow the complete felling of the tree.

Application for consent for tree work

If consent is required for work, an application must be made in writing to the LPA. This must specify the tree to which the application relates and the operations for which consent is required - most local authorities have forms for this purpose, but it is not essential to use these provided you provide the essential information. It is often helpful to discuss the proposed works with the relevant officer of the LPA before making the application. The Order also requires that reasons for the work should be given, and it is obviously sensible to support the application with as much relevant evidence as possible.

An LPA has eight weeks from date of receipt of the application in which to issue a decision (unless an extension is agreed). If no decision is given within this period, it is a deemed refusal. If consent is granted, it may be subject to conditions. Although an authority should only either grant or refuse consent for the operations specified in the application, in many cases they may approve alternative works. However, if you wish to submit alternatives, for instance for felling or for pruning, it is advisable to do so.

Appeals against decision of LPA

Where an authority refuses consent, or grants consent subject to conditions, there is a right of appeal to the Secretary of State for the Environment against such refusal or the conditions. Notification of the appeal should be sent to the relevant Regional Office of the

DETR (details should accompany the refusal) within 28 days. A form must be completed and returned in duplicate.

This form requires the "grounds of appeal" to be stated; it is on these that the appeal will be determined and it is therefore advisable that they are clearly set out and cover all relevant matters. There are no limits on the grounds of appeal but relevant and significant matters will obviously be given most weight, and may be more clearly presented if not lost amongst a mass of other irrelevant detail. Matters which may be particularly relevant are if:-

i) the tree is causing damage to your own or another building (although necessary works to prevent the latter should be exempt, you may prefer to seek approval).

ii) the tree does not contribute to amenity.

iii) the tree is excessively overbearing, casts excessive shade, or is otherwise unsuited to its location (if dangerous, the works should be exempt, but again you may prefer to seek approval).

iv) the tree is interfering with the growth of other more important trees.

v) removal and replanting is in the long-term interest of conservation of tree cover in the locality.

Although there is a right to a hearing at a Public Inquiry, these appeals are normally dealt with by written submissions. It is advisable that these submissions provide as much evidence as possible in support of the grounds of appeal in order to allow an adequate and proper assessment. If this evidence is not forthcoming, the appeal may be dismissed on the basis of inadequate information on which to reach a decision. Where damage by root action is alleged, it is highly desirable to provide a description of the damage, basic information on the depth of foundations and soil conditions below foundation level, the history of damage and the results of any monitoring. Similar evidence is also desirable if there is concern about a risk of future damage.

Chapter 11, and the details in Chapters 12 to 15, set out the information which may be most relevant. If necessary, additional evidence can be submitted after the appeal forms are sent in, but this may delay the appeal process.

If the appeal is by written submission, the LPA also have the opportunity to expand on their reasons for refusal and to comment on the grounds of appeal. The appellant may comment on this local authority submission. Either the appellant or the LPA may also seek comments from other interested third parties. Support for an appeal by neighbours can be very advantageous. Once this process is complete, arrangements are made for a site inspection by an Inspector on behalf of the Secretary of State. Where technical, as opposed to planning, matters are involved, the current practice of the Department is to appoint an arboricultural consultant as the Inspector.

Any interested parties may attend the site inspection, with the appellant and local authority usually both present (or with a representative), but if preferred the inspection can be on an unaccompanied basis. During the inspection the parties may not make oral representations, but they may draw attention to matters of fact (e.g. the location of cracks, the existence of defects in the tree, or the amount of shoot extension growth). The Inspector may also seek clarification on matters of fact, but will not discuss the appeal.

Once an inspection is complete, there is usually no further opportunity for submissions and a decision will be issued. There is a right of challenge against this decision to the High Court, but the grounds of this are very limited.

If an appeal is dismissed, the decision letter will set out the reasons. It is advisable to study these reasons, as it may indicate how a different outcome could be obtained with a fresh application to the LPA. If an Inspector other than the Decision Officer carried out the site inspection, there is a right to ask for disclosure of the Inspector's report.

The whole process, whether by written submissions or at a public hearing, can be lengthy. In the past a time scale of more than a year from submission of appeal to decision was commonplace, four to six months is now more typical. Target times are set by the DETR; if these are not met, the aggrieved party can ask the Department to proceed to a determination of the appeal, but the party which is causing the delay is usually given more time to respond.

As the time for an appeal plus the initial 8 week period for consideration of the application can be lengthy, it is advisable to ensure that the initial application for any work is made as soon as possible, particularly if action with the tree is required before another season of subsidence movement. Even if all of the evidence is not available initially, it can be submitted at a later date. Supplementary evidence, for instance from level monitoring, may need to be submitted at the last opportunity prior to the site inspection.

Once an appeal has been submitted, it need not stop further negotiation between the parties aimed at resolving the matter. For instance, further information from level monitoring may enable one, or both, parties to reconsider their original decision.

Compensation in respect of TPO's

Section 203 of the T&CPA 1990 states:

"A tree preservation order may make provision for the payment by the local planning authority, subject to such exceptions and conditions as may be specified in the order, of compensation in respect of loss or damage caused or incurred in consequence:-

(a) of the refusal of any consent required under the order, or

(b) of the grant of any such consent subject to conditions."

The exemptions and conditions which are specified in the Order are important. In particular, Article 5 of an Order allows that, when granting or refusing consent, the LPA may certify in respect of the tree(s) that the refusal or any condition is in the interests of good forestry, or that the tree(s) has an outstanding or special amenity value. If a statement to this effect is included on the decision notice (it must make it clear that the LPA is certifying the statement), Article 9 of the Order allows that no compensation shall be payable. The simple insertion of these relevant words in a refusal notice can therefore potentially prevent the right to compensation, and for this reason many local authorities frequently, or even routinely, include an Article 5 certificate of this sort.

There is no clear guidance on the meaning of "outstanding or special amenity value", although the obvious interpretation is that there must be some special feature about the amenity provided by the tree which makes it stand out well beyond the amenity which is a pre-requisite of any TPO. In practice probably few trees fulfil such criteria, and paragraph 62 of Circular 36/78 makes it clear that "The issue of such certificates.... should be undertaken discriminately and should not be used just to avoid compensation claims".

Where a Certificate is included, there is a right of appeal, with the procedures similar to those in the previous section. However, this is not made very clear on the current version of the appeal form, which merely lists one of the potential matters for appeal being where the appellant is "aggrieved by the compensation certificate of the [above named] authority" (this wording may be clarified in future). Few appellants appear to realise that, if they strike out this sentence along with the many other similar matters for deletion, they may loose a valuable right. Similarly, even if you do not wish to appeal against the refusal of consent for the work, if there is any possibility of a claim for compensation, an appeal should be submitted.

There are a variety of situations where a claim for compensation may be particularly relevant in cases of tree root damage:-

i) if the tree is causing damage to your own property (i.e. it is not a legal nuisance) and the works which have been applied for are essential for preventing the damage, and if the refusal makes underpinning the only viable alternative, it should be possible to claim the cost of underpinning. *Buckle -v- Holderness Borough Council* (Estates Gazette [1996] 39 EG 179) provides a case of this sort. Successful pursuit of such claim would require clear evidence that the tree is involved and that underpinning is essential because of the refusal.

ii) if further monitoring or other investigations are required to prove the involvement of the tree, the costs for this work can be claimed; *Fletcher -v- Chelmsford Borough Council,* (Estates Gazette [1991] 45 EG 191) provides a case of this sort.

iii) if an appeal is submitted (unsuccessfully) in an attempt to avoid the need to underpin and thereby mitigate the loss, the cost of the appeal might be claimed; see *Buckle -v- Holderness Borough Council.* Note however that the ordinary costs of an appeal by written submission cannot usually be claimed.

iv) if there are particular conditions which impose additional expenditure. In *Deane -v- Bromley London Borough Council* (Estate Gazette [1992] 21 EG 120) the additional costs incurred in using an Approved Contractor of the Arboricultural Association rather than the claimant undertaking the work himself, was claimed successfully.

Any claim for compensation must be submitted within 12 months of the refusal by the LPA, or within 12 months of the appeal decision. It does not therefore provide an open-ended right against damage occurring at some later date. Some individuals protect against this by regular submission of a fresh application.

Obligation to replant

If consent is granted for a tree to be felled, it can be subject to a condition requiring the planting of one or more replacements on the same site or in the immediate vicinity. In these circumstances the LPA can specify the species and size of tree for planting, but they will usually allow for some choice and take account of your wishes. If you object to such replanting there is again a right of appeal to the DETR against the condition.

There is an automatic obligation (unless the LPA dispense with it) to replant any tree which is removed, uprooted or destroyed in contravention of an Order, or where such action is authorised only by virtue of section 198(6)(a), that is for trees which are dying or dead or have become dangerous. However, this obligation does not apply to section 198(6)(b), which includes trees which are removed for the prevention or abatement of a nuisance. If you are concerned that replanting might recreate a similar problem at some time in the future, and so you wish to avoid a condition requiring such replanting, it may be desirable to make it clear (or agree with the LPA) that the tree is being felled under the exemption provided by section 198(6)(b), rather than applying for consent.

Where there is an obligation to replant, it is on a one-for-one basis, with a tree of an appropriate size and species and at the same place. Provided you fulfil these requirements, the LPA cannot insist on a particular size or species, but it may be desirable to agree these details before undertaking the work.

Under section 207 of T&CPA 1990, if it appears to an LPA that an obligation to replant or a condition which requires replanting is not being complied with, they may serve an enforcement notice. This must be served within four years from the date of failure to comply. Under section 208 there is a right of appeal to the DETR against such notice; this section specifies the grounds of any such appeal.

Trees in Conservation Areas

Section 211 of T&CPA 1990 has the effect of extending the actions which are prohibited by a TPO to apply to trees in Conservation Areas. It requires that, before carrying out any work on a tree in a Conservation Area, you give 6 weeks notice of intent to undertake the work. The intention of this is to allow the LPA to consider the works and, if they wish to prevent or control it, to serve a TPO on the tree owner. If a TPO is served during this 6 week period, the normal procedures of a TPO apply. If a TPO is not served, the LPA cannot, except with the agreement of the notifier, refuse the work or agree to alternative works, nor can they impose a condition requiring replanting. If, at the expiration of the 6 week period, no TPO has been served nor agreement reached to alter the scope of work, the work may proceed (within 2 years of the notification). It is advisable to get on with this work, as some LPAs are slow to respond to the notification and do not get round to serving a TPO until after this period has elapsed.

The LPA will have maps and can advise whether any site is within a Conservation Area; most arboricultural contractors will also carry this information for their locality. If a property is included in a Conservation Area, it should normally be disclosed in the Search at the time of purchase. However, when an area is designated or modified there is no obligation to notify all property owners within the area, and so you may not be aware of the existence of a Conservation Area. For this reason you should ensure that up-to-date records are used.

All of the exemptions which apply to trees subject to a TPO also apply to trees in Conservation Areas. In addition, there is no need to give notice for work on trees which have a diameter of less than 75mm, or of less than 100mm if the work is carried out to improve the growth of other trees (or in some other special circumstances). An obligation to replant will exist if trees are felled under the exemptions, but not if notice has been given.

Planning Conditions

Department of Environment Circular 11/95 (Welsh Office 35/95) provides extensive advice about the use and imposition of planning conditions when granting planning permission. Paragraph 14 of the circular notes the 6 tests which should be satisfied. These require that conditions should be:

i)   necessary;

ii) relevant to planning;

iii) relevant to the development to be permitted;

iv) enforceable;

v)   precise, and;

vi) reasonable in all other respects.

Paragraphs 71 - 75 of appendix A to the Circular provide suggested model conditions. Model condition 75 is particularly relevant to retention of existing trees on the site, as it includes provision that "no retained tree shall be cut down, uprooted or destroyed, nor shall any retained tree be topped or lopped ... without the written approval of the LPA". Some LPAs have sought to use this to provide long-term protection, comparable to that provided by a TPO. However, the model condition also notes that a specific time limit should be included; it suggests 1 year from the date of occupation. The model further notes that it is not considered to be reasonable to use conditions as an alternative to TPOs to secure long-term protection of trees.

Model conditions are also provided for provision of tree planting on new developments (model 73) and more generally for landscape design (models 25 and 26) and implementation (models 27 - 30). These normally require submission and approval of details before development commences. The developer should therefore be aware of the scope of tree planting before excavation and the laying of foundations; on clay sites it should therefore be possible to ensure that the foundations which are laid are of sufficient depth to protect the building against risk of future subsidence.

Regrettably, even where conditions of this sort have been made, the LPA does not ensure that plans are submitted and have been approved before work commences. The planning application and Building Regulation submission will often only stipulate "foundations to satisfy Building Regulation requirements", and, if no existing trees are present, 1.0m deep foundations may be deemed sufficient by Building Control. It is only at a later stage, when tree planting is being implemented, that it is appreciated that these shallow foundations are inadequate. This is then used as justification for omitting tree and shrub planting. A LPA can prevent this by judicious application of appropriate

conditions, and liaison with Building Control so as to ensure that the conditions are enforced and adequate foundations are provided.

To avoid any ambiguity, it would be advisable for a LPA to impose a condition requiring foundations to a depth suitable to allow appropriate tree planting in the locality. Chapter 18, page 310, or Table 3 in NHBC Standards Chapter 4.2, provides such depths. There is no model condition of this sort, and it is probable that a simple condition requiring foundations to a specified depth might be deemed not relevant to the development to be permitted, unless there was a second condition requiring tree planting. Two conditions might therefore be required, such as:

i)   "No works or development shall take place until full details of all proposed tree planting, and the proposed times of planting, have been approved in writing by the local planning authority, and all tree planting shall be carried out in accordance with those details and at those times." (This is the same as model condition 73, and ensures that planting is required. The associated model condition 74, in respect of replacement of failures, may also be deemed necessary.)

ii) "The foundations of the development hereby permitted shall be taken to such depth, or be so constructed, as to comply with the requirements of National House-Building Council Standards Chapter 4.2 in respect of the proposed tree planting." (This is to ensure that the foundations are adequate for the planting.)

When deciding whether conditions of this sort should be imposed, it is relevant to note that section 197(a) of T&CPA 1990 states:

"It shall be the duty of the local planning authority to ensure, whenever it is appropriate, that in granting planning permission for any development adequate provision is made, by the imposition of conditions, for the preservation or planting of trees."

This is the only section of the T&CPA which places a **duty** on the LPA. Although a LPA has a duty to impose conditions of this sort to ensure that appropriate planting can, and does, take place, regrettably such obligations are very rarely fulfilled.

Legal liability for damage

The whole issue of legal liability where damage has occurred is too large and specialised a topic for consideration in a book of this nature, particularly as many of the principles are in a state of evolution and change. As there are so many issues which can affect liability, the following sections should not be taken as providing dogmatic guidance, but are merely exploring issues of potential interest and relevance for further development.

Claims for tree root damage are founded on the tort of either negligence or nuisance (or both). In the simplest terms, negligence, as a tort, is a careless act, or a failure to act. It is based on conduct, rather than agreement (i.e. contract) or the protection of an interest (as with other torts, such as nuisance or defamation). In cases of tree root damage, the negligent act is most likely to be in respect of the management (or lack of management) of the tree.

Likewise, in very general terms, nuisance is something which interferes with the use or enjoyment of land. In cases of tree root damage, nuisance is most likely to be in respect of the ownership of a tree which interferes with the use or enjoyment of neighbouring land.

It must be emphasised that these are very general definitions; it is for the legal team of the Solicitor and Barrister to consider the details of the claim or of the defence, and to ensure that the essential evidence has been obtained, and is properly presented, to substantiate that case.

It is essential that those who are investigating a case of damage should liaise with the legal team to ascertain their requirements. However, investigations usually start long before legal proceedings. Furthermore, remedial works have often been completed before proceedings start and these may destroy much of the essential evidence. For these reasons it is necessary to appreciate the type of evidence which might subsequently be required, and to ensure that this is collected at the most appropriate time, even if legal action may not have been started by that time.

The full range of investigations outlined in Chapters 12 - 15 should ensure that all relevant information has been obtained. However, as noted in Chapter 11, cost-effective investigation should be targeted at the most relevant evidence to identify the cause and to determine the appropriate remedy. Additional evidence may be required to substantiate legal claims. The following sections consider some of the information which is most frequently required in this respect.

Evidence may be required to support the case either of the plaintiff or defendant. One is usually only instructed by one of these parties (jointly-appointed experts are still a rarity), and it is obviously essential to gather all of the evidence to support your client's case. However, if the case subsequently goes to Court, it is the duty of the Expert Witness to assist the Court in establishing all of the relevant facts and of expressing opinions based on those facts. For this reason, all the relevant information should be obtained regardless of the party who is instructing the expert.

Extent and cause of damage

An essential element in a claim in negligence or nuisance is that the plaintiff must have suffered damage. An adequate description of the damage is therefore necessary. Chapter 12 has described the methods for recording damage and the BRE system for assessing severity of damage (page 187). This information should be obtained before remedial works are put in hand.

Establishing the cause of damage should be a fundamental part of any investigation. I place great emphasis on the role of monitoring, particularly level monitoring, for demonstrating that the pattern of building movement is consistent with the involvement of the alleged tree. This information can counter any subsequent claims that other movements, for instance settlement, slope instability, or heave, are involved. If remedial work to trees is undertaken (pruning or felling), monitoring can be used to demonstrate the success, or otherwise, of this action. On the other hand, if underpinning is deemed essential, monitoring can confirm that significant movements are occurring and also demonstrate the scope of necessary work. Monitoring is an exercise which must start from the outset of an investigation; by the time legal proceedings are started it is often far too late, with the original conditions and building movements no longer occurring.

Chapter 13 has considered the scope of soil investigations. If one needs to determine the extent of soil desiccation, this is most relevant at the time that damage is occurring. If seasonal deficits are being measured, boreholes should be drilled in the autumn; spring boreholes can only demonstrate persistent deficits. It is usually deemed necessary to prove the existence of a shrinkable soil, but this information can be obtained at any stage.

Chapter 14 has questioned the relevance of root identification (page 220) for proving that roots have caused soil drying, but a claim against a tree owner will usually require positive identification of live roots originating from that tree.

Legal limitation and the time of events

For actions in negligence or nuisance, a writ must be issued within 6 years from the date on which the cause of action accrued, that is within 6 years of the physical damage occurring or when it could be discovered with reasonable diligence. However, where there is a continuing nuisance, there will be a fresh cause of action in respect of that continuance. In other situations different time scales may be relevant; for instance the NHBC Buildmark scheme provides cover for 10 years, and the liability of Approved Building Inspectors and the longstop provisions of the Latent Damage Bill have a 15 year maximum. Quite often there has been a change of ownership or of insurance cover, and the date of these changes may be relevant.

Chapter 12 (page 186) has considered the history of damage and considered the type of evidence which can show the original date of events, or the duration of movements. A feature of tree root damage is that, if the cause of damage is not dealt with, there is a likelihood that similar problems will recur, perhaps after the 6 year limitation period. A tree owner may be liable for this further damage, but, provided he abates the nuisance so that it will not occur again, liability should be restricted to the additional damage and not relate to the original. Evidence of the method of repairs used previously after similar damage may become relevant, particularly if a plaintiff now claims a massively superior remedy.

A level distortion survey can indicate the total extent of differential distortion (subject to assumptions about the accuracy of original construction), and this can be compared with the scope of current movement determined by monitoring.

A tree can also provide information on past events, particularly as the annual growth rings can provide definitive evidence about its history. Counting the number of rings can prove the age, whilst deductions about previous growth rate and photosynthetic activity can be made on the basis of changes in ring width. This information, combined with consideration of meteorological conditions, can often be used to assess the probable previous pattern of water uptake. It may be possible to link this to the past history of damage.

Foreseeability and the scope of duty

The decision of Lord Justice Dunn in the Court of Appeal in *Solloway -v- Hampshire County Council* (Estates Gazette [1981] 258) provides valuable guidance on these topics. That case was concerned with localised intrusions of clay, but the questions posed by L.J. Dunn have far wider relevance and major implications for tree management. These implications are considered in Chapter 20. This judgment is quoted extensively below, with some sentences in bold for added emphasis. At page 860 it notes:

"In *Leakey -v- National Trust* [1980] 1 QB 485, Megaw LJ reviewed the whole of the law of nuisance not brought about by human agency, and at page 522 he dealt with the case of *Davey -v- Harrow Corporation*. He said:

"... I have no hesitation in preferring [that] decision as stating the law as it now is; subject to the proviso that **the duty arising from a nuisance which is not brought about by human agency does not arise unless and until the defendant has, or ought to have had, knowledge of the existence of the defect and the danger thereby created**".

The judgment in *Solloway* goes on to note (at the end of page 861):

"The judge [in the lower Court] dealt with the question of foreseeability in two parts, by dealing first with what he called "the nature of the duty" and then with its scope. In reality the **scope of duty depends on the extent of risk of damage** and the two should be considered together.

In *Leakey's* case at page 524 Megaw LJ dealt with this question in this way:

"This leads on to the question of the scope of the duty. This is discussed, and the nature and extent of the duty is explained, in the judgment in *Goldman -v- Hargrave* [1967] 1 AC 645 at pp 663, 664. **The duty is a duty to do that which is reasonable in all the circumstances, and no more than what, if anything, is reasonable, to prevent or minimise the known risk of damage or injury to one's neighbour or to his property.** The considerations with which the law is familiar are all to be taken into account in deciding whether there has been a breach of duty, and, if so, what the breach is, and whether it is causative of the damage in respect of which the claim is made. Thus, there will fall to be considered the extent of the risk;

- **What, so far as can reasonably be foreseen, are the chances that anything untoward will happen or that any damage will be caused?**

- **What is to be foreseen as to the possible extent of the damage if the risk becomes a reality?**

- **Is it practicable to prevent, or to minimise, the happening of any damage?**

- **If it is practicable, how simple or how difficult are the measures which could be taken, how much and how lengthy work do they involve, and what is the probable cost of such works?**

- **Was there sufficient time for preventive action to have been taken,** by persons acting reasonably in relation to the known risk, between the time when it became know to, or should have been realised by, the defendant, and the time when the damage occurred?

Factors such as these, so far as they apply in a particular case, fall to be weighed in deciding whether the defendant's duty of care requires, or required him to do anything, and, if so, what.

In considering whether there is a breach of duty, **the extent of the risk and the foreseeable consequences of it have to be balanced against the practicable measures to be taken to minimise the damage and its consequences.**"

On page 863 the judgment in *Solloway* goes on to note:

"**Felling and lopping of trees**, as suggested by the judge, **might give rise to all sorts of complaints and difficulties, quite apart from its interference with public amenities**, and in the end such action might well not be appropriate, because the evidence was that the only effective method of locating the pockets of clay would be by sinking boreholes at every house adjacent to a tree.

Mr Smyth [Counsel for Plaintiff] did not go so far as the judge. He submitted that the defendants having done nothing, the onus was on them to lead evidence to the effect that remedial work was not practicable. He submitted that, at the very least, the defendants should have considered and discussed the question, and there was no evidence that they did; that they should have then circularised all householders whose houses were adjacent to trees, pointing out the dangers and asking them to pay for, or share, the costs of boreholes.

It seems to me that that evidence is not necessary in a matter of this kind. The expense would be considerable. **Common sense tells that action of the kind suggested by Mr Smyth would be likely to cause more problems than it solved. Householders circulated in that way would be likely to suffer apprehension for the value of their property, and probably with no reason.** The consequences of such circulation, it seems to me, are unpredictable and unsatisfactory. **Balancing the risk of pockets of clay under [the subject property] with the steps necessary to deal with that risk, in my judgment there was no breach of duty by the defendants in this case and so no nuisance.**"

In the supporting judgment Sir David Cairns included:

"To say that a risk of damage is reasonably foreseeable means that it is foreseeable not merely as a theoretical possibility but as something the chance of which occurring is such that a reasonable man would consider it necessary to take account of it. The risk of being struck by lightning when one goes for a walk is not a reasonably foreseeable risk. I should be prepared to hold that the risk in this case was not a reasonably foreseeable risk.

If however it could be said to be a reasonably foreseeable risk, **I am satisfied that it was a risk such that the cost and inconvenience of taking any effective steps to remove it or reduce it would be quite out of proportion to that risk. There is nothing in the evidence to show that [the subject property] was any more at risk than any other house in the avenue. Nor is there anything to show that any operation on the trees, short of felling them, would have made the roots safe if there were exceptionally dry weather and if the roots of any particular tree were passing through clay.**

Clearly **it would have been unreasonable for the council to remove all of the trees in the avenue** and it is unlikely that [this] avenue was the only road in the area where there were trees in proximity to houses. The alternative would have been to make an examination of the subsoil of every house which might possibly be at risk by boreholes in order to see whether the ground there was of clay, gravel or a mixture of both. Obviously a number of boreholes would have been needed close to each of the houses. It would all have been of great inconvenience to householders and the making of any proposal for it would have been likely to cause considerable anxiety to them The value of the houses might well have been reduced by reason of the operation."

Likewise Stephenson LJ added:

"I cannot agree .... that the appellant could effectively discharge its duty by investigating comparatively few properties and trees, and perhaps approaching a few property owners, or felling or lopping a few trees, at little expense. I do not think it needed evidence to decide that to have prevented or minimised the plaintiff's damage would have required correspondence with many property owners in the county, wholesale inspection of and boring under properties, and the felling of many trees, which would have put the appellant to very great expense and produced **many complaints from property owners upset by warnings of danger which might not exist and from a wide public deprived, perhaps needlessly, of the amenity provided by trees like those lining [the subject] avenue.**

Such precautions would not, in my opinion, be reasonable ..."

These quotations taken from judgments in the Appeal Court are very relevant and have many very important implications for cases of tree root damage.

The questions posed by Lord Justice Megaw are considered in further detail below.

"What, so far as can reasonably be foreseen, are the chances that anything untoward will happen or that any damage will be caused?" Chapter 18 has emphasised that, in most circumstances, the development of damage is very unpredictable, and the risks are very small. The maximum root spread as identified in the Kew Root Survey (page 143), but quoted by the Institution of Structural Engineers as a "minimum safe distance", provides a totally unrealistic indication of the risk of damage. Even more sophisticated risk prediction methods, such as the Arboricultural Association SRA, do not provide a reliable indication of whether damage will occur.

Furthermore, if one considers a population of 100 trees growing under conditions where each tree poses a 1% risk of causing damage, there is no way of identifying which of the 100 trees will actually cause damage. If one wishes to prevent the one case of damage, all 100 trees must be dealt with.

"What is to be foreseen as to the possible extent of the damage if the risk becomes a reality?" It is important to appreciate both the extent and significance of damage. The extent of most damage caused by tree roots falls within categories 1 or 2 in BRE Digest 251 (Figure 12.8, page 188). When damage first occurs, it is almost invariably within these categories; it only progresses to higher categories if remedial action is delayed or inappropriate. As noted in BRE Digest 251, Category 1 and 2 damage is aesthetic.

The extent of damage needs to be viewed in the context of the remedial action which is required to correct it. I do not suggest that aesthetic damage should be discounted, but merely that it does not warrant urgent measures to rectify the situation by underpinning; this view is supported by BRE Digest 352 and the BRE report on foundation movement and remedial underpinning in low rise buildings (Hunt *et al.* 1991). In the past the immediate reaction to damage was to underpin, and I agree that the costs of this (which are often considerable) might be deemed unacceptable. However, if it is now recognised that vegetation control, either by removal or pruning of offending trees, can stabilise the building, the cost of repair, and thus the significance of the damage, becomes far less.

"Is it practicable to prevent, or to minimise, the happening of any damage?" Any possibility of trees causing damage could be eliminated by removal of all trees on clay soils which are within possible range of

trees (i.e. closer than the Kew Root Survey "maximum distance"). Alternatively, the risks could be reduced (by an unspecifiable amount) by removal of all trees at some lesser distance (quite what distance, or other criteria, is not defined). As noted above, all trees which pose a risk would need to be treated. The need to consider such drastic action is, in my opinion, quite rightly rejected by Sir David Cairns' comment in the Solloway Judgement that "Clearly it would have been unreasonable for the Council to remove all of the trees in the avenue".

Rather than felling the trees, it might be suggested that pruning would be adequate. In Chapter 18 I have emphasised that pruning should not be considered a universal panacea. Just as it is unreasonable to fell all trees, it is unreasonable to prune all trees. This is not to deny that, in some identifiable high risk situations and with trees which are amenable to this treatment, pruning can become a proper management tool. However, it should be restricted to those types of situations identified in Chapter 18, pages 317 - 321. Just because these situations tend to have a high profile in local authority tree management, does not indicate that pruning should have more widespread application

"If it is practicable, how simple or how difficult are the measures which could be taken, how much and how lengthy work do they involve, and what is the probable cost of such works?" This question was highly relevant in the Leakey case, as the preventative measures in that case would have been difficult, lengthy and expensive. In financial terms, it would not be expensive to fell all trees, and even pruning all trees might be acceptable. However, it is the environmental and social costs, rather than the financial cost, which needs to be considered. In my opinion, these costs would be out of all proportion to any benefit.

"Was there sufficient time for preventive action to have been taken ...?" This question is also more appropriate to Leakey, than to tree root cases. However, it must be emphasised that the question is in relation to "the known risk"; as previously noted, it is not known which tree which tree will actually cause damage.

In relation to tree root cases it would be more relevant to re-phrase this question as: "Is there action which could be taken by the defendant (tree owner) after the damage has occurred to minimise the consequences?" In terms of tree management, the resounding answer to this question is "yes". In my opinion, the defendant should take action after, rather than before, the damage. The damage itself is only aesthetic; it is only serious if the consequence becomes a need to underpin, but underpinning is only needed if the tree owner is notified but then refuses (or declines) to take the necessary and appropriate action.

It remains to be tested in court whether there is liability on the tree owner if trees are managed with appropriate responsibility to the environment, and with proper appreciation that underpinning is not an inevitable consequence of damage. It is very relevant to re-emphasize the principle enunciated in *Goldman -v- Hargrave* that **"the duty is a duty to do that which is reasonable in all of the circumstances"**, and in *Solloway* as **"the extent of the risk and the foreseeable consequences of it have to be balanced against the practicable measures to be taken to minimise the damage and its consequences."**

Liability for underpinning against heave

Chapter 17 has emphasised that if there is a persistent deficit, there is no action which can be taken with the trees to stabilise foundations. The comments in this section only apply if there is a significant persistent deficit extending below foundation level, sufficient to create an unacceptable duration and amount of recovery. In these circumstances, felling will start the heave or recovery movements, retaining the trees will allow continuation of seasonal movement, whilst any form of pruning will produce a combination of these effects. Underpinning, with anti-heave precautions, is therefore the only viable remedy.

When considering the possible liability of a tree owner for the cost of underpinning, it is relevant to consider when the persistent deficit would have developed. Chapter 6 has noted that persistent deficits usually develop over a short period of perhaps 1 or 2 decades while the tree is in early maturity. Thereafter there is a long period through maturity of the tree while the deficit is maintained with little further change, before it declines as the tree becomes overmature.

If the deficit pre-dates construction of the building (or more precisely the foundations, as these comments may also apply to previous defective underpinning, e.g. Case Studies 4 and 16), heave is an inevitable consequence of the inadequate foundation design. No form of tree management would be effective, and it is probable that there would be no liability on the tree owner.

If the deficit established after the foundations were laid, it will have caused both seasonal movement and subsidence while it was developing. In the past many houseowners were more tolerant of damage, and al-

lowed this type of situation to develop (Case Studies 4 and 6). Once again, once the deficit has been allowed to develop, underpinning is essential and no form of tree management would be effective. There may be liability for recent seasonal movement, but the need for the underpinning is because of the historic movement associated with development of the deficit. If it can be established that the persistent deficit developed more than 6 years ago and that the need for underpinning has not altered materially in the past 6 years, it is possible that there would be a limitation defence. For this it would be necessary to establish that the distortion and damage is old, and that any continuing movements are seasonal. The house owner may be entitled to demand that the continuing nuisance is abated by removal of the tree, but I question whether there would be liability for underpinning. As there is no effective option for tree management, it might also be claimed that there can be no liability, even for the continuing nuisance and recent damage.

If these arguments are valid, it suggests that there should only be liability for underpinning if it can be proven that the persistent deficit and damage have only developed in the past 6 years. However, if the persistent deficit is of such recent origin, one might question whether there would definitely be an unacceptable duration for recovery. Deficits which have developed over a short period can usually recover over a corresponding or shorter period.

Summary

1.   Some trees are given statutory protection, by Tree Preservation Orders, Conservation Areas or planning conditions. These controls mean that, except in some circumstances, consent is required before felling or undertaking work of any kind on the trees. There are important exemptions, the most relevant of which is to allow work which is necessary for the prevention or abatement of a nuisance. Where consent is required, it should normally be granted, provided there is good reason and appropriate supporting evidence. There are rights of appeal against refusal of consent, and in some circumstances, rights to compensation.

2.   There can be legal liability, in negligence or nuisance, if tree roots cause damage to a neighbouring property. Details of claims for damage are a matter for legal advice. However, the evidence to support or defend such claims may need to be gathered long before the claim is made. For this reason, when investigating cases of damage, be aware of future requirements for evidence, and ensure that it is collected.

*Victorian property on steeply sloping London Clay site – Trees closely adjacent down-slope –
Long history of damage – Crack monitoring demonstrates seasonal and progressive movements –
Removal of trees produces no benefit – Seasonal movements apparently caused by natural drainage.*

The subject property is a two-storey detached house built in 1890 on a steeply sloping site in north London. It is on two floors plus an attic, and has a cellar beneath the front right hand room. Internal ground floor layout is shown in CS Figure 19.1. The steep slope on the site creates a change in external ground level of 2.1m across the frontage (CS Figure 19.2), and there is a further 1.8m high retaining wall 2m from the left flank wall. There are similar buildings closely adjacent on the up-slope side. The Geological Survey map shows the underlying soil to be London Clay.

In 1976 the owner alleged that extensive damage occurred and in 1977 he claimed on his insurance and structural engineers were appointed. In November 1977 the engineers attached concrete tell-tales to a number of the external cracks, and also sticky brown paper across some of the internal cracks. They also submitted a claim against the owner of the adjacent trees, and I was instructed to act on his behalf.

Case Study Figure 19.2
Front elevation and adjacent retaining walls.

The trees

The location and size of the trees alleged to be involved in the damage are shown in CS Figure 19.1. They were all vigorous trees, growing as coppice shoots from the stumps of young trees which had previously grown on the site. All of the trees appeared to be of similar age, and cores of wood taken from the lime and sycamore near the rear corner showed that these were approximately 45 years old. This suggested that all of the trees on the land had been felled in about 1933 and allowed to resprout. In addition to the trees shown on the plan, there were other sycamore and ash further down the slope. There were minor shrubs and herbaceous plants adjacent to the front and rear.

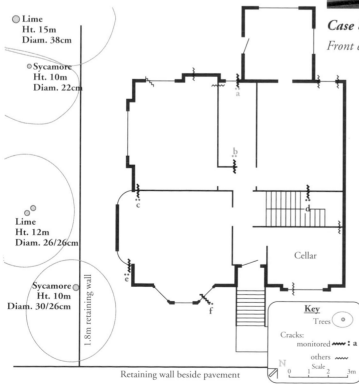

Case Study Figure 19.1
Site plan, including location of main cracks and crack monitoring markers

Damage to property

I inspected the property initially in November 1978. It had suffered extensive recent movement, but it was also apparent that there had been extensive movement throughout the building, probably occurring throughout its life. In some cases the recent cracking passed through areas of previous movement and it was therefore possible to distinguish between the old and recent cracking. Some of the tell-tales attached 12 months earlier by the engineers had cracked or torn, thus indicating that movement had occurred since they were applied, but these crude tell-tales did not indicate the time or direction of these movements.

Foundation depth

The engineers had dug trial holes at various locations around the building. These showed that the foundations of the left flank wall were 0.85m deep, with two courses of brick corbelling resting directly on the London Clay. Fill soil extended to the level of the base of foundations. They found tree roots (unidentified) in this trial hole. The foundations of the right flank wall were 0.85m deep, increasing to 1.75m around the cellar.

Further investigations

The lower parts of the ground floor were rendered which prevented a level distortion survey.

During my initial visit I attached Demec strain gauge markers across some of the main cracks; the position of these markers in shown in CS Figure 19.1. Readings were taken over the subsequent 20 month period; the results are shown graphically in CS Figure 19.3.

DISCUSSION

CS Figure 19.4 is a sketch diagram through the foundations of the building and the adjacent retaining wall, showing foundation depths and external ground level. It indicates an underlying slope of the ground of about 13°, and that the foundations of the left flank wall were about 17° above the base of the adjacent retaining wall. With the clear evidence of long-term lateral movement, particularly of the left hand flank wall, it suggested that slope instability or clay creep were likely to be involved. It was for this reason that I considered it imperative to monitor the movement to distinguish between the various possible causes.

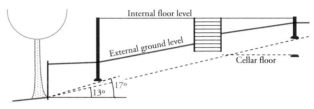

Case Study Figure 19.4

Section through front elevation showing angle of slope.

The engineers questioned the value of the monitoring and expressed concern that it would cause further delays. However, I pointed out that during the winter the trees would not be having any influence and gave assurances that action would be taken before the following summer.

The monitoring during the winter showed that the main crack through the building, monitored by markers a and b, was opening. However, most of the other cracks closed to some extent, confirming the involvement of seasonal changes in moisture content. In view of the close proximity of the trees, their involvement seemed inevitable and I therefore recommended their removal in March. All of the trees shown in CS Figure 19.1 were felled during April, leaving only some of the more distant trees.

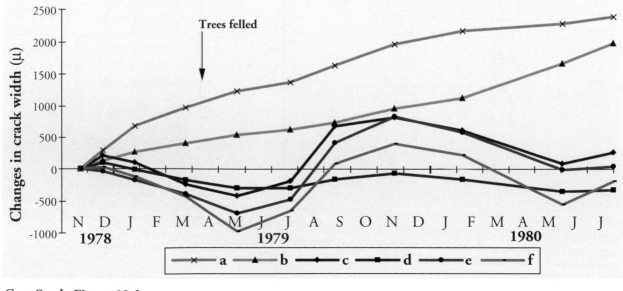

Case Study Figure 19.3

Results of crack monitoring.

The monitoring was continued, and, as shown in CS Figure 19.3, it was apparent that felling the trees had made no difference. Demec markers a and b on the main crack continued to open progressively, and the other cracks all reopened during the summer, with the amount of movement greater than the winter recovery. Continuation of the monitoring through the subsequent winter showed the cracks again closing, but with a net increase in width over the 12 month period since the monitoring had started.

Whilst it was just conceivable that the remaining distant trees might have been continuing to influence the flank wall, it was apparent that the movements were widespread, even affecting the deeply founded wall of the cellar. There were no other trees (or even vegetation) in proximity to this cellar. This indicated that any changes in moisture content which were causing the seasonal movement were widespread, and not related specifically to the tree root activity. On the sloping site, natural drainage was likely to be involved. In addition, the monitoring showed that the main movement was entirely progressive and clearly related to slope instability. For these reasons liability was denied, and the claim was subsequently dropped. A recent visit, 20 years later, showed that the building has yet to be reinstated, and not surprisingly the damage has continued to increase.

Whilst it was disappointing to have removed the trees and then discover that this produced no benefit, it would have been nigh impossible to deny liability without having taken such action.

At the time of these investigations I had not started level monitoring. It would have been interesting to have had such information, although in this situation it might have been difficult to find a reliable stable datum. With hind sight it would also have been useful to measure the extent of horizontal distortion of the lower flank wall (and perhaps the other walls) to determine the extent of lateral movement down the slope. Some of the old crack repairs were in excess of 50mm, and with the cumulative affect of a number of such cracks considerable movement had probably occurred.

Lessons to be learnt

- On a steeply sloping site, seasonal movements may be caused by drainage of the clay, rather than by vegetation. It might be difficult to distinguish their relative significance so long as the vegetation remains.

- Progressive movement from slope instability is also likely to be significant.

- If trees are removed, the effects of such treatment should always be monitored. In this case it prevented liability for what would otherwise have been a very substantial claim.

- It was only proper crack monitoring which could detect the pattern of crack movement; the crude monitoring by the engineer was useless (mercifully concrete tell-tales are now a thing of the past). Level monitoring might have been even more useful if a suitable stable datum had been present.

CHAPTER 20

A REVISED ROLE FOR THE PROFESSIONS

Introduction

The introduction to Chapter 1 identified the professions who are involved with, and have a responsibility for, trees and buildings. It listed (in alphabetical order) arboriculturists, architects, builders, building control, insurers, loss adjusters, planners, soil scientists, structural engineers, surveyors and valuers. That chapter went on to emphasise the need for a multi-disciplinary approach, and that members of these professions need to work with each other, and with the homeowner, to try to ensure a harmonious relationship. It also summarised the role of the professions in the past.

The subsequent eighteen chapters have considered the separate components of the system, and how they inter-react. They have suggested that a more detailed understanding of the role of trees in causing seasonal or persistent soil drying indicates a need to reappraise the methods of investigation, remedy and prevention. In some cases these chapters have identified a particular role for the various professions in investigations or remedial work. This final chapter seeks to bring together these various strands, and indicate how the different professions might reappraise their involvement and seek a revised role within a common approach to overcoming the problems of tree root damage to buildings.

A role for insurers

I have no hesitation in starting this chapter with insurers, as they have a key role in so many facets of the problem. They influence the roles and actions of all of the other professions which are involved in the problems of tree root damage to buildings, but at present these professions all work in isolation of each other. A major benefit would be achieved if insurers were to **adopt a central, well-informed, coordinating role.**

It was the decision by insurers to offer subsidence cover which changed the public's perception of subsidence (Chapter 1, page 6). Previously the public accepted that buildings move to some extent, particularly in a dry summer, and they were prepared to tolerate minor levels of damage. It was recognised that minor damage was not significant, and did not affect the function or safety of a building. These attitudes have changed, so that subsidence is now perceived either as a disaster requiring major remedial action, or as an opportunity for extensive refurbishment at the expense of insurers. Reverting to the pre-1971 situation by **withdrawal of automatic subsidence cover** would not produce an immediate return to the previous perception, but it would cause the public to think whether major remedial works are really necessary (if they have to pay for them), and be more realistic in their expectation about the performance of buildings. Alternatively, an option on existing policies to exclude subsidence cover, and allow a reduced premium, would encourage a more realistic attitude.

If subsidence cover in general is to continue, the demand for remedial action and refurbishment after very minor levels of damage could be stopped by **defining a minimum level of damage** which must be exceeded. BRE Digest 251 provides a widely recognised classification of damage (Chapter 12, page 188). Specifying a minimum category of damage, for instance category 2, would ensure that action is targeted at those situations where there is a justifiable cause for concern. If such a threshold level is adopted, it would also require strict adherence to the definitions; at present those who seek refurbishment tend to exaggerate the severity of damage.

Insurers (and mortgage lenders) further increase the public's concern by the demand for arboricultural reports. As emphasised in Chapter 18 (page 315), even the most sophisticated methods of assessment are not effective in predicting risk situations. The demand for these reports is therefore of negligible practical value, but serves to cause unjustified alarm for the public and can create problems in the completion of a house purchase. **The requirement for arboricultural reports on the risk of subsidence is best stopped.** This will need to be accompanied by instructions to surveyors and valuers that trees should only be highlighted in their reports if they are in particularly obvious high risk situations.

It is encouraging to note the initiative in August 1997 by the Association of British Insurers to introduce the "Domestic Subsidence Tree Root Claims Agreement - Third Party Liability" (text of agreement in Figure 20.1). It is to be hoped that this will lead to a less adversarial approach, and avoid antagonism between house and tree owners. Some of the implications of this agreement on claims management are considered in the next section, in respect of the role of loss adjusters.

If insurers continue their involvement by offering subsidence cover, it is suggested that major benefits could be achieved by instigating, and funding, further research. **Near-market research, particularly into the best methods for investigating and remedying damage, could be particularly beneficial.** In the past there has been extensive work on the development of methods of underpinning; comparable work on the various methods of vegetation control and on methods for accelerated recovery of persistent deficits are now required. Chapter 15 has emphasised the value of monitoring and demonstrated the patterns of movement where damage is occurring; further information on the movements which can be tolerated below the damage threshold would provide a better understanding of the development of damage.

A role for loss adjusters

Loss adjusters are appointed by insurers to act as the intermediary with the policy holder. As a result they have a very important role in resolving all insurance claims. In some cases they will require the insured to obtain a report on the cause of damage; in other cases they will instruct the relevant professional themselves. Once the cause has been investigated, they will consider any recommendations for remedial work, liaise with insurers on the costs of such work (and any apportionment between insurers and policy holder), and then make arrangements for the implementation of any work. Throughout this process they can influence, if not decide, who undertakes the investigations, who determines the type of remedial work, and who carries out the work. **It will therefore require the active involvement of loss adjusters to implement the changes which are advocated in this book for investigating and remedying damage.**

In my opinion this must require the loss adjuster to adopt a much more pro-active role. The strategy for investigating damage (Chapter 11, page 178) identifies **the priorities for cost-effective investigation to ensure that the essential information is available for**

ABI Domestic Subsidence Tree Root Claims Agreement - Third Party Liability

This Agreement relates to third party liability claims where both the liability and damage arise under policies covering domestic properties owned/tenanted/occupied by an insured in a personal capacity and situated in Great Britain, Northern Ireland, the Isle of Man and the Channel Islands.

Every insurer subscribing to this Agreement agrees -

1   that where a claim arises in respect of subsidence or heave and where damage to the building and/or contents has been caused wholly or partly by tree root encroachment the insurer holding the buildings and/or contents insurance for the damaged property undertakes to investigate, handle and where appropriate meet the claim on the basis of their policy cover;

2   not to pursue recovery against the insurers of the owned/tenanted/occupied property responsible for the liability of the tree root encroachment regardless of whether the damage has been caused wholly or partly as a result of the tree root encroachment;

3   that in the event of there being a recurrence of damage and no reasonable preventative measures have been taken by the person/persons who have liability for the tree root encroachment this Agreement will have no effect in regard to any subsequent claim.

4   that this Agreement will have no bearing or consideration in any uninsured loss claim which may be pursued against the person/persons having a potential liability for the tree root encroachment.

Provided that:

(i)   immediate notice shall be given to the other insurer by the insurer to whom the claim is notified, together with copies of all relevant reports (including covering letters) from loss adjusters, engineers, surveyors and the like.

(ii)   Nothing in this Agreement shall prevent any insurer from voiding a policy for fraud, non-disclosure or misrepresentation, or from relying otherwise on any policy term or condition except that late notification alone shall not prevent the operation of this Agreement.

(iii)   In the event of any dispute arising under this Agreement the matter shall be referred to the ABI Disputes Committee whose decision shall be binding. The Committee will be a body of last resort and disputes will only be referred to it if discussions between senior claims officials at Head Office level of the insurers involved fail to produce a solution.

Figure 20.1

Text of Association of British Insurers "Domestic subsidence tree root claims agreement".

deciding on the type of remedial work (vegetation control or underpinning). This can be contrasted with the specification prepared by a major firm of loss adjusters which identifies the standard procedures which they require from engineers:

> "Initial site visit and inspection, attaching of monitoring devices (Demec studs), organising and attending trial holes/bore hole investigation, organising and attending drains test (if required), analysis of soil and root data and preparation of initial report."

It is some relief that the specification includes monitoring, but the reference to Demec studs indicates that it is crack, rather than level, monitoring which is expected. As emphasised in Chapter 15, level monitoring will be far more useful and should form an essential part of any investigation. It is disappointing, when speaking to many engineers, to be told that they recognise the value of level monitoring, but cannot persuade loss adjusters to fund this work.

The present emphasis by loss adjusters on crack monitoring may help explain an article in the magazine of the Chartered Institute of Loss Adjusters, which includes:

> "It is my opinion that monitoring is meaningless unless there is an understanding of how the movement took place in the first instance. In order to do this, it is essential to have knowledge of the soils ..." (Hall, 1998).

I suggest this is putting the cart before the wrong horse! If level rather than crack monitoring is used, it will provide the diagnosis and show how the movement took place, and be far more valuable than any form of soil investigation. The same article goes on to note that:

> "remedial action should be taken before monitoring whenever possible";

again, an attitude with which I profoundly disagree.

One of the major potential benefits of the ABI Domestic Subsidence Agreement (Figure 20.1) is in identifying (in paragraph 1) that it is the responsibility of the house owner's insurers to investigate the claim. **If the Agreement is to work, it will be important to ensure that these investigations provide the evidence to allow the tree owner to make an informed decision on the need for any tree management.** I foresee that clarification may be needed on the scope of investigation which should be undertaken, and whether it is reasonable to expect preventative measures on a tree in the absence of adequate information. **However, my own opinion is that level monitoring should be an essential part of evidence in support of any claim, and, unless there is other overwhelming circumstantial evidence, it is unreasonable to expect a tree owner to take action in its absence.**

If notification to the tree owner is no more than a blunt demand for trees to be removed on the basis of inadequate investigation (as has tended to occur in the past), it will encourage the tree owner to adopt an unco-operative attitude, secure in the knowledge that he will not be held liable for the initial damage. Any such attitude will be counter-productive, both to the spirit of the ABI Agreement, and to a proper resolution of the problem. Paragraph 3 of the Agreement notes that, if no reasonable preventative measures have been taken by the tree owner, a claim can then be pursued in the event of recurrence, but it is better to ensure that the problem is properly dealt with on the first occasion. If the damage is allowed to recur, it does not alter the fact that action with any trees which are the cause of damage should still be preferable to underpinning.

The Case Studies have shown that, where trees are involved, seasonal movement is an invariable feature. **The level monitoring should demonstrate a pattern of seasonal movement of this sort, the location of which is consistent with the trees which are alleged to be involved.** It should be self-evident that, if it is claimed that a tree is involved, the results of the monitoring should show a pattern of this sort and support the claim. However, I have recently become increasingly concerned at the large number of allegations which are made where the evidence is inconclusive or points to some other cause. In these cases monitoring may show that movement is occurring, but it is also necessary to demonstrate that this movement is consistent with the potential influence of trees, rather than some other cause.

Figure 20.2 provides an example of level monitoring results where trees were alleged to be involved, and demands made for their removal. The site is on London Clay, and slopes down to the front of the building, with trees in proximity to the rear right corner. The front wall and a short return along the two sides had been underpinned with angled mini-piles in 1985, but damage had continued. Figure 20.2a presents an isometric diagram of the total movement recorded by an engineer over two years from January 1996 to 1998, and Figure 20.2b shows the pattern of movement for a selection of the stations during this period (locations identified by bars of corresponding colour in 20.2a). The results are all related to an 8m deep datum. It is apparent that movements have affected all parts of the building, including the underpinned areas, with maximum subsidence on the part furthest from the trees. The reason for the apparent upward movement of the right hand flank is not readily apparent as there is no reason to suspect that heave could be occurring; it may relate to movement of the datum on the sloping

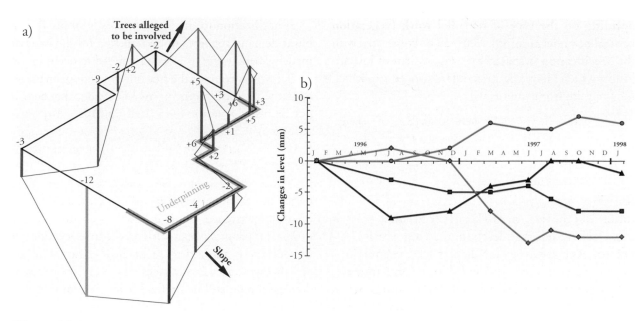

a)

Trees alleged
to be involved

b)

Figure 20.2

Monitoring results which are inconsistent with alleged involvement of trees.

site. It might be claimed that, although most of the right flank is above datum, the rear corner closest to the trees records 2mm subsidence over the two year period. However, the pattern of movement of this corner (dark blue line on Figure 20.2b) **shows no evidence of seasonal movement.** Detailed consideration of the results (not evident in these diagrams), unfortunately casts doubt on the accuracy of some of the readings; if one is to have confidence, results must be reliable.

Figure 20.3 shows results of monitoring two cracks, again where tree root activity is alleged to be involved. The cracks vary in width, but the pattern of movement is erratic, and unrelated to seasonal changes which might be occurring, thus exonerating the trees.

Figure 20.4 (overleaf) provides another example where a Wellingtonia tree was alleged to be causing subsidence (in this case the allegation was by an engi-

neer, but supported by the loss adjuster). It will be noted that the crack was opening progressively irrespective of the season, except for one brief period in July. It was further alleged that there was a direct relationship between the crack movement and the level of groundwater recorded in a standpipe in the area of alleged subsidence; the variations in water level are included in Figure 20.4. It is apparent that there is no consistent pattern between the crack movement and water level. As this water level was above the level of foundations at all times, it is difficult to understand how root activity could have been causing drying and shrinkage. Subsequent level monitoring confirmed that no seasonal foundation movements were occurring.

I do not, of course, suggest that all claims have similar anomalies; indeed, Chapter 11 (page 175) has noted that over 80% of subsidence claims on shrinkable clay soils are attributable to trees and shrubs. If trees are involved in 80%, it still leaves 20% which are not attributable to trees; Figures 20.2, 20.3 and 20.4 may be providing examples. Claims of this sort appear to be becoming increasingly common. To find these examples I did not need to trawl through past records; they were selected as the three most recent cases in which I have been analysing the claims made by others. They reflect badly on those who make them, and are detrimental to progress in the management of trees to remedy or prevent damage. **I hope these examples will help to demonstrate that results must be studied carefully before allegations are made.**

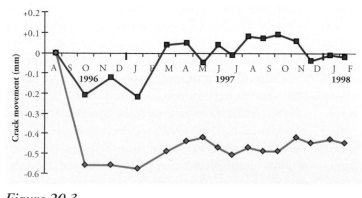

Figure 20.3

Monitoring of crack movements which are inconsistent with alleged involvement of trees

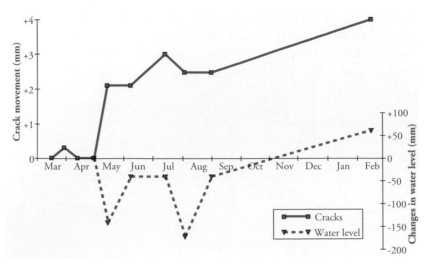

Figure 20.4

Monitoring of crack movement and of water level in standpipe. Results are inconsistent with alleged involvement of tree, nor do they support the alleged relationship between crack movement and water level.

When underpinning is being contemplated as the remedial action, it is normal for the loss adjuster to expect an engineer to prepare a scheme and obtain competitive quotes for the work. **In the same way, if vegetation control is contemplated, I urge that the loss adjuster should seek professional advice from an arboriculturist on the feasibility of the various options.** This should include advice on the amenity value of the tree, and the viability of pruning both as an immediate remedy and as a long-term measure. If a tree is being felled, the possibility of replanting with a more suitable tree in a suitable location should be considered. The arboriculturist should also be able to assist if the tree is subject to a Tree Preservation Order, or is in a Conservation Area.

Chapter 17 (page 292) has identified those situations where underpinning should be the preferred method. In particular, underpinning should be used in any situation where there is a persistent deficit. It follows that, as the tree may not maintain the deficit in the future, the **underpinning should include anti-heave precautions. It may be prudent for the loss adjusters to ensure that these precautions have been taken.**

Chapter 19 (page 342) has suggested that, where there is a persistent deficit which necessitates underpinning, there may not be liability on the tree owner for the cost of such work unless it can be established that the deficit has developed within the 6 years limitation period. The implications of this should be considered when advising on the potential for recovery from a third party tree owner.

If the foundations are stabilised by any form of vegetation control, Chapter 17 (page 292) has emphasised the need to continue level monitoring, and possibly also undertake crack monitoring, to confirm that the foundations have stabilised and crack movements have ceased. I suggest that **work of this sort is an essential part of the remedy, and should be allowed as part of an insurance claim.**

A role for structural engineers

Historically the structural engineer has played the key role in dealing with problems of tree root damage. The remedy which has been applied, both to this type of damage and to subsidence or settlement from other causes, has been to underpin. This book has emphasised that, in the majority of situations involving trees, vegetation control provides a viable alternative remedy, and that **in future the arboriculturist should become more involved. This will not mean that the engineer is ousted, but it should mean a reappraisal of his role.**

The previous section and Chapter 11 have emphasised that, if vegetation control is to be applied, investigations must be aimed at providing the necessary information. Greater emphasis is needed on level monitoring and on predicting the amount and duration of recovery movements. Information on soil conditions, except in respect of permeability, is of far lesser importance, particularly as the assessment of desiccation and prediction of soil movements is so unreliable. Although I undertake the necessary investigations myself, at present there are few other arboriculturists who are trained and able to carry out this work. For this reason, it is my opinion that **engineers should continue as the key player, but ensuring that the scope of investigations is modified to provide the required information. Once the information is available, they should liaise with the arboriculturists to decide which trees or shrubs are the cause of movement, and on the most appropriate method of controlling the water uptake.** The engineer will also need to ensure that the foundations are adequate to prevent seasonal movement either from other vegetation or from evaporation from the soil surface.

If vegetation control is adopted, the engineer will need to liaise with the arboriculturist to **ensure that the work has been sufficient and effective.** As noted in Chapter 17 (page 292), the most effective way for this is by continuation of level monitoring, to compare movement before and after the action to the trees.

I hope that engineers will appreciate the need to reappraise some of their existing practices, particularly in respect of monitoring. At present I am disappointed at the quality of much of the work. As emphasised in Chapter 15 (page 241), measurements taken with a heavy levelling staff resting on a projecting nail which is bending under the weight, and with no provision for interpolation between staff readings, is poor technique which will provide unreliable results. Suitable equipment and other precautions, such as always using the same optic level set up in the same location, will help to eliminate errors and ensure that the desired precision is obtained. If cracks are monitored, movements should be measured by calliper or demec gauge (page 246).

The previous section has emphasised the need for care when interpreting monitoring results, illustrating this by three examples where the results were inconsistent with the alleged involvement of the tree. Those comments were in the section on the role of the loss adjusters, because of my concern at the increasing number of allegations of this sort being made by that profession. However, those who have studied the Case Studies will no doubt have noted my critical appraisal of many of the conclusions and decisions made by engineers; in every one, apart from Case Study 6, **I consider that serious errors of judgement have been made by at least one of the engineers involved, invariably because of inadequate investigation or failure to interpret information in a rational way.**

In those situations where there is a persistent deficit and risk of heave, engineers will continue to need to design and supervise underpinning. In these cir-

cumstances the underpinning should include full anti-heave precautions, to protect the building in the event of the death or deterioration of the tree for any reason. Underpinning will also be required in some other circumstances, such as to correct very shallow foundations or where the value of the tree justifies its retention. If underpinning is needed, adequate soil investigation will be required both to determine the bearing capacity of the soil and the existing and potential future depth of influence of any root activity; as noted in Chapter 17, page 293, it is inappropriate to use NHBC Standards Chapter 4.2 for the design of underpinning.

I hope that engineers, along with other professionals, will play their part in reassuring the public that most cases of tree root damage are minor and need not lead to major expense and upheaval. The damage may warrant remedial action, but "subsidence" need not become a term for the public to dread. I draw attention to the following quotes which, if heeded, could help to restore a more enlightened approach:

> "The perception of cracks has gradually become more acute and the level of tolerance to them has dropped. The severity of damage at which owners become concerned is now very low and generally bears no relationship to that which may impair structural stability" (Hunt, Dyer and Driscoll, 1991, page 37).

> "It was apparent that many owners expect their house to be underpinned if cracking has occurred, regardless of its severity, cause and whether or not it is worsening" (BRE Digest 352, page 6).

> "Most Civil and Structural Engineers would consider these large sums [for underpinning works] totally unjustified if the problem were to be considered purely from a technical point of view" (Institution of Structural Engineers, 1994, page 8).

> "This meant that thousands of properties suffering from relatively minor damage, technically identified as being caused by subsidence, were underpinned which, from a technical point of view, was probably not necessary. Alternatively the problem could have been dealt with much more economically and objectively if the opportunity had existed to monitor the property over a period of time in order to identify the cause of the damage more precisely and to cure that instead" (Institution of Structural Engineers, 1994, page 8).

As previously noted, if vegetation control is adopted, it will remain the role of the engineer to confirm that it has been effective in stabilising the foundations. **Appendix C of the report of the Institution of Structural Engineers (1994) proposes a "Certifi-**

cate of Structural Adequacy" to provide assurance for the client or prospective purchaser of a property that the remedial measures have been sufficient. The draft certificate and section 8.11 of the report might imply that the certificate is only in respect of major structural work such as underpinning. However, section 7.9 of the report notes a wider potential scope and advocates:

> "If, after considering all the circumstances, it is thought that underpinning a property would have little or any benefit because the cause of the problem had been removed, e.g. drains repaired, trees felled, etc., then the Expert should be able to give the owner an assurance that, in his/her professional opinion, the property will remain structurally stable and free from significant movement in the future. The assurance would assume no changes in the property's environment or use and also that the property will be reasonably maintained. The assurance would be a considered professional opinion and not a warranty or guarantee. It can take the form of a 'Certificate of Structural Adequacy' - see Appendix C"

A role for arboriculturists

In my opinion it is essential that arboriculturists should recognize that trees are the biggest cause of foundation movement, and that they have a responsibility to remedy and prevent the damage. In the past there has been a tendency to deny the involvement of trees or any need to take action. As result it is not surprising that alternative remedies such as underpinning have become the norm, and that the public now expect any property with damage to be underpinned. This has lead to escalating costs, now reaching £500 million per annum (Figure 1.3, page 5); unless these costs can be reduced, there will be increasing pressure to eliminate the problem by eradicating all trees in proximity to buildings. **Arboriculturists must recognize that they have a pivotal role in controlling the damage and in reassuring the public that trees are not an unacceptable threat.**

I am not necessarily criticising the actions of arboriculturists in the past. The evidence which they have been given in support of claims has often been woefully inadequate, and Figures 20.2 to 20.4 illustrate that claims alleging the involvement of trees are sometimes not supported, or are even contradicted, by the evidence. **It is correct for arboriculturists to maintain a reasonable scepticism and seek to protect trees from unwarranted allegations, but this is best achieved by positive action to ensure proper investigations, rather than a denial that the trees are responsible.**

Trees are not invariably to blame, but in any situation where they might be involved, the possibility should be investigated. Chapters 12 - 15 have identified the range of investigation which may be undertaken, and Chapter 11 has considered the strategy and most cost-efficient approach. If these are adopted, it should be possible to identify whether trees are involved, and if so, which tree or trees.

If the ABI Domestic Subsidence Agreement is widely adopted, it identifies that the insurers of the house owner should undertake to investigate the damage. **Any arboriculturist who is instructed in these circumstances should seek to ensure that the necessary evidence is obtained,** not just to establish whether trees are involved but also where remedial action should be targeted. Level monitoring should be an essential part of the investigations. This work will normally be undertaken by the engineer or surveyor, but the arboriculturist should be familiar with the interpretation of the results. As all the information becomes available, the arboriculturist should liaise with the engineer to consider whether trees are involved, if so which, and on any appropriate remedial action to trees.

It may be necessary to provide a preliminary opinion based on limited information, for instance if the loss adjuster wishes to make preliminary contact with the relevant tree owner, or submit an application for work to a tree which is subject to a TPO. In some circumstances it may also be necessary to take immediate remedial action based on limited information, for instance during the summer months if damage is developing rapidly. However, whenever possible, any decisions should be substantiated by level monitoring. As noted in Chapter 15 (page 240), if monitoring starts in the autumn immediately after damage has occurred, the recovery movement can be used to identify the patterns of movement and help to identify the trees involved. Final decisions on remedial action can then be taken in the spring, and implemented before significant soil drying has developed (preferably by early May). If the tree owner has been notified in the autumn, the results of the level monitoring can be provided before the final decision is made. Likewise, if there is a TPO, results can be submitted in time for the appropriate committee decision.

An arboriculturist who is acting for a tree owner whose trees are alleged to be the cause of damage, should **indicate the information which he would wish to see to substantiate the claim, and try to ensure that the house owner's advisors are obtaining this,** i.e. try to ensure that level monitoring is in progress, and the reasonable scope of other evidence which may be needed. The scope of such evidence should depend on the particular circumstances. For instance, if the soil is almost certainly clay, soil investigations may be deemed unnecessary, particularly in the spring, whereas they may be essential if the Geological Survey provides reason to doubt the presence of clay. If there are additional trees owned by the house owner or others, it may be necessary to stipulate the location of level markers to ensure that any influence of those trees, and their role in any damage, is detected.

At the same time as requesting the necessary information, it is essential that the arboriculturist, or one of the other advisors acting for the tree owner, should write to the house owner:

i) to give assurance that, subject to the provision of reasonable evidence, **appropriate action will be taken with the tree in sufficient time to prevent further damage.** (This may not apply if notice is not given until mid-summer. In such circumstances it may be necessary to take immediate action, provided there is sufficient circumstantial evidence to implicate the tree.)

ii) to note that such action is being taken without prejudice to liability;

iii) to make it clear that the action taken with the tree should be sufficient to prevent any ongoing seasonal movement, and that **no liability will be accepted for the cost of underpinning.**

In the spring, before further soil drying occurs, the arboriculturist (whether acting for the house owner or tree owner), in liaison with other relevant advisors, should consider all of the available evidence. If there is a pattern of seasonal movement, it indicates seasonal changes in moisture content, probably associated with vegetation. **If the spatial pattern of this movement and other evidence implicates the tree, the type of remedial action should be decided, based on the guidance in Chapter 17 (page 295). If the movements are not seasonal, or the evidence indicates some other cause, the reasons should be clearly stated, rather than just an unsubstantiated denial.**

If it is decided that some form of pruning, rather than felling, is appropriate, it is essential to **ensure that the work which is undertaken is sufficient to achieve the desired objective.** As noted in Chapter 17 (page 288), if the means justify the ends, severe pruning in excess of the ideal may be required and justified.

If any form of vegetation control is used, whether felling, pruning, or any form of root control, it will be desirable for the level monitoring to be continued to check and confirm that the action has been sufficient to provide adequate stability. If there is any doubt about the adequacy, for instance if trees have only been pruned, or if the foundations are shallow or vulnerable to any other cause of damage, it will be advisable for monitoring readings to be taken at regular intervals (perhaps every 4 weeks) through the summer to check whether any additional action is required. The arboriculturist should reassure the house owner that, if such action involves further work to the trees, it will be undertaken promptly.

If trees have been pruned, **the arboriculturist should advise on the future management programme,** and ensure that the tree owner is aware of the need to maintain the specified regime. It may be necessary to include in this some arrangements for ongoing level monitoring, perhaps with readings each spring and autumn, to check that the regime is adequate (e.g. Case Study 9, but in that case extra readings in 1989 and spring 1990 would have been desirable). Although under the ABI agreement it is the responsibility of the house owner to investigate the cause, if there is a need for ongoing monitoring of this sort, it may be deemed that the responsibility (and costs) should be borne by the tree owner.

Where investigations have demonstrated that trees are the cause of damage, and there are other trees of the same species growing in comparable conditions and comparable proximity to buildings, it indicates **a need to consider whether there is a risk of similar damage to other properties.** Chapter 11 (page 176) has emphasised that the whole interacting system of trees, soils and buildings is inherently variable and unpredictable, and Chapter 18 has emphasised the difficulty of making any meaningful and practicable predictions. **Just because damage has occurred to one property under a particular set of circumstances, does not mean that damage will occur to other properties under apparently identical circumstances.** There is therefore no justification in applying preventative action to other trees in response to a single incidence of damage. However, it is sensible to consider the risks elsewhere, particularly if the other trees have the potential to grow and increase their water requirements. If there is more than one incidence of damage, it indicates a need for increasing caution, and the possible need to consider a management programme of preventative pruning. As noted in Chapter 18 (page 317), this will apply in particular to the management of trees in local authority ownership, where historical records exist to identify unacceptably high risk, and management experience can be used to define appropriate pruning regimes.

As emphasised in Chapter 18, although preventative pruning is justifiable and necessary under conditions of identifiable high risk, in my opinion in most situations, particularly those involving individual house and tree owners, the risks are too unpredictable and do not justify a preventative policy. As noted in the conclusion to Chapter 18 (page 324, paragraph 8), **in most situations it is better to accept that damage will be caused by a small proportion of trees, and to deal with these by prompt and appropriate remedial action.** For this reason I consider it inappropriate for insurers to ask for arboricultural reports on the risk of future tree root damage, and have urged insurers to cease this practice (Chapter 20, page 346).

If, despite this recommendation, insurers or others continue to ask for reports on the risks of damage, it is my opinion that arboriculturists should use the Arboricultural Association method of risk assessment (Chapter 18, page 312), but in any reports they should make it clear that even this method is not effective at defining risk situations. Particular care is needed if using this system of risk assessment for formulating a management policy for trees (page 316).

Arboriculturists who act for a tree owner whose trees are subject to a TPO or are within a Conservation Area should be familiar with the legislation and procedures, and ensure that client's rights are protected. Failure to do so may be deemed negligent. In particular:

- It should be remembered that works which are necessary for the prevention or abatement of a nuisance are exempt (Chapter 19, page 333). If this exemption applies, it is a matter of courtesy to notify the local authority before undertaking the work, but there should not be a need to seek consent (or give notice in a Conservation Area). However, the burden of proof lies with the tree owner, and it is therefore essential to ensure that proper evidence is available and that the work is only "so far as may be necessary" to abate the nuisance.

- If an application is required to the local planning authority, as much evidence as possible should be submitted. If monitoring results are not available at the time of submission of the application, they can always be submitted at a later date prior to the committee decision; if

necessary, suggest that a decision is deferred until the spring when monitoring results are available.

- If an application is refused consent, or is subject to unacceptable conditions or an Article 5 Certificate (page 335), an appeal may be required. This should be accompanied by appropriate supporting evidence. Although it may be possible for the latest monitoring results to be submitted during the site inspection for an appeal, they may be deemed too late and refused; it is therefore preferable that they should be submitted in advance of the site inspection, to allow adequate time for all parties to consider and comment.

- If ongoing monitoring provides fresh evidence in support of the appeal, or demonstrates that the tree is not involved or other works are deemed necessary, maintain a dialogue with the local authority to see if the matter can be resolved without the need to go to appeal.

- If consent for work is refused, or is granted subject to consent, there may be a right to compensation (page 335). This may be of particular relevance to problems of tree root damage, for instance if it is necessary to underpin or carry out special investigations such as monitoring in consequence of the refusal.

The comments in the previous paragraph are directed at the arboriculturist acting for a tree owner, but can also be interpreted by those working for the local authority. However, it should be remembered that a private tree owner may not have professional expertise or the advice of a competent arboriculturist. It is therefore helpful if the local authority can give guidance on the scope of investigations which may be required in support of an application. This guidance may need to distinguish between applications in respect of damage by drying and shrinkage of a clay soil, by direct root growth, or because of concern about potential future damage. A brief leaflet, identifying the cause and method of damage, the most suitable and cost-effective investigations, and the options for remedial action, could assist and help to reassure the tree owner.

Although it is necessary for the applicant to give reasons for the work, there is no obligation to supply evidence in support of these reasons. It may therefore be necessary to consider an application on the basis of little or no evidence. Whilst this makes it difficult to make a proper judgement, it should be noted that the application may have been deliberately submitted in anticipation of a refusal, but with the intention of then submitting a claim for compensation for the costs of obtaining the necessary evidence, as in *Fletcher -v- Chelmsford Borough Council* (page 335).

A role for surveyors and valuers

In the past surveyors and valuers have usually become involved as a result of noticing damage during a survey (e.g. Case study 8), or noting a tree in proximity to a building and expressing concern. Alternatively, they may have failed to notice such damage or the presence of a tree, giving rise to allegations of negligence (e.g. Case Study 2). They are expected to have a broad, but not necessarily detailed, understanding of the subject.

Recording the existence of damage should certainly fall within the role of the surveyor. Within the limited remit of the surveyor, interpreting the significance of any such damage will usually need to be on the basis of evidence which can be obtained immediately, without the benefit of monitoring. Whilst observing the pattern of cracks (Chapter 12, page 183) and deductions about the age of the damage (page 186) can provide some information, I suggest that **a level distortion survey (page 188) could provide valuable additional evidence on the movements which have occurred throughout the life of the building.** Simple investigations of this sort are well within the competence of a surveyor. Not only does a level survey provide a general indication of the condition of the building, but it can show whether distortion is consistent with trees in the proximity.

Those undertaking valuations are often expected to draw attention to trees in proximity to buildings where there is no existing damage, but it might be considered that there is a risk of such damage in future. Where trees are identified in this way, those commissioning the survey will often call for an arboricultural report; Chapter 18 (page 315) has noted my opinion that such reports are of little value, and Chapter 20 (page 346) has urged insurers to stop their requests for such reports. The need for surveyors to try to identify possible risk situations may therefore change in future.

If surveyors continue to provide predictions on the risks associated with trees, there are **steps that can reasonably be taken to allow a more informed decision,** and to at least indicated whether the risks are particularly low. In particular, inspection of the Geological Survey map (Chapter 13, page 199) can provide a general indication of the soil; if clay is unlikely, reassurance can be given that the risk of damage is very low. If there is likely to be a clay soil and a tree is deemed to be in a potential risk situation, a level distortion survey will usually reveal whether movement consistent with the tree has occurred in the past. Information of this sort is particularly relevant with older properties and mature trees; if they have not caused distortion in the past, they are unlikely to do so in future. Houses built in the past 20 years may not have developed distortion, but may have deeper foundations, designed in accordance with NHBC guidelines, which should not be vulnerable to damage.

If there is still concern that trees may pose a risk, the most effective action is to advocate a period of level monitoring. **Comments advocating tree removal or pruning should not be made in the absence of proof that such work is essential;** there is no reason why a decision on the future of the trees should not be delayed until such information is available.

If subsequent monitoring detects movement below the threshold where damage is occurring, appropriate action can then be taken. Likewise, if old damage has been detected but there is uncertainty whether it has stabilised, monitoring will provide a reliable method of checking on the situation. If the survey is in respect of a property sale, any necessary work can be undertaken by the new owner. Just because there may be evidence of movement, or concern that movement may occur in future, it need not blight a building. It may indicate a need for appropriate attention to adjacent trees or other vegetation, but, unless there is some other radical problem, does not indicate that the purchaser need suffer the expense and disruption of underpinning. **The public should be reassured, not alarmed.**

At present very few surveyors undertake level surveys or precision level monitoring. It is to be hoped that such investigations will become far more commonplace in future, both for the investigation of damage, and as a normal part of property management. Although land and property surveying fall within separate divisions of the Royal Institution of Chartered Surveyors, **there is no reason why simple work of this sort should not fall within the expertise and competence of building surveyors. It would allow a far more professional evaluation of the behaviour of buildings, and any possible involvement of trees as a cause of damage.**

A role for soil scientists

Chapters 4 and 13 have noted the problems in determining and interpreting the behaviour of soil when subject to soil drying. It is for this reason that I consider that, on the basis of current knowledge, it is preferable to concentrate on the behaviour of the building in response to the changes within the soil, rather than trying to interpret and predict soil behaviour.

However, for a thorough and proper understanding of the subject, it is obviously desirable to have a better knowledge of soil behaviour. For instance, the development of tensiometers which allow more precise and practical measurement of soil suction (Chapter 4, page 58) could provide a major benefit for investigations, and supersede the determination of moisture content. Even greater progress will be made when soil drying, whether determined by soil moisture content or suctions, can be related more accurately to soil shrinkage. **Our knowledge of the shrinkage curves, and their relationship to vertical and horizontal components of soil shrinkage under field conditions, of the wide range of clay soils throughout the country is most inadequate.** Soil scientists have a potential role in providing this information.

At present it is disturbing to note that geotechnical engineers place emphasis on plastic and liquid limit for determination of soil behaviour, whereas soil scientists note that these parameters are poorly correlated with soil shrinkage over the available water range (page 55). Both disciplines may be correct at the soil depths where their prime interests lie, but **the action of trees extends into both spheres of influence and may benefit from a closer mutual understanding between these disciplines.**

A role for planners

It is inevitable that the space required by trees will bring them into conflict with buildings. Much can be done to resolve this conflict by appropriate planning. The existing problems indicate that these conflicts have not been satisfactorily addressed in the past. It is valid for planners to claim that historically there was less knowledge of the problem, and that they could not have foreseen the changing public attitudes caused by the change in insurance policy. However, looking to the future, **it is important that planning decisions take proper account of the role of trees within the built environment, and the requirement to ensure a satisfactory juxtaposition of trees and buildings.**

There are two main elements. One is to allocate adequate space for trees within the built environment so that they do not come into proximity and potential conflict with buildings and their ancillary structures (roads, services, etc.). This involves allocation of areas of open space, and the integration of trees with other uses of this space. Space can also be found in street and verge design, and in the layout of buildings within their individual plots and in relation to adjacent plots. When considering the space requirements in all these situations, it is important to bear in mind the size of the mature tree: even a tree of modest size is substantially taller than a two storey house.

The other element is to recognize that trees and buildings will inevitably be in conflict, and to ensure that they can co-exist. It is outside the remit of this book to consider all of the potential areas of conflict, such as the requirements for light, concerns about safety, or the inconvenience from falling leaves or honeydew. However, it is relevant to consider the potential problems created by tree roots close to buildings; Chapter 18 has emphasised that this damage can be prevented by adequate foundation design. This needs to apply both to the design of new houses in proximity to existing trees (page 306), and to new buildings without existing trees but where tree may be planted or grow at some time in the future (page 309). In either situation, ensuring that the foundations are taken to adequate depth will greatly reduce, if not eliminate, the risk of damage.

Planners can ensure that these precautions are taken by the imposition of conditions when granting planning consent (Chapter 19, page 336). As noted in that section, the only place where the Town and Country Planning Act 1990 imposes a duty on a local authority is in respect of the imposition of conditions for the preservation or planting of trees. A condition requiring submission and approval of a planting scheme, and also one requiring that the foundations are taken to adequate depth to protect the building in respect of that planting, could ensure that all foundations are at a reasonable depth and not vulnerable to damage. The existing practice of allowing shallow foundations in the absence of existing trees should be stopped.

Consideration also needs to be given to possible changes in conditions in the future. If global warming alters the existing weather patterns so as to increase the extent of soil drying, greater foundation depths will be necessary (Chapter 8, page 132). Action is needed now to protect our buildings for the future, particularly as the importance of trees within the urban environment is likely to increase.

A role for building control

Close liaison between building control and planners can help to ensure that foundation depth and design of all new housing is adequate. NHBC Standards, Chapter 4.2 provides guidance on the depth of foundations in proximity to existing trees (Chapter 18, page 306). However, the previous section has emphasised that planners should also be seeking an increase in depth for all buildings on clay soils where trees may be planted or grow in future. If planning conditions are imposed which require such foundations, building control will need to ensure they are implemented. Minimum depth suitable for today's situation are advocated on page 310. Even greater depth would be appropriate if the house design is likely to lead to trees being planted in particularly close proximity (e.g. close to blank gable walls). A further increase, to allow for more extreme weather conditions in future, is desirable.

At existing foundation depths, the use of piled foundations is economically viable, particularly with the increased cost of removing the spoil created by excavating deep trench foundations. If foundation depths increase further, piled foundations become even more beneficial and cost effective. **The encouragement, or even enforcement, of the greater use of pile foundations, is highly desirable.**

Building control also have a role in the supervision of underpinning operations. As noted in Chapter 17, page 293, the foundation depths advocated in NHBC Standards Chapter 4.2 are intended for the average situation. If damage has already occurred, the trees or soils are likely to be the extreme, rather than the average, so that extra depth may be required. For this reason, the depth for underpinning is best determined by site-specific investigations.

Although the objectives of both foundation design and underpinning are to ensure that the foundations are taken down to a stable level, this will not necessarily need to be below the depth of all influence of tree root activity. **When deciding on the depth of underpinning, the depth of visible fine root activity is not necessarily a suitable criterion.** Determining whether these fine roots are active is very difficult, and traces of roots can remain in the soil for many years, if not decades, after a tree has been removed. Furthermore, a significant moisture deficit may extend well below the underside of foundations (Figure 18.5, page 307), but the building be capable of tolerating the movement, for instance if the design ensures sufficient rigidity by the incorporation of suitable reinforcement to restrict the amount of angular distortion.

A role for architects and for builders

As builders are implementing the plans of architects, it is reasonable to consider them together, particularly as they have a common aim of ensuring that a new house enjoys the best possible environment. Promotional pictures by builders and architects almost always site the new house against a background of trees, reflecting their recognition of the importance of trees. Unfortunately design and building practices do not always allow implementation of this ideal.

As noted in the previous two sections, foundation depths should take account both of existing trees, and of trees which are likely to be planted in the future. On clay soils, all foundations should be of adequate depth to ensure this. The best, and most economical, way to achieve this is by the use of bored piles, ensuring that the prescribed length is sufficient to provide the required support from the soil below the depth of root activity.

Care is also needed in the construction of underground services. Modern materials are usually sufficiently flexible to ensure that they are not vulnerable to damage by root activity, and to prevent roots from penetrating into drains. However, it is important to consider locations where differential movements may occur, for instance where underground services enter a building, and ensure that adequate provision is made for movement.

Builders can also ensure that work in close proximity to trees makes allowance for their future growth and the potential for direct damage (Chapter 10, page 164). In most situations it is possible to make special provision to provide sufficient space for future growth, for instance by the use of lintels or compressible materials. Alternatively, the structure should either be sufficiently rigid to ensure that it is the roots rather than the structure which distorts, or it should be accepted that the structure will move and design it accordingly.

Summary

1   In most cases where trees are the cause of damage, vegetation control is the most effective remedy. As it is also the most economical remedy, it is not surprising that this method is becoming increasingly popular with insurers.

2.   However, if it is to be implemented, there must be a proper understanding of the interaction of trees, soils and buildings, and of the methods of control.

3.   Before contemplating the removal or pruning of trees, it is necessary to have definitive information on their involvement as a cause of damage. Provided proper evidence is presented, arboriculturist should give a positive response in implementing remedial action, so as to ensure that the damage is minimised and that underpinning is unnecessary.

4.   The diagnosis of tree root damage and information which is required for decisions on the appropriate remedy requires a different approach to that traditionally adopted as a precursor to underpinning. Monitoring, in particular level monitoring, should play a much more important part of investigations, both as a diagnostic aid, and as a means for determining the efficacy of remedial action.

5.   The different approach entails a reappraisal of the traditional roles of the various disciplines. Engineers will continue to play a central role, but acting in closer liaison with the arboriculturist, who can advise on the type of remedial work which is most suitable. Surveyors could, and should, undertake level distortion surveys as part of their routine, and become more involved in level monitoring.

6.   In some situations where the risks of damage are high and readily identifiable, it is appropriate to manage trees to reduce or prevent damage. However, in the majority of situations, the interaction between trees, soils and buildings is so variable and unpredictable that it is not practical to make any meaningful predictions about the risk of damage. On both economic and environmental grounds, it is preferable to adopt a policy of accepting that damage will sometimes occur, and then to deal with the offending trees or shrubs as necessary.

6.   Planning and construction of new housing should include greater precautions in foundation design and construction to allow the growth of trees in proximity to buildings without risk of damage.

Semi-detached house with reinforced raft foundations on Kimmeridge Clay –
Comparison of level distortion surveys indicates about 30mm seasonal movement –
Root barrier inappropriate – Trees felled – Level monitoring showed slight continuing recovery.

The building

The subject properties form the two halves of a semi-detached building (CS Figure 20.1), built in 1956 as council houses, but later purchased by the occupiers. The building is located on the Kimmeridge Clay in Wiltshire.

It was built using prefabricated components produced by Unity Structures Limited. External wall construction comprise a series of storey-height pre-cast columns located at intervals of 0.9m around the periphery of the building. The front elevation is brick faced, but the side and rear walls are clad in concrete facing panels, tied to the columns by copper straining ties. The first floor incorporates rolled steel joists which run from front to back at 0.9m intervals, bolted to the concrete columns and forming a splice for the columns of the upper storey. Internally the structural columns are faced by 50mm thick clinker concrete blocks which are also used in the non load-bearing partition walls. A detached garage stands adjacent to the right flank; this was constructed of pre-cast concrete panel segments bolted together on a concrete slab. The area between the garage and house is covered for use as a store.

Case Study Figure 20.2
Front elevation and adjacent oak trees.

Investigations by the engineer established that the foundations are a reinforced raft which extends 0.9m beyond the peripheral walls. This raft is 200mm thick on the edges, increasing to 470mm beneath the peripheral walls.

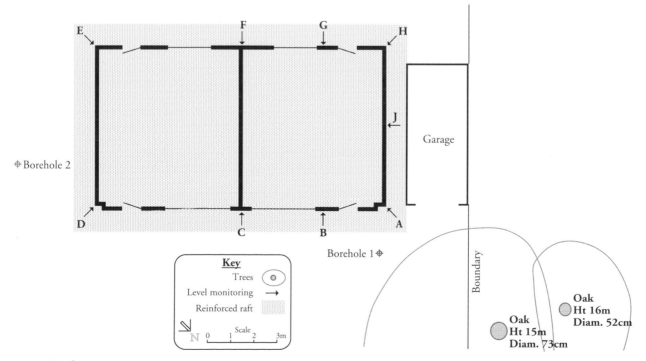

Case Study Figure 20.1
Site plan, including location of level monitoring markers

Damage

The right half of the building had a history of minor damage which had been corrected during routine decoration but in the early 1980s the cracks became worse and an insurance claim was made. Various cracks, up to 3mm wide, were present on the front and rear elevations, with these cracks most apparent in the internal blockwork. Graduated tell-tales fixed by the engineer recorded the worst cracks opening by about 2mm during the summer of 1983. A crack was visible in the exposed edge at the front and rear of the raft, but was not apparent when internal floors were inspected. The garage was distorted and had a crack from front to rear in the concrete slab. The concrete drive in front of the garage was also extensively damaged. By the time of my involvement I assessed the overall damage to the right half of the house as category 2.

The owner of the left half of the building was unaware of any damage until alerted by the owner of the right half. When he stripped the wallpaper from the rooms adjacent to the party wall it revealed fine cracks above the window lintels and beneath the window on the front elevation. The overall damage was category 0.

The trees

The only trees of significance were three oak trees (*Quercus robur*) owned by the local authority and growing in an area of open ground to the right of the house. The nearest of these oak trees was 7.3m from the front corner. It had a height of 15m and a large and well-developed crown structure which dominated the adjacent tree. This adjacent tree was 9m from the front corner and was an etiolated specimen with a height of 16m and a lop-sided crown as a result of this suppression. A further tree grew 17.2m from the front of the right flank; it had a height of 13m and was an attractive open-grown specimen. All were estimated to be about 100 years old.

Previous investigations and recommended remedial works

In September 1983 the engineer acting for the owners undertook a level distortion survey. This showed the right half of the building to have a pronounced downward tilt; the results of this survey are included (as the blue lines) in CS Figure 20.3.

The engineer also investigated the foundations and established the presence of oak roots in the underlying clay soil.

With this information, combined with the results from the crack monitoring which showed that the cracks had opened during the summer, he recommended a claim against the local authority.

With regards to remedial measures the engineer reported:

"This investigation has shown that at least a third of the raft under your house has been seriously affected by subsidence. Had the building been of traditional construction with strip foundations, one method of ensuring future stability would be to underpin them to a depth below the zone likely to be affected by the tree roots. However, this is not possible for a raft foundation and therefore other means have to be found.

It is considered that the most practical method in this instance to ensure that the roots are rendered ineffective, is to form a root barrier. This would be done by excavating a deep trench close to your boundary which would cut the existing roots, and to fill this with concrete to prevent future root growth. This barrier should extend from the front boundary to beyond the rear of the garage [i.e. a total length of about 20m] and to a depth of 2m increasing somewhat opposite the trees.

The closest of the oak trees would have so many roots cut by the root barrier that it would be unstable and liable to fall. This would require the co-operation of the local authority, and it may well be that there are Tree Preservation Orders in force which would have to be lifted beforehand.

In order to construct the root barrier it would be necessary to demolish the existing store building and to take down the garage and covered way. The concrete root barrier alongside the boundary would act as a deep strip foundation for the garage, and there would therefore be a likelihood of future settlement if it was rebuilt on a ground slab. The new foundations should therefore either be strip footings or a reinforced concrete raft.

As far as the repairs to your house are concerned, time will have to be allowed for the clay to regain its moisture content during the wetter part of the year and to reach its equilibrium moisture content. At least one winter will be needed before work can commence, provided that this is a wet one. Although the swelling force of the clay is likely to lift the subsided portion of the raft, it may not be possible for it to regain its original level, and some reconstruction of the present levels of the ground floor is likely. In addition, the cracks in the raft itself will need to be investigated within the lounge as it is likely that the cracks visible in the paths continue across beneath the rather inflexible composition flooring."

I was instructed in May 1994 by the local authority to advise on the claim and on the appropriate remedial action.

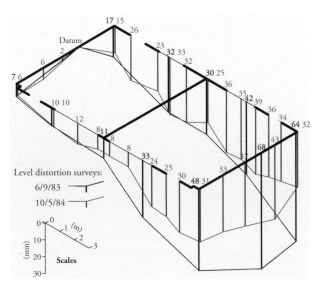

Case Study Figure 20.3

Comparison of level distortion surveys by Engineer (6/9/83) and myself (10/5/84) showing extent of seasonal recovery.

Further investigations

On 10th May I measured the level of the projecting edge of the raft slab around the periphery of both halves of the building. The results are included on CS Figure 20.3. Although the measurements were not taken at exactly the same locations as those used by the engineer the previous September, it appears legitimate to compare the results. For this reason, they are adjusted to the same datum point.

To allow more accurate subsequent measurements, I also attached level monitoring markers at the location shown in CS Figure 20.1. Subsequent readings were taken off these markers in the autumn and following spring. The results are presented in CS Figure 20.4, and changes in level by 31/5/85 shown diagrammatically in CS Figure 20.5.

Changes in level compared to initial readings on 10/5/84:			
Station	2/11/84	31/5/85	Seasonal movements*
A	+3.0	+5.7	17
B	+1.8	+3.6	9
C	+0.4	+1.2	3
D	Datum	Datum	0
E	+0.3	-0.2	0
F	+0.7	+4.1	5
G	+1.1	+4.9	7
H	+2.4	+7.3	32
J	+3.5	+4.3	31

Case Study Figure 20.4

Results of level monitoring (seasonal movements derived from comparison of level distortion surveys in CS Figure 20.3).*

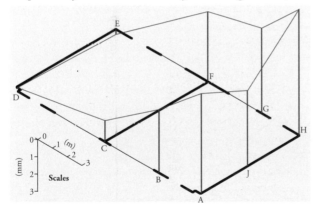

Case Study Figure 20.5

Recovery recorded by level monitoring on 31/5/85, 12 months after felling of trees (note different scale to CS Figure 20.3).

I also drilled two boreholes at the location shown in CS Figure 20.1. Both these boreholes encountered essentially similar conditions comprising:-

0	-	0.4m	topsoil
0.4	-	0.75	yellow, slightly sandy clay
0.75	-	0.9	gravel
0.9	-	4.0	dark grey clay, highly fossiliferous (shell fragments), with fine bands of mudstone, marl and sand.

The moisture content of the two boreholes is shown in CS Figure 20.6.

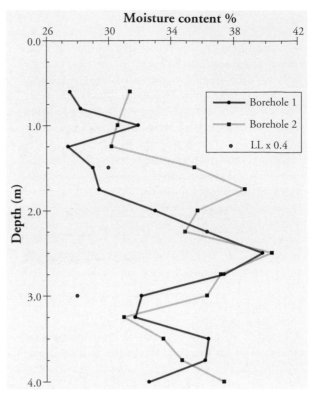

Case Study Figure 20.6

Moisture content profiles in May 1984.

Representative samples of the soil from boreholes 1 were used for classification tests. The results were:-

Depth (m)	Plastic Limit%	Liquid Limit %	Plasticity Index %	% Linear Shrinkage
1.5	31	75	44	12.8
3.0	31	70	39	13.5

While drilling borehole 1 a 10mm diameter live oak root was encountered at 1.2m. No other roots large enough for identification were recorded, but fine root activity was observed to a depth of at least 3.5m.

DISCUSSION

Cause of damage

The level distortion surveys undertaken by the engineer in September 1983 and by myself in May 1984 are essentially similar in the left half of the building, but show the right half to have recovered during the winter, approximately halving the amount of distortion which had been present. They imply recovery during the winter by about 32mm at the rear corner and 17mm at the front corner of the flank wall.

These results are entirely consistent with the involvement of the oak trees as the principal cause of the damage. The foundation raft was clearly inadequate to withstand the considerable seasonal soil movements which were occurring. Similar movements would undoubtedly have been occurring for many years, and it was accepted by the owner that various cracking had occurred in the past. These movements had probably increased during recent years as the trees continued to increase in size and as the trees recovered any root activity which might have been destroyed at the time of construction. Clearly, if no action was taken, the amount of seasonal movement would further increase, particularly during dry summers, and there would be a regular continuation of significant cracking.

Comparison of the moisture content profiles suggests that borehole 1 close to the trees was slightly desiccated compared to the control borehole 2. However, both boreholes show considerable fluctuations which reflect inherent variations in the clay characteristics. Comparison of moisture content with plastic and liquid limits suggests possible slight desiccation at 1.5m, but equilibrium conditions at 3m.

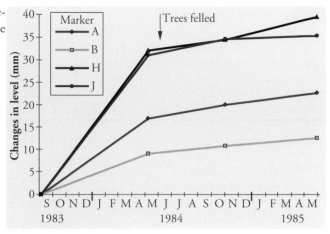

C.S. Figure 20.7

Changes in level recorded from distortions surveys and monitoring, during winter prior to tree removal and over subsequent 12 months.

Remedial action

I agreed with the engineer that it was essential to restabilise the raft by curtailing the root activity in the underlying clay.

I expressed the opinion that the nearest oak was too close to the corner of the house for pruning to be a viable option. Curtailing the water demand should therefore involve either felling the trees, or the installation of a root barrier as suggested by the engineer.

I agreed with the engineer that, if any such barrier was located on his clients property, it would involve demolition of the garage, and would then necessitate very elaborate foundations if the garage was reconstructed, in order to prevent differential foundation movements in that structure. If alternatively the barrier was located on the local authority side of the boundary, it would de-stabilise the nearest tree (unless the section nearest the tree was on the opposite side of the drive). I also considered that a 2m barrier was far too shallow, particularly as fine root activity had been observed to a depth of at least 3.5m in my borehole, which was significantly beyond the possible barrier.

For these reasons I agreed that the nearest tree would have to be removed. The adjacent tree was of very poor shape with an asymmetric and lop-sided crown as a result of previous suppression. It would not provide any significant amenity, and certainly did not justify the installation of a root barrier. It was considered that the most distant oak tree, 17.2m from the building, could be retained.

The two nearest trees were recommended for removal on 15th May, and were felled on 6th June before they could start any significant soil drying during that summer.

As shown in CS Figure 20.5, the subsequent monitoring confirmed some continuing recovery at the right end of the building. Although the level monitoring clearly showed this movement, the crack monitoring by the engineer could not detect any crack movement. CS Figure 20.7 plots the overall movements (derived from the level survey and the monitoring) and shows that the rate of movement was progressively diminishing (with no evidence of the direction reversing in the summer).

Although complete stability had not been achieved, as most of the movement had ceased the superstructure of the building was reinstated and redecorated. To the best of my knowledge no further problems have occurred.

Lessons to be learnt

- A raft foundation needs to be very stiff to resist underlying movements.

- The extent of damage was reduced because of the relatively flexible superstructure compared with traditional housing. Apart from the external skin of facing brickwork on the front, the remainder of the structural components, as well as external facing panels, were bolted or tied together with metal straps.

- The uniform surface of the raft made it possible to make meaningful comparisons between level distortion surveys undertaken at different times of year. However, level monitoring using defined markers would obviously be more accurate.

- The proposed root barrier was unlikely to have been effective and could not be justified.

- Removal of the two nearest trees stopped all further seasonal movement and allowed the soil to restabilise rapidly.

- Recovery movements did not reverse during the summer, confirming that there was no further influence of remaining vegetation.

- The remaining most distant tree retained some reasonable tree cover. Other trees, which were less likely to cause problems in future, could be planted.

Bengough, A.G. and C.E. Mullins (1990). Mechanical impedance to root growth: a review of experimental techniques and root growth responses. J. of Soil Science **41**, 341-358.

Biddle, P.G. (1979). Tree root damage to buildings - an arboriculturist's experience. Arbor. J. **3**, (6), 397-412.

Biddle, P.G. (1981a). Trees and buildings in harmony. J. Insurance Institute of London **69**, 39-58.

Biddle, P.G. (1981b). Recommendations for revision of National House-Building Council Practice Note 3. Limited edition for NHBC purposes only.

Biddle, P.G. (1983). Patterns of soil drying and moisture deficit in the vicinity of trees on clay soils Géotechnique **33**, (2), 107-126.

Biddle, P.G. (1984). Subsidence, heave and trees. Proc. Conf. on Found. Damage. Legal Studies & Services Ltd.

Biddle, P.G. (1985a). Trees and buildings. Advances in Practical Arboriculture. For. Comm. Bull. **65**, 121-132.

Biddle, P.G. (1985b). Arboricultural implications of revision of National House-Building Council Practice Note 3 'Building Near Trees'. Arbor. J. **9**, (4) 243-249.

Biddle, P.G. (1986). Subsidence, heave, trees. Problems and solutions. Proc. Conf. on Foundation Failures and Damage. Legal Studies & Services Ltd.

Biddle, P.G. (1988). Damage by trees - problems and solutions. Proc. Conf. on Foundation Failures. Legal Studies & Services Ltd.

Biddle, P.G. (1989). Trees - The summer of 1989, effects and implications. Proc. Conf. on Foundation Failures. Legal Studies & Services Ltd.

Biddle, P.G. (1992). Tree roots and foundations. Arbor. Research Note **108**, AAIS. 6pp. Reprinted (1998) with minor amendments, as Arbor. Research Note **142.**

Biddle, P.G. (1995a). Should arboriculturists be asked to carry out mortgage assessments? Arbor. Ass. News **81**, 12-13.

Biddle, P.G. (1995b). Long-term monitoring of soil moisture deficits on clay soils near trees. Proc. Arbor. Research Conf. 1995. 69-75. Published as: Arboricultural Practice, Present and Future, Ed. J. Claridge, 1997.

Bode, H.R. (1959). The relationship between leaf development and the formation of new absorbing roots in *Juglans*. Ber. Deut. Bot. Ges. **72**, 93-98.

Bonshor, R.B and L.L. Bonshor (1996). Cracking in buildings. Construction Research Communications Ltd. 102pp.

Bray, J.R. (1963). Root production and the estimation of net productivity. Canadian J. Bot. **41**, 65-71.

Brennan G., D. Patch and F.R.W. Stevens (1981). Tree roots and underground pipes. Arbor. Research Note **36**, AAIS. 3pp.

British Standards Institution BS 1377:1990. Method of test for soils for civil engineering purposes.

British Standards Institution BS 3998:1989. Tree Work.

British Standards Institution BS 5837:1991. Trees in Relation to Construction.

British Standards Institution BS 5930:1981. Site investigations.

Bronswijk, J.J.B. (1988). Modelling of water balance, cracking and subsidence of clay soils. J. of Hydrology **97**, 199-212.

Bronswijk, J.J.B. (1989). Prediction of actual cracking and subsidence in clay soils. Soil Science **148,** (2), 87-93.

Bronswijk, J.J.B. (1991). Relation between vertical soil movements and water-content changes in cracking clays. Soil Sci. Soc. Am. J. **55**, 1220-1226.

References

Building Research Establishment Digest 63 (1965). Soils and foundations:1.

Building Research Establishment Digest 64 (1965). Soils and foundations:2.

Building Research Establishment Digest 67 (1966). Soils and foundations:3.

Building Research Establishment Digest 240 (1965). Low-rise buildings on shrinkable clay soils: Part 1.

Building Research Establishment Digest 240 (1980). Low-rise buildings on shrinkable clay soils: Part 1. New edition 1993.

Building Research Establishment Digest 241 (1980). Low-rise buildings on shrinkable clay soils: Part 2.

Building Research Establishment Digest 242 (1980). Low-rise buildings on shrinkable clay soils: Part 3.

Building Research Establishment Digest 251 (1981). Assessment of damage in low-rise buildings.

Building Research Establishment Digest 298 (1985). The influence of trees on house foundations in clay soils.

Building Research Establishment Digest 343 (1989). Simple measuring and monitoring of movement in low-rise buildings. Part 1: cracks.

Building Research Establishment Digest 344 (1989). Simple measuring and monitoring of movement in low-rise buildings. Part 2: settlement, heave and out-of-plumb.

Building Research Establishment Digest 352 (1990). Underpinning.

Building Research Establishment Digest 361 (1991). Why do buildings crack?

Building Research Establishment Digest 386 (1993). Monitoring building and ground movement by precise levelling.

Building Research Establishment Digest 412 (1996). Desiccation in clay soils.

Building Research Establishment Information Paper IP 4/93 (1993). A method of determining the state of desiccation in clay soils.

Carson, E.W. (1974). The plant root and its environment. Univ. Press, Virginia.

Carter, M. and S.P. Bentley (1991). Correlations of soil properties. Pentech Press. 130 pp.

Chandler, R.J. and C.I. Gutierrez (1986). The filter paper method of suction measurement. Géotechnique 36, 265-268.

Chandler, R.J., M.S. Crilly and G. Montgomery-Smith (1992). A low cost method of assessing clay desiccation for low-rise buildings. Proc. Instn. Civ. Engrs. Civ. Engng. 92, 82-89.

Chapman, R.L. (1982). The public utilities and trees. Arbor. J. 6, (3), 205-209.

Cheney, J.E. (1989). Long term heave of a building founded on clay soil after tree removal. Proc. ICE Conf. on Instrumentation in Geotechnical Engineering, Nottingham, 1989. Pub. Thomas Telford, London, 1990 as Geotechnical Instrumentation in Practice: Purpose, performance and interpretation, 275-287.

Crilly, M.S. and R.J. Chandler (1993). A method of determining the state of desiccation in clay soils. BRE IP 4/93. 4pp.

Crilly, M.S., R.M.C. Driscoll and R.J. Chandler (1992) Seasonal ground and water movement observations from an expansive clay site in the UK. Proc. 7th Int. Conf. on Expansive soils, Dallas, Texas.

Croney, D. (1977). The design and performance of road pavements. HMSO. 674pp.

Coppin N.J. and I.G. Richards (1990). Use of vegetation in civil engineering. C.I.R.I.A. 292pp.

Cutler, D.F., P.E. Gasson and M.C. Farmer (1990). The windblown tree survey: analysis of results. Arbor. J. 14, (3), 265-286.

Cutler, D.F. and I.B.K. Richardson (1981). Tree roots and buildings. Construction Press. 94pp.

Cutler, D.F. and I.B.K. Richardson (1989). Tree roots and buildings. Longman Scientific and Technical. 2nd ed. 71pp.

Cutler, D.F., P.J. Rudall, P.E. Gasson and R.M.O. Gale (1987). Root identification manual of trees and shrubs. Chapman and Hall. 245pp.

Driscoll, R. (1983). The influence of vegetation on the swelling and shrinking of clay soils in Britain. Géotechnique 33, (2), 93-105.

Fayle, D.C.F. (1978). The case of the thickening root. Symp. Root physiology and symbiosis, Nancy, France. 216-227.

Forestry Research Co-ordination Committee (1988). Report of the review group on arboriculture. 55pp.

Fritts (1966). Growth rings of trees: Their correlation with climate. Science **154**, 973.

Gasson, P.E. and D.F. Cutler (1990). Tree root plate morphology. Arbor. J. **14**, (3), 193-264.

Gasson, P.E. and D.F. Cutler (1998). Can we live with trees in our towns and cities? Arbor. J. **22**, (1), 1-9.

Greacen, E.L. and J.S. Oh (1972). Physics of root growth. Nature **235**, 24-25.

Groninger, J.W., S.M. Zedaker and J.R. Seiler (1997). Herbicides to control tree roots in sewer lines. J. Arbor. **23**, (5) 169-172.

Hall, D.G.M., M.J. Reeve, A.J. Thomasson and V.F. Wright (1977). Water retention, porosity and density of field soils. Soil Survey Tech. Monograph No. 9. 75pp.

Hall, J.F. (1998). Monitoring: an aid not a solution. The Loss Adjuster **9**, 31-32.

Hamilton, D.W. (1984a). Side walk/curb-breaking tree roots. 1. Why tree roots cause pavement problems. Arbor. J. **8**, (1), 34-44.

Hamilton, D.W. (1984b). Side walk/curb-breaking tree roots. 2. Management to minimise existing pavement problems by tree roots. Arbor. J. **8**, (3), 223-234.

Hammer, M.J. and O.B. Thompson (1966). Foundation clay shrinkage caused by large trees. J. Soil Mech. Founds. Div. Proc. Am. Soc. Civ. Eng. **92**, 1-17.

Head, G.C. (1965). Shedding of roots. Ch. 7 of Shedding of Plant Parts, Ed. T.T. Kozlowski.

Head, G.C. (1967). Effects of seasonal changes in shoot growth on the amount of unsuberised root on apple and plum trees. J. Hort. Sci. **41**, 197-206

Head, G.C. (1969). The effects of fruiting and defoliation on seasonal trends in new root production on apple trees. J. Hort. Sci. **44**, 175-181.

Helliwell, D.R. and S.J. Fordham (1992). Tree roots and tree growth. Reading Agricultural Consultants. 18pp.

H.M.S.O. (1989) Defects in buildings. 508pp.

Hoffman, G. (1966) Verlauf der Tiefendurchwurzelung und Feinwurzelbildung bei einigen Banmarten. Arch. Forstwiss. **15**, 825-856.

Hough, M., S. Palmer, A. Weir, M. Lee and I. Barrie (1997). The Meteorological Office rainfall and evaporation calculation system: MORECS Version 2.0 (1995). Update to Hydrological Memorandum 45. 80pp.

Hunt, R., R.H. Dyer and R. Driscoll (1991). Foundation movement and remedial underpinning in low-rise buildings. Building Research Establishment Report.

Institution of Structural Engineers (1994). Subsidence of low rise buildings. 106pp.

Jones, R.J.A. and A.J. Thomasson (1985). An agroclimatic databank for England and Wales. Soil Survey Technical Monograph No. 16. 45pp.

Kelsey, P.J. (1979). The investigation of damaged buildings and the diagnosis of cracking. Proc. Sem. Brick Dev. Assn., Cambridge.

Kozlowski, T.T (1971). Root growth. Ch. **5** of Growth and development of trees. Academic Press. 196-305.

Kozlowski, T.T. (1982). Water supply and Tree Growth. Forestry Abstracts **43**, (2), 57 - 95.

Kramer, P.J. and J.S. Boyer (1995). Water relations of plants and soils. Academic Press. 495pp.

Kuntz, J.E. and A.J. Riker (1956). The use of radioactive isotopes to ascertain the role of root-grafting in the translocation of water, nutrients, and disease-inducing organisms among forest trees. Proc. Int. Conf. on the Peaceful Uses of Atomic Energy, Geneva 1955. **12**, 144-148.

Land Use Consultants (1993). Trees in towns: a survey of trees in 66 towns and villages in England. Department of Environment. Research for Amenity Trees, No. 1. 51pp.

Lawson, M. (1993). Trees, clay and climate. Proc. Sem. The Geological Society, Yorkshire Regional Group. 11pp.

Leonard, O.A and N.R. Townley (1971). Control of tree roots in sewers and drains. Calif. Agr. **25**, 13-15.

Marsh, T.J. and R.A. Monkhouse (1993). Drought in the United Kingdom, 1988-92. 15-22.

Marshall, D., D. Patch and M. Dobson (1997). Root barriers and building subsidence. Arbor. Practice Note 4, AAIS. 8pp.

Materechera, S.A., A.R. Dexter and A.M. Alston (1991). Penetration of very strong soils by seedling roots of different plant species. Plant and Soil **135**, 31-41.

Mattheck, C. (1990). Why they grow, how they grow; the mechanics of trees. Arbor. J. **14**, (1), 1-17.

Mattheck, C. and H. Breloer (1994). The body language of trees - A handbook for failure analysis. H.M.S.O. 239pp.

McCombie, P.F. (1993). The relative water demand of broad-leaved trees - a new analysis of the Kew tree root survey. Arbor. J. **17**, (4), 359-374.

MacLeod, R.D. and W.J. Cram (1996). Forces exerted by tree roots. Arbor. Research and Information Note **134**, AAIS. 8pp.

Michael, D.A., D.I. Dickmann, J.G. Isebrands and N.D. Nelson (1990). Photosynthesis patterns during the establishment year within two poplar clones with contrasting morphology and phenology. Tree Physiol. **6**, 11-27.

Misra, R.K., A.R. Dexter and A.M. Alston (1986). Maximum axial and radial growth pressures of plant roots. Plant and Soil **95**, 315-326.

Mitchell, A. (1974). A field guide to the trees of Britain and Northern Europe. Collins. 415pp.

Moffat, A.J., N.A.D. Bending and M.C. Dobson (1998). Barriers against tree roots - an experimental investigation. Arbor. Research and Information Note **141**, AAIS. 7pp.

Monteith, J.L. (1965). Evaporation and environment. Symp. Soc. Exp. Biol. **19**, 205-234.

National House-Builders Registration Council (1969). Root damage by trees - siting of dwellings and special precautions. Practice Note 3.

National House-Building Council (1974). Root damage by trees - siting of dwellings and special precautions. Practice Note 3 (revised).

National House-Building Council (1985). Building near trees. Practice Note 3 (1985).

National House-Building Council (1992). Building near trees. NHBC Standards Chapter 4.2.

National Joint Utilities Group (1995). Guidelines for the planning, installation and maintenance of utility services in proximity to trees. Publication No. 10. 23pp.

NHBC - see National House-Building Council.

Nichol, B.C. and A. Armstrong (1997). Street tree root architecture and pavement damage. Arbor. Research and Information Note **138**, AAIS. 6pp.

Penman, H.L. (1948). Natural evaporation from open water, bare soil and grass. Proc. Roy. Soc. Ser. A **193**, 120-145.

Owen, R.C. (1984). Vegetation and seasonal ground movement effects on buried mains. Proc. 3rd Int. Conf. Ground Movements and Structures, UWIST, Cardiff.

Periera, J.S. and T.T. Kozlowski (1978). Diurnal and seasonal changes in water balance of *Acer saccharum* and *Betula papyrifera*. Physiologia Plantarum **13**, 289-299.

Pritchard, J. (1994). The control of cell expansion in roots. New Phytol. **127**, 3-26.

Pugh, R.S., P.G. Parnell and R.D. Parkes (1995). A rapid and reliable on-site method of assessing desiccation in clay soils. Proc. Instn. Civ. Eng. Geotech. Engng. **113**, 25-30.

Redmond, D.R. (1959). Mortality of rootlets in balsam fir defoliated by the spruce budworm. Forest Sci. **5**, 64-69.

Reeve, M.J. and D.G.M. Hall (1978). Shrinkage in clayey subsoils of contrasting structure. J. of Soil Science **29**, 315-323.

Reeve, M.J., D.G.M. Hall and P. Bullock (1980). The effect of soil composition and environmental factors on the shrinkage of some clayey British soils. J. of Soil Science **31**, 429-442.

Reynolds, E.R.C. and D.Alder (1980). Trees and buildings 6. A matter of opinion – settlement or heave of houses and the role of tree roots. Arbor. J. **4**, (1), 24-30.

Richardson, I.B.K. (1995). Dead or alive? Is it really that simple? Arbor. J. **19**, (4), 395-400.

Richardson, I.B.K. and R. Gale (1994). Tree recognition - a pocket manual. Richardson's Botanical Identifications. 140 pp.

Ridley, A.M. and J.B. Burland (1995). A pore water pressure probe for the in situ measurement of a wide range of soil suctions. Proc. Int. Conf. on Advances in site investigation practice, London.

Samuels, S.G. and J.E. Cheney (1974). Long-term heave of a building on clay due to tree removal. Proc. Sym. British Geotech. Soc. on Settlement of Structures. Pentech Press. 212-220.

SEMSELB (1990). (Seminar for Structural Engineers of London Boroughs). The effects of trees on foundations in clay sub-soils. Design Practice Note.

Stone, E.L. and P.J. Kalisz (1991). On the maximum extent of tree roots. For. Ecol. and Manag. **46**, 59-102.

Steudle, E. (1993). Pressure probe techniques: basic principles and application to studies of water and solute relations at the cell, tissue and organ level. Ch 2 of Water deficits; plant responses from cell to community, βios Scientific Publishers. 5 - 36.

Tang, Z. and S.B. Land (1995). Photosynthesis and leaf water relations in four American sycamore clones. Forest Science **41**, 729-743.

Tariq, A. and D.S. Durnford (1993). Analytical volume change model for swelling clay soils. Soil. Sci. Soc. Am. J. **57**, 1183-1187.

Task Force Trees (1987). Action Pack. Countryside Commission.

Terzaghi, K. (1936). Settlement of structures. 1st I.C.S.M.F.E., 79-87.

Thompson, N., I.A. Barrie and M. Ayles (1981). The Meteorological Office rainfall and evaporation calculation system : MORECS (July 1981). Hydrological Office Memorandum No. 45, 69pp.

Wagar, J.A. and P.A. Barker (1983). Tree root damage to sidewalks and kerbs. J. Arbor. **9**, (7), 177-181.

Ward, W.H. (1947). The effects of fast growing tree and shrubs on shallow foundations. Journal Inst. Landscape Architects **11**, 7-16.

Ward, W.H. (1953). Soil movement and weather. Proc. 3rd Int. Conf. Soil Mech. and Found. Eng., Switzerland.

Wells, A.K. (1959). Outline of historical geology. 4th Ed. George Allen & Unwin Ltd. 398pp.

Wilkinson, D.M. (1995). Modelling tree crowns as geometric solids. Arbor. J. **19**, (4), 387-393.

Wilson, B.F. (1967). Root growth around barriers. Bot. Gaz. **128**, (2), 79-82.

Wong, T.W., J.E.G. Good and M.P. Denne (1988). Tree root damage to pavements and kerbs in the City of Manchester. Arbor. J. **12**, (1), 17-34.

Wright, C.E. (1976). Once in 1,000 years? Water.

Zahner, R. (1968). Water deficits and growth of trees. Vol.2, Ch. 5 of Water deficits and plant growth. Ed. T.T. Kozloski. Academic Press. 191-254.

Zahner, R. and J.R. Donnelly (1967). Refining correlations of rainfall and radial growth in young red pine. Ecology **48**, 525.

Zwieniecki, M.A. and M. Newton (1995). Roots growing in rock fissures: their morphological adaptation. Plant and Soil **172**, 181-187.

CROSS REFERENCE OF BOTANICAL AND COMMON NAMES

Botanical	Common
Abies	Fir
Acer	Maple
A. campestre	Field maple
A. platanoides	Norway maple
A. pseuodoplatanus	Sycamore
Aesculus hippocastanum	Horse chestnut
Ailanthus altissima	Tree of Heaven
Alnus	Alder
Araucaria araucana	Monkey puzzle
Arbutus unedo	Strawberry tree
Betula	Birch
B. papyrifera	Paper bark birch
B. pendula	Silver birch
Carpinus	Hornbeam
Catalpa bignoniodes	Catalpa (Indian bean tree)
Cedrus	Cedar
Chamaecyparis lawsoniana	Lawsons cypress
Corylus	Hazel
Crataegus monogyna	Hawthorn
X Cupressocyparis leylandii	Leyland cypress
Cupressus macrocarpa	Monterey cypress
C. nootkatensis	Nootka cypress
Eucalyptus	Eucalyptus
Fagus sylvatica	Beech
Ficus	Fig
Fraxinus	Ash
Ginkgo	Maidenhair tree
Gleditsia	Locust
Ilex aquifolium	Holly
Juglans	Walnut
Juniperus	Juniper
Laburnum	Laburnum
Larix	Larch
Liquidambar styraciflua	Sweet gum
Magnolia	Magnolia
Malus	Apple
M. sieboldii	Crab apple
Morus	Mulberry
Picea	Spruce
Pinus	Pine
Platanus x acerifolia	Plane
Populus	Poplar
P. alba	White poplar
P. nigra 'italica'	Lombardy poplar
P. x euramericana	Hybrid black poplar
Prunus	Cherry
Prunus	Plum
Pyrus	Pear
Quercus	Oak
Q. cerris	Turkey oak
Q. palustris	Pin oak
Q. robur	English oak
Robinia pseudoacacia	False acacia
Salix	Willow
Sambucus	Elder
Sequoiadendron giganteum	Redwoods
Sophora	Pagoda
Sorbus	Sorbus
Syringa	Lilac
Taxus	Yew
Thuja	Thuja
Tilia	Lime
Tsuga	Hemlock
Ulmus	Elm
Umbellularia californica	Californian laurel tree

Common	Botanical
Alder	Alnus
Apple	Malus
Crab apple	M. sieboldii
Ash	Fraxinus
Beech	Fagus sylvatica
Birch	Betula
Paper bark birch	B. papyrifera
silver birch	B. pendula
Californian laurel tree	Umbellularia californica
Catalpa (Indian bean tree)	Catalpa bignoniodes
Cedar	Cedrus
Cherry	Prunus
Cypress Lawsons	Chamaecyparis lawsoniana
Leyland	X Cupressocyparis leylandii
Monterey	Cupressus macrocarpa
Nootka	Cupressus nootkatensis
Elder	Sambucus
Elm	Ulmus
Eucalyptus	Eucalyptus
False acacia	Robinia pseudoacacia
Fig	Ficus
Fir	Abies
Hawthorn	Crataegus monogyna
Hazel	Corylus
Hemlock	Tsuga
Holly	Ilex aquifolium
Hornbeam	Carpinus
Horse chestnut	Aesculus hippocastanum
Juniper	Juniperus
Laburnum	Laburnum
Larch	Larix
Lilac	Syringa
Lime	Tilia
Locust	Gleditsia
Magnolia	Magnolia
Maidenhair	Ginkgo
Maple	Acer
Field	A. campestre
Norway	A. platanoides
Monkey puzzle (Chile pine)	Araucaria araucana
Mulberry	Morus
Oak	Quercus
English	Q. robur
Turkey	Q. cerris
pin	Q. palustris
Pagoda	Sophora
Pear	Pyrus
Pine	Pinus
Plane	Platanus x acerifolia
Plum	Prunus
Poplar	Populus
hybrid black	P. x euramericana
Lombardy	P. nigra 'italica'
white	P. alba
Redwoods	Sequoiadendron giganteum
Sorbus	Sorbus
Spruce	Picea
Strawberry tree	Arbutus unedo
Sweet gum	Liquidambar styraciflua
Sycamore	Acer pseudoplatanus
Thuja	Thuja
Tree of Heaven	Ailanthus altissima
Walnut	Juglans
Willow	Salix
Yew	Taxus

See also Figure 14.1, page 219, and Figure 14.4, page 222.

Important or definitive entries in **bold type**, Case Studies in *Italic type*

Important or definitive entries in **bold type**, Case Studies in *Italic type*

Important or definitive entries in **bold type**, Case Studies in *Italic type*

Persistent moisture deficit (see persistent deficit).

pF. **15,** 45.

Phase system. 37.

Phenotypic variation. **135,** 141.

Phloem. 11, **12,** 16, 29, 31, 280.

Photosynthesis. 13 - 16, 18, 29, 67, 73, 76, 95, 136, 149, 229, 230, 283, 318.

Pine. 25, 143, 147, 159, 231, 287, 313.

Pipette samples. 41, 204.

Plane tree. 76, 77, 136, 143 - 148, 279, 281, 286, 287, 304, 313.

Planners. 1, 5, **356.**

Planning condition. 310, 331, **336,** 342, **356.**

Plastic limit. *21,* 47, **54, 56, 205,** 211.

Plasticity index. **54,** 55, 56, 59, 92, 105, 111, *180,* 204, 212, 255, 308, 312.

Plum. *100,* 143 - 148, 219, 313.

Pollarding. 76, 229, 262, 282, **286 - 288,** *297,* 318.

Poplars. 13, 27, 96, 143 - 148, 162, 256, 262, 279, 280, 287, 308, 313.

Poplar, hybrid black. *7,* 52, 70 - 72, 76, *80,* 85 - 93, 96, 130, 231, 265.

Poplar, Lombardy. *80,* 232.

Poplar, white. *7,* 280.

Pore water pressure. 106 - 108.

Porosity (see also soil pores). 75.

Potential, matric. 44, 45, 46, 58, 207.

Potential, solute. 44, 46, 58.

Potential, water (see water potential).

Pressure, axial (roots). 28, **158.**

Pressure bulb. 108.

Pressure, hydrostatic. 44, *216.*

Pressure, radial (roots). **158 - 159,** 160, 167, 169.

Pruning. 17, *19,* 29, 96, 114, 169, 176, 229, 239, *254,* 257, 258, 262, 277, 280, **281 - 288,** 295, 296, 309, **317 - 321,** 333, 355.

Pruning, effect on persistent deficit. **97 - 98,** *156,* 276.

Pruning, effect on seasonal changes. **76 - 78, 277,** *281.*

Pruning, reduction. *80, 155,* **284,** 285, 286, 287, 288.

Pruning, severity. 288.

Pruning, thinning. **284,** 285, 287.

Pyracantha. 151.

Radiation. 67.

Radicle. 26, 158.

Rainfall. 2, 3, 16, 17, 67, 68, 71, 73, 78, 95, 113, 114, 121, 132, 228, 289.

Ray. 11, **12,** 29.

Reading Beds. 38, 39.

Real land use. 123, 124, 125, 128.

Recovery. 6, *83,* 85, 98, 114, 240, **255 - 268.**

Recovery, amount. *119,* 256, 264, 342.

Recovery diagnosis. **260.**

Recovery, duration. 92, 98, 114, *119, 181,* 240, 256, **261 - 262,** 268, 276, **291,** 292, *300,* 342, *362.*

Recovery, prediction. **261 - 262.**

Recovery, rate of. *22,* 57, 93, *120, 156, 182, 216,* 240, 245, 256, 263, *362.*

Recovery, seasonal. *22,* 71, *82,* 114, 194, 255, 256, 268, 278.

Redwood. 143, 147, 279, 313.

Remedial action. 176, **275 - 296.**

Respiration. **17,** 27, 32.

Respiration, anaerobic. 28.

Ring porous. 11, 12, 67, 226, 228.

Risk prediction (see also subsidence risk assessment). 6, 141, 145, 264.

Root activity. 199, 201, **203,** 221, *270,* 290, *298,* 357, *361.*

Root age. 29, **223.**

Root alignment. 26.

Root barrier. *7 - 10, 155,* 166, *250, 251,* 257, 277, **289,** 294, 296, *360, 362.*

Root, brown. 27, 32, 204.

Root, buttress. 30, 32, 162.

Root cap. 26.

Root, conducting. 29, 77, 78, 159, 220.

Root, damage to. 17, 111, 163, 166, 229, 257.

Root, dead. *7, 10, 20,* 29, 31, 203, 224, *236.*

Root depth. 24, 30, 96, 136, 141, 146, 151, 282, 290.

Root diameter. 29, 142, 159.

Root dieback. 232, 282, 283.

Root extension growth. 27, 157, 158, 159.

Root, fine. *9, 20,* 25, **27,** 28, *32, 63,* 77, *101,* 107, 111, *118,* 166, 176, 178, 203.

Root grafts. 25.

Root growth. 17, **27,** 29, 32, 58, **113,** 164, 221, 282, 290.

Root, growth ring. 12, 29, 223.

Root hairs. 27.

Root identification. 29, *101, 118,* 142, *154,* 176, 178, *197,* 217, **220 - 223,** *236, 251, 270, 298, 339, 360.*

Root meristem. 26.

Root mortality (see also dead roots). **31,** 77, 278, 282, 283.

Root plate. 30.

Root radial growth (see also pressure, radial). 157, 158, 159, 160, 167, 357.

Root, radial spread. 24, 78, 106, 136, **141 - 143,** 146, 147, 151, 282, 341.

Root regeneration. 17, **31,** 111, 166, 168, *250, 251,* 290.

Root severance. 163, 166, 194, *249,* 257, *271,* 277, 289, **290.**

Important or definitive entries in **bold type**, Case Studies in *Italic type*

Stomata. 14, **15,** 16, 18, 76, 136, 229.

Strawberry tree. 159, 279.

Structural engineers - see engineers.

Structural voids. 44.

Stress, uniform surface. 13.

Stump treatment. 278.

Subsidence. **105, 110,** 111, 175, 185, 192 - 195.

Subsidence risk assessment. 277, 309, **312 - 316,** 323, 341, 346, 354.

Suckers. 160, *237,* 258, **280.**

Suction. **15,** 16, 18, 44 - 46, 58, 74, 95, 107, 145, 201.

Sugar. 12 - 18, 31, 229, 230.

Sugar beet. 25.

Sunlight (see light).

Surrey. *235.*

Surveyors. 1, 4, 311, **355.**

Sweet gum. 147, 279, 280, 313.

Swelling, horizontal. *64,* 185, 195, 260, 294.

Swelling potential. **54,** 201, 256, 267.

Swelling pressure. 54, 111, 255.

Sycamore. 143 - 148, 162, 167, *235, 289, 343.*

Tap root. 26, 30.

Taplow Gravel. *100.*

Tarmac. 74, 162, 163.

Temperature. 14, 16, 18, 27, 29, 67, 73, 76, 121.

Tensiometer. 58.

Terminal bud. 13, 231, 287.

Thanet Sands. 38.

Thuja. 147, 313.

Topography. 78.

Town and Country Planning Act. 310, **331 - 337.**

Trachieds. 12.

Transpiration. 2, 3, **14 -16,** 18, 67, 73, 76, 78, 107, 121, 136, 149, 277, 278, 281 - 284, 294.

Tree, age. 13, **225,** 228, 231, 287, 339.

Tree, control of water uptake. 275, **276 - 289.**

Tree felling. *22, 80,* 92, *100,* 111, 114, *118, 120, 155,* 176, *181, 182,* 239, 257, 277, **278 - 280,** 295, 296, *300,* 317, 355, *362.*

Tree felling in stages. 280.

Tree groups. **149,** 152.

Tree of Heaven. 143, 147, 279, 280, 313.

Tree height. 142, 147, 149, 164, 224, 277, 308, 314.

Tree identification. 178, 217, 220.

Tree management. 283, 288, **317 - 323,** 341, 342, *353.*

Tree moisture deficits. **15.**

Tree planting. 164, 170, 309, **322,** 324, 334, 336, 337, 350.

Tree Preservation Order. *171,* 177, *213, 216,* **331 - 336,** 342, 350, *352,* 354.

Tree Preservation Order, appeals. 331, 333, 354.

Tree Preservation Order, applications for consent. 333, 354.

Tree Preservation Order, compensation. 331, **335,** 354.

Tree, proximity to structure. 142, 163, 283, 304, 306, 314, 316, 317, 323.

Tree, ring barking. 31, 278, 280, 333.

Tree rows. **149,** 152.

Tree safety. 163, 166, 217, 232, 290.

Tree size. 137, 217, **224,** 283, 316, 356.

Tree vigour. 2, 287, 314, 316.

Trenches. 113, 221, 258, 290.

Turgor. 26, 28, 158, 159.

Underground services (see also drains). 113, 164, **169,** 196, 289, 290, 303, 305, 357.

Underpinning. 6, *99,* 176, 239, 275, **292 - 296,** 309, 341, 353, 357.

Underpinning, anti-heave precautions. **293,** 296, 342, 350, 351.

Underpinning, mini piles (failure). *327.*

Underpinning, partial. 112, *115, 119,* 239, *249, 252,* 293.

Underpinning, pier and beam. *9, 61, 154, 180, 235, 250, 269,* 293.

Underpinning, strip. *19, 115, 269,* 294.

Units. **15.**

Valuers. 1, 355.

Vapour pressure. 16, 121.

Vermiculite. **43,**

Verticality survey. *172,* **194.**

Vertical stress. 108.

Vessels. 11, **12,** 29, *67.*

Voids. 37, 58, 107.

Voids ratio. **37,** 48.

Void, structural. 46.

Wadhurst Clay. 39.

Wall, boundary. 161, 162, 164.

Wall, retaining. 161, 162, 165, *171.*

Wall, root penetration. 163.

Walnut. 143, 147, 279, 289, 313.

Water. 2, 6, 13, 14, 32 37, 43, 106, 203.

Water absorb. 44, 58.

Water adsorb. 44, 46, 58.

Water, available. 16, 18, 44, 46, **50,** 114, **122 - 124,** 289, 308.

Water demand. 141, **145,** 152, 306 - 309, 313.

Water flow. 16, 113.

Watering, artificial. 275, 277, **289,** 290, 295, 296, **300.**

Water level. *9,* 175, **189,** *198.*

Water loss. 16, 17, 18, 67, 121.

Water potential. **15,** 27, 58, 75.

Water requirement. 16, 17, 217, 230, 289.

Water shrinkage factor. *9,* 52, 53, 71, *119,* 141, *253,* 266 - 267, *271, 299.*

Important or definitive entries in **bold type,** Case Studies in *Italic type*

Important or definitive entries in **bold type**, Case Studies in *Italic type*